To my most wonderful
Glen & Anna,

I cannot thank you enough
for the support you gave to
me both through the events in
this book & in the production
of it.

With all my love
Always
Lu
x

LOVE AND WHEATGRASS

LORRAINE A. EREIRA

This is a true story. However, all names and identifying details
have been changed to protect the privacy of individuals.

Cover Illustration by Olena Kaminetska/www.shutterstock.com
Cover design by Pixel Studio
Photography by Marc Mina and www.shutterstock.com
Editing by Abi Truelove, www.findaproofreader.com/ajt-editing

THIS BOOK IS WRITTEN FOR MY HUSBAND SIMEON,

WHO IS MY BEST FRIEND, MY SOULMATE AND MY ROCK.

Foreword

This book is a powerful, inspiring and insightful story about how every one of us can take control of our own health and healing.

A diagnosis of illness can create such fear that we are often led to believe that there are no options available to us other than conventional medicine, and we place our trust wholly in our doctor and/or other medical practitioners. However, this story illustrates that we are ultimately responsible for our own health, and whether we choose a solely alternative approach or embark upon a conventional treatment programme we must support our body every step of the way, giving it the best chance of a full recovery.

For the author and her family this discovery came through the shock of discovering that her husband, Saul, had cancer. Their story provides a rare glimpse into how dealing with cancer can ultimately be an empowering experience, by taking an integrated, complementary approach.

A delightful, honest account about love and hope and this family's successful journey out of cancer – the latter part of the book is particularly helpful for readers in a similar situation, as it is full of delicious and healing recipes and how-to strategies and practices to give you the tools to help yourself or someone you love through a similar experience. The author shares her discoveries and knowledge of superfoods, with practical recipes that are easy to follow – who said eating healing and healthy foods was boring!

The Greek physician Hippocrates, who is also known as the Father of Western medicine, remains a **huge inspiration to everyone who wants to follow an integrated, complementary approach to their own health and healing**. He understood the restorative power of certain foods, and summed it up with one valuable piece of advice:

"Let food be thy medicine and medicine be thy food."
Happy, healing reading!

Foreword by Dr Britt Cordi, PhD, www.livewheatgrass.com

Acknowledgements

Writing this book has been a truly amazing experience, but I could not have done it without the help of some key people.

Firstly, my thanks goes to Dr Britt Cordi, PhD of www.livewheatgrass.com for her faith in me as a writer and her unending support throughout the production of this book.

Next I would like to thank my editor Abi Truelove, without whose eye for detail this book would not be complete.

Thirdly, thanks to my photographer Marc Mina, for his artistic ability to make a photograph come to life.

Thanks also to my family and best friends who have supported me throughout and helped me to write this story.

I give special thanks to my brother Glen and his wonderful wife Anna Lisa for their unending support both through our ordeal and through the writing of this book.

Thanks to my two wonderful sons who supported my husband through the cancer but also encouraged me to get this book written.

Lastly, and most importantly of all, I would like to give my heartfelt thanks to my amazing husband for allowing me to write about his story, and for pushing me to get it finished.

Contents

How to Use this Book
in the Spirit in Which it is Written...

The first part of this book is a story.

I am a woman who has a wonderful life, a lovely home, two gorgeous sons, a supportive family, the very best of friends, and, most of all, the greatest husband, who, together with my sons, is the centre of my world.

So when one day we found out that he had cancer, our wonderful life became dark and frightening.

The story is told through my eyes about the things I did as a carer, how the whole experience affected my family, and how my husband dealt with his illness. It is a story first and foremost about love, in all its forms: the relationships, the bonds, and the emotions that ran high for all of us. But it is also a story of discovery, of learning and of knowledge: how what we did and achieved throughout my husband's illness flummoxed his medical team, and how he exceeded everybody's expectations.

The second part of this book is reference guide. Here you will find recipes, strategies and practices to give you the tools to help yourself or someone you love who is going through a similar experience.

This is the path that we walked, and for us it meant we could have our lives back, even better than before – and that is why I want to share this with you.

Everyone's journey is different. You must make your own choices and be guided by those who are qualified specialists. There are no wrong choices, but there are choices. Whether you choose conventional medicine or alternative treatment, or a combination of both, remember that your body needs to be supported. Cancer is a symptom that your body is sick; your immune system is not coping. Conventional treatment is destructive – the body will need assistance, on many levels; it will need strength to fight, and nourishment to heal. It is hard to know where to begin, or where to turn when you hear *that word* from your doctor – there is so much information out there, it feels like a minefield, when all you want is a peaceful meadow, with a clear path.

I hope that my journey, my discoveries, and my experience will help you to find your way. But if you only take one thing from this book, and choose to ignore the rest, let it be a better understanding of yourself, your body, your health, and your world.

Part 1

Prologue

Once, a long time ago, I climbed a mountain. It was hard, really hard, but I persevered and finally I reached the summit. And when I got there, I found the most amazing thing: that all the time I'd been climbing, pushing onwards and upwards, someone else had been climbing up the other side! I hadn't known at the time that he was there, but when I reached the top and saw him, from that moment I knew that it wasn't just my mountain anymore: I would share it forever with this man.

We travelled on together then, and even though the journey got harder, and much more dangerous, as we walked along our path, we had each other. We held each other, never letting go. Sometimes one of us would stumble but the other always stopped us falling.

There was one point on our journey where my man lost his footing, his feet slipping on uneven ground and he almost fell into the abyss below. He hung onto a ledge, his fingers grasping at whatever they could find; but, I too had a hold of him, and I would not let go. It took nearly all my strength, with my back aching and my arms burning with the effort of holding his weight, but with sheer determination I held on tight and, with my help, he scrambled back onto the path, shaking with relief and falling into my arms with exhaustion.

Then our path became much smoother, and we walked on level ground, laughing together as we enjoyed the beauty of the vistas around us. We even ran sometimes. Our love grew stronger every day: we were united in its strength.

One day, a little boy joined us, holding hands with both of us, walking along between us. We smiled down at him, loving him, knowing he was part of the mountain too. A little further along our path another little boy appeared, and we held him in our arms, welcoming him onto our journey.

We took pleasure in the boys' innocent fascination at the beauty in all they saw, making us notice and appreciate our surroundings with fresh eyes.

The four of us walked on together, stopping only to visit friends who we made along the way.

The road was easy, a smooth ride. Sometimes I thought back to when I was climbing alone, or to when my soulmate had lost his footing near the beginning of our journey together, but mostly I hardly thought of it. I became used to walking the easy route, once again taking each new day for granted. The sun would rise each morning, painting the sky with warmth and brilliance, and set each night saying farewell with golden strokes. The rain would fall, the birds would sing, but I just walked oblivious to the wonderful world that was mine. I knew my man was by my side, and our boys were with us playing their childish games. Friends came and went, some returning to walk with us regularly, others just on the odd occasions. We had food, we had shelter, we had each other, the four of us, and somehow I thought we were indestructible.

So when one day the clouds turned black, covering the sky, blocking the sun, so that for a moment we couldn't see the path, I wasn't ready.

Fumbling in the darkness I found his hand, but his grip had no strength, his fingers lacking somehow. Something was wrong. I searched for my boys and finding them I held them close, needing their strength to fight once more for my man.

Phase One
The Catastrophe Phase

Chapter 1

It's so easy to become complacent. It doesn't seem to matter what we have – we are always looking for that next high, never just sitting back and taking stock of all the wonderful things we have already achieved.

It isn't until something happens to make you take notice of your life in its present state that you begin to appreciate these things. For example, I would imagine that you are currently lusting after something, be it a new pair of shoes, a promotion at work, a holiday... maybe it's that your partner would be more attentive, more fun, more helpful... or that you would like your children to do better in school, get the lead role in the play, stop leaving their room looking like the aftermath of a burglary...

But just stop your world spinning for one minute and look at what you do have. Count your blessings. Count them and contemplate them. And appreciate them – all of them, because it's not until those fabulous achievements, those beautiful and amazing people, that security that you currently have becomes threatened, that you really look at life through different eyes.

I needed a holiday. I'd had a hard year! Saul had turned 50 and I had spent ages planning his party, and a surprise trip to the Barcelona Grand Prix. Admittedly I had enjoyed it – the planning, the party and the trip, but now I felt the burning need to go and lay in the sun with a good book by a sparkling blue pool, or a golden beach, somewhere! I didn't care where it was, but I knew I needed it!

"Floss, you know we can't afford it! This year has already been a huge expense, with my birthday and David's 18th as well! We went to Barcelona; why don't we just save up and go somewhere extra nice next year?"

"My birthday is coming up and you know how I love to go away with you and the boys! We can find a cheap deal! I will look into it!" I protested.

It was always the same – we never seemed to have much money. We both worked, me as a Sports Therapist in my own small clinic and Saul as a carpenter also working for himself. We both made a living from own careers, but had always lived pretty much hand to mouth. We never had much in the way of savings and I didn't believe in buying things on credit (I had my dad to thank for that trait), so we could never afford big, expensive holidays or spending sprees.

Saul sighed, resigning himself to the fact that, as I did most of our planning, bookings and money management, by the end of this week we would probably have a holiday booked for September.

I managed to find a really good deal on a low-cost website. It was a cheap hotel – all-inclusive too, and because it was such a good bargain we could afford to take the boys' friends as well. Jack had just broken up with his girlfriend and was feeling really down: it would do him good to get away and to bring a mate. And, we could take my nephew, who had just turned 18 – it could be a lovely surprise for him, I thought excitedly.

September came round quick and before we knew it the six of us were setting off to the sun. I'd heard only good stuff about Turkey, and on the budget flight on the way there I laid my head back on the head-rest, with my iPod headphones in my ears, and pictured azure blue skies reflecting off a sparkling sea, and soft golden sand to lie on. I could almost smell the fresh lime in the mojito in my hand. I smiled to myself as Rhianna sang to me about yellow diamonds.

As we stepped off the plane the heat hit me. It was very welcome, and I loved the feeling – like summer smacking you full in the face! You know you are on holiday when that happens.

On the transfer bus from the airport we were all in good spirits. None of us had been to Turkey before. My nephew George had only ever been abroad a handful of times and was always so excited to come away with us. Jack's friend Sam was a very lively and amusing chap, a bit like Jack in his disposition, slightly dappy but always happy! The four lads would have a great time together and Saul and I could relax and enjoy some much-needed alone time.

I loved holidays for obvious reasons, but spending time with Saul, away from the busy demands of home life, was the best bit for me.

Saul and I were so lucky. We still had the most amazing marriage even after 22 years! We were the envy of many of our friends, as we were still very much in love. I knew we had something very rare, that never grew old or tired, that somehow even through the stresses of daily life we managed to keep fresh and alive.

I remember meeting him, so clearly. From the minute we saw each other we both felt such an attraction that went way beyond the bounds of lust: the connection sparking something deep within our souls. We both knew that instant that we had each found our raison d'etre: the point of our existence on this earth. Nonetheless, even unwavering love like ours still needed time: time for us to be alone together; time to reconnect with each other and remind ourselves of how very fortunate we both were.

Holidays made us like young lovers again, revelling in the luxury of being together with no stress. We would enjoy long walks on the beach, romantic meals on palm-fringed terraces, making love on balmy nights; it really did us so much good that it was always worth every penny. Also, I loved spending time with the boys. We had a great relationship with them. Now they were older and could go off and do their own thing, the time we did spend with them was really appreciated. Even at home the four of us would often go for an early drink together on a Friday night after work, something I rarely saw other families do. We all had strong personalities, which often resulted in family conversations ranging from heated discussions to full-blown rows; but we all loved each other dearly and when we were not engaged in heated debates we got on famously together.

Jack was funny. There was never a dull moment when he was around. He was never embarrassed or self-conscious about anything, making himself the butt of many jokes both with our family and with his friends; but we all loved that about him. When he was around, we looked to him to entertain, and he loved nothing more than being in the limelight. He was cheeky to the point of making us cringe, but with his good looks and charming smile, he got away with his manner, making people like him all the more for it.

David, much quieter than his gregarious brother had a dry intelligent sense of humour, and would often say things unexpectedly that would make you laugh until your sides hurt. He was much deeper than Jack, and didn't like being the centre of attention at all. However, he could be so insightful; even as a little boy he was very principled and seemed to see the world with a maturity way beyond his years.

Both boys were gorgeous, and everyone loved them, but no one more than us.

George, my nephew, was like a third son to us. He and David were the same age and had grown up as close as bread and butter. I will never forget, when they were babies, they both had dummies: they would toddle around together, bumping into each other, and then would suddenly look at each other and, laughing, would swap their dummies! It was the cutest and funniest thing, and I often wish we had managed to capture it on video, but we were always too busy laughing at their antics! Hugely unhygienic of course, but I think the only effect it had on them was to create a lifelong bond. As little ones they had been inseparable – from the minute George arrived at our house he would barely notice the rest of the family, making a beeline for David. They would sit in David's room, sometimes shutting themselves in the boys' toy cupboard, making it into whatever imaginary world they had at the time. You wouldn't hear anything from them until it was time for George to leave. As they grew up their bond deepened even further, and they spent most weekends together, still sharing their worlds and their friends.

George had two older sisters, Alisha and Layla. My oldest niece, Alisha, was a pretty, dainty little girl, like a fragile flower with petals falling off at the slightest puff of breeze – it made you want to wrap her up and protect her from the world. She held herself slightly apart from the others, always seeming a little more mature. As she grew up she was for a while a troubled young girl, dealing with obstacles that seemed insurmountable, but with maturity she learnt to manage her anxieties and blossomed into a beautiful and confident young lady. The boys loved her dearly and she was always the big sister to all of them.

My youngest niece, Layla, was as a little girl a source of great amusement. If Alisha's personality seemed as though she was floating in the clouds, Layla was as down to earth and grounded as they came: a little girl with a deep voice, and a sunny smile that could charm anyone. She was the one who Jack was the most drawn to. Perhaps it was the tomboy in her, or maybe because they both had an innate sense of fun, but as youngsters they developed a strong bond.

As they grew up they were not so close as Layla realised she wanted to be more girly, and then discovered boys: while Jack was still very much a child, she was growing up much faster. She was still a girl when she became a mother but she took to it like a duck to water.

I would have loved it if the girls could have come away too, both to give me some female company and because it would have been just perfect to have them all there, but I was very happy to have George with us and Sam was good company too.

As the night began to draw in, the bus began to drop passengers at hotels. We wondered at each hotel we arrived at: was this ours? We couldn't really see much of the town, but the hotels were all bright and seemed nice from the outside.

Finally, we drew up in a side street. Even from the coach we could hear the thumping of disco music and the shrieking of drunken laughter coming from inside this hotel. I looked at Saul anxiously. Hopefully this wasn't our one!

The driver called our names, and descended from the coach to start unloading our cases. This *was* our hotel! Hopefully when we got inside we would find that it was more tasteful.

We walked into the reception area, which opened directly onto the restaurant, and a small Turkish-looking man looked up from the desk. It was dimly lit, and there was no one else around. He told us to put our bags to one side as he dealt with our check-in. He was polite but not welcoming: it didn't help to make us feel like we'd arrived at somewhere we could unwind for the next week.

Our room was on the fifth floor so we would need to use the lift. We couldn't all fit in at once, so Saul and I went first. The lift was hot, airless and smelly, and the door didn't close properly. We pressed the buttons and it rattled and graunched its way up five floors. I clung to Saul, not really being a big fan of lifts at the best of times, and feeling afraid that we would get stuck in this one.

Luckily it made it to the fifth floor and creaked its way to a halt. The doors began to open and Saul had to wrench them the rest of the way, so we could get out.

Our room wasn't a lot better. It was dark, uninviting. Brown curtains draped the window, and bed covers were an equally dull match. The bathroom had broken tiles and the shower stall was a cubicle with an old curtain around it, and brown water marks on the wall.

There was no double bed, just two singles separated by an old nightstand.

I plonked myself heavily onto the bed, my head in my hands and burst into tears.

Saul came and sat next to me. Gathering me up in his arms, he stroked my hair.

"It's okay Floss – it's not that bad," he soothed.

"This is all my fault! I booked it. I wanted a holiday so badly, I didn't research it properly."

"Floss, that's not fair. You tried to get somewhere that was lively enough for the boys!"

"I feel like I'm on a lads' holiday!" I sobbed. "It's probably like the places Jack goes to with his mates!"

"Babe, we're here now. The beds are clean, and we are together. Tomorrow, the sun will be shining bright and everything will seem much better. Let's go down and get a drink. I'm sure after a glass or two of wine this will seem like paradise!"

I refused to get back in that lift, so we took the stairs. The boys were all down by the pool bar, with a beer, smiling and laughing. They had no problem with the place. George took one look at me and knew I'd been crying.

"Auntie Floss, it's okay," he said putting his arms round me. "We're gonna have the best time, you'll see."

David had already got me a drink from the free bar. As he put it in my hand, I grimaced – a plastic cup! I sipped it expecting the worst, and was mortified to find it even worse than I'd imagined: vinegary, warm, cheap wine that made me wish it was just water instead! Oh god, could this get any worse?

We sat with the boys listening to the loud music, and watching the hotel residents downing the free booze and shouting to each other over the din. The vast majority were British sun-seekers who had come away to spend their days cooking in the sun and their nights getting tanked-up on cheap liquor and here we were, all set to spend a week with them!! I didn't think we'd be making many friends here!!

I couldn't bring myself to drink any more of the cheap wine, but we sat with the boys a while longer before finally deciding we'd had enough for the night and would re-assess things in the light of day.

The next morning, after a night of tossing and turning on lumpy beds with very spasmodic air-con in the stuffy room, we arrived downstairs to see what breakfast was like. It was not cordon bleu, that's for sure! Considering we were in a hot country, most of the fruit on offer was from a tin, and what 'fresh' fruit there was looked like it may have been around most of the week. There was a selection of processed cold meats, and rubbery hard-boiled eggs, or cheap bread with little packs of jam.

I poured myself a coffee and sat down looking at Saul glumly.

"We need to find a rep. I can't spend a week here. I'd rather not have a holiday!"

"I know," said Saul; "well, it said on the paperwork we were handed at check-in that a rep is meant to see us today, so let's see what they can do."

We took our coffee out to sit by the pool, but already the ample-bodied, heavily tattooed holiday-makers were lounging on all the sunbeds. Rolls of well-oiled flesh glistened in the sun, in colour spectrums ranging from translucent white to lobster-red. They oozed out of swimming trunks and bikinis, exposing flesh that oscillated with every tiny movement.

Mid-morning, the rep turned up to meet us. I was quite impressed with this, thinking she was coming to see if we were okay, happy and settled – this was quite a service compared to the current holiday experience so far. However, it soon transpired that she was not there to see how she could be of service to us, but more to see what she could sell us.

She smiled sweetly, showing us tobacco-stained teeth, in her otherwise immaculate appearance. Dressed in a red blazer and a white skirt, she proffered a perfectly manicured hand in greeting.

We sat down with her and before she had a chance to open her glossy brochures, I very quickly began to express my feelings:

"This is not what we expected, at all. It's a shabby hotel in a noisy resort, with cheap wine, no fresh food and a clientele that have clearly stopped in from a pub crawl via Costa del Blackpool!!"

I'm not sure she fully understood my references, but she definitely knew I was not a happy customer. Saul was a little embarrassed by my description, and tried to tone down our complaint:

"I think what my wife is trying to say, is that if possible we would like to move somewhere quieter: this is really not our scene." He smiled.

"Of course!" she said sweetly. "It's no problem."

So clichéd! I thought cynically – they always say that, when you're abroad, and it usually means: how can I soft-soap these mugs, and make more money out of them at the same time?

"I will call my manager and have you re-located as soon as possible. We have some lovely hotels the other side of the resort where you would be very happy. Now while I call him, can I suggest you relax in the sunshine and take a look at these wonderful trips that are all on special offer today. In fact, as I can see you have not had the best start to your stay, I am going to make you a very special price." She smiled so charmingly, she even had me for a moment.

She disappeared into the hotel reception, and we looked at the brochures. There were trips involving moonlit cruises, Turkish baths, jet-skiing, go-karting, natural springs, stunning beaches, quad bike safaris – you name it! There were, of course, no prices on anything.

"Shall we book a couple of things?" Saul suggested. "At least we know we will have some nice days out to enjoy – you don't want to stay by the pool all week, do you!" he laughed.

I guessed we should do something while we were here, and my birthday was in a few days too.

"Let's book a Turkish bath day, with all the boys too. It might be fun," I suggested.

In the end we decided on that and jet-skiing.

The rep returned, all smiles.

"It all arrange for you," she said in almost perfect English. "Tomorrow we collect you and take you to another hotel. Very cheap upgrade, only another £50 per person. Very good hotel. Must book today though, as all places going fast, and there are six of you. Now, what lovely trips have you decided on?"

After we showed her what we wanted, she scribbled down some sums on a scrap of paper. "As you have not good time, and it's your birthday, I give you a present. A moonlight cruise for you two, the night of your birthday, no extra cost. My present to you."

She really was charm personified!

We handed over the cash, and parted company feeling as if we had at last had something good.

Having resigned ourselves to the fact that they would sort out our accommodation tomorrow, even if it was going to cost us a fair bit to move, we decided to try and make the best of it until then, and stay by the pool. We plugged our ears with iPod headphones and buried our noses in books, trying to pretend we were somewhere a little more exotic. Later that afternoon, an important looking, smartly dressed man approached us. After introducing himself as the hotel owner, he apologised for disturbing us, and asked if he may speak with us in private.

We followed him into his office, wondering if we had offended him by complaining about the hotel. He asked if we would like a drink and ordered a bottle of wine – good wine! So they did have it – just not as part of the all-inclusive package! The office we were seated in was obviously his little haven. The theme was very black and white – masculine but very plush, with some softness in the finishing touches. Pictures of his family were on the walls, along with educational certificates.

"I am so sorry you are not happy here," he began. "I am to understand you have been offered a different hotel for a premium?"

He was very well-spoken with impeccable manners, and he had obviously been well educated.

"You speak very good English," I commented

"Ah yes, thank you. I was educated in England, and have spent many years in America, too," he smiled. "I can see that you are not like our customary clientele." He gestured towards the pool. "We welcome guests who have a little more decorum than the typical crowd."

Did he really just insult his hotel guests in an attempt to try and appease us?

"It's not really for us," Saul began politely. "Although we think our boys may well be happy here, my wife and I were looking forward to a quiet break, somewhere to read and relax, away from the din of noisy holiday-makers."

"Yes of course, I understand, and I wish we were in a position to offer you that, but I must warn you that all the hotels in this resort will be the same. You see, the resort is lively. The hotel you have been offered is no different. In fact, just last week we had guests re-locate from there to here, and they say it is much better. I can arrange for them to speak with you if you like? And of course you are at liberty to visit the hotel in question and decide for yourselves. Please, do not take me at my word."

He was so genuine, warm and refined that we had no choice but to believe him.

"If you decide to stay, I will make you my personal guests and go out of my way to ensure your stay is as comfortable as I possibly can. It will be an honour to have you here. I have already met your boys, last night, and found them utterly charming. I have already had comments from the guests that compliment your sons and their friends. I think you will all be good for my hotel."

Saul squeezed my hand under the table, questioning my opinion of the offer.

I must admit I was most impressed that he had gone out of his way to make us feel respected and valued but still rather surprised that the hotel did not seem to reflect the quality of its management.

"Please, take your time to decide. There is no rush. I can contact the rep and let them know what you would like to do. If you wish to move I will make sure you have a smooth transition. If you wish to speak to the guests who have come from the other hotel, I can arrange it."

"We'll stay," I said, surprised at my own reaction. "You have been so kind, and hospitable, I think the least we can do is to give your hotel a proper chance." I smiled and turned to Saul who was nodding in agreement.

So we had decided to make the best of it. We settled in to a week of people watching, trips out during the day and walks in the evening into the old part of town.

We actually had a great week. The boys were hilarious – they spent their evenings entertaining the hotel guests, chatting them up, making cheeky comments, and getting drinks bought for them left, right and centre – from the paid bar, that sold proper drinks! Late evening, they would go off to clubs and bars while Saul and I took long walks to the old harbour, for a nice meal or a few decent drinks.

The old part of town couldn't have been more different. About an hour away on foot, we would watch the scenery change from burger bars, tattoo parlours and thumping clubs, to narrow, cobbled streets overhung with bougainvillea, and little restaurants with chequered tablecloths and candles melted into old wine bottles. As we walked along the seafront the plastic sun-loungers crammed on the narrow bank of sand gave way to the harbour where beautiful yachts bobbed in their moorings, and the rich owners sipped cocktails in the balmy moonlight.

One night, as we sat on the terrace of a little restaurant sipping the Turkish tea that was served in the traditional tavernas in the old part of town, Saul and I chatted about our dreams, as we often did on holidays, having the time to get lost in fantasies about living in sun drenched villages in unspoilt parts of Europe.

"It's funny but I think this might the first time we've come away and I haven't wanted to check out the estate agents for bargain, quaint holiday homes!" I smiled.

"I know, Flossie – this is one place I am not one bit tempted to live!"

It had always been our dream to live abroad. When we first met we had travelled, and although that trip had a whole host of complications, we still loved the idea of doing more. Our plan had been to buy a flat in the UK, rent it out and travel for a few months, but then I fell pregnant with Jack and from then on life took over, and our dreams were put on hold. We still discussed it a lot, though, while watching holiday home programmes and looking at places where we thought it might be nice to live.

When the boys were young we'd looked seriously at going to live in the South of France (always a favourite of mine). Saul and I had booked a trip to look at schools and check the area out, but it was a disaster from the off. The day we arrived I came down with a horrific stomach bug and spent the next three days draped most inelegantly around the toilet bowl. We managed to go to one school, as we had made an appointment to see them, but were put off by the fact the boys would both have had to go down two full years, studying with much younger children, because their education system was so much more efficient than ours. I suppose we should have seen that as a plus, but we couldn't bear to do that to them. Additionally, the school seemed very Victorian with high ceilings and dark corridors and very little outdoor space, which struck us as odd in such a beautiful mountain valley town. The kids got a half-day every Wednesday when they could go off and do sport, but it was not part of their curriculum, which we felt was rather sad, even if the academic side was far superior to ours. There was something oppressive about all that academia, dark corridors and concrete – even if the work we were shown was mind-blowingly perfect! My sickness bug seemed like an omen, that we decided to heed, and consequently the decision not to move there was made. Nonetheless, we still continued to dream of one day moving away, and although we still hoped the boys would come too, we knew that the older they got the less likely that became.

Apart from the fact the rep had totally ripped us off, overcharging us for the trips, and sending us on the most unromantic "boat cruise" – which turned out to be a cheap, crammed boat, with long benches where they served processed chicken, a bit of soggy salad garnish and the obligatory pile of chips for dinner – they turned out pretty well: the Turkish baths was a scream and the jet-skiing was great fun too.

The hotelier was true to his word, buying us drinks, always coming to see that we were okay; even sending the boys off on a free go-karting trip.

The day we left, he came to say goodbye personally, expressing his hopes that we would return. Although we were very grateful for his personal attention and hospitality, I knew that it was one place that we would not be re-visiting.

We had managed to have fun, though, and to relax into our holiday, making the best of a situation which could otherwise have been a nightmare. But we were very happy to get on the plane to go home.

"I'm so tired – I can't wait to get home, have a nice power shower and climb into our king-size, comfy bed!" I said snuggling up to Saul on the flight.

"Me too," he smiled pulling me close. "I think that spending a week in that place has challenged my immune system: my glands have come up," he said rubbing the side of his neck.

"Always happens on a flight! Its most likely the combination of being in that grotty resort and the air-con in this cabin. You are probably getting a cold."

"Great! Just what I need going back to work!"

Chapter 2

The evenings had started to draw in, marking the onset of autumn. Three weeks had passed since we'd got back from Turkey, and we were well and truly back to the grind.

One night, lying in bed, Saul said to me,

"You know, it's funny, but I've still got that gland up in my neck, and it never came to anything – not even a sore throat!"

"Maybe your body is still trying to fight it off?"

"Yes, maybe, but it's odd – it doesn't feel tender to touch like a swollen gland usually does, and there's no swelling on the other side."

"I think you should get it checked out, Saul. It's probably nothing, but you're right it does seem a bit unusual."

"Oh Floss, I hate going to the doctors. They'll probably put me on antibiotics – that's what they usually do!"

"Yes I know, but I still think you should go, babe. I'll make you an appointment tomorrow."

Although Jack had had a great time on his holiday with us, he was still moping around after splitting from his girlfriend. It had been over two months and although he was his usual bright self on the surface, I knew he wasn't right.

Anabelle had become so close to us all when they were together, we all missed her terribly, but when your children decide for whatever reason not to be with someone, you have to try and let them go. David had become close to her too, and they were like brother and sister. Even George, Alisha and Layla loved her, and my mum thought of her as another granddaughter – she had been perfect for Jack, and although they were young, she was just what he needed in his life right now, and we all knew it.

"I heard from Anabelle today," I said to Saul over dinner.

"You have to stop messaging her, Floss! It's not fair on Jack.

I know you miss her, we all do, but unless she and Jack can work things out, you have to let go!"

"I know! You are right, but she misses all of us too, and do you know something? I think she would like to try again with Jack, but doesn't know how to!"

"Well if she does, Floss, that's great, and we will welcome her back with open arms, but you have to let Jack sort it out."

"Hmmm..." I agreed, on the surface.

I couldn't tell Saul that Anabelle told me she had asked to see Jack. I didn't know if he had answered her as yet, and was so nervous that he might say no. I knew he wanted to desperately, but I also knew he couldn't face just being friends with her, and if he thought that's all she wanted, he wouldn't agree to see her.

When Saul came home the next day, he'd seen the doctor.

"He's not worried, thinks it might be glandular fever or something – but still thinks I should go for tests."

"Really?" I asked, feeling a tendril of fear raise its head in my gut. I knew the doctor he had seen and trusted him. If he wanted Saul to go for tests, then he must be concerned.

The letter came through quickly and by the middle of October Saul had had everything from blood tests to magnetic resonance imaging (MRI) and positron emission tomography (PET) scans. We didn't really discuss it much, both thinking our own private thoughts about it. I guess in some way we thought if we didn't talk about it, it wouldn't come to anything. There is some saying about not giving something energy to become anything, or some such nonsense – well, we were going down that route! Saul had his appointment booked to get his result, and until then we were just ignoring it.

The day before, Jack casually told me he was seeing Anabelle for a drink, so may be late home for Sunday dinner.

"Oh, that's nice," I said trying to sound simultaneously nonchalant and like I knew nothing about it.

"Mum, I know she's been talking to you, so you probably already knew I was going."

I couldn't lie to my son.

"She said she wanted to ask if you might meet her, that's all I knew," I said defensively.

He sloped off to get ready, but there was a look about him that told me he was hopeful.

I clock-watched waiting for him to come back with news of how it had gone. Three hours later and still he hadn't returned. The phone ringing disturbed my impatience. It was Jack.

"Hi Mum! Erm, is there enough Sunday dinner for Anabelle too?" he asked. I could hear the grin behind his words; he knew how happy I would be!!

They came home together, and it was as if they had never split in the first place.

The next day David was taking his driving test. The poor lad had already failed three times. He was a really good driver, very safe and careful, but lacked confidence. He had always lacked confidence, in so many things. As a little boy he would always assume that everyone was better than him. It didn't help him that Jack was so confident and seemed to sail through most things without really trying, whereas David put his heart and soul into everything, and although he also succeeded in most things too, he never really thought he did, or always felt he could have done better. We always thought this was actually a great quality, as he was always striving for the very best he could be, but he didn't quite see it that way, and consequently it affected his self-esteem.

The morning of his test, I drove him to the test centre. Rain splattered the windows, washing away any shred of confidence he may have had.

"At least not so many people may be out today – hopefully the rain will keep them in," I said trying to find a small positive.

"Don't, Mum. Just don't even try," he said staring at the grey road ahead.

He seemed to take ages on the test. Others who had come in with him had long finished, and still I sat there on the edge of my seat in the grim waiting room, where there wasn't even a coffee machine to take your mind off your child's nerves! Finally, his car pulled into the car park. I could see the examiner talking to him, and him nodding or uttering responses, but I couldn't make out what the outcome was.

"I reckon he's done okay, love," said a driving instructor who was waiting for his pupil to return. "They usually chuck 'em out of the car pretty quick if it's a fail."

Feeling buoyed by his comment, but not wanting to count any chickens, I smiled politely, and continued to wait.

The driver's door opened slowly. David was holding a sheet of paper in his hand – was it a pass certificate, or a document outlining his majors and minors, to add to the previous three fail sheets?

I ran out of the centre and up to him. He had his head down as I approached him, but slowly raised his eyes to mine. He was obviously going to try and pretend he'd failed, but he couldn't keep the smile off his face.

"Oh David!!" I cried flinging my arms round his tall frame. "I'm so proud of you!!"

He picked me up, spinning me round. "I did it!" he said triumphantly.

I was really happy. In the last two days my eldest had been re-united with his lovely girlfriend and now my youngest had finally passed his driving test. Things were looking good. I felt confident that all my wishes were coming true. Things always happened in threes! Now just one more – the most important one – that Saul's test results would come back negative.

David was off, driving around to see all his friends, and being the willing chauffeur for a few weeks while the novelty of being a driver was still fresh. I made a mental note to milk this one – remembering how quickly Jack had tired of driving everywhere after he passed his test! So Saul and I planned a few nights out where we could enjoy having a drink together knowing David was willingly on hand to pick us up.

Jack was so much happier since he and Anabelle had got back together. Although he was generally a very happy boy he had missed her so much – more than he would say. Always the clown and never a great talker, he covered his true feelings with a joke and a cheeky grin, and most people, including Saul, were none the wiser. The two of them worked together, Jack being Saul's apprentice carpenter, and always got on great, but it always amazed me that they never really talked; they just joked around a lot – I guess that was a bloke thing, especially as most of the time they were on a building site: probably the most 'blokey' place on earth apart from a football stadium!

Anyway, I was probably one of the few people Jack did ever talk to, and that wasn't really because he wanted to, but because I always knew when shadows were lurking beneath that sunny exterior. It was so lovely to see the light shining from deep within his eyes now he was back with Anabelle. His smile was not just for everyone else's benefit, but because he was truly happy.

The morning of Saul's consultation, I drove to the site where he and Jack were working, to pick him up.

It was only round the corner from the hospital so we were there before we knew it, and didn't discuss how we felt on the way. To be honest, I hadn't allowed myself to think too much, pushing it to the very back of my mind, not wanting to give it any credibility.

On the way to collect Saul, I couldn't now stop thoughts of hospitals entering my head however hard I tried to distract myself. I hated them. Clinical places with no soul, where sick people went, and some never came out again. They smelled of medicine, disinfectant and illness. No one was ever happy, not the patients, the visitors or the staff. From the cleaners to the doctors, no one who worked there ever seemed to feel good about their jobs, or if they did very few conveyed this. Maybe I was biased. I'm sure there were many a cheery nurse, and tea ladies with ready smiles, but I couldn't help it. The last time I came to this place was the last time I ever saw my dad. The day will forever be imprinted in my mind. I had sat with my mum, Saul, Michael, Tess, Jack, David, George and Alisha round his bed. The only one who wasn't there was Layla, because she was so close to giving birth; but the rest of us sat watching my dad. He was hooked up to a heart monitor, a drip and breathing apparatus, because his lungs had all but given up. He had been asleep for almost two days, and we all knew that he wasn't going to wake up. But he was still there – I could feel him, he was there inside his body. He could hear us. He knew my mum was crying. He heard Saul and Michael take it in turns to read the newspapers. He heard Jack, David and George making jokes and chasing the darkness out of the room. He heard Tess, Alisha and I talking softly to him. I had always loved his hands. My dad always had the coolest hands. They were never clammy, always smooth, calm and gentle, with strong fingers with square, neat nails. I held his hand as I spoke quietly to him. I remember my promise to him:

"Dad, I know you are holding on because you are worried about Mum. You don't need to worry. We will all take care of her. You can go, whenever you feel too tired, Dad; sleep whenever you are ready, don't try to fight anymore."

My mum sat on one side of him crying onto his chest, while I held his hand and gazed down at his face. He must have heard me, he must have known what I was whispering to him, because at that moment the gentle pressure on my hand released and his face changed. He had gone. My dad's body was empty: a vessel no longer required. Everything that made him the man who he was – his thoughts, his feelings, his personality, his soul – had gone, to another place.

When we left the hospital that day, somehow I felt as though it had taken him from me. He had gone in there and never come out. He would never come out. It was his Hotel California: "You can check out any time you like, but you can never leave."

For about a year, I couldn't drive past the building without feeling some small resentment. I knew it was stupid, childish even, but for a while that's how I felt.

Now, just over two years later, here I was again, this time with Saul. Back to the place that had taken my dear dad. Well, it wasn't having my husband.

Chapter 3

We walked into an annexe at the back of the hospital. That was good, I thought. It wasn't a cancer wing or anything sinister, just an assessment unit.

The waiting room was a large, open space with abstract art on the walls in garish colours – not very relaxing, but I suppose it was quite cheery, if you like that sort of thing.

I sat there holding Saul's hand and absently thumbing through a magazine. It seemed to be a long wait and the room was mainly empty, so I couldn't really see why. I was sitting next to a glass door that opened onto a small patch of grass. Movement at the window caught my eye, and I turned to see a magpie – just one, on his own, looking at me beadily. I raised my hand to salute him – always superstitious, but before I could touch my brow he was gone.

"Saul Hammond," called an austere voice from behind us.

We stood and walked into a tiny, cramped room at the back of the clinic. Two men sat in there: the one who had called us had grey hair, and glasses perched on his nose; the other was a younger man with dark hair who smiled as we entered and offered his hand in greeting.

"I'm Mr Southerland, Consultant Surgeon, and this is my registrar," said the older man, waving towards the younger without looking up from his desk.

"You've had several tests done I see, and you have cancer. It's a secondary lesion, a squamous cell carcinoma," he continued without pausing for breath, looking up or even giving us time to take on board the news that Saul had cancer!

"What? Cancer, Saul's got cancer?" I said stunned.

Saul gripped my hand and calmly replied, "Can you please explain, Mr Southerland?"

"Yes," he said without a shred of empathy in his tone. "As I said, it's a secondary, a squamous cell carcinoma. It means there is a primary somewhere which we've yet to find. Treatment is fairly standard: we will do an exploratory under general to locate the primary, which is usually located within the vicinity, and then will commence a course of treatment which will be a combination of chemo and radio."

"Oh my god! Cancer, Saul's got cancer!" I cried. Big, fat tears rolled down my cheeks, and I began sobbing uncontrollably. "No, he can't have; there must be a mistake. He can't have cancer." My nose started to run, tears and snot converging in rivers dripping off my chin with nowhere to go but my lap. I didn't care. I didn't care about anything. This couldn't be happening. This was not real.

The registrar silently handed me a tissue. Perhaps the sight of me dripping and leaking everywhere was too much – probably not very hygienic in a hospital. Mr Southerland, on the other hand, ignored me altogether. I don't really think he even knew I was there. He didn't even really seem to know that Saul was there. He was just talking like a computer-generated animation, on auto-pilot, spurting our information with no thought or feeling. He barely even looked up from his desk.

"Right," said Saul decisively, "so that's fine – another test to find the primary, and then when can I start treatment? I want to start as soon as possible." He was so calm. He had just been told he had cancer. Cancer. And he was asking rational, lucid, reasonable, sensible questions. How was he doing that? He squeezed my hand as I let out another loud sob.

"Yes, we will arrange all that as soon as we have the results from the exploratory. Now, any other questions?"

Any other questions?? "Yes!!" I screamed inside my head. "Why was this happening? How was this happening? You're lying to us. You've made a mistake. This isn't right."

"No. Thank you," said Saul quietly. "I think that's all for now. I'm assuming you will send my appointment for the procedure in the post?"

"Yes, that's all in hand," My Southerland said dismissively, waving us out of the room, so that he could offer our seats to some other poor, unsuspecting victim to be told their fate in the same cold tone that we had been. He was probably rolling his eyes at his colleague as he shut the door. Another blubbing, emotional patient to deal with, what a nuisance!

As we walked out of the building Saul pulled me into his arms. I sobbed into his shoulder, soaking his t-shirt. I couldn't speak. My throat felt swollen and closed. He stroked my hair, finding his own strength by comforting me. He turned me round to start walking back to the car, still holding me close, neither of us speaking. He drove back to his site.

"Let me ask Jack to drive you home, Floss," he said when we arrived. "You're too upset to drive."

"What? No! I mean, you can't go back to work, not after that! Come home with me!!"

"No Floss. I need to go to work. Do you understand? I need to just get on with my afternoon. Jack will come home with you. I will give him the afternoon off."

"No. You come home," I begged.

"No Floss. Please understand. This is my way of dealing with this. I have to go to work. I will see you at home."

Jack looked over from his work, and walked towards the car. He took one look at my face and quickened his step.

"Mum, what? What did they say? Dad?" he asked, worried.

"Dad's got cancer!!" I cried and again the sobs started.

"Jack, I need you to go home with Mum. She's too upset to be alone. Drive her home."

"No, Saul," I said recovering myself a little. "If you are staying here, then I want Jack to be with you. You need him right now."

Poor Jack looked from me to Saul and back again, not knowing what to do or who to listen to.

"Look after him Jack," I said.

"Okay Mum," Jack said quietly, his head down. Poor lad, he looked so distraught. This was so hard on him too. I got out of the car and put my arms round him, suddenly finding a little strength from somewhere.

"Whatever happens, we will get through it," I whispered to him.

I touched Saul's hand, shut the car door and drove away.

As I drove home, tears continued their journey down my cheeks. I had been crying for over an hour already and they showed no sign of stopping – all the way home they just kept coming, an eternal reservoir of water from deep within my soul. Soon I would be sitting in a pool of tears.

My mobile rang as I was driving. My best friend knew where we were going today and she was calling to find out what had happened.

We had known each other since Jack and her son became good friends during the summer holidays before they started senior school. I remember the day I first met her. She arrived to collect her son from our house – this stylish woman, who looked as if she had just stepped out of a magazine, with her strawberry-blonde hair piled on top of her head and designer sunglasses on. I thought at first glance she was a typical Surrey housewife: rich husband, lady-who-lunched type who would have nothing in common with me. Then, she got out of her car, revealing her not-so-glamorous, muddy running shoes and tracksuit bottoms, and came over to chat – a warm, friendly girl, whose infectious smile gave away the humour that was such a big part of her personality. From day one she became a huge part of my life. We had lived in the same village then, and although later, after her marriage ended, she moved into town, we still saw each other most weeks and spoke every day. No one ever laughed at the same things that we thought were funny. We would have stupid names for things, and the same silly jokes would crop up time and time again making us laugh each time until our sides hurt. I had a lot of good friends, but no one else as loopy as her, or who understood my very off-the-wall sense of humour like she did. But she was also always there for me, through every single little blip however small it seemed: she listened, made sense of it, talked me out of it, or made me laugh, and whatever it was would pale into insignificance. But this time not even Rica could make this better.

I pulled over and rang her back.

"I can't talk. I'm driving and I've just stopped to call you. It's bad. Saul's got cancer," I sobbed. "I can't —"

"Okay, okay Floss. Call me when you get home. Just call me and tell me you got home okay, and then call me later when you want to talk. Call me whenever, day, night. Just call. Okay?"

"Okay," I said, hanging up.

Finally I got home. I walked in the door, the same door I had walked through every day for the last 12 years, but never had I walked through it and felt like I did today. Like life had changed forever: that normal, everyday, mundane sameness was now not the same. How I longed for my unexciting, routine existence. I wanted to speak to David and to my mum, but I didn't have the strength as yet. Mum would be so devastated, and she would cry. I couldn't deal with that. I couldn't deal with being the strong one, not right now. And David, I needed to tell him, but he was at work, and he would be on duty. He was a lifeguard at the leisure centre. I couldn't speak to him when he on poolside, and again, I didn't know that I was ready to talk to anyone, even my son.

The only person who at that time I knew I needed to talk to was my brother, Michael.

Firstly, he was the most level-headed, rational person I knew, and would speak to me not with emotion, although of course he'd be upset, but with clarity. He would be calm, and give me good advice on how to deal with this. He was always like that, a bank manager, he knew how to deal with people, how to get people to problem-solve themselves, by speaking objectively. He had this really great knack of being able to get people to come to their own conclusions about how to deal with things. He never told you what to do, but somehow made you see the way forward, however thick the trees. Even when we were kids, although he was five years older than me, he would be there for me, a guiding hand, who never judged. As a teenager you didn't always want to disclose things to your parents, as they may worry too much, or get emotional, or maybe give you a hard time and your friends often gave bad advice for the wrong reasons, but he was somewhere in between. Not a parent, yet more than a friend.

The second reason I needed to speak to him is that he had been exactly where I was right now. My sister-in-law, his wife Tess, had had cancer, and not only once but twice – the first time was before they met. As a young 22-year-old woman she had suffered with an aggressive form of leukaemia: others who had it like she had had not survived. She had a bone marrow transplant, and went through seven shades of hell, but she pulled through. Then before she married my brother she was diagnosed with breast cancer. Once again, that was nothing minor for her, and she had had to undergo surgery, but once again she came out the other side. Her strength and courage was incredible, and I had nothing but the deepest admiration for how she'd fought back each time to be here to tell the tale. She was a wonderful girl, and my brother loved her with all his heart. I loved her not only because she was my sister-in-law, for all she had been through, or because she was warm, caring and incredibly big-hearted, but because she brought out the very best in my brother. All the things that made him a great man, she somehow magnified, and made him even greater. Now, though, I saw her in a different light again; my admiration for her swelled in my heart as a beacon of hope. She knew how to fight this frightening disease! And my brother, the calm font of knowledge, had known how to keep strong and get through as her carer. I needed now to speak to him more than anyone.

The minute I heard Michael's voice on the phone the tears began again.

"Flossie, whatever's wrong?"

I could barely make myself understood as my voice broke with emotion,

"It's Saul – he's got c-cancer!" I sobbed.

"Okay, I hear you," he began calmly. "I need you to take a very deep breath and try to calm your tears, so that we can talk."

I did as he suggested and began to regain a little control. I explained what had happened, from the minute Saul had found the swelling on his neck until today's conclusion.

"Flossie, why haven't you told me about this before?"

"I didn't want to say anything, and worry anyone in case it was nothing, and to be honest I didn't want to give it wings!" I said trying not to cry anymore.

"Yes, I understand, that makes sense. Right, what I need you to do is to find out as much information as you can, so we know exactly what we are dealing with."

I loved him so much – he had already taken some of it away from me, by making it something that "we" were dealing with.

"It doesn't sound as if the consultant told you much, but then they do this. They need to let you get over the impact of the news before you can begin to process it enough to ask questions. So make yourself a coffee, or pour yourself a large glass of red, and write down everything you want to know. Get the facts. The name of the cancer, the exact location, the prognosis, the treatment options available, time-frames, the structure of his support team, contact details... write it all down in a book, and whenever you go to the hospital take the book with you. Get all the answers, and then ask more questions. Every time you find out any information, email it to me."

I tried to take it all in. Basically he was telling me to do what I always did in times of crises. Take control. This was not about falling apart and letting it destroy our world; it was about looking at facts, and finding out how to deal with every aspect of it, armed with as much information as possible.

"The other thing you need to do is to think about what he's putting into his body," Michael said interrupting my thoughts, "You need to make sure he is getting all the supplementation he needs. I will speak to Jason and get some advice, as soon as I have more information from you."

Jason was Tess's oldest brother. He was a naturopath who had been one of the main reasons Tess had done so very well through her own illnesses. He had been there for her as a brother, but also as someone knowledgeable about complementary treatments, and he had contributed to the success of her recovery flummoxing the medical profession. Although no one really knew, it may well have been the reason that she survived both episodes in the face of such adversity, when others in the same despairing situation had not fared as well as her by a long way.

"Yes please. Please speak to Jason. I want to do everything possible to help Saul." I felt a surge of hope rise from pool of anguish in my soul.

Speaking to Michael had helped. It had made me able to begin to formulate some rational thought instead of feeling as though my world had just ended. Before Saul's diagnosis, although I hadn't wanted to give any credibility to the possibility of cancer, I had done a little research into things. I'd also looked into it previously for friends. One of my closest friends had only just finished treatment for breast cancer, and Saul's cousin, who we were close to, had had a diagnosis just six months previously, so I had been reading about ways to support the body and to either prevent or help treat the dreaded disease. One of the things I had read about was something called a "blackstrap molasses/ bicarbonate of soda Trojan": this was based on the theory that cancer cells are attracted to sugar.

The Trojan theory suggested that if you remove all sugar from the diet, and then blend bicarbonate of soda with a very high-grade sugar such as Blackstrap molasses, the cancer cells will be attracted to the sugar and the bicarbonate of soda will kill the cells. Cutting sugar from the diet in itself was a good thing, as there is evidence to show that cancer cells feed on blood glucose[1] and also that cancer cells can readily metabolize fructose to increase proliferation[2].

In addition to this, I was planning on implementing an alkaline-based diet. Although it can be argued that it is not possible to change the pH of one's blood[3], eating an alkaline-based diet is not really about trying to change your blood's pH so much as minimising the stress on your body caused by an acidic diet. The body will make a multitude of sacrifices with regards your long-term health in order to maintain your short-term health by keeping the pH of your cellular fluids at 7.365. This can include drawing calcium from the bones, pulling magnesium from the muscle tissues, and the increase of yeasts, bacteria and microbial overgrowths in the digestive tract; and, most importantly, weakening immune function. An alkaline-forming diet, that also stabilised his blood sugar, was definitely something we needed to do, but right now I figured trying the bicarbonate Trojan theory was a good starting place because it was something I could do straight away, and I needed to start being practical, to focus my mind on healing protocols rather than negativity.

So, jumping into the car I drove down to my local health food shop and bought a large jar of organic molasses, which in itself has beneficial properties due to its rich mineral and anti-oxidant content.

By the time Saul came home, I'd spoken to Mum, called Rica back, spoken to my other best friend Evie, written a preliminary list of questions in an old notebook that I'd found, and worked out a rough diet plan for Saul to embark on.

---

1   http://www.sciencedirect.com/science/article/pii/0006291X85919308

2   http://cancerres.aacrjournals.org/content/70/15/6368.abstract

3   http://www.biomedcentral.com/content/pdf/1550-2783-9-50.pdf

I hadn't yet spoken to David, as I couldn't tell him at work – it just wasn't fair to do that to him. We would sit down as a family tonight and tell him together. And as a family we would stand strong as we always did, and face the world united. Throw what you want at us: we will fight it, and we will emerge triumphant!

Chapter 4

Saul and I always reacted very differently to crisis situations. I remember when Jack was very little, he and I were at my mum and dad's house when he fell on a toy with his leg twisted beneath him, and spiral-fractured his femur. I didn't know at the time, as there was no outward sign of fracture, and put him in his car-seat and drove him to hospital. The poor little chap had screamed all the way there, and really loudly whenever we hit a bump in the road or took a corner. When I found out his leg was broken, I went to pieces, crying uncontrollably, which didn't help Jack at all! When Saul had arrived at the hospital he calmly spoke to the doctors, and sat with his distraught son and distracted him by talking about his favourite book that he had with him at the time. Instantly, Jack calmed down, I calmed down, and the situation became much easier to handle. Saul was my rock, our rock, and now he needed us to be strong for him.

I had thought that because this was about him he would be different, but no, not my brave man. When he came home, it was as if, in his eyes, the world was no different from this morning.

"Hey Floss," he said putting his arms round me, "how are you doing?"

How am *I* doing? I thought. He was incredible.

When David got home I let Saul tell him, and he did so in a way that down-played his news, taking the sting out of it totally

"How did it go today Dad?" asked David, his dark eyes serious and concerned.

"Well son, looks like I'm gonna get a few weeks' holiday!" he said grinning

"Gonna get some treatment for this little fella growing out of my neck, get him zapped, have a little rest, then back to work!"

David smiled, amused by his dad's easy manner. "Did they say what it was?" He needed to know the cold truth, however Saul wanted to put it.

"Yeah, it's cancer, but hey, it's treatable!" Saul said putting his sandwich box in the dishwasher.

David looked at me, knowing that my face would convey the truth. I quickly smiled, not wanting to worry him more than he would anyway.

We sat down to eat dinner, and Saul encouraged the boys to joke with him.

"So, I get to play the cancer card now!" he said laughing. "I can't take my turn at washing up, I've got cancer! I can't cut the lawn, I've got cancer!!"

The boys were buoyed by his temperament and joined in.

I sat there quietly. I couldn't make it into a joke, no matter how much I knew why Saul was doing this and that he was right. My dinner stuck in my throat, and I swallowed it down with water, trying to keep a lid on my emotions, for the boys' sake and for Saul.

After dinner, the boys went up to their rooms, and Saul came over to me and wrapped me in his arms.

Now the boys had left the room my internal waterfall began to flow once more.

"C'mon Floss," Saul said. "Crying won't change anything."

"But they haven't even found the primary – what if they can't find it? What if it's really bad, like in a major organ or something?" I said voicing the fears that I had suppressed all day.

"What-ifs are a waste of time, babe! There is no point worrying like this – let's just see what they say."

"I can't help it Saul, how can I? You are my whole world, I can't bear it," I choked on my own words.

"Floss, we will get through this. Please try not to let it get to you. I need you to find a way to be strong, OK?" he said raising my face to his.

I couldn't answer, for fear of tears starting again, so I kissed him, nodding that I would do my best.

I knew that Saul was right. I did need to find a way to cope with this, and be strong for him, for the boys and for myself. With the help of Michael and Tess and, indirectly, Tess's brother Jason, I embarked on a personal journey which would take me through this time and help Saul to recover more quickly and more fully then I could ever have hoped for.

I spent hours researching diet and supplements that would help support his body and immune system. When the demons in my mind started tormenting me at night, I would get up and go downstairs to do more research. I wrote it all down, everything I learnt. I cross-referenced articles, read people's anecdotal stories, and looked at clinical evidence. I read about his type of cancer, about the treatments, but most of all about what I could do to support him through this. I knew that he would be subjected to some gruesome treatments and that he would need to have an immune system built of steel in order to come through as undamaged as possible. It wasn't just about fighting the cancer, but about making sure his body could cope with the horrors of the treatment. With no time to waste, I got him started on his new diet. We had always eaten very healthily, but now, this was a whole new regime.

During periods of stress the body will dehydrate and blood pressure will increase, the cells become more acidic and more prone to inflammatory conditions. He needed an alkalizing diet to help his body to detoxify: to reduce the stress currently on his immune system and vital organs – as they were going to need all their resources to deal with the drugs that would be pumped into him – and to stabilise his blood sugar; a diet that would give his body the tools it needed to thrive.

To begin with, we increased his water intake to 2 litres (filtered) a day – this was in addition to herbal teas – and removed diuretics (tea, coffee and alcohol). We cut out all refined sugars, dairy, red meat, and anything vaguely processed. He ate mostly raw vegetables (a lot of leafy greens), oily fish, chicken, nuts, seeds, raw oils (olive, flaxseed, hemp), apple cider vinegar, berries, lightly steamed veg, brown rice, and pulses. (See Part Two for meal plans.)

In addition, on Jason's recommendation, he took digestive enzymes on an empty stomach[4,5] and IP6 with inositol[6] as a supplement. He also had increased doses of Vitamin C (2000mg a day), along with Vitamin E, selenium and quercetin.

He was so good about his diet, accepting that it was going to help him, and feeling comforted by the fact that I was being proactive rather than falling apart. We both needed this for different reasons – him physiological and me psychological.

Saul's exploratory examination came at the end of November, almost a month after the initial diagnosis, and before long we were called back to the hospital to see the consultant again, and hear the news of what they had found. We had to wait until they had assimilated all his test data and he was then referred to an oncology (branch of medicine that deals with the prevention, diagnosis and treatment of cancer) consultant, a Dr Wick. Mr Southerland was an Ear, Nose and Throat (ENT) surgeon.

The day of his appointment, we sat once again in the tiny claustrophobic room in the hospital's ENT department, and waited for Mr Southerland, and Dr Wick, to arrive.

The registrar sat in with us – this time a lady.

"Mr Southerland will be along in a few moments to give you more details of what he found – but basically, the primary cancer is at the base of your tongue where it joins your throat," she said. She certainly had a better bedside manner than Mr Southerland, although she was still very matter-of-fact.

The door opened and Mr Southerland walked in.

"Saul Hammond?" he said as though he'd never seen him before! This guy was unreal, such a charmer! The very least he

---

4 http://articles.mercola.com/sites/articles/archive/2011/08/21/enzymes-special-report.aspx

5 http://www.healingcancernaturally.com/pancreatic-proteolytic-enzymes.html

6 http://www.ncbi.nlm.nih.gov/pubmed/14608114

could do was remember the patients to whom he was dishing out shit news!!

"Yes, that's me!" Saul grinned, with enough charm for everyone in the cold, clinical, claustrophobic room.

"Yes, the primary cancer is in fact a small lesion at the base of the left side your tongue, as I think my colleague here has explained. Quite remarkable really, as generally when we find the primary lesion the cells surrounding it are also quite suspicious too, but yours are surprisingly normal looking. The tumour itself is very small: less than 2 cm, but due to its location it cannot be surgically removed. The swelling in your neck, as you know, is the secondary tumour. My colleague here will discuss your treatment plan." He nodded at the registrar, indicating that she should take over, and without a backwards glance he left the room, probably forgetting we existed as soon as the door closed behind him.

I squeezed Saul's hand. I felt that what we were doing with his diet and supplements was the right thing – Mr Southerland himself had commented on the unusual health of the surrounding cells and even though I had no proof, the news was positive so I felt encouraged!

Finally, Dr Wick came in to join us. A softly spoken lady with a pleasant manner, she offered her hand to both Saul and I as she entered.

"I gather you have been fully updated as to your results, so now we need to discuss your treatment."

I got my notebook out of my bag with all my questions. I knew that there would be quite a few.

"The general approach to treatment is a six-week course of radiotherapy, comprising 30 fractions of treatment, and this is supported with chemotherapy at the same time."

I looked in my book.

"What sort of radiotherapy is it?" I asked. She looked at me, clearly surprised that I even knew there were differing types.

"It will be intensity modulated radiation. This matches the strength to the shape and position of the tumour, maximising effectiveness and minimising damage to healthy tissue," she explained.

I nodded, pleased that he would at least be getting the best type of radiotherapy.

"And what about the chemo – what type of that will he be getting?"

"Our gold standard for his type of cancer is Cisplatin. It's a platinum-based treatment and has the best research outcomes."

"What are the side effects of the treatment, for both the radiotherapy and the chemotherapy? Please can you explain all of them, beginning with the short-term effects and then the long-term?" She glanced at the registrar clearly not used to such extensive questioning.

She turned to Saul although I had asked the question, who was sitting quietly listening. I wasn't sure how much he was taking in, and I knew he was happy to let me take the lead and get the information we needed.

"Well, during the initial stages of radiotherapy you probably won't feel too much. In fact, during each treatment, you won't feel a thing," she smiled trying to reassure as much as she could, "but as the treatment goes on it will have an accumulative effect and you will begin to notice some changes: usually a tingling in your skin, which then becomes sorer, like sunburn. Your mouth will begin to feel sore too, and eventually swallowing will become difficult. We will talk more about that in a moment, as there are things we can do to help with this. You will probably lose your hair, but only from the part that is treated, like your beard, but probably only from the mouth down, although the chemo will affect the rest. The worst part of the radiotherapy comes after the treatment finishes, because of its effect being cumulative – it's much worse at the end and for a couple of weeks afterwards, before you then start to feel better."

We both nodded. We had some vague prior understanding of the treatment, but she had explained it well.

"Long-term," she continued, "you will experience a dry mouth. This varies with everyone, but you will get it. Some people recover their saliva to some extent, others don't. It's very hard to predict how you will react, but the fact that you will be having the intensity modulated radiotherapy should reduce this side effect. However, you will need to take extra care of your teeth and oral health afterwards as lack of saliva can pre-dispose you to dental issues. We will get you looked at by a dentist prior to treatment, to check there is nothing underlying that needs attention first. Your tastes will change. You may find that there are things you liked before that afterwards you don't and vice versa and again these changes may be permanent, semi-permanent or just transient; there are no hard and fast rules, everyone is different. There are also some minimal risks of an underactive thyroid, cataracts and the possibly of radiotherapy-induced cancers in the future, but these risks are very low compared to the treatment's positive outcomes"

"So I will only have half a beard?" Saul said grinning. I marvelled at him. With everything she was explaining, that's what he had grasped, and was now making a joke of! How I wished I could be more like him, but then I guess that was his way of dealing with it, and this was mine. I continued to press her,

"Okay, so how about the chemotherapy?"

"The Cisplatin's short-term effects will be nausea, sickness and hair loss. The long-term effects can be reduced kidney function, lowered immune function, altered sensitivity in fingers and toes, tinnitus and possible hearing loss. Obviously we will provide all the anti-sickness support he needs."

I sat there looking at her in total shock. How can this be a good thing? Here was my man, healthy, all bar a stupid lump, and they were going to poison him and burn him and reduce the quality of his life to god-knows-what, and that was just acceptable? There must be something else we could do, surely? Even Saul couldn't seem to make light of these revelations.

"So Cisplatin, is this the only option we have? I mean, is it the only chemotherapy available for his type of cancer, or are there others, with different, well, less horrendous long-term effects?"

Dr Wick looked at her colleague, as if there was something else that she didn't want to disclose.

"Well, there is another drug, but it's not as well researched," she began. "It's called Cetuximab and it's a monoclonal antibody. It tends to be more targeted, working on specific proteins on the surface of the cells rather being indiscriminate like the platinum-based drugs."

I sat up, already more interested, as it sounded as if it would be less destructive by its very nature.

"And its side effects?"

"Short-term, it can still make you nauseous and give you diarrhoea, but it does also give you an extremely nasty rash in the treatment zone and sometimes even more widespread. It will be like a cross between eczema and a nasty bout of acne – quite painful, and coupled with the burns from radiotherapy – it is often not tolerated well at all. There can also be a reduction in red blood cells and in electrolyte balance, particularly a lowering of magnesium."

She seemed to be doing her best to paint a grim picture of this option, but I was not put off by short-term ill effects.

I scribbled a few notes in my notebook.

"Okay, what about the long-term effects?"

"Well, there may be some scarring of the skin in the treatment area," she said. I waited for more. "Other than that, there are few known long-term effects."

I was aghast! "So the platinum-based chemo can give him suppressed immune function, deafness and reduced kidney function, but the antibody drug might scar his face?" I reiterated her words, trying to form a comparison in my head. It seemed like a no-brainer to me!

"Well yes, but Cisplatin is our gold standard, because it has had such extensive research. The Cetuximab is much newer and hasn't been subject to the same research, so there are maybe things we don't know about."

Was it just me or was she trying to put us off?

"Okay, well let me ask this then," I said, trying to be as objective as I could. "The trials that have been done on the outcomes of Cetuximab – have they been successful?"

"Yes, yes of course," said Dr Wick.

"So even though there are far fewer trials to date, the outcomes have shown as much success as those for Cisplatin?"

"Yes, they have, but as I said, they are far fewer, and the drug is much newer, so we haven't been able to gauge the full impact of all its long-term effects as yet."

"No, I realise what you are saying, but as you have also said, we do know the long-term effects of the Cisplatin, and to me they seem pretty grim, and we also know the Cetuximab is more targeted, so less likely to have such global effects in the body; right?"

"Well, yes, I suppose that is true."

I looked at Saul. I wasn't sure how much he had taken on board, but he was nodding.

"I have tinnitus anyway, could it make it worse?" he asked.

"That is a possibility, yes."

"Well, to me it seems obvious. Cetuximab is far less of a risk to his long-term health and quality of life, and the results from the research to date are favourable; so I think that is the one for Saul; what do you think, Saul?"

"I don't want anything that might make my tinnitus worse, or affect the sensitivity of my fingers – I'm a chippy: if I can't feel my fingers properly, how can I work?"

Dr Wick looked at her registrar. She seemed hesitant to give us the okay to go with this option, but I think that now she had laid it out on the table, she had no choice but to allow us this decision. I wasn't really sure why, maybe it really was because of the limited research, but there certainly seemed to be a reluctance on her part.

"Okay, if you're sure? The rash is very nasty, and uncomfortable. We don't want you to have to abandon the treatment halfway through because you can't cope with the effects," she said.

"I'm sure that just knowing they are short-term will help, but there must be some topical agents we can put on his skin to soothe it as well?"

"Yes, we can prescribe something."

"What about just a Vitamin E or an aloe vera gel?" I asked, always preferring the natural options. The thought of some steroid cream or other chemical-based compound going onto his weakened skin made me shudder.

"Well, we do have a cream we recommend, but if it doesn't work for you, then just pure aloe has helped some patients in the past, but we wouldn't recommend anything else."

"Okay, I will get some pure aloe," I said smiling. So it was confirmed, he would have the less toxic type of drug – the lesser of two really ghastly evils.

"There is one other thing I need to discuss with you," she said rather solemnly. I didn't like the tone of her voice: there was a darkness to it suggesting more bad news.

"You know earlier I explained that one of the side effects of the radiotherapy would be a problem with swallowing?"

"Yes, what about it?" said Saul with concern.

"Well, we find that all patients who go through this will at some point during the treatment no longer be able to eat anything. Some cannot even sip water, as the throat all but closes up."

I squeezed Saul's hand. We hadn't even entertained this line of thinking.

"To maintain proper nutrition throughout the treatment, we offer something called a PEG. PEG is an acronym for percutaneous endoscopic gastrostomy. This is basically a tube passed into the stomach, through the stomach wall, which remains there until after the treatment."

I felt Saul bristle next to me.

"Well I might not need one! So let's just see how I get on. If I do need one, we can do it then," Saul said decisively. This was the most determined I had seen him throughout the consultation.

"Yes Saul, I understand why you would feel this way, but you see, I'm afraid they have to do it before treatment commences. The procedure has to go through your mouth, which will become very sore during treatment and to do it then could be very complicated. A catheter is used to puncture the abdominal wall through a small incision, and a soft guide wire is inserted through this and pulled out of the mouth. The feeding tube is attached to the guide wire and pulled through the mouth, esophagus, stomach, and out of the incision. So you see we really need to do it in advance. If you find you don't need it, then that's fine – but it would be most unlikely."

"So I have to live with a tube coming out of me?"

"Yes Saul, I'm afraid so, but it's discreet, and can be tucked into the waistband of your clothing. After a while, you won't even notice it's there!" she said trying her best to reassure him.

I could tell he was unhappier about this than anything else she had told us, but what choice did he have – to have that or risk malnutrition or even starvation in an already weakened body?

We left the hospital with appointments to see the rest of the team, in the coming week, and were told to expect a letter to inform us of the start date for treatment. As it was getting close to Christmas, I had asked if we could wait until just after to begin, as we were planning to spend it in Dorset with my brother and Tess. I wanted to be able to just enjoy a family Christmas, without poor Saul being sore, or feeling sick. Dr Wick had assured us that it would be unlikely to be before then anyway as there was still the PEG fitting to be scheduled in before then.

The issue of the PEG tube was a source of great distress for Saul. I think he was able to cope with the thought of the treatment, but for him the prospect of having a tube protruding from his body was really hard for him to accept. I felt his frustration – for me, this went against everything I had learnt and knew to be good for him, and felt like it could so easily be something we had no control over. Not only did it mean that the "food" he got would be artificial and probably packed with chemicals, and that poor Saul would have a semi-permanent invasive piece of plastic going into his body, it also meant that my ways of supporting him would be severely hindered from a nutritional standpoint, and that was where I was beginning to find a little strength to cope! If I was upset by the thought of it, then Saul was distraught! For him the implications were even worse. To him it meant he was really ill. It was an outward sign of something no one could currently see, and although it would be concealed in his clothing, he would know it was there, marking him as a sick, dependent man. It made him feel weak and vulnerable.

"I don't see why they can't wait to see if I actually need the damn thing!" he said later that evening.

"Dr Wick explained that, babe! If your throat and mouth become too sore, how will they get it in for you? It could be so much worse! It's only there as a precaution. No one even has to know about it!" I tried to justify it for both of us.

"I'm not gonna need it – it's just something to put me through for no reason."

I knew it was futile to try and push the point, so I let it sit with him. I guess he just needed to vent about it, but he knew he had no choice.

Two days later, Saul had to return to the hospital to have a mask fitted. They did a full dental check first to make sure there was nothing that needed attention that might change the shape of his face even slightly. He was asked to come clean-shaven so that the mask could be moulded directly to his profile. We had been loosely informed about this, but again it's something we hadn't thought too much about. It was to make sure his head stayed in one place during the radiotherapy treatments, so that they could focus the beam with precision. I didn't go with him for this; he went from work. There were no specialists to see; it was just the procedure.

When he came home, he had a mask with him.

"Look Flossie! They made a mistake on this one so they let me keep it. They had to re-do it!" He held the mask over his face so I could see it.

It was horrible. Really grotesque. Made from white plastic with tiny perforations all over it, it was an exact replica of his face, but with no features. The edges of the mask were flat, with holes that would be clipped down onto the bed, to hold his head completely still. There was no mouth or eyes, just a small hole where his nostrils would be so he could breathe. I hated it, more than anything. It was frightening to look at, and what it represented made it all the more terrifying. How could they make the face of my gorgeous man into something so chilling? I turned away from Saul as he tried to make light of it, so he couldn't see the tears that were threatening to fall.

Chapter 5

The letter with his appointments arrived shortly after that. To begin with, he had to have a meeting with the rest of his team. I was happy that a specially qualified dietician would be looking after him – it would be so reassuring to have someone with whom to discuss his healthy-eating plan. I was looking forward to meeting the dietician and to working with her.

They wanted to see him on December 10th for his pre-loading dose of Cetuximab, and then the following day he would have his PEG fitted. His treatments were due to begin in earnest on December 17th.

Once again I felt the impact of the unfairness of all of this. December 10th was Jack's birthday – what a date to begin everything, – and worse than that, Dr Wick had said treatment was unlikely to begin before Christmas, but the letter confirmed otherwise: this would mean we couldn't go away for Christmas as his treatment was to be daily; plus, he would probably be feeling really rough by then, too.

"Saul, can't we ring them and ask for it to be put back 10 days? It won't make any difference to the cancer, but it will make a huge difference to our Christmas?" I pleaded.

"No Floss, I just want to get on with it. I don't see the sense in waiting – the sooner I start, the sooner it will be over."

"But you might not even need it! They should re-test you!" I cried clutching at straws. I had harboured a deep hope that all the healthy eating and supplementation might have cured him, and we wouldn't have to go through this, but they weren't going to check, so we would never know how much it had all helped.

"Please, Saul. This is about all of us, not just you. Please can we just have Christmas?"

"No Flossie. I have decided. I want to start now." Saul was adamant. He left the room with a determination I rarely saw.

I sat on the bed, slumping forward heavily, and buried my head in my hands. This time I didn't try to stop the tears. It seemed they were always there, just waiting for another excuse to fall.

I sat there quietly crying, and was so cocooned in my despair I almost didn't hear the soft knock on the door.

"Mum?" said Jack quietly as he entered my room.

He didn't say anything. He just sat next to me, and wrapped his arms around me, letting me cry, being strong for me. Eventually, when my sobs began to ease, he spoke gently to me,

"I know you want Christmas to be perfect, and I know a lot of the reasoning is because you think that's what me and Dave want. But it's not, Mum. We just want Dad to get this over, and the sooner he starts the sooner that will be."

I looked into his deep brown eyes, twin pools of concern under his furrowed brow. My poor, lovely lads, this was so hard on them, and they were being so stoic. I felt a surge of pride push through my anguish, reminding me that in spite of everything, I was a lucky lady to have such a wonderful family.

We arrived early at the hospital to meet Saul's "team". This time we were in the cancer unit of the hospital, somewhere that we would get to know pretty well. I had passed it before and always felt a kind of fear mixed with aversion at the place, but never did I think it was somewhere that we would need to go.

Sitting in the long waiting room, I looked at the people around me, wondering what cancer they had, what treatment they were enduring, and how they were coping. One man caught my eye, and I studied him surreptitiously. He was skinny, so thin that he almost folded in on himself, his arms and legs having no flesh to give them any form, just skin and bone. But what really struck me were the burns on his neck. He must have been having radiotherapy and his neck was bright red with weeping sores. His hollow cheeks were inflamed and sore and he had a slightly startled look in his empty eyes, as if the very life had been burnt from them. I looked away, unable to stop the morbid thoughts that my handsome Saul could look like that in the coming weeks. How would we get through this? I already felt my heart breaking, and we hadn't even started yet.

"Saul Hammond?" called a nurse.

We stood up and followed her into a small room, being asked to sit and wait.

Eventually a cheery-looking lady entered and introduced herself as the head and neck specialist nurse. She was slightly plump, very jaunty, and I warmed to her instantly.

"Hi Saul, I'm Carol: you're going to be seeing quite a lot of me over the next few weeks," she smiled. "Whatever you need: support, drugs; if you have any questions, you just have to call me. I will give you my direct line and my pager number. If I am on duty, which I am much more often than not, I am available for you to talk to. Other than that, I will see you every week here in clinic during the course of your treatment." I instantly felt reassured by her. She was going to be there for us every step of the way.

The door opened again and two other ladies entered the room.

"Hi, I'm Jill, the speech therapist. I will be keeping an eye on your voice and speech during and after treatment."

I looked at her slightly aghast. Might he lose the ability to speak? I hadn't even considered this horrendous possibility.

"My voice?" he said obviously thinking the same as me.

"Oh don't worry! I'm sure your voice will be fine," she smiled. "It's just that some patients have a few issues but they are usually all just minor. I am available for any questions, too, though."

"My name is Sarah. I'm the dietician," the other lady, tall and blonde, said, offering Saul her hand.

Ah! Yes, this was who I wanted to chat to.

"We will let Sarah take over from here, but here is my card with all my details, and Jill's are on there too. Remember, you can call at any time," said Carol, leaving the room.

Sarah sat down and took out a notepad.

"So, I want to start by asking you about your diet. We have already weighed you and you seem to be a healthy weight. It's important that we work to maintain your weight throughout your treatment. Obviously this is important for your overall health and wellbeing, but also so that your mask fits correctly throughout. You already know that eating will become an issue as we progress through your treatment, so keeping your weight up now will give your body a good head start."

"My wife will discuss my diet with you, as that's very much her department," Saul said taking hold of my hand.

"Oh, right, well it sounds as if you are on some sort of diet, then? Is that right?" she asked not looking too pleased.

"Well, yes, I suppose you could say that," I began. "It's basically just a natural, healthy diet."

"Like what?" she asked putting down her pen and turning to face me. I wasn't sure I liked the tone of her voice. Already she seemed to be disapproving!

"Well, he has no caffeine, sugar, wheat, dairy or alcohol. However, he has a high intake of raw veg, especially leafy greens, and plenty of fruit. He also has lots of fish, nuts, seeds, pulses and brown rice," I said feeling sure she would be impressed.

"Why doesn't he eat dairy, or wheat? Does he have some kind of allergy?"

"No, not at all. But you know that both dairy and gluten-grains are allergens and if there is major pathology in the body, they should be avoided."

"If he doesn't have an allergy to them, why should they be avoided?"

"Well, for one, there is research to indicate that dairy products can increase the risk of certain cancers[7], and you can get more calcium from leafy green veg and Vitamin D from natural sunlight than you can from milk; and most wheat products are highly

---

7 http://jnci.oxfordjournals.org/content/93/17/1330.full

processed and have a high sugar content, and wheat is a known gastrointestinal inflammatory, so it seemed sensible to cut both out of Saul's diet."

"I suppose you think sugar causes cancer too?" she said in a patronising tone. For someone who I thought would be helpful and supportive, she was clearly arming herself for battle!

"Hyperglycaemia has been associated with malignancy, so controlling your blood sugar is important!!" I said, adopting her condescending tone.

"That's not necessarily due to the sugar one consumes," she said haughtily.

"Are you trying to suggest the two are unrelated?" I asked astonished.

"Well no, of course not, but I think we are getting off-track here. Like I said, it's more important that Saul's calorific intake is not compromised, and it seems to me that he is going to be losing weight before he's even started. He should be enjoying whatever it is he likes right now, not worrying about a bit of sugar here and there!" she scoffed.

I felt my own blood pressure rise. How dare she? I was doing what I truly believed to be the right thing. Anyone would think from her reaction that I was feeding him an unhealthy diet, instead of one that was based on detoxification, when he was to be filled with toxins, and immune strengthening when his immune system was already under heavy attack, which would only get worse as he went through treatment.

"So I can have McDonalds, ice cream, coke?" asked Saul, secretly enjoying adding a little fuel to the fire.

"Well, if that's what you fancy, then enjoy it!" she said smirking at me. Was she doing this to upset me? Surely this could not be standard dietetic advice? I was horrified.

"You are joking. Please tell me you are not advising a patient with cancer, who is about to undergo what is essentially poisoning and burning for six weeks, to eat food with no nutrition that will actually cause him further harm! I thought you would be advising him to increase his fruit and vegetable intake, and be prescribing a healthy-eating plan!"

"The government recommended daily requirement is 5 fruit and veg a day. It sounds to me as if Saul is getting well above this." Oh please, now she was quoting school-girl nutrition at me!!

"The government recommended daily intake!!" I was almost shouting now. I felt Saul take my hand and press it, trying to calm me down.

"That is aimed at people who eat no fruit and veg, to give them a starting place. It is not aimed at someone with a serious pathology who is about to embark on treatments that are going to all but destroy his body!"

"We can't have him losing weight."

Oh dear god, she was like a pre-programmed robot.

"If you take a look at his weight today and compare it with his weight when we saw Dr Wick a couple of weeks ago, you will see that he has actually *put on* weight!!"

"Well, I don't see how that's possible, with what he has been eating."

"So you don't understand how avocados, oily fish, nuts, organic butter and olive oil can make you put on weight? Do you really think that you can only put on weight by eating McDonalds and doughnuts?"

I think I had finally made her lose her nerve, because there was no simpering retort.

"Thank you, Sarah. I think we will be leaving now," Saul said politely, standing up and getting his jacket. He took my hand and all but pushed me out of the room.

I was shaking. Adrenaline shot round my body as if it was looking for an escape route. I felt hot and clammy and I could hear my heartbeat loudly in my ears.

We walked out of the building and I stood for a minute, taking great lungfuls of fresh air, cleansing my body of the stale air that filled the hospital, with all its illness, drugs and stupid, ignorant "specialists".

All the way home in the car, I could barely speak; I was so shaken and angry that I knew if I started I wouldn't stop.

"I think we should make sure we don't see her again. There must be another dietician who has more of a clue!" Saul said quietly. He didn't need this stress – I had to try and keep a lid on it, at least while I was with him. He knew how angry I was, and he was feeling let down by the system too, expecting support when we had instead been met by bureaucratic, narrow-minded arrogance.

Later that evening while Saul relaxed watching TV, I shut myself in the study to phone Tess.

I needed to vent and I knew she would be sympathetic, if not angry for me.

I relayed the conversation to her.

"Bloody hell Floss, that's shocking! How can she call herself a dietician? She should be struck off!! Why the hell would they encourage patients to eat unhealthily?"

"I don't know, Tess, but I'm still so angry. I have a stinking headache after dealing with her – she's caused me more stress than any other event relating to this, and she's supposed to help!"

"Right. Have you contacted Macmillan? They are really good. They will give impartial advice that's not driven by bureaucracy. You should give them a call, just so you have a point of contact you feel you can speak to – even if it is only to check if there is anything you shouldn't be giving him that might conflict with his treatment, you need to speak to someone you can trust. If you feel really unsure you can always run things by Jason – he will be happy to advise where he can, but he will do so with caution. He's not an oncology specialist, and although you and I both know he knows his stuff, he will always err on the side of caution, – so by all means speak to him, but also speak to someone who is in the trade."

It made sense. I did feel as though I was on my own. I had researched everything thoroughly, but I now knew that the hospital was not going to give me any decent nutritional advice – they had totally blown any trust I may have had in them.

Chapter 6

The day of Saul's loading chemo, we both went to the hospital. I had never set foot in a cancer ward, and in my vivid imagination I expected it to be full of balding, half-dead patients hooked up to machines, lying on white, cold beds, staring lifelessly into space. So I was relieved to see it wasn't like that at all. A small bright room had 7 or 8 comfy chairs with coffee tables and magazines next to them. Everyone in the room seemed in good spirits, some reading quietly, some chatting to their companion or another patient. They were of course all hooked up to drips, but other than that it could have been any waiting room – none of them were even bald!

The nurse took all Saul's details, and then hooked him up to a saline drip to flush his veins. After this came another drip with an antihistamine and a steroid to prevent adverse reactions to the drug. Finally, came the drug. I'm not sure what either Saul or I expected, but he sat there with it going into his body, and after a while he fell asleep. I wandered downstairs for a coffee, and came back to find him still sound asleep. I woke him just as the nurse was coming to unhook him.

"How are you feeling?" I asked concerned that all the nasty side effects would have already taken hold, but he was fine.

"Sleepy," he said rubbing his hand across his eyes. He still looked like my husband.

That night we all went out for a curry for Jack's birthday. There were eight of us, including David and Anabelle, and my mum, and a couple of Jack's mates. It was a funny night with Jack being his usual self, making everyone laugh. Was it my imagination or was he trying a little harder to be jovial, for Saul's sake? Saul was quiet, not eating much. I think being tired after his treatment and being worried about the PEG fitting wasn't doing much for his appetite, but at least we had been out and celebrated.

The next day Saul was admitted to have the tube fitted. I dropped him off in the morning, and when I went back, he was sitting up in bed drinking the soup I had made for him. I didn't want him to have any of the hospital food. His diet was the one thing I had control over, and I would make damn sure nothing bad went in. I was more determined now than ever to look after him the best way I knew how. His body was already being traumatised, and being filled with horrible drugs – the least I could do was to keep the food he ate as natural and healthy as possible.

Saul was very uncomfortable. The tube felt sore where it exited his stomach wall, not just on the skin, but deep inside too.

"I have to be really careful not to catch it on anything, cos it will hurt like hell," he said glumly. "I can't work for a few days, as I can't lift anything or do anything manual. I don't want to take too much time off for this stupid thing, when I'm going to be off for so long with the treatment."

"Just stay at home for a couple of days until it feels less sore, babe – then you can go back to work; but just take it easy! You've got Jack there to do all the heavy lifting and stuff. You point fingers!" I said trying to make light of it. He was clearly uncomfortable and unhappy.

Three days later Saul was still so sore from the PEG that he hadn't noticed his skin begin to change. I could see a redness to his skin, like the beginnings of a rash, but I didn't mention it; he had enough to worry about. However, just as he started to feel the soreness from the PEG begin to abate, a couple of days later the rash took on a new lease of life and his face and neck broke out in hives. And before we knew it it was time to go back for a second dose, and begin the gruesome radiotherapy too.

I sat with Saul again while they pumped him full of drugs, and watched him doze off into a blessed sleep. When he came round after the treatment, we headed downstairs for his first radiotherapy session.

When they called him in I knew that now this was it. There was no going back. They were going to take him into another room, clamp that terrible mask to his face and burn him. How could I just sit there while they did that to my husband? It seemed barbaric, like they were leading him into a torture chamber. Suddenly a loud sob escaped me and I found myself in floods of tears.

A nurse came out and saw me crying. She handed me a box of tissues and gently put her arm around me.

"He'll be okay, your man, you know. He's a strong one," she said kindly.

"Why don't we go and sit somewhere quieter and I will make you a cup of tea."

Dumbly I nodded, allowing her to lead me into a dimly lit room with two soft armchairs and a coffee table.

"You sit here and I will get you some tea." She disappeared and returned again within minutes holding a steaming mug.

"Here you go love, you drink that, will do wonders for you!"

I didn't take milk or sugar in my tea, but I was too upset to tell her that so I began sipping. The combination of milky sweetness and piping hot liquid had a soothing effect on my nerves.

"I think she's in there," I heard a voice from the corridor say.

The door opened and in walked Saul. I looked at him half expecting to see a look-a-like of the man I had seen in the cancer unit a few days ago, but Saul looked the same as he had when he went in.

"Floss, what you doing in here?" he asked, looking from my tear-streaked face to the kindly nurse sitting with me.

"Oh, your lovely lady here got a wee bit upset when they took you in. See, I told you he'd be fine!" she said turning back to me.

"Oh Floss, you soppy mare! Come here," said Saul pulling me up into his arms.

"You have to think of it like they are zapping it, killing the bad cancer – it's not hurting me; I can't feel a thing! C'mon, let's go home," he grinned down at me.

The next few days passed by fairly uneventfully. Although the rash on Saul's face was quite angry and sore, we put a natural olive oil and chamomile cream on it at night and aloe gel in the day, and it gave him some relief. He hadn't gone back to work at all since having the PEG fitted, as no sooner had that calmed down than he had begun to feel more tired and a bit nauseous, and his face being so sore wasn't helping. Also, although the radiotherapy sessions were only 20 mins at a time, by the time we went into town, waited around, had the session and came home again, the whole afternoon had gone, so it didn't really leave him time to work.

I had stopped the Vitamins C and E supplements the day before he started his chemo properly, as the hospital had asked us not to mega dose with anti-oxidants, as there was some evidence that it may interfere. I had never found research to back this up. In fact, I had read research to the contrary, stating that it could not only help the patient cope with the side effects but may actually improve the effects of the chemotherapy[8,9]. With the benefit of hindsight, I now firmly believe that supportive anti-oxidants are not only beneficial but critically important, but at the time I had been advised by Jason to listen to the doctors on this one, and I was still afraid of doing the wrong thing. However, although I had cut the anti-oxidant mega doses, I had started him on wheatgrass. I had learnt that wheatgrass is 70% chlorophyll and is a very similar chemical structure to haemoglobin: it helps to cleanse the blood, improving its oxygen supply, and is also packed with enzymes, vitamins and minerals. It has been shown to help many patients,

---

8 http://www.ovariancancer.org/2014/02/11/high-dose-vitamin-c-may-boost-chemotherapy-effectivenes

9 Cancer Treatment Reviews, 2007 Aug;33(5):407–18. Epub 2007 Mar 23.
   Impact of antioxidant supplementation on chemotherapeutic efficacy: a systematic review of the evidence from randomized controlled trials.
   Block KI1, Koch AC, Mead MN, Tothy PK, Newman RA, Gyllenhaal C.
   http://www.ncbi.nlm.nih.gov/pubmed/17367938

even the terminally ill[10]. It is also a good source of magnesium, and Dr Wick had told us that the Cetuximab depleted magnesium during treatment, so I wanted to stay on top of this. I gave Saul live organic wheatgrass, which I had specially delivered frozen every month. In addition, he was taking reishi mushroom[11] in liquid form to help with his immune function and increase his chances of responding to conventional treatment, milk thistle to help his liver cope with the extra toxicity, a probiotic to keep his digestive flora healthy and coconut water to help maintain electrolyte balance in the body (another side effect of Cetuximab was its effect on electrolytes).

He was also still taking his digestive enzymes and the IP6 with inositol daily, and drinking vegetable smoothies with spinach, broccoli, avocado, beetroot, hemp oil and apple cider vinegar. I'm not going to pretend he liked it, he didn't, not one bit, but he took it, every drop, every pill, every day, because he knew that his body was going to need all the help it could get.

---

10 http://meeting.ascopubs.org/cgi/content/short/24/18_suppl/8634
11 http://www.ncbi.nlm.nih.gov/pubmedhealth/PMH0046740/ Pubmed, Cochrane Database of Systematic Reviews: Plain Language Summaries [Internet]. *G. lucidum* (Reishi mushroom) for cancer treatment 2012

Chapter 7

We had decided that as Saul's treatment was so time consuming, everyone would come to us for Christmas. Although he would get Christmas Day and Boxing Day off, it would still mean having to rush back from Dorset, and also we didn't know how he would feel to travel. It was agreed that I would do Christmas dinner, Mum would buy the turkey (free range, of course!), and Michael and Tess would bring desserts and nibbles.

So the morning of the 23rd I went to the supermarket to stock up on supplies. Unfortunately, I hadn't been organised enough to buy all organic veggies, but I got what I could, scrabbling with the other customers for the last-minute essentials. It really was crazy, the store was heaving, and people were just pushing and shoving to grab what they could. Luckily for me many people don't want to buy organic due to its cost, so there were actually a few bits left, when a lot of the non-organic veg was down to its last odd and ends. Then after queuing for what seemed like hours in the aisles, I finally got to check out and go home.

By the time I got home the wind had picked up and it had started raining. I was glad to get indoors and shut the world out for the night. Saul had lit the wood burner in the living room. The Christmas tree sparkled in the corner of the room with presents piled beneath its boughs and the house looked cosy and inviting. Let the storm rage, I thought as I poured myself a large glass of red and snuggled down by the fire.

After dinner Saul and the boys sat down to watch a game of football, so Anabelle and I decided to go upstairs and watch a girly film in my room.

Outside the rain lashed the windows and the wind howled, making an eerie sound. Anabelle and I laughed, scaring ourselves at the sound of the storm as it whipped the house from all angles, feeling like nervous children.

We turned up the TV to drown out the noisy weather and relaxed – talking about our Christmas plans. She was set to go home on Christmas Eve to be with her family, and return to us on Boxing Day and I had everything done, just had a few more pressies to wrap tomorrow – we were well ready for Christmas. Although it was not going to be a normal Christmas with Saul not being well, he was okay, and coping with his treatment – he should still be able to enjoy Christmas dinner. I was determined to make it as lovely as possible.

We chattered, sang and giggled through the movie, and no sooner had it finished, Jack had come upstairs to find Anabelle, to go to bed, and all of a sudden – bang! The power went off.

We all went to bed. I lay awake for a while – disturbed by the wind and rain, but eventually, snuggling under the covers, feeling cocooned against the wild weather outside, I drifted off.

I woke a couple of hours later, worried that I hadn't shut the freezer door after opening it earlier to freeze some leftover dinner. The power had now been down for a good couple of hours and if it didn't come back on soon and I *had* left the door open, the food would spoil. I got up to check, and sure enough it had popped open! I re-arranged the food, and closed it firmly – hopefully the power would come on again soon, and the food would be fine. I had disturbed Saul, though – he was awake and going to put cream on his poor sore skin.

A few minutes later we were both back in bed. Once again I drifted off, now safe in the knowledge the freezer door was shut!

Some time later I was once again awakened, this time by flashes of light outside. Was the power trying to come back on? The wind still thrashed and the rain still beat against the window. I had to see what was causing the flashes of light.

I looked out of the window – I could see people, lots of people, walking with torches – what was going on? Why were there so many people in the street, on such a night, walking around! Then

I saw why! The road was a river! It flowed fast and furious down our street, washing over gardens and pavements, creating one rushing stream!

I woke Saul, yelling that the street was flooding. We pulled on robes and rushed downstairs. In my haste I tripped, painfully twisting my ankle as I fell down the last three steps. It was all I could do not to sit and cry on the bottom step, but I had to see what was happening outside! Saul was already looking out, telling me it was too late – there was nothing we could do to stop it. The cars on the drive were already submerged up to their wheels' rims.

Jack and Anabelle heard us and came down – we began to move things: the Christmas presents, the lamps from the floor. We tied up the curtains, and took the covers off the sofas. Dave came down sleepily, wondering what all the commotion was about, but was quickly wide awake and began to help move things.

Jack and Saul were putting wooden blocks under the kitchen table, and Anabelle and I were making sure nothing was left on the floor. Jack walked out into the utility room and suddenly exclaimed: "Oh my god!" I began to hobble over to where he was but he tried to stop me. "Mum, don't look in here!"

How could I not? I couldn't pretend this wasn't happening, as much as I wanted to. The back of the house had started to flood, the utility room and shower room filling as the water came over the threshold, spilling into our home.

There was nothing we could do but watch in horror as it made its unwelcome invasion.

Jack decided to do what all good British people do in a crisis – put the kettle on! Or he would have if we'd had power, so he boiled some water on the gas hob and made tea for everyone. It did little to soothe our nerves or calm us down as we sat there watching the water slowly rise.

We had moved all we could. There really was nothing more we could do to help ourselves or save our home. We sat until the rain eased, until it seemed that at least it wouldn't get worse, if the rain didn't get heavier.

Finally, all spent, we went to bed. I didn't want to; I wanted to do something: stand at the entrances and stop any more water coming in – but Saul took my hand,

"C'mon Floss, we can't do anything else, we've protected what we can. Try and get some sleep."

"Yes, c'mon Mum," said David putting his arm across my shoulders and pulling me into a hug; "sitting here will just make you feel worse. Go to bed, stay warm and rest your ankle. Tomorrow we will work out what to do."

Reluctantly I followed my family upstairs, leaving the house to the mercy of the storm.

The others fell into an exhausted sleep. I lay awake, wondering what was to become of my home, my life now? I had a husband who I had to protect: I couldn't let him stay here, in a house that was wet, where floors would need ripping up – he couldn't be exposed to that! His immune system was going to be weakened by his treatment, and he needed somewhere warm, dry and safe to recover. We had to get out. Where would we go? How could we all find somewhere as a family? How would we live? What would happen? It was Christmas Eve, and we had other family members set to arrive – I would have no home, no food to offer them. I lay awake until 7.00am, when I could lie there no more.

I got up and went downstairs with a torch. In the dark I walked on sodden floors, with my shoes on, acutely aware of the squelchy puddles beneath my feet. I searched for the phone. Thankfully we had a plug-in phone. I picked it up and checked for the dial tone. I called Michael, telling him that we couldn't have Christmas – it was over, cancelled. He listened patiently to me ranting, and then calmly told me to pack up what we could and try and get down to them as soon as we could. Saul had treatment all day at the hospital – we should go down after that, if we could get there, and if Saul felt up to it. They would sort Christmas; they would make Christmas a warm, dry sanctuary that we could escape to.

By the time I got off the phone to him, the insurance company was open. I called them, registering the flood, beginning the long, arduous task of trying to restore our home. Luckily we had insurance – I knew many would not have.

As the day began to grow lighter, although dark clouds still hung like groups of threatening thugs in the heavy sky, the rain held off. As soon as it was light enough to see, I began to empty the freezer and fridge, pushing what I could into cold storage boxes, ready to take to my mother's house.

I woke Dave up and asked for his help. With my now swollen ankle, carrying heavy boxes was not something I could attempt alone.

I had already called Mum, so she made room in her freezer for my food. I hadn't been able to save it all, but some at least had been salvageable. It made me feel as if I hadn't been totally defeated by the cruel storm – it may have taken over my home, but it hadn't stolen all our food!

With an ice-pack on my foot and a cup of tea in my hand, I finally gave in to the emotional exhaustion that was consuming me. There is something about being in your mum's house when everything around you feels as though it's closing in: I was once again a scared little girl, who needed to be with her mum, feeling surrounded by the familiarity of all that my childhood had given me. From the smell of clean laundry to the pictures on her walls that she hadn't changed in years, I drew in great lungfuls of comfort, and I realised as I sat there that it was the only place I wanted to be at that moment, safe from the storms of my life.

I remembered as I sat and cried in Mum's warm, dry house something a friend had once told me:

"A strong person is not the one who doesn't cry: a strong person is the one who cries and sheds tears for a moment, then gets up and fights again."

That's what I had to do now – get up and sort out the mess that life had thrown at us yet again.

Truth was, I didn't know where we were going. The future seemed so uncertain. We now had nowhere to call home, and I wasn't even sure where Christmas would be! Christmas Eve had always been magical to me, right from my own dreams as a child of Father Christmas's imminent visit, through watching my own children's mounting excitement as they went to bed the night before Christmas, to the promise of spending a few warm, cosy days with those dearest to me, without the interruptions of work or the everyday pressures life often presented. But today, it didn't feel like Christmas Eve at all. Saul had gone for his chemotherapy, and I didn't know how he would feel about going to Dorset after his treatment, but I really didn't know what else we could do. In fact, even if it wasn't Christmas we would have to go somewhere, and right now, I only wanted to be with family. I tried not to think about what we would do after Christmas. I knew we would have to come back as Saul's next treatment was the day after Boxing Day, but where we would come back to was not something I could deal with at the moment.

I decided to go home and pack up whatever I could in preparation for going to Dorset. We would need to take two cars, so that the four of us, Mum, the presents and food could all fit in: I would drive Saul so that he could sleep en route, and one of the boys could drive their car and take them and Mum.

Walking back into the house was soul destroying. It already smelled damp and musty, and although all the water had drained away, the floors were squelchy to walk on, and the rooms all felt cold and depressing. There was no power still, so I couldn't even put on heating or lights to combat the dark, overcast day outside. Was it really only last night that my home felt like a magical cosy haven, all twinkly lights and roaring fire? Already it seemed like a lifetime ago.

I found some boxes and began packing up our photos, ornaments, books and whimsies that made this house our home. I felt tears of anger pricking the backs of my eyes, at the unfairness, the timing of this disaster! How could this be happening when we were already trying to cope with something huge? Did God, fate, or whoever or whatever was throwing this stuff at us not think we had enough on our plate? And on Christmas Eve too! Was this a test of my strength, because right now, if it was, I was failing miserably!

Jack and Anabelle were still in the house, getting ready to take Anabelle home. They came downstairs to see what I was doing.

"Do you want some help Flossie?" Anabelle asked sweetly.

I looked up from packing the photos, and she came rushing over as soon as she saw my mask of despair.

"It's okay, Flossie. Soon, your house will be all fixed up, like new, and you will look back on this and laugh – well, maybe," she smiled, trying to lift my spirits.

However, my spirits were so far down that not even the appearance of Johnny Depp dressed as a half-naked Santa Claus and bearing a crate of Prosecco would have worked at that moment.

"I'm not coming back here," I said softly.

"Of course you are! This is your home!" she replied thinking somehow that I wanted to come back.

"No, you don't understand," I looked at her squarely, with my jaw set in resolve, "I will never live in this house again. I know that. I feel it in my heart."

"But where will you live?" she asked, concern clouding her soft brown eyes.

"I don't know, Anabelle; I only know it won't be here."

David had gone to work, and I shuddered at the thought of being alone in the depressing house. Jack asked if they should stay with me until Saul got home.

"No sweetheart, I think you should get back. The roads are not good: there are a lot of trees down and surface water everywhere.

You better go while it's still light; otherwise, it will just get harder. And I need you to be back as soon as you can, too, babe. If we are to get down to Dorset at all, we need to leave as soon as Dad and David are back. Hopefully we can at least leave while it's still light and be on the motorway before dark."

I wished Anabelle a happy Christmas with her family, and told Jack to drive safely and carefully. After they left I went upstairs to pack bags for all of us with enough clothes for a couple of days and some toiletries. I packed what I could of the Christmas presents, and then sat on a kitchen chair, staring at the kitchen wall as the grey light began to fade.

It wasn't long before they all arrived home. I barely gave them a chance to cross the threshold, ushering them straight back out the door. I couldn't wait to get away from the house. I could feel it draining the energy from me as the evening drew in, and I wanted to get on the road as soon as we could. We piled into two cars, and made our way to Mum's to collect her and her things and then we headed off away from the disaster that had befallen us, towards what I hoped would be a happy Christmas in spite of everything.

Phase Two
The Treatment Phase

Chapter 8

I had imagined the worst in terms of travel conditions, expecting our journey to be fraught with hazards, but was pleasantly surprised. As soon as we left the county border, and headed towards the coast, the number of fallen trees and flooded roads began to diminish. All the phone masts had been down near home, but as we drove further south on the motorway, phone signal resumed and I was able to call ahead to tell my brother that we were well on our way.

Three hours later we arrived at Michael and Tess's in Dorset. As soon as we walked in, the smell of a delicious chilli filled our nostrils making us all realise how hungry we were! Food had not been high on our list of priorities today, so none of us had really eaten. Tess came rushing out of the kitchen to wrap us all up in huge bear hugs. Clucking and fussing round us in her warm and generous manner, she made us all feel like we had indeed arrived at a sanctuary.

So Christmas Eve turned out to be magical after all. With our bellies full of Tess's chilli, followed by home-made apple pie, with a few bottles of red wine, and conversation laced with laughter, while sitting by the fire, we all fell into bed tired but safe, full up and toasty warm.

Although they hadn't been so badly affected in Dorset, some of the neighbouring counties, particularly Somerset, had been even worse hit than we had.

However, Christmas morning was a bright and sunny one. It was as though the storms had never happened.

After a leisurely breakfast we dropped Mum at church so she could go to mass, and we all piled down to the beach for a walk along the seafront. It was beautiful. The sea was as blue as a cloudless sky on a summer day, and the sands, devoid now of summer bathers, were a smooth golden carpet being gently lapped by the water.

The occasional child or dog ran along the beach, enjoying the freedom of uninterrupted space, but most of those similarly out for a stroll did so along the promenade, admiring the vista.

Nothing could evoke the emotions quite like the sea: it seemed to change its mood, reflecting it back to the onlooker with powerful allure. Stormy seas made you feel alive, rousing passion and vitality; while calm, blue waters gave you a sense of tranquillity that went deep into your very soul. I stood still for just a minute, letting the others walk ahead, and took a deep breath, inhaling the serenity that I beheld, the salty air a soothing balm to my anxieties, and tried to capture the moment, imprinting a solace in my memories where I could return whenever I felt the need.

Christmas Day was everything and more that a family Christmas should be. Tess's brother, who lived locally, joined us for dinner, and we all ate far too much. Lovely presents, lots of wine, game playing and finally dozing off in front of the telly, in that contented slumber that only comes with excessive feasting.

Boxing Day was equally relaxing, if a little less voracious, but a very pleasant day overall. As we sat down to a late brunch, my mobile rang. It was Marie, a friend who we knew well but never saw much of. She had been quite concerned about Saul and had heard of our recent plight and wanted to see if we were okay.

"Where will you go when you get back from Dorset?" she asked the question that I knew I should be thinking about seriously, as I really wasn't sure. Mum had said we could stay with her if necessary, but she lived in a tiny two-bedroom apartment, so it would be cramped to say the least.

"I guess we will be at my mum's until the insurance company can sort out an alternative place for us to stay," I explained.

"No way! Your mum lives in a retirement village; you can't possibly stay there, all four of you – you'll all go mad!"

"I think Jack will stay with Anabelle's family, at least until she goes back to uni in January, and David will most likely stay at his mate's house. At least it will be near his work then."

"Has the insurance company said anything about accommodation for you?"

"Yes, they are trying to book us into a hotel. I have asked for one as close to the hospital as we can get, so that it will be easier for Saul."

"Well then, there's no question – you can stay here with us until your hotel is ready. We have enough room, and it will be fun having you here."

"What? No, we couldn't possibly!" I protested. Although Saul had been good friends with Marie's husband Tom for many years, Marie and I hadn't been close, and I felt like this would be a huge imposition. Besides, they only had a little three-bed cottage, and they had two young boys who I'm sure wouldn't want us invading their home.

"I'm not asking you Flossie!" she laughed kindly; "I'm insisting. I won't take no for an answer. As soon as you get back, go home, pick up whatever you need and come straight here. You can all stay, we have sofas, and spare beds a-plenty!"

She really wasn't going to take no for an answer. I felt that she really wanted to help, and was reaching out to us.

"Okay," I laughed, feeling relief that we had somewhere to go until we had a hotel sorted, "but it will just be Saul and I; the boys will be fine at their friends.'"

"Lovely, we will look forward to seeing you later! I will have something hot for you to eat, and a glass of wine poured and ready for you!"

How was it that misfortune brought out the very loveliest traits in people when you least expected it?

We were reluctant to leave my brother's house. We had been made to feel so welcome, and had had such a lovely time; we had almost forgotten our troubles. Even Saul hadn't seemed too poorly, and had enjoyed his Christmas as much as anyone. He had been a bit uncomfortable with the rash being so sore, but he was applying the cream at night and the aloe in the day, and although the rash bothered him, he was brave and hardly mentioned it.

After dropping Mum at her house we went back home to collect and drop off various belongings, so that we could go our separate ways to our friends' houses. It was odd, because although David and Jack were often out for nights away from home, this was different. It felt as though we were being forced apart, like refugees seeking asylum. I hugged my boys, pulling them both close. They were both so tall it was hard to pull them both into my arms, but I needed to convey a silent promise to them, that whatever life threw at us, we would be together: a tight unit that no hardship, however tough, could ever break.

We ended up having a lovely evening at Marie and Tom's. She had made a hearty lasagne with a green salad and some freshly baked bread. Saul's diet had well and truly fallen by the wayside while we were guests in the homes of friends and family – but it was unavoidable. As soon as we got settled somewhere I would get him back on track. He was still having his daily wheatgrass, and all the supplements, too, but trying to maintain the rest of his diet was just not possible. At least what we were eating tonight was healthy and home-cooked, for which I was very grateful. Even most of the food at my brother's had been home-made apart from the odd treat, and Saul had refrained from alcohol and stuck to green tea, and smoothies that I prepared for him.

Marie had put both her boys in one room and given us the other bedroom, which had bunkbeds! I hadn't slept in a bunk for years, so it was a quest climbing up the ladder (as I'd drawn the short straw and got the top bunk!)!

The next morning, Saul went off to the hospital for his treatment and I spent what seemed like hours on the phone to the insurance company about accommodation. Eventually, they confirmed a reservation for all four of us, for the next week at least, in the hotel that was right next door to the hospital! A little piece of luck at last! I called Saul, and then I rang the boys and told them where we would be staying, and said we would meet them there this evening for dinner. Relieved that we finally had somewhere we could settle at least for a few days, and not travel around like drifters, I thanked Marie with a warm hug, and packed up our things to leave.

After packing up more things from the house, I left to go and meet Saul at the hotel.

Saul was sitting waiting for me on a big comfy sofa in front of an open fire, in the large, open hotel reception area. As soon as he saw me arrive he stood to come and help get the bags from the car. I explained to the girl on reception that the boys would be along shortly.

Our room was on the ground floor, and was spacious and comfortable, and well-equipped with a king-sized bed, a sofa and table, a large TV and a good sized en-suite. I thought we would be very cosy here until they could find us a house or apartment to rent while our house was being restored.

As we began to unpack our phone rang. It was the boys to say they had arrived, and to tell us their room number, and also that they were starving! The insurance had agreed a daily food allowance figure per person, so I was looking forward to a nice meal in the hotel bar. The food was decent, a good selection for most palates, and although I knew it wasn't going to be organic, at least there was plenty of fresh veggies and other healthy options.

The boys ordered a couple of beers and I had some much-needed wine, but Saul, still being very good, stuck to water. I felt bad for him, when we were all enjoying a drink, but he didn't want any.

"To be honest, Floss, I don't really fancy it; it doesn't taste the same. My mouth is becoming a bit sore inside, and I think I have little ulcers on my gums and tongue. Alcohol just irritates and burns, whereas nice cold water is soothing," he explained.

The next few days passed without too much trouble. The boys were enjoying being in a hotel, sipping beer at the bar and making friends with the staff. Anabelle came to stay a few nights, and although she didn't come to breakfast, we smuggled some fruit and croissants back to their room for her. Saul and I could walk to the hospital for his radiotherapy treatments, often stopping at the supermarket on the way home to pick up odd and ends. He was still able to enjoy most food, although his taste had begun to diminish. Spicy food, or sharp fruit still tasted good, but plainer food seemed too bland, and had begun to feel heavy in his mouth. He was now a third of the way through his treatment, and so far was coping really well.

It was New Year's Eve and we were going to spend it with Rica and her fiancé Jaco. They had recently moved into a swanky new house in town and were very happy there. It had become traditional to spend New Year together if we were all free, and this year my other best friend would be joining us too. She had booked into the hotel for the night, so I had made sure she got the room next to us. We arrived at Rica's posh new house. It was a mews style, built in a complex, and had lots of very nice finishing touches. The spacious kitchen on the ground floor was a deep red with granite surfaces, had an island in the centre and a long dining table by the window. The lounge, which was on the first floor, was a lovely bright room with sliding doors opening onto a roof terrace.

Rica handed me a glass of chilled Prosecco, which I gratefully took.

"How's things?" she asked intently.

"It could be worse, but not much!" I laughed.

"Saul seems to be holding up. Apart from his poor sore face, he looks well."

"Yes, he is doing okay. It gets a little worse each day, but I think we are still on top of it."

"What's the hotel like?"

"Really nice. I love the fact that I don't have to cook, or clean; it actually takes a lot of stress off me."

"Yes, I hadn't thought of that. You are good, Floss, to see positives, with all you are going through!" Rica smiled.

"Well you have to. There's no point in dwelling on stuff you can't change. We just have to get on with it, and make the best of things."

"Well, tomorrow I will come by and collect any washing you need doing. I should have thought to get you to bring it tonight, but I didn't think of it until now."

"That would be great Ric, thank you, but let's not think of chores tonight. Let's have some fun, and leave our cares 'til tomorrow."

"Yes, you're right," she said clinking my glass with hers. "Chin chin! Now where is Evie? She said she'd be here by 8."

"Well you know Evie: when she says 8, read 10!!"

"We'll be sozzled by the time she arrives!!" laughed Rica.

"Oh, I'm pretty sure she won't waste any time in catching us up!"

Saul and Jaco had gone upstairs to watch TV, so we gave the curry another stir, and went up to join them.

At just after 9, Evie's taxi finally pulled up, and we all went downstairs to meet her. We were pretty hungry by now and the fizz had started to make my head feel light, without food to soak it up.

Evie swanned in with no apology for being late, as had become her signature trait. She knew no one would mind a bit, especially when she waved two more bottles of fizz at us, grinning her infectious grin.

The night passed by effortlessly, with delicious food, lots more bubbles and enough laughter to fill a small stadium. We welcomed the New Year in, wishing each other health, good fortune and happiness.

"Good riddance to 2013!" I shouted.

"Yes, good riddance, and may 2014 be your year!" they all said to Saul and I. I felt a surge of adrenaline, making my skin tingle with goosebumps and tears sting my eyes as emotion flooded through me. Evie put her arms round me,

"This year is going to be good for you, Floss. You and Saul and those lovely boys of yours are going to come out of this smiling!"

At about 1am the taxi arrived to take us back to our hotel.

"Don't forget I'm coming round to get your washing," Rica slurred at me with a sleepy smile.

"I might not let you have it!" I laughed.

"I'm gonna steal it!" Rica giggled, swaying in the doorway. Jaco held her up, rolling his eyes, and waving us out of the door.

"I better get this one to bed, or she won't make the rest of the year."

Back at the hotel, Evie headed straight for the bar.

"Yay! It's still open; let's have another drink!"

"Saul, do you want anything?" she asked.

"What are you having?"

"I fancy a shot of black Sambuca!" I said.

"Make that two!" said Evie.

"Make it three!" said Saul.

I looked at him, surprised, but thought, well he hasn't had a drop of alcohol, and it is New Year, so what the hell.

"On three," said Evie as the barman served the shots.

We all downed the sweet liquorice syrup, and slammed our glasses back on the bar.

"Again?" said Evie.

I looked at Saul. He had gone crimson, and was holding his throat.

"Water, please, quickly!" I said to the barman.

Saul took a huge gulp of iced water. His eyes were streaming and his nose had started to run. I handed him a tissue.

"Oh god!" he said when at last he could speak, "do I have steam coming out of my ears? That burnt my throat, like liquid fire!"

"Okay," I said worried, but trying not to laugh at the same time, "I think that verifies our decision to keep off the alcohol, then!!"

"Yes it bloody does!! I think petrol might be more soothing!!"

New Year's Day, Saul woke up in good spirits. He had been feeling pretty self-conscious about his PEG and so we hadn't been very intimate and I was letting him take the lead – I didn't want to push him because I knew he was so sore and uncomfortable generally; but also, if he felt insecure, I didn't want to make an issue out of it. So when he pulled me back to bed, I was pleasantly surprised. I was stirred by the confidence in him, and felt proud that nothing could make my man feel emasculated or defeated. He was showing me a strength that impressed me beyond belief.

The rest of the day was lovely, just what I needed – an Evie day. We had been friends for 20 years, ever since I was pregnant with Jack. I remember clearly the day we met – I sat, heavily pregnant, in Marie and Tom's kitchen hugging a mug of fruit tea, when she walked in with her then boyfriend, all long blonde hair, long eyelashes and the widest smile I'd ever seen. I knew immediately that she would be someone I would connect with, and I couldn't have been more right. Evie was warm, funny, and delightfully ditzy, but at the same time incredibly insightful and intelligent. This meant that whatever you were feeling she could make it better. If you were down she could make you laugh, or envelope you in the warmest of hugs; if you were talking rubbish she could somehow turn it around so it made sense; and she could talk with you for hours over a few bottles of fizz, until the world seemed right again.

We spent the whole of New Year's Day doing all of the above, over a long breakfast, a relaxing morning in the hotel spa, and then most of the afternoon in the bar. Finally, after an early evening meal, Evie left to go home to London, and Saul and I retired for a much-needed early night.

Chapter 9

I'm not sure whether the events of the last few days had taken its toll on Saul, but the confident exuberance he had shown on New Year's Day had vanished the next day. He began to notice that his facial hair was falling out, showing me clumps of it in his fingers. His mouth was really starting to become more painful, and he was really tired.

"You have to listen to your body. Why don't you just stay in bed today? You don't have to get up. Relax, watch TV, sleep, do whatever it is you feel you want to do. I'm going to go to Rica's to do some laundry, and make a stew for you. Then I know you will be getting some good, home-cooked food. I will ask the hotel if I can freeze it, so you can have some each day."

"I thought Rica was coming here to pick washing up?" Saul asked yawning.

"She has probably forgotten, she wasn't very coherent when we left! Anyway, if I go there I can use her kitchen to cook while the washing is in the machine."

I gave Saul a kiss and he closed his eyes, surrendering to his fatigue.

A couple of days later, Saul began to notice changes in his skin.

"My face is burning," he said miserably.

"The rash looks a little calmer today, but I think the radiotherapy has started to affect your skin now, babe," I said, while I prepared his wheatgrass drink.

"Yes, it feels different. Not as lumpy, or inflamed, just like I've got nasty sunburn."

"They did say it would feel that way. Well, hopefully the chemo rash will start to improve a little."

"I'm not having any more," Saul said quietly.

"Any more what?" I thought perhaps he was talking about the wheatgrass. I knew he hated it, but he was aware of how it was helping him.

"Any more chemo. It's just poisoning me. I'm beginning to feel really sick. I don't want any food, I'm tired, I'm sore. I know I have to have the radiotherapy, but I don't need this chemo. It's just a toxic chemical pumping into my body. It's wrong. I don't want it."

Although I was the first person to want Saul to try and deal with this naturally, I was really scared by his comment.

"Are you sure, Saul? It's early days and how do you know how much it's helping? Maybe we should talk to Dr Wick, and see what she says."

I didn't want to take responsibility for this decision. It was too big. What if it meant the treatment wouldn't work? To go through all this for nothing was just unthinkable.

"I'm seeing her in a couple of days, at my clinic check-up, and I'm going to tell her. I'm not having the poison."

"Okay," I said trying to remain passive. I didn't want him to be upset. I wasn't disagreeing with him; in fact, on some level I was pleased that he didn't want it anymore. I hated the drugs going into him, but I couldn't help the fear that if he stopped it would reduce the chance of killing the cancer.

Saul had been asking for blander and more liquefied food in the hotel. Swallowing was becoming more difficult for him. He had begun ordering soups, mashed potato with gravy and fruit with yoghurt. Just a few days ago he had wanted spicy food, as spices were all he could taste, but now he couldn't tolerate anything with even a slight kick to it. I was glad that he was at least able to eat the chicken broth with pearl barley and soft organic vegetables I'd made at Rica's. Tonight he was eating another portion of my broth.

While I ate my dinner I watched him pushing bits of chicken and veg around his bowl: he had only taken the broth.

"Saul, you have to eat, babe," I said worriedly.

"I'm not hungry, and nothing tastes right. Everything has a metallic taste. Even this!" he said sipping his water.

"I know it's hard darling, but if you don't then you need to start using the PEG and supplementing your intake with the Fortisip drinks that the hospital have given you."

"No! I don't want to use that. I won't need it!" he protested, but even as he said it, I could see the resignation in his eyes. He knew he had no choice.

"Hopefully you won't need it much sweetheart, just a little a day to keep your calories up."

"Have you tasted it? It's disgusting; it makes me feel sick!"

"Well, that's why if you use the PEG, you won't have to taste it: you will be getting the calories without having to drink them!" I said trying to coax him.

From day one he had never accepted the PEG. He was so brave about everything else, but this was always a stumbling block for him. He hated with a passion everything it stood for, and although he had to flush clean water through it daily, other than that he tried to forget it was there. Now, all of a sudden he was faced with the fact that it was to become his lifeline – without it he would not be able to sustain his body; he was to become totally dependent on something he abhorred.

By the next day Saul's eating had almost stopped altogether. He managed a piece of melon for breakfast chopped into tiny pieces and a few spoonfuls of tomato soup from the restaurant's children's menu, but even that he said was spicy. It wasn't, I checked with the staff – there was no spice in it at all, but Saul couldn't eat it. He had tried the Fortisip drinks again and although he had managed a couple he couldn't swallow them without retching.

It was time to try the tube. Reluctantly he pushed the vanilla favoured drink in with the plastic syringe, turning his head away as he administered it. Even the smell of the drink was making him feel nauseous. He was supposed to have up to nine drinks a day if he wasn't eating, but he was barely managing two or three. I was worried.

"I'm sure you will get used to them babe. I know you hate them, but at least you can't taste it."

"I can taste it! If I burp, the taste is regurgitated in my mouth! I can't do this for the next few weeks!"

"Shall we ask for another flavour?" I asked tentatively.

"I tried them all: this was the best of a bad bunch! They are all revolting!" With that he ran to the bathroom and promptly emptied what little was in his stomach.

I had started to put the wheatgrass drink in through the tube too, and he hated that as well, but somehow he managed to keep it down. At least I knew he had approx. 90 of the hundred or so minerals required by the body, and a healthy dose of vitamins, a great source of protein, and not forgetting that all-important chlorophyll that was oxygenating his blood – and because I mixed it with pure coconut water, I knew he would maintain his hydration. I clung to that bit of knowledge like a raft in a sea of mounting despair.

The next morning when we got up he tried the Fortisip in the tube again but promptly brought it straight back.

"It hurts my throat so much to be sick," he cried.

"Right, we have to do something about this!" I said resolutely. "This can't go on." I looked at his poor sore face. His eyes had a sunken look to them, and the skin around them had a grey pallor that I hadn't seen before.

He went back to bed, sipping cold water, and when he was calmer I gave him his wheatgrass, praying silently that it would stay down. Ten minutes later he was rushing to the bathroom again. This time the wheatgrass came back. I couldn't bear it – he needed good nutrition more than ever to stay strong through this, and he wasn't getting it.

I let him sleep. He was exhausted. I sat quietly in the room with him, watching his chest rise and fall. I loved him so much, this was breaking my heart to watch this happening to him. I couldn't believe how quickly he had gone from being okay, socialising, eating, even making love, to being so sick. I think a lot of it was down to the fact that he had slowly been eating less and less, and now he couldn't keep food down, but the speed at which it was happening was overwhelming. I had to do something. I needed Dr Wick to take charge and help us manage this. If we could only get food in him, he wouldn't be so weak. I rang the boys' room. David was working early shifts and had just got back.

"David, Dad has his appointment with the hospital this afternoon. Will you come with me? I'm so worried about him, I don't want to go alone."

"Of course I will Mum! You don't need to ask! What time shall I come and meet you?"

"I'm going to wake him up now, so give us 20 minutes. Then come up."

"I'll drive us there Mum. If Dad's feeling weak, he won't want to walk."

"Yes, David, yes please. You are right, he is too weak to walk at the moment."

15 minutes later, David knocked on the door. Saul was so tired, he didn't want to get up. He was sitting on the edge of the bed, trying to find the energy. Suddenly he started to retch again. David grabbed the bin and shoved it under his chin, just in time. I turned away – I had never been very good with people being sick. When the boys were little it was always Saul who dealt with them if they vomited, as my stomach would just turn too if I tried. Now the tables had turned.

"It's okay Mum, I've got this," said David taking the bin away to wash it out.

Saul lay back down on the bed, exhausted. I felt tears sting my eyes. David was an 18-year-old boy: he shouldn't have to see his dad like this, let alone clean up after him. My little boy was having to grow up fast, and it seemed like a huge injustice.

Between us we managed to get Saul dressed and to the car, and up to the hospital. He had to have his radiotherapy first and then see the team.

"What if I'm sick when I'm lying on the table, with the mask clamped to my face?" Saul looked at me with sunken, haunted eyes.

"Darling, don't worry. There is a bell in the room – if you feel even slightly woozy, just press the bell and they will stop the treatment and come in."

"I might choke!" he was really worried.

"You will be okay. You haven't been sick since we got you here. You won't be. Think positive." How easy it was for me to say these words.

David and I sat and waited. Both worried stiff about Saul. "Please let him be okay," I whispered silently.

It wasn't long before he was coming out again with the nurse walking with him. I jumped up.

"Is he okay?" I asked her.

"Yes, he's fine! He was feeling a bit weak so I just thought I'd walk him out to you."

I held his arm and David walked round to his other side. "C'mon babe, let's go and see Dr Wick; I'm sure she will know how to make this better."

When we got up to the cancer unit, Saul sat slumped in a chair until they called us in. He climbed onto the couch in the consultation room and closed his eyes. David and I sat quietly watching him, not wanting to disturb him.

Dr Wick came in, with Carol, the head and neck nurse, and Saul stirred, opening his eyes.

"Oh dear, you're not looking too good, Saul; how are you feeling?"

"Sore, sick, tired," he said dejectedly.

"He's really not managing to eat much at all, and he hates the Fortisip: they make him feel sick. Mostly, he is just bringing them back up."

"How often are you taking the antiemetics?" she asked, looking at Saul.

He looked puzzled.

"The anti-sickness drugs," she explained assuming we were not sure to what she was referring.

"I'm not," Saul answered.

"None at all? Well no wonder you are feeling and being sick! What about pain relief?" she asked, taking a look inside Saul's mouth with a torch.

"Nothing," he said, after she was done looking.

"Well, Saul, that explains how you are feeling! I have never heard of anyone getting this far in to their treatment without taking pain relief and antiemetics. Your mouth is quite ulcerated. I'm not surprised you are so sore. You are almost halfway through your treatment. I'm prescribing you some cocodamol, and some aspirin mouthwash, and also some metoclopramide for the sickness – you will feel much better if we manage your symptoms."

I grimaced, hating the thought of him putting more toxic drugs into his weakened body, but knowing that if we didn't, he wouldn't get through it. At least he had done well to get this far without them.

"Thank you. I hope it helps; I feel like shit."

"It will, Saul, you will feel much better, and you will be able to eat, or at least keep your drinks down, so you won't feel so weak. Now is there anything else you want to ask or discuss?" she asked kindly.

"Yes, there is. I'm not having any more chemo," Saul said somehow finding the strength for his resolution.

Carol raised her eyebrows in surprise. I looked at Dr Wick expectantly. I was sure she would tell him he had to have it – that he had no choice – or at least try to discourage his decision in every way she could.

"Why is that, Saul? What has made you decide this?"

"You told me that chemotherapy only increases the success rate of my treatment by 8%. Well in my opinion it's not worth going through all this shit and putting all that poison into my body just for an 8% increase in my chances. Anyway, I've had half the course of treatments, so I should have a 4% increase now," he reasoned.

"Well Saul, I'm not sure it works quite like that. The 8% increase is only clinically proven to work if patients have the full treatment. There are no trials detailing patients who only have half or a portion of their chemo, only for those who have the full dose. I think it would be in your best interests to continue with the treatment and to try and manage the symptoms with supportive medication as best we can, but I can't force you."

I was surprised that she wasn't trying harder, but I suppose she knew that every patient was ultimately in charge of their own decisions.

"So the only way through taking this poison, which might give me another 4% success rate, is to take even more chemicals to stop my body getting so ill that I physically collapse?" Saul said.

"It's my job to advise and support you Saul, and I can do only that. My advice is that you try to stay with the treatment programme, and that we do all we can to minimise your discomfort, but it seems you have already made up your mind. Just to let you know that if you do come off it, you can't go back on it if you change your mind. Your decision will have to be final, so I hope you have thought it through and talked with your family about it?" she looked to me and David, who was sitting quietly taking it all in. Was she trying to get me to take her side? We had briefly mentioned it to the boys and they both agreed that is was totally up to Saul.

I had thought about it since Saul had declared it, and although I couldn't help feeling a bit scared, I was both proud of him and pleased that he felt the way he did. We were doing and had done so many other things outside of the realms of the conventional treatment, I felt confident that we could make up the 4–8% by making sure he continued with his healthy diet and supplements that we had started a whole month before this, and would continue as soon as he could eat again. He was still having his wheatgrass daily, and had only stopped the IP6 with inositol yesterday, as he couldn't swallow it and I was worried the powder formula may block the tube. He was also having probiotics in his wheatgrass complex, to help his immune function and reishi mushroom[12] extract too, as there was some evidence that the Ganoderic acid found in them triggered apoptosis (cell death) of cancer cells. All these measures were far less toxic than the chemotherapy he was having, so surely this was a better option. However, I was fairly sure that his "team" would not support this line of thinking, as it wasn't the allopathic approach, so decided to keep my reasoning to myself.

"I think Saul has made his mind up, Dr Wick, and I can only support whatever he wants to do. No one except the patient can ever really know how treatment feels, so he must be the best judge."

"Okay. I will liaise with the chemotherapy team, and let them know you will be discontinuing your treatment. Here is your prescription for your meds: just take it to the pharmacy and the girls there will sort you out. Is there anything else we can help with?" she asked Saul.

"There is one more thing," I interjected. "I would like copies of all Saul's blood test results please."

"Well, we don't usually give them out, but of course you are within your rights to have them – Saul?"

"If Floss wants them, then I am asking for them," he said, knowing I would have good reason to ask.

Carol, who had been in the room, disappeared to get copies for us.

Very soon she came back with another lady whom we had not met before.

"This is Lucy. She will be taking over as your dietician."

---

12 http://www.ncbi.nlm.nih.gov/pubmed/17007887

I bristled. Was she going to have the same condescending attitude to Saul's diet as the other one had? Then I realised that she must have been asked to step in to take over with Saul. I wondered whether the other woman had asked to be replaced because of my challenging her, or whether she had been replaced because she had managed us so poorly.

Lucy smiled. She had a warmth to her that the other woman had totally lacked.

"I would very much like to discuss your PEG feeding with you," she said to Saul. "How are you managing it?"

"I hate it, but I know I have to do it."

"How many bottles are you taking each day?"

"About 3, maybe 4."

"Hmmm, you know that will not be enough to sustain you? I think you are aware that it is very important not to lose too much weight. If you are finding swallowing food difficult, you must persevere with the bottles. Hopefully now Dr Wick has given you antiemetics you will better tolerate them, but you must let me know if this doesn't work. We may have to change the antiemetic, or give you additional drugs, so that we can stop your body rejecting them."

I looked at Saul, who was looking green at the very thought. Surely the fact that his body was rejecting them so vehemently proved that the artificial food was just wrong on so many levels! Why couldn't I just make him nice broths and smoothies to put in instead? Good, natural food. I asked Lucy about this possibility.

"Oh no! You must never put anything in the tube unless we have prescribed it! If that tube gets blocked by a piece of food, it can cause huge problems. If it gets infected, changing it can be very tricky not to mention traumatic for Saul. The feed is specially formulated to work both orally and for the PEG system. The only things which can go in are water, medication and the feed."

I wasn't going to tell her about the wheatgrass complex I had been putting in every day. I put it through my blender, and made sure it was as smooth as water. I would listen and not put anything else through, but there was no way I was stopping that – I knew it was the only natural nutrition he was getting and by god did he need it!

I smiled sweetly. "Of course, I understand; only his meds and the Fortisip."

David dug my leg, knowing how blatantly I was lying. I ignored him, hoping Lucy and Carol hadn't noticed.

"Anyway, for now his weight is fine, but if he continues to reject the feed we will have to re-assess him, and see what else we can do. There is another system we can use where the food is administered much more slowly. It goes in overnight, on a drip system. It's essentially the same stuff, but sometimes the body can cope better with a slower constant pace than with one quick hit. It's not as convenient of course, but with patients whose stomachs can't handle the feed in one go, we have a lot of success with the other system."

Saul was almost asleep. The conversation had taken it out of him, and we needed to get him back to bed.

"Thank you, Lucy. We will try now with the anti-sickness drugs. Hopefully they will help, but if not, we will have to look into this other way."

Over the next few days we tried the anti-sickness drugs and the painkillers, but although the painkillers took the edge off his pain, the anti-sickness seemed to do very little. Also, the soreness inside his mouth seemed to be worse if anything. The Macmillan nurse came to visit, and I explained our predicament. I was getting very worried about Saul now as he was barely able to keep anything down. She sat down with us and looked at all Saul's drugs, and asked to see his blood test results too. I had been studying these, mainly because I knew the chemo he was on could deplete the body's magnesium stores. Magnesium, unlike most minerals which are only required in trace amounts, is needed by the body in significant quantities, and is required for hundreds of chemical reactions throughout the body including cellular function, so I wanted to watch his levels. His last test had shown his levels were low even with the wheatgrass, so I had bought some liquid magnesium and added it to his wheatgrass complex. I would only give it to him if levels were low, when the wheatgrass needed an extra boost alongside it.

Marianne, the Macmillan nurse sat studying his results.

"His bloods are surprisingly good! Considering how little nutrition he is taking in and retaining, and how poorly he has been, I can't quite believe it! I would have expected his magnesium to be on the low side due to the levels of Cetuximab in his body, but even more surprising are his haemoglobin levels!"

I smiled at Marianne. I had done lots of research and knew that radiotherapy was likely to be more effective in patients with good haemoglobin levels[13,14], meaning that if a patient had become anaemic their likelihood of survival was lower. I also knew that patients undergoing radiotherapy and chemotherapy were likely to experience anaemia[15], so prevention was key. The chlorophyll in the wheatgrass was clearly doing its job perfectly.

"I don't think I've ever seen a patient with such good levels at this stage of treatment!" she exclaimed as if she was seeing some sort of miracle.

"I give him a blend of vital nutrients," I confessed.

She looked up from the blood tests sheets, quizzically. I knew I could be honest with her. The Macmillan staff seemed to be much more open to supportive measures outside of the conventional approach.

"What do you give him?"

I explained what I mixed up for him every day and put into his PEG.

---

13 http://www.ncbi.nlm.nih.gov/pubmed/17577257
14 http://www.ncbi.nlm.nih.gov/pubmed/15932808?dopt=AbstractPlus
15 http://theoncologist.alphamedpress.org/content/5/suppl_2/1.full

"Well how wonderful! He is a very lucky man to have such a switched-on wife," she smiled. "Do you mind if I jot that down?"

"Not at all!" I laughed, pleased to be endorsed by her.

"Okay, can I have a little look in your mouth Saul?" He was lying on the bed, not really taking in much of our chat, but nodded in response.

She pulled a little torch from a pouch, and shone it into his mouth.

"Oh no wonder your mouth is still so sore! You have some thrush in there! We must treat that – I will prescribe something for that. Now, let's take a look at these drugs."

She went through them all, writing them down for me: when I should give him what, and exactly how much. She was so supportive. She left then, giving me her mobile number and telling me I could call whenever I wanted. She arranged to return next week.

Chapter 10

David had planned a trip. When he was in junior school, his best friend Chris and he would chat for hours about their plans for when they were older. They would start a business and make lots of money; they would have big houses, drive nice cars and travel the world. The last dream was something they continued to discuss as they grew up, and their discussions becoming less outlandish and more realistic. Not long before Saul had been diagnosed, David announced that he and Chris were going to south-east Asia to fulfill their dream of travelling. When Saul had become ill, David was hesitant about booking the trip.

"I can't go until I know how Dad is. What if you need me? What if he gets really ill?" he worried.

Both Saul and I told him we wanted him to go. We had travelled as young adults and although our trip had been full of challenges that I would not wish for my son (or anyone for that matter), it had taught us so much about life and about ourselves that we would not otherwise have learnt. David was a sensible and responsible young man, and we thought that travel would be an enriching and fulfilling experience for him.

Eventually, we had managed to persuade him to go ahead and book his trip, which he and Chris had done together just before Christmas. He was due to go in just two months; the time was passing fast. Ordinarily I would have been on hand to help him organise his visas, his immunizations and generally help him plan, but I had been so pre-occupied, mainly with Saul, but also with the flood, dealing with the insurance and everything, that I hadn't been there for him at all. He was still only 18, and I felt terrible about it, but at the same time I felt it probably made him even more independent, having to organise everything himself.

One evening when Jack, Anabelle, David and I were eating in the hotel restaurant, while Saul slept, David was really snappy.

Jack couldn't say a word without David making sarcastic snide comments back, and his tone to me was aggressive and unkind. The only person he wasn't short with was Anabelle, but even she asked him what was wrong.

"I don't know what you're talking about!" he retorted.

"You just don't seem very happy tonight Dave," she said kindly.

"Yeah, you've been really grumpy for ages!" Jack added.

"That's cos you've been a twat!" David told Jack, cruelly.

"David! That was uncalled for!" I said feeling angry now.

"You don't have to share a room with him, so what would you know?"

"Face it David, you have been so irritable for ages! I don't particularly like sharing a room either, but I don't go round making your life miserable for it!"

"Why don't you fuck off!" David said aggressively.

"Do you know what? I will! C'mon Anabelle! I've had enough of this shit – see you later Mum!"

I couldn't blame Jack. David really was being nasty. He stood up to leave as well, clearly not wanting to sit with me and have me tear him off a strip.

"David – please sit down. We need to talk." I ventured, knowing this wasn't going to be an easy chat. "Would you like a drink?" I offered, to calm him down.

"No thanks, I'm tired. I just want to go to bed, but I guess Jack and Anabelle will be up for hours, giggling," he said sullenly.

"Okay, well, I will try to make this brief, but we do need to talk, David."

He slumped back into his seat, and stared ahead.

"Something is clearly eating you. I know this is a very difficult time, but what is it? You are obviously upset about something."

"I hate living here. I want to go home."

"David! You are not a child. You understand very well that we can't go home. Our house is uninhabitable. I know this isn't ideal, but can't you just try to make the best of it? Anyway, you are going away soon! You have a wonderful trip to look forward to! Why don't you focus on that?"

"Yes, great! And where will you be when I get back? Here, home, another house, another country?" he said his voice raising an octave.

Now I saw why he was so upset. He had always been so independent that sometimes I forgot he was still young. Jack had Anabelle to talk to, to confide in when he was worried. I guess David thought I had Saul, although in reality I didn't at the moment at all. All of our worlds had been turned upside down, and he was worried that when he came back from his travels, he wouldn't have a home, normality or stability. Saul and I had always talked too about moving away, abroad, and I guess David imagined we might do something like that now we had no home here to speak of. He knew things were unstable now, but he was here, living it day to day, and somehow you just cope when you are in it, but to go away, a million miles from your home, family, friends, and then not know what you may come back to find, was just too much for him.

I touched his hand. I felt him recoil, but he didn't draw it away.

"David, when you come home, Dad and Jack and I will all be here – well, maybe not here," I said indicating the hotel, "at least I hope not!" I smiled, "but we will be in this area. You will have a home and us to come back to. Dad will be fine; he is going to get through this, and we will be living somewhere locally as a family – I promise!"

"You won't move away?" he said in a small voice,

"No darling, we wouldn't go anywhere without you. We will be here, near all our friends and our work. I can't promise we will be back in our house, as you know we want to sell it and move somewhere else, but that will take time, and Dad has to be strong and healthy which will take time too. The likelihood is that the insurance company will find us a house locally, and that's where we will be when you come home. We will all move in together before you go – long before, and when you come back I'm sure we will still be there."

He turned to me then, meeting my gaze.

"I'm sorry Mum."

He was such a profound boy. I felt my heart contract with love for him. He was scared – of course he was, we all were, but he had had no one to talk to. Although he could talk to me, I hadn't had time to notice his worries, and he probably hadn't wanted to burden me, so instead he'd locked it up, and it came out as anger. He had great friends, but boys never really talked to each other, it just wasn't in their nature, and he wouldn't of his own accord admit he was worried. I put my arms around his tall frame, my head resting on his chest. I didn't care that we were in a hotel, and he would probably hate me for it – he needed a hug from his mum. Surprisingly he didn't pull away, but rested his chin on top of my head.

"I love you David, and I promise it will be okay."

As I released him he nodded, his eyes glazed with emotion. "I'm off to bed now Mum. Thank you."

"Sleep tight, David," I said, going up on my toes to plant a kiss on his cheek.

The next few days were pretty awful. We were on a rollercoaster of drug management and Fortisip and wheatgrass complex administration, and yo-yoing between sleep and the hospital, and moderate and severe bouts of vomiting. I tried everything, from leaving out the wheatgrass (this was very hard for me to do!) to giving him both that and the Fortisip, really slowly, releasing less than 5 ml at a time into the PEG, then waiting, with my fingers crossed that that would stay down. Saul spent his time between being in pain, sleeping, and being sick, to being dragged back and forth to the hospital. The boys were great. Whenever they were not at work, either one or both would come with me to the hospital. I needed them more than they realised; their support was invaluable.

After three days of Saul showing no signs of improvement, all three of us decided we had to do something. He was just getting weaker all the time, and was in so much pain. We were due for a clinic meeting again with Dr Wick, so would discuss our predicament with her and her staff.

I think even she was surprised by how poorly Saul had become.

"I think we will need to admit him," she said after examining him. He is becoming too weak and is in danger of dehydration.

I was not keen at all to let this happen.

"Mum," Jack said quietly while Saul's 'team' discussed things, "we have to do what's best for Dad. If they can make him better, then perhaps we will have to try this."

"His immune system is really low. He is going to be exposed to all kinds of horrors if he is admitted. I can take care of him and we are only next door!" I protested.

"Ask him what he wants to do," said David, sensibly. "He is still capable of deciding what he thinks is best."

I walked over to where Saul was lying in a semi-conscious state.

"Saul?" I whispered quietly. "Have you been listening, babe? Do you want to stay in the hotel, or do you feel you need to be admitted? We will do whatever you want."

Saul opened his eyes, turning his head slowly to look at me. "I don't know, I just need to feel better than this," he said miserably.

My heart ached for him. I wanted to do the right thing, but I was so scared of what he would be exposed to if he was admitted; however, I didn't want to put him at risk by standing in the way if that really was the answer. Saul didn't know, he just wanted to be looked after one way or another, so he could feel better – we just had to decide how we were going to make that happen.

I looked back at the boys. They both shrugged, in unison, as confused as I was.

Dr Wick returned to the room.

"I've been discussing this with Lucy and Carol and we know you're not happy about him being admitted, so we thought we could try one last thing, but if it doesn't work, Flossie, you may have to relent and let us take him in."

I sat up hopefully, waiting to hear what they had in mind.

"There is another feeding system – I think Lucy mentioned it to you before?" I nodded in response, recalling the conversation we had had.

"You will all need to be trained, as it does take a little bit of getting used to. Katy our nutrition nurse is on duty now. Lucy has just gone to find her. She will show you how to use the system. We will give it the weekend, but if Saul is still struggling to retain anything after that, we will have to admit him."

I nodded. This didn't sound too bad, just a slow way of him getting some sustenance, while he slept, which was getting to the point where it was more often than not.

"I'm also going to give you morphine, as I think Saul needs the stronger pain relief now. I see that the Macmillan nurse has given him some Fluconazole for oral thrush, so we will keep an eye on this too."

Lucy entered the room after knocking softly, accompanied by a lady with some sort of apparatus in her hands.

"Ah! Good, this is Katy," said Dr Wick. "I will leave you with her, so she can show you how to operate the Flocare system."

Katy was smiley and cheerful. She was like a breath of fresh air in a room brimming with stuffy anxiety.

"Hi! I'm going to give you all a little lesson! Bet you didn't think you'd be coming in to learn a new skill today!" she laughed.

Saul struggled to sit up so he could at least watch what she was showing us.

"Okay, so this is the Flocare Infinity dispenser," she explained, showing us the plastic frame with a little computerized box attached to it.

"You take one of these bags of feed, and attach it here." She demonstrated how to hook the bag onto the machine and then proceeded to show us how to set the flow-rate, amount and timing controls on the computerized panel.

"I know it all looks a bit complex, but it's really very simple. Now Lucy has suggested that we start you on the slowest setting and only give you the 500ml bag, to see how you tolerate it," she said to Saul, who nodded imperceptibly.

"If you are okay with that, we can slowly increase the speed and the dosage, so that you are getting the full amount of a litre and a half per day. Now, I can give you enough for about 4 days, but then we will have to order some more for you. I know you are not living at home, so can we get them sent to the hotel?"

"Er yes, I guess so," I said scribbling down the hotel address for her, to place the order.

"Hopefully this will sort you out, and you'll start to feel a bit more like yourself again!" she smiled her cheery smile at Saul and then the rest of us.

I was pleased the boys were with us as there was quite a bit to carry.

"Well she was a bit patronising," said David, a little tersely, as we walked to the car.

"Do you think so? I thought she was rather lovely."

"I just think she thought we were all a bit stupid, and couldn't work a dumb machine."

"No, darling, I think they just need to be very sure we have a full understanding of it. We can't afford not to. They are not there with us to set it up, and Dad needs this to work."

"Yeah, I guess so."

Back at the hotel, I got Saul settled in bed, and set about giving him all his painkillers and anti-sickness meds. Then we fiddled about with the machine and finally got it going, set to give him just half a litre over 10 hours.

He was asleep within minutes of it starting. I stayed with him for an hour or so, to make sure he was okay, before going to get something to eat, in the bar.

All the hotel staff had got to know us pretty well. They really looked after us, always asking about Saul and offering to go over and above their duties to do anything they could to help. Some nights when the boys were out, or working, and I sat alone to have my dinner, they would chat to me, between serving other guests, if they were not too busy, taking the edge off my solitude.

After my meal, I checked on Saul, and he was still fast asleep with the machine gently whirring away beside him. As much as I hated the artificial nutrients that were slowly making their way into his body, I felt grateful that at least he was getting some sort of sustenance. He needed it so badly, and if this could prevent him having to be admitted, then I would be happy.

I took a long bath, feeling content for a while to lounge in the warm water, knowing Saul was safe. I let the water soothe my tired limbs, and felt myself drifting off, relaxing for the first time in ages.

Chapter 11

I woke the next morning to find Saul still snoring gently next to me. He must have woken in the night to unhook himself from the machine, but it looked as though he had had all of it, and kept it down!

I got up quietly trying not to disturb him, but he opened his eyes, and smiled a sleepy smile.

"Darling, how are you feeling today?"

"Better. Not so drained. I haven't been sick!"

"That's fantastic! I'm so relieved! I'm going to get some breakfast, I won't be long," I said pulling on a top and some jeans.

"Can you get me some melon?" he asked.

"Yes, of course I will!" Wow, he really *was* feeling better!

He managed a small bowl of chopped melon and then later, after his meds, we got him started on the next feed. I had held off giving him his wheatgrass complex for the last couple of days, as I didn't want to challenge his system too much. If today was a success, then tomorrow I would try him with it again.

As it was the weekend, Saul didn't have to go to the hospital for any treatment. He loved not having to go, and it seemed to me that having the mental break from radiotherapy was as big a part of his improvement as not being sick and getting some sustenance into him. We had visits from his cousin and from my family too – but they were only very brief, as anything more than about half an hour was just too exhausting for him.

By Monday, although Saul was very tired and his mouth was still extremely sore, he was definitely better. The sunken look had all but gone from his eyes and his skin had lost that grey tone which he had presented over the last few days. He had had some wheatgrass too, on Sunday, and kept that down – I had literally drip-fed it to him over half an hour, and made sure he rested afterwards.

However, when I started to try and get him to get ready to go to the hospital his demeanour changed. He sat slumped on the bed, looking so dejected.

"C'mon baby. You are almost two-thirds of the way through this now! You are doing so well, and now that we have some food going into you, you will feel better."

He slowly raised his eyes to mine and nodded anxiously. Then, getting up, he took himself to the bathroom to shower and take his meds.

I heard the shower running – always on the alert in case he felt faint or weak, but somehow he always managed. Then I heard him being sick.

I rushed into the bathroom to find him kneeling by the toilet. He looked at me, with such doleful eyes it broke my heart. I fetched him some water and stroked his head.

"You've done so well all weekend! I think you have got stressed about going for treatment, sweetheart! Tomorrow, let's try not giving you anything in your stomach until after treatment; that way, if you get anxious there won't be anything in your digestive system to lose!"

I heard a knock on the door. Jack and Anabelle were coming with us today, and I was really glad. I needed them so much.

"You go let them in. I will get myself straight," said Saul, making himself face his fear.

For a few days he seemed okay. We even managed to walk one way to the hospital a couple of times, with the boys picking us up afterwards.

Then by Friday of that week, he took another turn for the worse.

I had been to work, leaving him sleeping with strict instructions to call me if he needed to. David was in the hotel too, today, and Saul knew he could call on him any time and David would be there in minutes, so I wasn't worried about leaving him.

When I arrived back in our hotel room that evening, Saul was hunched over the toilet being sick.

"Oh darling! Not again!" I said feeling despair engulf me.

David was with him, sitting on the bed in our room.

"This is the fourth time today. He hasn't had any food at all." David's brow was knitted in distress.

"Has he had any anti-sickness meds?" I asked.

"No Mum, he hasn't had anything – only a few sips of water."

"Oh sweetie, why didn't you call me? I would have come back straight away!"

"You think I can't look after my dad?" David looked hurt.

"No darling, I don't think that at all. I think you are amazing! But it would have been easier for you if I was here to help you."

I didn't want him to think I was ungrateful for his support. Little did he know how much I needed him right now. I could have fallen into his arms and cried, for the desperation I was feeling, but who would that help? Not Saul for one, and not me or David either, but that's how I felt.

David helped Saul back into bed, while I got his antiemetics ready. I gave him a dose, and then half an hour later some coconut water, to stop him becoming dehydrated[16].

He settled then for an hour or so, but then began being sick again. I rang the hospital. They suggested giving him the other antiemetic, but even that he couldn't keep down for long. By now it was late Friday evening and there was no one at the hospital who knew us who I could talk to. I had to decide how best to treat him – if I could keep his hydration levels up overnight, then in the morning I could speak to an oncology doctor. So I settled him back to bed and got a glass of iced water from the hotel bar. I added a few drops of coconut water so it was really weak, and with a straw, got him to sip at it slowly, just wetting his lips. He

---

16 *Molecules* 2009, *14*, 5144–5164; doi:10.3390/molecules14125144. *molecules*. ISSN 1420–3049. The Chemical Composition and Biological Properties of Coconut (*Cocos nucifera* L.) Water. Jean W. H. Yong, Liya Ge, Yan Fei Ng and Swee Ngin Tan *

did this for about 2 hours, me rousing him every few minutes and him dropping off to sleep between sips. Throughout the night, I woke myself every half hour to make him take a sip of his fluids. He wasn't sick at all, and by morning, I was feeling more positive, if somewhat shattered!

However, as soon as he got up to visit the bathroom, I heard him vomiting.

So I tried more antiemetics, then more water, but he was sick again.

Now I knew I needed help. I was at a loss. I was exhausted, desperate and scared. What would I do if they wanted to admit him? I knew that was a distinct possibility, but if they did, I realised that apart from being so fearful he would get some other dreaded bug, and I would be unable to give him any of his natural nutrition that I knew his body would need again as soon as he could keep anything down. I called the hospital, knowing someone should be there. I spoke to a duty doctor who told me to come in and talk to her.

Jack came up to sit with Saul while I went to the hospital. On the way, my mobile rang and it was Michael. I told him what was happening and how afraid I felt.

"Flossie, I know you don't want him to be admitted, but they may have to. You have to face the possibility. They will get him on a drip, sort out his hydration and his vomiting and then let him out again. He will be looked after by staff who know what to do, and you can get a full night's sleep! I'm worried about you!"

I dismissed him. "I'm fine. I am getting enough sleep, and anyway, I can always sleep in the day when he is asleep too. I don't want him going in, not unless he absolutely has to."

I explained my fears about him going in.

"Yes Flossie, I do understand how you feel and why you feel that way, but you must try to think about what would be best for Saul."

"I am thinking about what's best for Saul! It won't be best for him if he gets a superbug! Unless they can assure me he will be put in isolation, and I can be with him as much as possible, then it will have to be an emergency for them to take him in!"

"Okay Floss," Michael said resignedly. He knew how stubborn I was, and how strong my feelings were. "But just try to accept that if he does have to go in, they are going to take good care of him. Call me later and tell me what they say."

The doctor asked me about Saul: What had his night been like? Had he managed to keep anything down?

I explained the regime I had followed to keep him hydrated. She looked at me as if she now understood why my eyes had small black suitcases under them. Thankfully she suggested we try yet another antiemetic. This one worked differently. It crossed the blood-brain barrier, working on the part of the brain that induced vomiting, whereas the one he had been taking was a motility drug, that moved food through the gut – but as he wasn't having any food, obviously this was not working. He needed something that would stop his body rejecting everything.

I raced back to the hotel with the new drug, and got to work straight away at administering it. It worked! He managed to keep down fluid and then later a 500ml bag of feed, on the slowest setting! We had got through another episode without him having to be admitted. I breathed a sigh of relief.

The next day Saul's poor mouth was so sore. The inside of it was raw and bleeding and the lining of his tongue was peeling away in layers. He didn't speak; he could barely move his mouth. I got him glass after glass full of ice cubes topped up with water, which he sipped at constantly. He looked defeated, like a man who just couldn't take any more. His eyes were sunken and his skin was red raw with big blisters forming, around his neck and jawline. I couldn't hold him in my arms, because he was in so much pain. I sat holding his hand, trying so hard not to cry. He didn't need my tears, he needed my strength, but truth be told, I didn't have any left to give. I just wanted to curl up next to him and sleep. Maybe I was not the best carer for him as I had thought. A nurse would be psychologically removed, would be capable of rational thought: she would have slept; she would be part of a team. I was an exhausted wreck, an emotional mess whose heart was breaking.

He slept, most of the day. I gave him another feed and his wheatgrass complex – super-slow. While he slept, I cried, silently, so as not to wake him. Big, fat tears of lonely desperation. Was I really any good for Saul?

In the morning Saul was brighter. He seemed less forlorn, and a little more awake. The Macmillan nurse came to visit, and I told her a little of how I was feeling too. She smiled at me, so kindly.

"Flossie, I don't know that I have ever seen a wife as devoted as you! You are doing an amazing job! Look at Saul – I know you think he looks poorly but apart from a few sores, the rest of his face looks great. His chest and back have not been affected; his bloods are still really good, in spite of how poorly he has been. You've kept him hydrated and better nourished than anyone else I've ever seen at this stage of treatment. And he is feeling better today – you said so yourself, didn't you Saul?" she said turning to him.

"Yes, I do feel a bit less like a zombie today. I don't know what I'd do without Flossie." His eyes glazed over with emotion.

"There, you see! And there is only one more week of his treatment left!" she smiled encouragingly.

After Marianne left, Saul was tired.

"I just want to sleep. Why don't you go and have a break – have a swim, go and see Rica, read a book?"

Although he did seem brighter today, I was still reluctant to leave him, but he was right, I did need to get out of this hotel room, and do something that felt normal.

"The boys are around, so call them if you need anything," I said planting a kiss on his head.

"I will," he murmured closing his eyes.

I was a keen swimmer, so I was happy to take advantage of the hotel pool, and it felt so good to be doing something physical, and a huge relief from the mental anguish I was experiencing most of the time. After my swim I popped my head round the door of our room, but Saul was still asleep, snoring peacefully, so I decided to go out for an hour and see Rica.

As soon as I got to Rica's she enveloped me in a huge hug. The warmth of her friendship was like the key to the floodgate of my emotions. The tears came, and she stood in her kitchen with her arms wrapped around me, stroking my hair. She didn't say anything, just letting me cry. Eventually the tears began to slow and my ragged breaths returned to normal. Rica let me go and put the kettle on. Only then did she start to speak,

"This is the toughest part, Floss. Saul is going through the worst: the treatment has accumulated in his body, and his symptoms are at their most severe, but you are so nearly at the end now, and you are doing such an amazing job with him!"

"I can't bear to watch him go through this. The cancer itself had no symptoms: no pain; no side effects; no suffering for him on a physical level. I know that emotionally he feels as if an alien is invading his body; a malevolent intruder with ill intent, and I'm not belittling that in any way. Even though it's happening to him, and we are so close, I still can't begin to imagine how it must feel mentally every day knowing that's inside you – but physically, apart from a stupid lump, there's nothing! But the treatment – that's what's so physically crippling; it's barbaric! His body has been poisoned with chemo, burnt with the radio, and to manage the burning and poisoning, he has to take a load more poisons!!"

"I know, sweetie, but you are giving him all the good stuff to minimise those effects, and although it's tough now, I bet it will all pay off! Just one more week, then the treatment stops, and he can start to heal."

"But that's just it, the worst is yet to come," I sobbed. "The two weeks post treatment when the accumulative effects peak is the toughest bit! I'm not even convinced that what I'm doing for him is really helping that much – surely he shouldn't be suffering this badly if it was working!"

"Flossie, you said yourself that the wheatgrass and other stuff you are giving him works by minimising the long-term, harmful effects of the treatment, and will help him recover from it more quickly. Also, you said it helps maximise the therapeutic effects of the treatment, so maybe his symptoms are worse now because the treatment is really working. Anyway, look at his blood tests! You know what you are doing is working – you have proof!"

"It just doesn't feel like it when I look at my poor man. I don't know how much more I can take," I said glumly.

Rica took hold of my hand, and looked at me earnestly,

"You are such a strong woman, Floss. I've always thought it, but now you are showing it in so many ways. You are doing a sterling job with Saul, being there for the boys, dealing with the house insurance, living in a hotel, and all you've done is cried a bit! I'm pretty sure most women in your shoes would have gone to pieces – I know I would!"

I hugged her tight. I had needed her reassurance more than she would ever know.

Driving back to the hospital, I turned the radio on. Katy Perry's "Roar" was playing. I turned it up, and began singing with her:

"You held me down but I got up
Already brushing off the dust
You hear my voice, you hear that sound
Like thunder, gonna shake the ground
You held me down, but I got up
Get ready 'cause I've had enough
I see it all, I see it now
I got the eye of the tiger, a fighter
Dancing through the fire

'Cause I am a champion
And you're gonna hear me roar
Louder, louder than a lion
'Cause I am a champion
And you're gonna hear me roar..."

"That's right, cancer – you might have held me down, but I've had enough, I'm going to fight you, and fight for my man, and you are going to tremble before me," I thought resolutely to myself. I felt emboldened: a surge of courage, of steely strength pulsed through me, sending goosebumps all over me.

After Katy had finished her motivational song, I turned the radio down and began to think about cancer. Did wild animals get cancer? They didn't eat all the rubbish we put into our bodies. They didn't use toxic products on their skin, or clean their habitats with chemicals. Surely because they were not exposed to the toxins that we humans were on a daily basis, the prevalence would be much less if not zero. I guess it would be difficult to quantify, as in order to study animals, you had to have contact with them, which immediately puts them in contact, indirectly, with the toxins humans are exposed to , which would the nullify the study: catch 22! However, after looking into it I did find one article that suggests that the only animals in the wild who did show signs of the abnormal tissue growth were those who were exposed to anthropogenic activities[17]. It would be interesting if researchers could find more on this, without putting the animals at risk!

But it begged the question – were we humans killing ourselves and all those with whom we came in contact? Were we the cancer to mother earth? That was not a comforting thought.

---

17 http://www.nature.com/nrc/journal/v9/n7/full/nrc2665.html

Chapter 12

The insurance company had been very good. They were trying to secure a house for us to rent, but it wasn't happening very quickly. In the meantime they kept extending our stay at the hotel. We had been at the hotel for almost a month already, and it was far from ideal, mainly because I didn't feel as if we were living as a family. I only saw the boys briefly at mealtimes if they were around, or if they came to the hospital with us, or popped in to visit Saul. This was hard, as I missed them – at home, even though they very much lived their own lives, I knew they were in their rooms, or they would watch TV with us sometimes, or just wander through the kitchen to get some food etc. Either way we had constant interaction with them that we didn't get living in the hotel. Additionally, having to go back to the house every so often to get things was an inconvenience, as was going into work, as it was now a 25-minute drive, whereas it was only 5 minutes from home – although, at the moment, I was hardly working.

However, there were also perks. The hotel's proximity to the hospital meant that getting Saul to and from his treatments was less stressful than it might have been from home; also, knowing the hospital was on our doorstep was reassuring, especially recently when he'd been so poorly. On the housekeeping front, I had no cooking or cleaning to do, meaning I could focus nearly all my time and energy on taking care of Saul, and not have to worry about day-to-day chores. The hotel staff were nothing short of wonderful, really looking after us and doing all they could to help. Finally, I loved the fact that I could just pop down the corridor and go for a swim, which I tried to do as much as I could, if I knew Saul was okay – usually when he was sleeping.

It was also nice for friends to come and visit. I didn't even have to make them a cup of tea, so it was no stress for me. We were lucky – so many friends came by, for tea, or a glass of wine or some dinner. They all came to support me, and although they wanted to see Saul, mostly they understood that he just needed to stay in bed sleeping, and wasn't really up to social interaction.

I realise that it was these people who got me through this terrible time, who gave me the strength to carry on and not collapse in an emotional heap – my boys, my family and my wonderful friends.

I learnt so much about people during that time. My best friends and close family I knew I could count on. They would always be there in my life whatever it threw at me. But it was other friends who surprised me. Friends who I hardly ever saw, who came out of the woodwork when they knew what was happening and offered me their support, their kindness and their love, by the truckload. How that touched my heart, I can barely even put into words. These folk showed me such compassion and empathy at a time when I felt as though my world was caving in. They were people who had found their way into my heart, and I knew that I would treasure them always for it.

There were two friends in particular who really came up trumps when I least expected it. One was Marie, who although we hadn't been close stepped in and offered her home for the night when we were in need of somewhere warm to stay, and constantly called and messaged me to lend her support. The other friend was again someone who I hadn't been close to since the boys were small. I remember a few years ago finding out that she had been diagnosed with breast cancer, and feeling the weight of the punch that came with the shock of that news. I had called her a couple of times, to express my sympathy, and ask if there was anything I could do, but I was not there for her; yet she never held that against me, and when she had found out about Saul, I couldn't believe how unbelievably kind and supportive she was. I didn't deserve her friendship, her love or any of the sweet things she did for us, but she gave it, willingly and unquestioningly. I thought back to when I had heard her news and asked myself why I hadn't given her my support at that time. The truth is, until it happens to you, you never really understand how tough it is. You hear the news, feel the impact of their pain momentarily, and then your own life with its trials and tribulations takes you away, smoothing the sharp edges of your new knowledge until it becomes a thought in the back of your mind that you only pay attention to when it arises. How can you know, how can anyone know unless they have been there? I apologised to her from the bottom of my heart for my negligence, and she forgave me with all of hers. It made me all the more thankful not only for her friendship but also for all of my close friends who were there for me, although they hadn't been through it. They were there just because they loved us; they may not truly understand what it was like for us, but nonetheless they were there, and I knew I could lean on them, those precious rocks who were the very fabric of my life.

Every night before I went to bed, and every morning when he was awake enough, I followed a skincare regime for Saul. The sores on his neck were open and weepy, his face was still sore and dry and chest, back and upper arms were as dry and flaky as old paint. I sprayed his neck and inside his mouth with colloidal silver, which has been shown to have anti-bacterial properties[18]. Then once that had dried I used another soothing natural spray, which has skin cooling and healing properties, and was specially formulated for burnt and radiotherapy-treated skin[19]. After this, I very gently applied some Vitamin E cream with lavender to his skin, just patting it on and leaving it, followed by massaging pure coconut oil with aloe onto him where his skin was dry but intact. His face and neck hurt to put these treatments on but very quickly the soothing effects began to kick in, and he got some relief. Also,

---

18 http://www.jnanobiotechnology.com/content/10/1/19
19 http:// skinlabs.com/?product=rescue-relief-spray

we managed to avoid any type of skin infection that is common with patients who have radiotherapy wounds.

At his next clinic session Dr Wick was pleased. Saul seemed a little brighter and the feeding system was obviously working out well. He was able to keep his food down most of the time, only vomiting occasionally – but this level of sickness she said was to be expected. She commented on Saul's haemoglobin levels from his blood test, saying they were truly remarkable and that she had never seen a patient with such good levels at this stage, particularly as Saul had been so ill and taken so long to settle into any kind of feeding pattern. I didn't mention my wheatgrass regime – we had been under strict instruction to only put the prescribed feed and drugs into the PEG, and I didn't want to be told not to continue, so I kept quiet, smiling innocently at her.

The next few days were fairly good by comparison. His skin was very sore around his neck and his mouth was ulcerated and bleeding. He sipped constantly on his iced water, but this was good as it kept his swallowing mechanism intact – many patients who undergo this treatment cannot swallow at all at this stage, and can only hold water in their mouths then spit it out, but Saul drank continuously and copiously.

Saul's cousin Chris came to visit from London, and as Saul was doing so well, we took a drive to the local cathedral. The sun was shining and although it was January it was a beautiful, mild day. We stepped out of the car and wandered slowly up the sweeping driveway to the building. The cathedral, an imposing but plain building in itself, stood out against the pale blue January sky. You could see how a different background would have made it the perfect setting for the ominous role it played in the film "The Omen" in 1976. The inside of the cathedral was light and airy – quite the opposite of its daunting exterior – with its walls adorned with local art exhibits. The left-hand side of the building is comprised of the chapel of the Queen's Royal Surrey Regiment, and is framed by three archways, where the sun filtered through. For a while we lost ourselves in the magnificence of the building and its trimmings, forgetting for a moment how doing something so simple, so ordinary, could feel so good. This was the first time we had been somewhere other than the hospital together, and done something that was not related to his treatment, his illness, or our sorry situation, and it felt like the most healing tonic. Drinking in the cathedral's splendour, filling our lungs with fresh air, and walking in the sunshine, Saul and I held hands, savouring the feeling of normality.

I thanked Chris for suggesting it. I don't think he realised just how much we had needed this little trip into everyday existence.

Later that evening, we had a lovely surprise visit from our dear nephew George. He had arrived on the train from London, desperate to see his uncle, and to lend us his priceless support. It was so good to see him. Saul even sat in the hotel bar for half an hour, to be in his company.

At about 6.30pm Saul was exhausted and took himself to bed. I went with him to administer his skin and medicine regime, and get him settled for the evening and night.

The next day Saul decided he was going to use the hotel gym! I was astounded.

"Let me come with you," I said, so afraid he would collapse.

"No, I'll be fine. You swim. I am just going to take it easy."

"Are you sure it's a good idea, Saul? I'm very happy that you want to do it, but are you going to be okay?"

"We'll soon see!" he said with remnants of his cheeky personality showing through.

He was barely able to speak, his mouth was so sore, but still he was managing to find some motivation. Was it because he knew that tomorrow was his last treatment?

He managed a 3km walk on the treadmill which took him 40 mins. He came back to the room looking like he had run a marathon, and then some! But he was smiling. He showered and flopped into bed, with a sense of achievement that had probably done him more good mentally than physically.

The next day, Saul was tired. However, he wanted to walk to the hospital for his last session. At the clinic, he had put on a little weight and his bloods were excellent – well above expected levels. He'd done it – made it right through to the end of this horrible treatment, and he was still okay.

We were flooded with text messages, phone calls and emails from friends and family who knew that today Saul had reached an all-important milestone. They wanted to share in the relief that we were feeling. Their support enriched our feelings, making us even more elated than we already were.

Later that evening both the boys and Anabelle came to our room and we all watched a movie together. Having that time as a family, something we were getting so little of, was extremely precious. Although Saul's mouth was so sore he was barely speaking, his eyes shone with the gratification that having his boys with us gave him.

Yet, we fooled ourselves into thinking that by reaching the end of the treatment it was all over. It's not as if we hadn't been warned that things would get worse first, but because we had been on a high, I think the fall was that much harder when it came.

Saul's energy levels slumped over the next two days, leaving him drained, and depleted.

He didn't get out of bed – just sleeping, and feeding, and taking his meds and his wheatgrass when I gave them to him. I began to worry about bed sores, suggesting he got up and just moved around the room a little, or sat up to change his position, but my suggestions were met with the blunt rejection of a man who just didn't have the energy to move.

I left the room for less than half an hour to swim, but other than that I sat with him, with the curtains pulled shut, blocking out the light so he could sleep. I didn't put the TV on as I didn't want to disturb him. I couldn't speak on the phone as that too would disturb him.

I turned to look at my sleeping husband, a dark shape on a large white bed, drugged into a false slumber, hooked up to a machine that pumped beige coloured slurry into his ravaged body. I felt the tears pricking angrily at my eyelids, wanting to escape in full-blown howling despair, but having to make their way quietly down my cheeks to drip onto my lap, so they didn't wake Saul.

I'd had enough! I was done keeping it together. We had finished the treatment! Where was the relief of it being over? I thought irrationally. Surely life should be better now? I didn't want to be a nurse anymore, or live in a hotel, or deal with insurance companies and hospitals! I wanted to see my friends, go to work, go to yoga, go out for a meal. I wanted to be at home with my husband and my boys and cook a family meal. I wanted my life back! A sob escaped my lips, I quickly turned, but Saul was in another place – he wasn't here with me. No one was. I was alone. More alone than I had ever felt in my life. I couldn't even put my arms around my husband. He was so covered in weeping sores, and with his feeding tube I couldn't get close to him.

For four hours I sat quietly staring into the darkness of our room. Sometimes I cried, sometimes I just sat, but I knew that the high of reaching the end of his treatment had thrown me back down hard, too: I felt lonely and destitute.

At last, my phone beeped with an incoming text. Someone was reaching out to me when I needed them most. It was Jack.

"Want to have dinner with me?" he was asking.

Never had I been so happy to get a dinner invitation! I quietly tiptoed to the bathroom to wash my face. Then after checking Saul was okay, I slipped out of the room to go and meet my son.

I didn't share my feelings with him, but I did tell him I wasn't having such a good day and that meeting up with him was just wonderful. In his usual style he managed to make me laugh at some crazy story about what he and his friends had got up to the night before. I'm not sure he ever knew how much I needed him that day, and how his making me laugh had saved me from slipping into a pool of despair.

I decided that now Saul had finished his treatment it was time to help him as much as I could with his rehabilitation. The first thing I did was to increase his wheatgrass from one to two pods a day. The brown sludge that he had to ingest daily to keep him alive made me shudder every time I thought about how artificial and full of synthetic nutrients it was, so having the natural, live nutrition that the wheatgrass gave, seemed to me like fresh air for him in a room devoid of oxygen. I knew that keeping one down had sometimes been more of a challenge than he could manage, but because I gave it to him at such a slow pace, he usually managed to hold onto it. Now his body needed to start the process of getting rid of all the toxicity so it could heal – and his immune system could begin its road to recovery. The volume of liquid hardly increased with the double dose of wheatgrass, and I deliberately didn't tell Saul, so that psychology wouldn't make him think that he wouldn't be able to tolerate it. It worked! Within a day or two he seemed to noticeably pick up a little, and was able to stay awake more, even sat with me one morning looking at old holiday photos on my laptop.

His energy levels had definitely lifted: he was able to sit up in bed and watch a little TV, and even move around the room to sit on the sofa, but he didn't want to leave our room. His skin had somehow become worse, and he was very uncomfortable. We were told that this would happen, but I guess as he was showing signs of improvement I was disappointed that his skin was worse. I massaged his back and shoulders with coconut oil, and sprayed his weeping skin with colloidal silver to stop it becoming infected. After using the spray, and letting that dry I gently patted the Vitamin E cream onto his skin. This gave him some relief from the pain and discomfort, but it did little to heal the sores.

Although I felt disheartened I understood that radiotherapy was not actually the same as a burn, so would not respond in the same way. Radiotherapy wounds are actually not damaged skin but missing skin, because the treatment causes the skin to stop producing new layers, which is why it gets worse as time goes on, rather than reacting to the early stages of the treatment. I understood that no topical treatment could in fact heal the wounds, as we had to wait for the body to begin to reproduce skin again from the bottom layers – the wheatgrass would probably help this more than anything we applied externally. However, I did know that the colloidal silver would inhibit the growth of any bacteria in the weeping sores, and this was very important as we needed to avoid any complications.

We had been advised that his skin would most likely get worse in the two weeks post treatment, so we were expecting this. However, within a week the worst of it was over and his skin began to heal. Once it had started to show improvement, it healed very quickly and by day 10 post treatment the sores had stopped weeping and his skin was much less painful.

It was around this time (day 9 post treatment) that we finally moved out of the hotel. The insurance company had found us a house not far from our own house, and signed up to a six-month contract for us. This was the end of six whole weeks of living in a hotel! I had battled relentlessly on the phone with the company to complete this contract for us. I had found the house myself, and pretty much handed it to them, so that all they had to do was sign on the dotted line and we could move, but it had taken almost four weeks of phone calls, back and forth between the estate agents, the insurance company both the accommodation department and the finance department – none of whom was capable of talking to either of the others without my intervention. It was a huge relief that we were finally going! I would miss the staff, who had been so kind to us, and would miss not having to cook or clean, but boy was I glad to be moving into a house with my family. Finally it was time to enter a new phase – the rehabilitation phase. Not just for Saul, but for all of us. We had been held in the "treatment" phase all the time we lived at the hotel. This next phase felt as if we were moving in the right direction – healing from the treatment, living once again as a family unit. It was just what we needed in so many ways.

Phase Three
The Rehabilitation Phase

Chapter 13

When we arrived at the house, Jack and Anabelle, had already made really good headway with the unpacking. They had all but sorted the kitchen, with Anabelle putting things in logical places that only another female would comprehend. Jack was happily passing her things as she arranged them in my cupboards.

I'd previously made a chicken broth from organic chicken and carrot and onion for Saul, which was in the freezer. I defrosted it and he managed to drink some of the broth. Other than a few slivers of melon and spoonfuls of tomato soup at the hotel, this was the first thing he had managed by mouth in the way of food. It was very exciting to see real nutrition going into his body.

Later that evening, David came home to our new temporary house, and began to sort out his room. Anabelle had Jack's room all organised and cosy, and they were curled up exhausted on his bed.

Moving out of the hotel and into a normal house was such a tonic. It marked the beginning of the healing process. Saul pottered around gently in those first few days, helping me however he could. He began very slowly to eat a little piece of banana, a small smoothie with fresh fruit and nuts blended in, a piece of avocado. His skin began to clear up, drying out and becoming flaky instead of weepy. When he felt tired he listened to his body and simply flopped onto the sofa allowing the force of his exhaustion to overcome him. A few close friends called by, eager to see Saul in a more normal environment. I was careful to tactfully ask them not to stay long, reminding them that he tired easily and that any stimulus was a big deal at this stage.

He did so well in that first week it was easy to forget just how weak he still was. So when, a week into our new phase, Saul hit a rough patch, it shook us all up more than we had bargained for. He became very tired, his mouth became more ulcerated, and his throat more sore. He vomited with every morsel of food, and felt shivery and sick.

We had a follow-up at the hospital that was an effort to get Saul out of bed to go to, but when we got there we voiced our concerns to the team.

We expected them to be as disappointed as we were by his setback, but they seemed to think this was normal.

"All of Saul's symptoms at the moment are totally in line with what we expect at this stage of recovery," explained Dr Wick.

"But you don't understand!" I cried. "He has been socialising, helping me with us moving into our house, eating and drinking!!" I told her.

She looked at her colleague as if to say: "as if – the woman is delusional!!" She didn't believe me! She thought I was making it up and Saul was too poorly to back me up!

"Honestly, Flossie, this is what we expect! If he were able to do the things you are wanting him to do, it would be way too soon! He has only just finished his treatment. He will be worse now before he shows any signs of improvement!"

"But he has shown all of that! Honestly, why would I make it up?"

"Yes of course," she placated, "but he needs his rest."

She clearly didn't believe me. Well, there wasn't much I could do, except hope he would return to *our* brand of "normal for this stage" very soon.

For the next couple of days Saul was very tired. Looking back, I guess we had done a lot. Returning from hospital to the hotel, and then moving into a new house, having guests over, beginning to eat... of course he would be exhausted! I encouraged his rest, but kept up his very gentle return to oral food with spoonfuls of natural yoghurt, porridge and home-made bone broths.

Meanwhile, the terrible weather continued in the UK. Storms raged across the south of England, wreaking havoc. Houses continued to flood, particularly along the Thames, and the coast.

I used to love the sound of the rain. There used to be nothing more cosy than hearing it lash against the windows while we snuggled up indoors, with a fire roaring in the stove, and the curtains drawn against the force of the storm; but now, when I heard the rain it invoked dread deep within my soul. My heart contracted with fear for my home, worrying every time about flooding, knowing now how much damage the rain could do. I don't think I would ever find anything beautiful in the sound of the rainfall again.

Saul struggled to get back on track with his recovery. I maintained his two wheatgrass pods with hemp, coconut water, reishi, probiotics and milk thistle, through the PEG, and persevered with my home-made soups for him. Finally, it began to pay off, as I came from work one afternoon to find he had been out for a little walk! It was still only 20 days since he stopped his treatment, and bearing in mind he was meant to be at his very worst at around two to three weeks post treatment, he was doing fabulously!

Within a couple of days he was walking about a mile into the village, having a coffee and then walking back again. He was eating mashed veg with gravy, and natural yoghurts. In between walking and eating small amounts he would sleep, or just rest, watching TV. He couldn't yet concentrate enough to read, as radiotherapy affects the concentration span.

David was going to be leaving us for a few months to go and travel in south-east Asia. This filled me with mixed emotions in the days leading up to his departure. I was happy that he was following a dream that he had nurtured with his best friend since primary school; but, at the same time I was worried that my precious boy would be so far away from home, in countries that I knew from my own experiences were not all silks, spices, and breath-taking sunsets. There was a darker side that I hoped my boy would not encounter, and if he did that he would be able to return home unscathed.

Some friends invited us out for an evening to have a meal in town. We weren't sure we should go, but Saul wanted to get out and do something "normal". We hadn't really been out in the evening until now so this was a pretty big step in Saul's recovery.

It felt so good to be socialising in the evening. Saul managed to eat a little chicken, which was great too, as eating any meat until this point had been too much for him to break down, so another little milestone for him. He was quiet at the restaurant, but happy to be out.

However, the next day he was exhausted. His throat was very sore, and he stayed in bed until the early afternoon. He had felt a bit nauseous through the night so hadn't had his whole feed. He did manage a little walk but was very sleepy all afternoon, and couldn't really eat much either. I guess going out for an evening was a little premature, or at least we needed to make sure we factored in a rest day after an active day.

At his next check-up we saw the whole team. They were amazed. They said they had never seen anyone do so well only one month post treatment. They couldn't believe he was walking over a mile a day, and eating and drinking too. There were no signs of any tumour or anything to be concerned about at all! I messaged our news to family and friends, and especially to David who was waiting to hear how his dad was before he left on his trip.

"Now you can go and not worry, sweetheart," I said to him.

"Ah Mum, that's the best news ever. If it hadn't been good news I would have cancelled my trip."

I knew how hard that would have been for him, but I believed that he would have done just that. He was such a loving son. They both were. They had been through so much in such a short time, and were still young. He needed to get out and see the world, and follow his dreams, and I was very pleased he was able to without restraints.

Chapter 14

We were now into the beginning of March, and just as it had felt so good to leave January and the horrors of the treatment behind us, it felt equally as good to have completed February, and be well into Saul's recovery. The sun was shining bright and warm, and Saul and I strolled hand in hand into town for a coffee. He even went to the rugby club with a couple of mates to watch the local team play at home, while I did a bit of cleaning and tidying at home. Slowly we were taking our life back, one day at a time, enjoying simple pleasures that to anyone else would seem normal, even mundane. I realised how lucky I was, to have my man slowly return to me, when for some the journey was to a much darker place, and the end of their road. But still I longed to go out for dinner with him, to make love, to have a row, to do all the things that meant I had him back fully, the man I loved with all my heart, the man who took care of me. I could feel that he was now on his way, gradually returning to what I hoped would be the strong, healthy, protective husband who had always been my rock.

We had Pancake Day a day early, so that David wouldn't miss out as that was the day he was due to fly, and I knew how he loved his pancakes!

The next morning, David and I got up at 4.30am, to go to the airport with Chris and his parents too. As I watched him zigzag away from me through the belted area at security, I felt my heart lurch painfully. I sent a silent prayer as I watched him go, for his protection and safe return. No one tells you that when you give birth to that precious little bundle how many times they will break your heart, as they grow up. These words came to me, as words often do when I'm feeling the power of my own emotions.

A newborn baby, in your arms, he learns to walk; you let him go
Mischievous toddler holds your hand, until he runs; you let him go
The child at school, you know he's there, until he leaves; you let him go
The growing teen who lives at home: he stays out late; you let him go
The young man travels across the world, to pastures new; you let him go
A full grown man with wife and child, in his own home; you let him go
Being a mum, loving your son: never gets easier to let him go.

Now Saul was able to tolerate smooth liquid foods, I invested in a new blender, to make daily smoothies. It would mean I could give him everything he needed nutritionally in one meal, and that any solid food he ate was a bonus, for the calorific qualities, which he also needed if he was to ever come off that god-awful artificial feed that the hospital had him on.

We experimented over the next few days, with me trying more calorific (and what I deemed palatable) foods such as banana, avocado, and vanilla protein shakes and Saul feeling sick trying to ingest it, because the texture was just too thick and creamy. He was still having his wheatgrass blend into his PEG, so at least I didn't have to try and get him to swallow that, but I needed to work a little on what he could have in his smoothies. I cut down on the sweet, heavier fruits, and juiced fresh orange, whizzed up with a little mango, some spinach and almond milk with a spoon of natural yoghurt. That seemed to work ok, and he was able to sip it slowly. He was having soups at lunchtime, and mostly was doing ok.

Then he took another turn for the worse. His mouth was painful on the left, and his energy levels plummeted. I took him to the GP. He had a mouth infection, and was put on penicillin. How I hated antibiotics and how they destroy the natural flora of the gut, and right now his was all over the place, with the diet he'd been on, so I knew this was going to set him back – but what choice did we have? He couldn't have an infection in his mouth; it could be very dangerous for him if left unchecked and could lead to necrosis of the jaw bone!

The doctor advised him to start back on the opiates again, to help with the pain, but he was desperate not to take them anymore. Although during the treatment he could not have coped without them, he knew that they were contributing largely to his depression even to the point where he'd had hallucinations!! We had learnt so much about pharmaceutical drugs on this journey – how they masked some symptoms, but just gave you a load of others, which when you told the doctors about, they just gave you yet more drugs to mask those symptoms. Although we knew how they were often necessary, they just seemed to lead to a vicious cycle of dependency if you let them. Going back onto those opiates was not an option. It was hard, because it was the drugs and the treatment which had caused all of this, but we could now understand why people got swept along, to that whirlpool of addiction, where one set of symptoms could lead to a lifetime of drug use; the body never getting a chance to try and heal itself, as you throw more and more poisons into it. To me, it seemed a little like trying to extinguish a fire with petrol instead of water!

The antibiotics picked him up for a few days but on the third day he was very sick. This went on for a couple of days, really dragging him down.

One afternoon I got home from work and found him at the end of his tether. He put his arms out to me and I dropped my bag on the floor and ran to him, wrapping him up in the biggest hug I could find. He cried into my hair, not understanding why he had been so set back when he had been doing so well. It broke my heart a million times to see him like this. He was my man, my strength, my whole world, and he was broken. Eventually, his tears stopped and I took his hand and lead him into the garden to sit in the sunshine for a while. Slowly he warmed up, and I made him some tea, and he began to feel his spirits lift a little.

Over the next day or so the sickness eased a little and the pain in his mouth subsided. But during the nights he started showing signs of restless legs syndrome (RLS). It got very bad, so bad that he couldn't sit still even in the evenings and couldn't sleep at night. He was becoming exhausted and his energy levels by day were showing the effects!

I did a little research – it seemed that withdrawal from opiates, e.g. morphine and fentanyl (he had taken himself off them after the feelings of depression became too much, and his pain was manageable without them) coupled with taking antiemetics (which he had been advised to increase to try and control the sickness caused by the antibiotics) causes RLS!!

Saul was so brave; he didn't want to be taking any more drugs, as he understood the negative dependency cycle they drew you into, and he'd clearly had enough.

"I'm coming off the antiemetics too," he announced firmly, one morning.

"Are you sure? But how will you cope, babe? You need to keep food down!"

"It's ironic," he replied, "that the only 'food' that makes me feel sick is the brown sludge I have to take through my PEG. I am so desperate to stop pouring that artificial crap into my body. I wish my mouth was not so sore, so that I could stop this horrible, synthetic soup!"

My heart went out to him. It was such a struggle to try and get enough calories into him with good natural food that he could eat with no pain and without bringing it all back, that we had no choice but to continue with the sludge.

Once again I felt that our little saving grace was the live, organic wheatgrass that we pumped into him every day. It was the only good thing going into his body, apart from the minute amounts of food he was eating on the good days.

If only an organic food company could have made a liquid feed that he could have had through this! I knew it would have helped him so much, but it was impossible – sadly it would have no place in conventional medicine and would never be sanctioned, and the hospital feed was packed with chemicals to give it a ridiculously long shelf life, so any type of live food would be very difficult, but if there had been one available it would have been wonderful! I remembered only too well how the doctors forbade me to put anything else into that PEG except the sludge and the drugs. I had disobeyed them, and it gave me such a comfort to know that his poor body was actually getting something natural each day. I know now that without that, his recovery would have been a very different story!

He continued to struggle through this phase for almost three weeks, with slight reprieves when he would have a couple of hours where the RLS wasn't as bad or the pain in his mouth was less, but it would only take a little too much talking, or a sip of warm soup, to make his mouth start hurting again. Then he would produce a horrible mucus which would then make him feel sick and be sick, this would then make it almost impossible to keep any kind of food down including his wheatgrass complex, and so he would be more tired and frustrated. I think the toughest part of this period was that he had been so much better before this mouth infection hit him, so it felt like a huge step backwards which psychologically really brought him down.

I made him teas with fresh ginger for the nausea, and gave him extra Vitamin C with echinacea. We tried some homeopathy and peppermint for the nausea. It was so important to keep on top of it and not get dragged down, but it wasn't easy. He felt worse at night, with the RLS coupled with the feeds, which he hated so much. Then after having it drip into his system for hours on end, he would sit up and bring the whole lot back up. He was so tired, and because he wasn't getting the calories he needed from the artificial food, he was getting weaker and more and more down.

He began to have wakeful hallucinations where he saw himself as a gate between two warring countries, having to defend the boundaries, or as boat on the sea whose waves were engulfing him. His mind was giving him impossible challenges, filling him with negativity and frustration. I was so afraid, as he spoke to me of these things. They were not dreams; they were his reality. I tried to comfort him, but my words were lost inside a mind that was drowning in irrational thoughts; thoughts that were so real, I couldn't reach him.

It was during this time that his parents visited from the States. They had naturally been so worried, and we had spoken to them a lot on the phone, but they were desperate to come and see him. I picked them up and brought them to the house. His mother broke down when she saw him, and choking her emotions she wrapped him up in a huge hug that she told him she had been longing to give him.

It was so good to have them there. He was lifted by their arrival and it took a huge strain off me, to have someone with me who really cared and who I could talk to. I confided in them about how hard it was, how afraid I was, and how alone I'd been feeling. Although my family and my friends had been wonderful, it was impossible for anyone to really know what we were going through. Jack was wonderful, helping where he could, and always managed to make Saul laugh with a daft comment or a funny story, that helped break the intensity more than he realised, but he was a young man, with no real concept of the gravity of the situation; and David was having the time of his life somewhere in south-east Asia. When we spoke, I couldn't tell him how tough things had become, as he was too far away to let him worry. My own mother had been really supportive, always asking every day how he was, but she had her own health issues that were to be expected by a lady of her advanced years, and couldn't do much to help physically. In addition, I never wanted to worry her by letting her know how down I felt at times, as I knew the stress would not be good for her. My brother and Tess of course were fabulous and always at the end of the phone, as were Rica and Evie, but there were only so many times you could call anyone.

I was so grateful that his parents were here; it meant that I had the support from the only other people who could really help me. They didn't stay with us as I couldn't cope with having houseguests, but they were only 20 mins away, staying with Saul's aunt, in town.

Saul's parents came to the hospital with us for his check-up. The team maintained that everything he was going through was perfectly normal for this stage of recuperation (2 months post treatment), and that all he had experienced before in terms of health, energy, being able to tolerate food and drinks, were incredibly unusual. When they examined his mouth and throat they said it was all healing well. They were more concerned about his mental state, and suggested counselling. Saul explained that he felt his mental state was due to his setback, coupled with not keeping food down and having to take the horrible feed which he found insurmountably depressing. He had never accepted the PEG and all it stood for. The doctor was reluctant to let him try without the feed, saying that he needed the calories and he just wouldn't be able to get enough in the small amounts he was eating.

"But I'm bringing most of it back up anyway!" Saul cried.

"Yes Saul, but before you do, because it's liquid you will be absorbing some of it, so it's still preferable to you not having it! You are not gaining weight; in fact you are losing it. We have to get your weight to stabilise."

"I'm losing weight because even the sight of the stuff makes me gag! If I could just try to come off it," Saul begged her.

Eventually she agreed that he could try and replace the feed with some oral supplementation, and gave us a whole bagful of powdered shakes and liquid protein-type drinks to try. But she warned us that if he started to lose more weight he would have to go back on it.

When we left the hospital I read the ingredients on some of the supplements. In the first line was the maltodextrin and sucrose, both of which are sugars, usually made from genetically modified

(GM) sources. Closely behind were canola and sunflower oils, both highly processed and high in omega 6, which is known to cause inflammation and free radical damage. And then there were all the chemical ingredients for flavouring, preservatives (for a 12-month shelf life!) and artificial vitamins, which the body has to try and process, putting a huge strain on the liver as it tries to detoxify this along with all the other horrible drugs that have been pumped through his body!

I understood that they were trying to help, and that he had had no choice when it had to be through the PEG, but now, this was oral, so there had to be something I could do to replace these artificial drinks with a combination of real food and more natural supplements.

On the way home I visited the health food shop and bought an organic protein supplement. After this I went to the butcher and bought some bones to make broth. Saul said he felt he should at least try one of the hospital supplements, as they had been so kind about giving us some, but even the smell of them made him start heaving. I picked up the bag and dropped it into the bin, before I set about making a batch of bone broth, and a small smoothie with a spoonful of the organic shake I had bought him.

That night, for the first time in ages, Saul was not sick. He wasn't having the artificial food pumped into him, so he slept all night, and kept the broth and the smoothie down, where they could help him start to heal.

The next day Saul already seemed brighter. He had slept all night, hadn't been exhausted by vomiting and had a little food in him!

We began a new regime of little and often, with his meals every two hours.

He started his day with some organic oatmeal and full fat milk with ground almonds; then, two hours later, a small organic yoghurt. The next meal was a cup of bone broth and one slice of wholemeal bread and butter, then a fruit smoothie with the protein powder;

and later, more bone broth and bread and a milky drink before bed. (See Part Two, Chapter Three for recipes.)

He struggled to eat, not wanting any of it, but knowing he had to. He ate slowly, sipping water between mouthfuls to wash it down. He kept it all down!

I baked ginger biscuits. I made scrambled eggs and ground nuts into it, and chicken noodle soup. I gave him mashed veggies with home-made gravy. I mashed up tuna with avocado, and olive oil. The only thing we still used the PEG for now was his wheatgrass!

His energy picked up, he slept better and his mood lifted. We started walking again, and even went out for a meal for Mother's Day with my mum and his parents. And best of all we made love for the first time in three months! My husband was coming back!!

Chapter 15

It was around this time that I really began to look into the toxins in and around our home. From cleaning products to toothpaste, from plastic bottles to laundry soap, they were everywhere! We were drowning in a sea of chemicals! Although I had always practised good nutrition and made everything myself, I had never appreciated how many chemicals we exposed ourselves to everyday. I knew that you could give a drug or a substance such as nicotine to someone by placing it on the skin (transdermal medication), so that meant everything your skin came into contact with could potentially be absorbed, to varying degrees, by your body. In fact, your skin is the largest organ in your body, with a huge semi-permeable surface area. And what about your respiratory system? What do you draw into your lungs when you use deodorants, hairsprays and oven cleaners! At least when you eat something the enzymes in your saliva and stomach help to break it down and flush it out of the body, but applying products to your skin means that they are potentially absorbed into the blood where they can travel to your organs without any kind of filtration.

I thought about my routines and my own personal exposure to chemicals: in the shower (shower gel, shampoo, conditioner); then afterwards I would moisturize. Fortunately I stopped using harmful deodorants years ago when my sister-in-law told me about its links to breast cancer, but that was all I had done so far! Then, cleaning my teeth: one of the quickest ways for something to enter the bloodstream is through the lining of the mouth where there are many blood vessels! Toothpaste and mouthwash are a wonderful blend of saccharin, fluoride, propylene glycol, sodium laurel sulphate and triclosan – all of which are harmful and toxic to the body.

This was before I applied any make-up, sunscreen, and hair products or painted my nails. And let's not even begin to think about what I was exposing myself and my family to when I cleaned the house, did the laundry, washed the dishes and plugged in the air fresheners!

In fact, in just using personal care products alone, the average adult is exposed to approximately 200 chemicals each day!

I slowly began to throw away all my supplies one by one, and replace them with home-made products, that after a while became surprisingly easy to make and saved me a lot of money too. I found that with a few key ingredients I could clean my home and wash my clothes, and that my skin care was down to one basic ingredient with just a few things added, but all totally natural, and all at a fraction of the cost of what I had been using! So although I was now spending more money buying organic food, I was saving on my products.

(For a full breakdown of all my recipes for personal care and cleaning products, please see Part Two, Chapter Four.)

Saul was continuing to slowly improve; every day, a step closer to being the man he was before the devastating treatments ravaged his body. However, with each small improvement came frustration at not having the physical strength, emotional stability or energy to cope with daily life. Somehow although the darkest days were coming to an end, Saul was now starkly aware of his limitations, and this was another challenge he had to overcome.

Jack, our colourful son, was part of a drama and acting school, and he was to take to the stage for the first time in his young adult life. Apart from the odd donkey nativity performance, as a little boy, this was to be his stage debut.

Set in a small theatre in town, the actors had put together a showcase of their talents, into a set of short scenes for our enjoyment. I was so proud of him, always having been able to see how artistic he was when it came to entertaining people, and wanting him to develop and share that talent with the world.

As the day approached, he rehearsed his lines both with his acting buddies and on his own. I had never seen him apply himself to anything in this way, always having the attitude that he would be fine, with very little effort. It was so good for him to really immerse himself in something he clearly had a passion for. For the first time he showed a healthy uncertainty coupled with a desire to succeed, instead of the flippancy and offhand manner he usually exhibited as he sailed through his life. We all felt a mixture of nervousness for him but pride that he was doing something so positive.

The night of the performance, as I got ready to watch my son on stage, I felt my stomach quiver with butterflies of excitement and nerves. I glanced at Saul lying on the bed. He had showered and changed, ready for the evening, but as he went to sit up on the bed, the colour drained from his face, and his skin took on a sheen from the effort of the movement.

"What's wrong darling?" I asked softly, as I went to sit next to him on the bed.

"Nothing, nothing, I'm fine," he said, more to himself than to me.

"You're not fine. What are you feeling?"

"I'm just tired. I will be okay," he said trying to reassure both of us.

The truth was that "tired" just didn't mean the same thing as it had before. It no longer meant you just needed sleep, or a rest from something you were doing. For Saul, at this point in his life, it meant utter exhaustion; total fatigue. It literally meant not having the reserves to lift a finger.

"I know this isn't what you want to hear, Saul, but maybe you just have to stay at home, this time. Jack will understand. I will video it, so that you can see him. David will have to see it that way too, so I will make sure I get good coverage, so neither of you will miss out," I said holding his hand and looking into his dark, shadowed eyes.

"No. I'm coming. I want to see him on the stage, even if I have to leave early. I can get a taxi home as soon as he's finished, but I am coming," he said setting his jaw in resolve.

This was part of his recovery. Finding the energy from a fuel tank that had run dry, to do something that meant the world to him. He wasn't going to let the fact that his body was still so weak stop him tonight. Tonight was his debut too: his tentative steps back onto the stage of his life.

Jack was incredible. The youngest and newest member of the cast, he played the part of Dawson, an uneducated young prisoner whose innocent but cheeky charm delighted the audience as he bantered with Wentworth, his older cellmate.

All of us bar David were there to watch him, including three of his grandparents – there to share his big moment. We were all so proud of him. He had taken to the stage like a duck to water, his natural desire to entertain emanating from him, lending him a stage presence that captivated the audience. Saul squeezed my hand as he watched his son with pride shining in his eyes, showing not a trace of the exhaustion he felt before we left the house.

Tonight had marked a big step for both of them, as they overcame private hurdles taking them closer to their personal goals, making them both men I was immeasurably proud of.

Although my son loved the limelight he certainly didn't take after my husband who liked nothing more than to blend in with the scenery. In fact, although Saul wasn't a shy man, he was never one to play to an audience, or do anything that attracted attention to him. So when one day, while he was in the thick of his treatment, he agreed to do a fashion show to help raise money for the Fountain Centre, I was more surprised than anyone!

The Fountain Centre was a wonderful organisation. They offered various supportive treatments, including massages, reflexology, counselling, and acupuncture, free to all patients and for a very reasonable donation to family members. They deserved to have support in return for all they did.

I remember clearly the day he volunteered. He had been really sick before we left the hotel, and had continued to feel sick throughout his radiotherapy session. He'd been worried that he would need to vomit while he had that horrible mask over his face. However, he had got through it and managed not to throw up.

We saw the advertisement for the show on the way out of the radiotherapy department. They needed two more men for the show. The date would be just two months post treatment for him. When he agreed to do it, filling out his details with a trembling hand, I worried that he wouldn't be well enough. He could barely sign his name, but he wanted to give something back to an organisation that gave so much to people in their hour of need.

And here we were. Just one week after Jack's show his father was now going to take to the stage and be my totally amazing husband in front of hundreds of people.

We arrived at the hotel in town and met up with his parents and my mum and Jack for some dinner. Saul had some soup and a roll and then left to get ready for the show!

What an amazing night it was! There were 25 models (20 ladies and 5 men). Every single one of them was brave beyond belief. Not only were they walking down a catwalk in front of hundreds of faces, but more importantly these people had all battled cancer: some more than once; some were terminal; and some were so young they should be out getting drunk with their friends, not dealing with the most hideous of diseases! But here they were strutting, wiggling and doing their turns on the catwalk, while the audience clapped, cheered, wolf-whistled, cat-called and sang along to the upbeat songs that the models paraded along to! It was incredible. Every single person in that room was elated, from the models, to the organisers, to the friends, family and supporters of the amazing people they were watching.

When Saul appeared on stage, my heart trembled with anticipation for him. My hands went clammy in my lap, and I could feel a few beads of perspiration forming on my top lip. As he walked on, his eyes scanned the crowd until he caught my eye and I saw the self-conscious, unsure man, which made him more beautiful than just his good looks alone could ever do. I waved and cheered, jumping out of my seat, unable to contain the force of emotion bubbling through me.

As he began to make his stage debut, the music swelled and he began to relax, as he moved along the floor. No one outside of this room would ever know he had just battled cancer and not long finished the devastating treatment protocol. He looked gorgeous in his tailored suit, which hid the PEG tube perfectly, and black bow tie. His hair shone, his cheeks glowed healthy and pink. His fully healed skin glowed under the stage lights and his smile showed none of the horrors his mouth had undergone during the treatment, just over eight weeks ago.

I felt my heart physically grow inside my chest as it filled with love and pride for my fantastic man.

Every day was another step closer to normality. Life would never be exactly the same and although we knew that and discussed it regularly, there was no way to know how different it would be. Would he ever get his taste back? Would he ever get his saliva back? What about his teeth and gums, would they be more delicate, or more vulnerable? Would he have ear problems or throat issues in the future? Could he be exposed to carotid artery stenosis in the future? Whenever we discussed things like this, instead of worrying about them, I did my usual and went to research it and find ways to reduce the risks. For example, my home-made toothpaste we now used consisted of a very carefully selected blend of ingredients... each one having its own cleaning, remineralising, strengthening properties, without exposing him to toxins.

The risk of stenosis (narrowing) of the carotid artery was something that concerned me: if this happened, a patient became more likely to suffer from a stroke due to lack of blood supply to the brain.

My research found that taking tocotrienol (a form of Vitamin E) had been clinically proven to reduce atherosclerosis (deposition of fatty material on the arteries' inner walls) and improve blood flow to the brain[20].

20 https://www.rejuvenation-science.com/n_vitaminE_stroke_3.html

So slowly, together, hand in hand, we continued our journey of Saul's return to health.

Saul was desperate now to have his PEG removed. For him it still represented the whole experience: from the day it was inserted, when he was still working, a healthy strong man, who could never believe he would need it; to him accepting he had to use it, but hating it; to him being totally dependent on it, while hating the stuff it carried into his body. At his most recent check-up, he all but begged to have it removed, but they were adamant that they would not until two weeks after his PET scan which was in two weeks – that was another four weeks! He was devastated! Another four weeks of this constant reminder hanging from him, like a useless, lifeless plastic limb. I felt his disappointment like a weight in my own heart. Although the team were really happy, and most impressed with how well he was doing, he wasn't going to be cajoled out of his downheartedness.

After his parents flew home, Saul and I went away to Michael and Tess's down by the coast for the weekend. The last time we had visited here had been Christmas. How different things had been then. In stormy weather we had travelled down to them, away from our flooded home, with Saul just one week into his treatment, his face having blistered with hives from the Cetuximab drugs, and his appetite already waning. They had given us the cosiest, warmest, loveliest Christmas they could, but with the best will in the world nothing could have taken away that edge of desolation that we all felt as a family.

Now we travelled down with the sun shining, and the radio playing, in good spirits.

We spent a lovely couple of days with them, with gentle walks in the spring sunshine, along the beach, and good, home-cooked food by a cosy fire in the evenings. It was everything we both needed and although Saul was tired after we returned we both felt the benefits of the trip.

Not long after this Saul began to complain of tingling down his spine whenever he flexed his head forward. I was naturally concerned as although my musculoskeletal knowledge was good, this wasn't something I had come across before now. My feeling was that his spinal column was being restricted, at the level of his neck, possibly due to scarring at the site of the radiotherapy treatment, or otherwise muscular atrophy (wasting) was causing neural tightness. I made a note to discuss this at his check-up, which luckily was in a few days. It turned out that he had something called Lhermitte's sign, which is transient myelitis (an inflammation of the tissue around the spinal cord), caused by the radiotherapy. If this occurs over one year post treatment it can be serious, but if it occurs around the four–six months post treatment, it is a common symptom, and clears up on its own as the inflammation heals. We were just over three months post treatment, so it was not a concern.

Finally came the day of Saul's scan results. As we sat once again in Mr Southerland's office, we couldn't help but think of the last time we were here: the delivery of that shattering blow, that would change our lives drastically for the next six–twelve months, and maybe forever; the cold and unfeeling way the consultant had dealt the blow, as if we were just another number in his system, another statistic on his computer screen, waiting to be added to his lists. What would they say this time? Dare we hope that everything we had been through had been a total success, or at the very least had improved things?

We listened in anticipation, Saul squeezing my hand, as Mr Southerland read to us from his open folder.

"Our clinical impression is such that Saul's tests showed no evidence of residual metabolically active disease and no new sites of disease were actively demonstrated," he imparted in his usual clinical tone.

I felt the cogs turning in my brain as I processed what he was telling us. I looked at Saul, who still looked perplexed, and then back at Mr Southerland, who was now looking at Saul with something resembling a smile on his face!

That was enough for Saul! That shadow of a smile told him all he needed to know. He was clear! The cancer was gone, and there was no sign of any other troubling spots!

I jumped up and flung my arms round the poor, unsuspecting, unyielding doctor, who immediately cleared his throat again, plainly embarrassed by my outburst. As before, though, when my emotions had erupted during our previous consultation with him, I didn't care. I turned to Saul and we both collapsed onto his chair crying and laughing at the same time as waves of relief splashed over us, washing away the pent-up dam of terror that had held our deepest fear in frozen silence.

I couldn't wait to share our news, especially with David, who was still travelling, and would be ecstatic to hear of his father's good health.

That night we celebrated, with all our friends and Jack's friends too in our local pub! It was as though Saul had won a race, or an OBE – everyone was jubilant, and genuinely overcome with joy for him.

They had all been such an important part of our journey – without the strength and support they lent us, it would have been almost impossible to cope.

Our friends have been like shining stars, lighting our path for us:

We have been walking along a very rocky road;
At times we've almost crumbled under our heavy load.
The days have stretched out endlessly,
The nights have been so black,
And all the time we have known there is no turning back.
But as our legs almost gave way and our bodies felt so drained,
And we thought we'd never see an end to the relentless rain,
We looked into the darkened sky to see bright shining stars –
They lit our path and warmed our hearts and helped us come so far.
For sometimes when we have felt like our journey will never end,
We know that we can get there with our shining stars; our friends.

Each and every one of them had helped in ways they probably never even realised: a text message to show they were thinking of you; a warm hug to envelop you and make you forget for a moment; being at the end of the phone while you pour out your heart; placing a glass of something uplifting in your hand when you needed it most; taking in a load of laundry when you had no energy to do it; making you laugh when all you thought you had were tears, and being there every day, every step to hold your hand and steady you.

Once again, I had really had cause to appreciate my friends. I had a wonderful family. No, I had an amazing family, and although just because they are related doesn't obligate them in any way to be so wonderful, they were the very best we could have asked for. But our friends had no requirements at all to be there for us like they were, but yet they all were.

He was supposed to wait another week to have his PEG removed, but he convinced the nurse to remove it a week early, and as he was doing so well, his doctors gave permission. I remembered hearing from another patient who had had the PEG previously how painful the removal was, but that's something I kept from Saul. This man had explained that it had been one of the worst things he could remember other than the effects of the radio and chemo. When Saul came home he confirmed that this man had been pretty accurate! It had hurt like hell, like someone was stabbing him from the inside of his stomach. However, he was elated to be rid of it. As much as its insertion had represented sickness, vulnerability and weakness to him, its removal represented his return to normality, health and strength. He could start to feel whole again.

Chapter 16

In September, four months after we had celebrated our good news, we felt ready to take a much-needed holiday. So we headed off to the Costa del Sol for a fortnight.

We all needed to get away as a family and relax. We went with a group of friends who had organised a quiet apartment for us next to a big party villa, where the boys could stay. That way we could relax, and the boys could have fun, but we could all be together.

The taxi took us up a windy road that seemed to snake into nowhere. It was dark so we couldn't really see the surrounding area, but we knew we were going somewhere peaceful and remote, just by gauging the distance it was from the main road.

We turned off the track to head through a set of big gates and up a steep incline, before the taxi finally came to a stop.

Getting out and stretching our legs we took in what we could see. Behind us was a large white wall with the lights of a large villa behind it. Bougainvillea hung like a candy-coloured waterfall, over the wall. The sweet scent of night jasmine captured our senses, delivered like a perfumed letter on the balmy evening breeze. In front of us were a set of stone steps built into the side of the hill, that led down to a lit pool and barbeque area, and beyond it was another smaller chalet that would be our own little space for the holiday.

It was such a far cry from the trashy hotel in Turkey!

One night the boys had gone out clubbing with the others, and Saul and I had gone out for a quiet meal on our own. As we sat in a Chirringuito restaurant, on the beach, and listened to the waves gently washing over the sand, the sun glowed a pastel pink in the evening sky just before it left the world for the night and disappeared into the silvery sea. A lone man and his dog wandered along the shoreline, almost a silhouette now against the sunset sky. Although it was September and still quite busy, for a snapshot moment that scene froze, like looking at a postcard of an idyllic fragment of time.

Before Saul spoke, the thought had already fluttered through my mind, the silver butterfly of our shared dream;

"Flossie," Saul began as he took my hand, "let's do it! Let's move here! We don't live in our own house, I haven't properly gone back to work, and the boys are no longer in education. We have dreamed about it forever. I don't want to get to the end of our lives and say – I wish we had done it. Life is too short."

I looked into the eyes of the man who I loved even more than the precious life that flowed within us.

"Okay," I smiled broadly, squeezing his hand.

Epilogue

December 2014

I stood looking out of the kitchen window. It was a crisp, cold morning, and a silver-white frost iced the garden. One single red rose stood strong and proud in the garden. It was a deep red that stood out against the dark brambles around it. Its crystalled petals overlapped in velvety folds that were gently opening, not afraid of the frosty morning. A strong English rose, so beautiful and so resilient it took my breath away. It held such significance for me, today.

"Mum, c'mon! Dad needs a hand to get the stuff packed into the car!" David called, breaking my thoughts.

Just one year ago, Saul had not long received his diagnosis, and we were about to embark on a rollercoaster ride into hell as he began his treatments, and were flooded out of our home. But today, a year later, we were looking ahead to different challenges; today, we were leaving England. We were leaving the only life we had known, the only town I'd ever really lived in. We were going to live our dream life in southern Spain.

I knew we would always love England and miss all that is beautiful about it. It will always be home to us on some level, but now we were ready for change. We had been through so much in the last year that we knew the time was right for us to go. We knew that this move would be laden with more challenges, but they would be exciting: learning a new language; meeting new friends; getting to know a new culture.

I took a photo of the rose in my English garden, capturing its otherwise transient beauty in a permanent image, and followed David out to the car to help pack up our home.

March 2015

"Mmmm, that looks good, Flossie!" Saul said as he inhaled the sizzling prawns I put next to the salad on the table.

I was so pleased he had his appetite back in full force. He could taste everything, and although for a while his tastes had changed, they were now pretty much back to normal. He was a bit slighter in build than he used to be, but still looked great, his muscle definition had returned with his physical work.

"Mum, is there any bread?" said Jack.

"Jack, it's under your nose, try looking! David, please put your phone down when we are about to have dinner!"

I loved it! Normal family life: home-cooked food, home-made banter and healthy debates round the dinner table. This was my life, our life, and it was about as perfect as it could get. But instead of being indoors with the central heating on, while we looked out of the window onto a street lined with parked cars, as we shared our evening meal, we were sitting round a large glass-topped table, on a generous wooden terrace, that abutted one side of our villa, under a canopy hung with a grapevine. Our view was of a sparkling blue ocean in the distance, across which on a clear day we could see the coastline of Africa, against the horizon. My garden was no longer the home of the perfect English rose that sparkled with glittery frost, but of a jacaranda tree, laden with purple flowers, night-flowering jasmine that made you want inhale deeply to absorb its essence, and birds of paradise, with plumes of orange and red against their long palm fronds.

Finally we had done it. We had climbed back up to the top of our mountain, and plunged our flag of victory firmly into its summit. Not only had we coped with the most harrowing of diseases, and watched Saul emerge strong, his vitality almost unscathed, and his wellbeing restored, but we had finally achieved a longed-for dream, as a family, and moved to our place in the sun!

Part 2

Introduction to Part 2

PLEASE NOTE: these are some of the protocols that we followed. I am not making recommendations or even suggesting that others should do the same as us unless they have been advised so by their specialists. ALWAYS seek specialist advice before making any diet modifications, taking any supplements or adopting any protocols which may interfere with or negatively impact on treatment or medication. Please check with your doctor before embarking on any new procedures, and do your own research.

The Immune System and Cancer

As long ago as the 19th Century the physiologist and medical scientist Claude Bernard believed, after making many medical discoveries, that a person's internal environment was more important in determining disease than any external pathogen. He believed that the internal terrain of the host's susceptibility to infection was more important than the germ. A good analogy for this would be to consider a mosquito (germ) that seeks stagnant water (host), but does not make the water stagnant; if the water is clear, moving and healthy, the mosquito will search for another pool. Naturopathic medicine considers disease to be the result of an accumulation of toxins which the body becomes unable to eliminate. A person's vitality is determined by the strength of their defence system (immune system) to throw off pathogens.

The immune system is complex. It comprises the lymphatic system, the spleen, the thymus and the bone marrow. It protects the body from harmful substances, such as bacteria, parasites, viruses, toxins etc. and becomes inflamed when these substances injure tissues. It works very closely with the digestive system and is critically important in protecting the intestines from being injured by these substances.

The system itself is a collection of reactions and responses that the body has to damaged cells or infections.

It is important to understand that both cancer and conventional cancer treatments can damage the immune system. Chemotherapy and radiotherapy weaken the immunity by causing a drop in the number of white blood cells that are made in the bone marrow[1].

If the immune system is strong and functioning well, it can recognise and kill cancer cells; however, if it is weakened, through exposure to the harmful substances mentioned above, as is the case for many of us, then its ability to do this becomes greatly compromised. As mentioned, conventional allopathic medicine weakens immune function, so the first step in complementary or alternative treatment is to strengthen this before embarking on conventional treatment. Alternatively, if you plan to take a wholly alternative approach to treatment, this should form the basis for your practices.

Step-by-step approach

1. Reduce the stress on the immune system by decreasing toxicity and supporting the pathways of elimination.

   - If following a conventional route, this should happen prior to treatment and, where possible then throughout treatment too, as tolerated.
   - If following an alternative route, this should happen throughout treatment*.

   Stress reduction is done through diet (Chapter 1), supportive additional treatments (Chapter 2), and reducing your exposure to toxins (Chapter 4).

2. Strengthen the immune system, with the right nutrients (Chapter 1).

---

1 http://www.cancerresearchuk.org/about-cancer/what-is-cancer/body-systems-and-cancer/the-immune-system-and-cancer

3. Supporting the nervous system, to reduce production of the stress hormones. This is done through meditation and deep breathing techniques (Chapter 2).

4. Rehabilitating the immune system post treatment – for those who undergo conventional treatment (Chapter 3).

*For patients who have make the decision not to undergo conventional treatment, I recommend a juice fast as part of the detoxification diet. The benefits of doing a juice fast are many, including increased energy and better hydration, but primarily:

- The digestive system, including the stomach, gut and liver, is allowed to rest, not having to process dense and complex foods; and during rest it can heal, so the body is able to detoxify more efficiently. The liver, kidneys, skin and lungs are always working to detox the body, but ingesting nutrients that support these processes, without the interference of foods that hinder the body, means greater opportunity to function more efficiently.
- The body is flooded with phytonutrients, which it can utilise easily, as they are absorbed by the body without it having to break anything down.

If doing a juice fast, I also recommend preceding it with organ cleanses, beginning with the colon, followed by the kidneys and the liver. The liver and kidneys should be supported throughout detoxification – see Chapter 2.

Please consult with a naturopathic practitioner or a nutritional therapist before embarking on a juice fast and an organ cleanse regime.

Introduction to Food Recommendations

I have compiled a selection of recipes. Chapter 1 is the detoxification diet. This is recommended prior to beginning any therapy, and then throughout as well if tolerated. It is designed to help remove toxins from the body and strengthen the immune system, so that the patient has the best chances going forward. Some doctors may advise you to change your diet as you enter the treatment phase. You must liaise with them and check that what you are eating will not interfere with your treatment plan. **However, before you begin treatment it is most definitely advisable to eat this diet, and, if your doctors agree, to follow it as much as possible going through treatment.**

Chapter 3 is for patients during/post treatment who cannot continue with the plan in Chapter 1, because they feel their appetites have diminished, eating becomes difficult, it interferes with their medication, or for another medical reason they have been advised not to continue with the detoxification diet.

You will note that throughout the diet advice, there are certain ingredients which are suggested frequently. Here is a list of those ingredients and the reasons why they are commonly advised.

- **Apple cider vinegar**

Apple cider vinegar improves digestion, normalises intestinal bacteria, strengthens the immune system, and helps detoxification.

- **Himalayan rock salt**

Table salt, which is 97% Sodium Chloride (NaCl) is chemically produced, bleached and devoid of most other nutrients. It also contains aluminum in many cases, which has been linked to Alzheimer's disease and other problems in the body. Himalayan rock salt is rich in magnesium, potassium and calcium; in fact, it contains all 84 trace minerals needed by the body.

Benefits include:

- Detoxifies the body by balancing systemic pH
- Improves hydration by providing trace minerals
- Improves mineral status of the body
- Reduces muscle cramps by improving minerals and hydration
- Helps balance blood sugar
- Supports hormone balance for everyone, no matter what hormonal issues you face
- Helps balance blood pressure because it provides unrefined, mineral-rich salt in an ionic solution
- Improves sleep by supporting blood sugar and hormone balance
- Acts as a powerful antihistamine
- Supports weight loss by balancing hormones and improving energy
- Supports thyroid and adrenal function

For more information, go to: http://empoweredsustenance. com/himalayan-salt-benefits/

- **Coconut oil**

The best choice for cooking is coconut oil. High in saturated fat (90%), it is very resistant to high temperatures, making it very stable. It also lasts for years without going rancid, and contains 48% lauric acid which has been shown to be helpful in dealing with viruses, and bacteria that cause diseases such as herpes, influenza, cytomegalovirus, and even HIV. It also helps in fighting harmful bacteria such as listeria monocytogenes and helicobacter pylori, and harmful protozoa such as giardia lamblia[2].

- **Spices**

Where possible, always use natural organic spices. Each spice has healing and therapeutic properties as well as offering great flavours. Patients following Chapter 3 may find their palate requires blander food to begin with, but stronger foods should be re-introduced as soon as possible. Please check with your doctors, though, as some spices can interfere with medication.

Here are some examples of the magic of spices:

- **Turmeric** – powerful anti-oxidant; has been shown to retard cancer cell growth and stimulate cancer cell death (apoptosis). Protects the cardiovascular system; anti-inflammatory, regulates immune function. *Note: turmeric can inhibit blood clotting and exacerbate gall bladder issues. Please also check with your doctor if taking PPI's (protein pump inhibitors), diabetes medication or any blood thinning medication such as warfarin, aspirin etc.*

- **Black Pepper** – The sharp flavour and healing prowess come from the piperine in this spice. Black pepper has been shown to improve digestion; have anti-tumour effects; reduce inflammation; improve brain function; lower blood pressure.

---

2 http://www.organicfacts.net/health-benefits/oils/health-benefits-of-coconut-oil.html

- **Ginger** – helps with nausea; aids digestion; anti-inflammatory. *Note: ginger can interfere with blood thinning medication.*

- **Garlic** – rich in manganese, Vitamin B6, Vitamin C, selenium. Boosts immune function; reduces blood pressure; rich in anti-oxidants; helps detoxify body from heavy metals. *Note: garlic can interfere with blood thinning medication.*

- **Cayenne pepper** – aids digestion; helps patients with angina and diabetes type 2; relieves skin irritation, has anti-cancer properties.

- **Cinnamon** – rich in anti-oxidants, protects against free radical damage; reduces blood sugar and improves insulin function, helps insomnia.

- **Saffron** – immunity boosting; anti-carcinogenic; anti-oxidant; anti-depressant.

For more nutritionally rich recipes, I recommend a very good book from the Penny Brohn Centre called *Nourish: The Cancer Care Cookbook* with Christine Bailey.

http://www.christinebailey.co.uk/shop/nourish-cancer-care-cookbook/

CHAPTER 1

The Detox Diet Plan

1. **Eat Organic**

    All food should be organic to reduce the level of toxins going into the body and also to ensure that the vitamin and mineral content of the food is as high as possible. Food that is grown in soil that is mineral rich and not chemically permeated will be worth much more to you nutritionally than food that is not.

    There are a few cases where it is not so important, e.g. pineapple, because the skin is so thick, but even then the pesticides get into the fruit through the ground water, so if possible buy everything organic. If you cannot get organic meat, at least make sure it is locally sourced, and you know the origin.

2. **Natural, Unprocessed Food**

    Try to keep all cooking as natural as possible – plan ahead, so that you have a good supply of things such as home-made stock and legumes in your freezer. Avoid pre-prepared sauces and tinned foods where possible.

    - Instead of using canned tomatoes, use large, whole tomatoes blanched, peeled and blended. You can even make tomato puree yourself very easily, by following the above and then cooking them down to a paste.
    - Every time you do a roast, boil up your carcass and veg ends, with some fresh herbs, simmer for a couple of hours,

and cool and freeze in durable freezer bags. You can make batches of soups for lunches in advance too.

- For legumes, just soak overnight and then boil up for 20 mins, then wash, cool and freeze – they can be used like frozen peas!

3. Avoid Sugar

Consumption of sugars and foods with added sugars has been shown to increase the risk of cancers.[1,2]

4. Avoid Gluten and Dairy

Both these foods have been shown to contribute to chronic inflammation and autoimmune disease.[3,4]

5. Fluids

Try to drink *at least* 2 litres of filtered water daily, and cut out tea and coffee. You can include green teas and herbal teas, or hot water with fresh lemon and ginger root.

---

1 The American Journal of Clinical Nutrition. Consumption of sugar and sugar-sweetened foods and the risk of pancreatic cancer in a prospective study. 2006;84:1171–6. Printed in USA. Susanna C Larsson, Leif Bergkvist, and Alicja Wolk http://www.kickthecan.info/sites/default/files/documents/Am%20 J%20Clin%20Nutr-2006-Larsson-1171-6.pdf

2 American Association for Cancer Research. Cancer Epidemiology, Biomarkers & Prevention – Dietary sugar and colon cancer September 1997 6; 67. M L Slattery, J Benson, T D Berry, D Duncan, S L Edwards, B J Caan and J D Potter. http://cebp.aacrjournals.org/content/6/9/677.short

3 Nutrients. The Dietary Intake of Wheat and other Cereal Grains and Their Role in Inflammation. Published online 2013 Mar 12. PMCID: PMC3705319; 2013 Mar; 5(3): 771–787. Karin de Punder and Leo Pruimboom. http://www. ncbi.nlm.nih.gov/pmc/articles/PMC3705319/

4 The American Journal of Clinical Nutrition. Dairy attentuates oxidative and inflammatory stress in metabolic syndrome. First published June 29, 2011 Renée A Stancliffe, Teresa Thorpe, and Michael B Zemel. http://ajcn.nutrition. org/content/early/2011/06/29/ajcn.111.013342

6. Avoid Red Meat

When you are detoxifying the body, you need to facilitate digestion. Red meat is difficult for the gut to break down, making it harder work on the body. The object is to reduce the stress on the digestive system. Ordinarily red meat can be included in the diet, in small quantities, from grass-fed, organic sources, but not during detoxification.

Pre-Breakfast Juices

Drinking a vegetable-based juice first thing in the morning can give you a natural energy boost via an infusion of vitamins, minerals and enzymes that go straight into your system without having to be broken down. It is important to focus on vegetable-based juices rather than fruit juices, as you want to avoid a high intake of fructose, which, without the fibre to slow down absorption, can cause spikes in blood sugars.

My recipe includes a green apple, which is low in fructose, to add a little sweetener.

• Juice Recipe

- 1 small beetroot (inc. the leaves!)
- 1 small cucumber
- 2 carrots
- ¼ of a broccoli
- 1 inch ginger root
- 1 green apple
- I small lemon

Pre-Breakfast Juices

Breakfast Recipes

Breakfast Smoothie
Scrambled Eggs and Kippers with Tomatoes
Fried Egg with Asparagus and Avocado
Banana and Almond Pancakes
Savoury Breakfast Pot
Grain-free Flapjack Granola

• Breakfast Smoothie

- Kale, spinach, watercress, rocket (choose at least two)
- Sprig of parsley
- 1 small avocado (or banana for a sweeter smoothie)
- Juice and zest of an orange
- Handful blueberries
- Ground nuts (almond, brazil, walnut)
- Seeds (sunflower, pumpkin)
- 2 wheatgrass pods
- 2 tbsps hemp or flax oil
- Reishi mushroom drops
- ¼ cup coconut water
- 10 drops milk thistle
- ½ tsp golden paste (see recipe at the end of chapter)

Blend and enjoy.

- ## Scrambled Eggs with Kippers and Grilled Tomatoes

  - 4 organic eggs
  - 2 kippers, halved
  - 2 large tomatoes
  - Almond milk
  - Butter
  - Himalayan salt, black pepper
  - Fresh or dried herbs

Whip up eggs with a dash of almond milk, and scramble in melted coconut oil.

Meanwhile, grill kippers with a generous knob of butter.

Grill tomatoes with a twist of Himalayan salt and black pepper and a pinch of herbs.

- ## Fried Egg with Asparagus and Avocado

  - 2 organic eggs
  - 6 asparagus tips
  - 1 avocado
  - Coconut oil
  - Olive oil
  - Apple cider vinegar
  - Himalayan salt
  - Black pepper

Fry eggs in coconut oil. Meanwhile, sauté asparagus on griddle until lightly charred and tender.

Serve with avocado drizzled in virgin olive oil and apple cider vinegar and sprinkled with Himalayan salt and black pepper.

• Banana and Almond Pancakes

- 2 bananas
- 2 heaped tbsps nut butter (try to avoid peanut at this stage, or if you do use it, choose a pure, organic variety – make sure there are no other ingredients)
- 4 organic eggs
- Pinch of cinnamon

Mash bananas in a large mixing bowl.
Combine bananas with 2 heaped scoops of nut butter and blend with eggs in the bowl.
Mix well and scoop a quarter of a cup of the mixture onto a hot griddle or flat pan over a medium heat. Wait for bubbles to appear, then flip and cook for another 1–2 minutes.
Top each pancake with cinnamon, and fresh fruit if you're looking for a little extra sweetness.

• Savoury Breakfast Pot (serves 4)

- ½ cup spring onions, chopped
- ½ cup red pepper, chopped
- 4 large organic eggs
- 1 clove garlic
- Himalayan rock salt
- Black pepper
- Paprika

Preheat oven to 180°C.
Combine onion, garlic, red pepper, black pepper and salt in a medium-sized mixing bowl.
Grease individual ramekins with butter or coconut oil and add mixture to cover three-quarters of each cup.

Crack a single egg on top of each one, and break up with
fork, whisking lightly.
Sprinkle the top of each with paprika.
Bake for 20 minutes, remove from oven and serve

• **Grain-free Flapjack Granola**

---

3 cups assorted nuts and seeds (almonds, walnuts and
brazil nuts; sesame, sunflower and pumpkin seeds) *option –
you can replace one cup with a cup of buckwheat flakes*

- ½ cup dried cranberries
- ½ cup goji berries
- 2 cups unsweetened shredded coconut
- ¼ cup coconut oil
- ¼ cup butter
- 2 tsps raw honey
- ¼ tsp pure vanilla extract
- ¼ tsp Himalayan rock salt
- 1 tsp cinnamon
- ¼ tsp chopped fresh ginger

Melt butter in pan and use a little to grease a baking tray with sides.
Melt coconut oil with butter.
Melt honey and stir.
Add spices and seasoning.
Add nuts, seeds and flakes and coat evenly.
Lastly, add berries.
Pour into greased tin, and press firmly.
Bake for 15 minutes on 180°C.
Allow to cool.
Store in a glass jar.
Eat with nut milk as a cereal or enjoy as snack bars.

Grain-free Flapjack Granola

Copyright: Marc Mina

Lunch Recipes

Salmon and Avocado Wraps
Sweet Potato Hash
Parsnip, Watercress and Red Pepper Stockpot
Salmon Noodle Power Soup

• Salmon and Avocado Wraps

- 1 small piece of lightly steamed (and cooled) wild salmon
- ½ ripe avocado
- 2 tbsps organic mayonnaise
- ¼ cup green olives
- 2 tbsps diced green chilies
- 1 spring onion
- 2 large leaves of lettuce (or your favourite green!)

Cut olives in half and remove stones, and finely chop spring onion.

Mash the avocado until it's a creamy consistency and then mix with mayonnaise.

Mash the salmon and add along with olives, spring onion, and diced green chillies to the avocado-mayo mixture.

Place one scoop of salmon and avocado mix into a large leaf of lettuce, wrap, and enjoy!

• Sweet Potato Hash

- 1 large onion, sliced
- 3 tbsps olive oil
- ½ tbsp coconut oil
- 4 large mushrooms
- 2 sweet potatoes

Salmon and Avocado Wraps

- 3 tbsps fresh rosemary
- Pinch of cayenne pepper
- Himalayan salt
- Black pepper
- 3 organic eggs

Preheat the oven to 220°C.

Line a baking sheet with greaseproof paper.

Heat one tablespoon of oil in a pan over a medium heat.

Add the onions and mushrooms.

Cook on a low heat until brown.

Meanwhile, peel the sweet potatoes and chop into bite-sized pieces.

Place into a large bowl with the remaining two tablespoons of olive oil, the cayenne pepper and rosemary.

Add the cooked onions and mushrooms to the bowl, and toss.

Season with salt and pepper.

Spread the mixture evenly onto the prepared baking sheet.

Roast for 30–35 minutes until the potatoes are soft and browned.

Place the potato hash into an ovenproof dish, make three small wells in the mixture and crack the eggs into these.

Season lightly with salt and pepper.

Bake for 15–18 minutes at 220°C until the eggs are set.

- **Parsnip, Watercress and Red Pepper Stockpot**

  - ½ ltr chicken stock (made from organic carcass)
  - 1 clove garlic
  - 50–80g watercress
  - 25g butter
  - 1 tbsp buckwheat flour
  - 1 onion

- 2–3 large parsnips
- 2–3 carrots
- 1 red pepper
- Pinch of turmeric
- Himalayan salt and black pepper

Chop vegetables.

Melt butter and sauté onions; then make into roux sauce with flour, butter and stock.

Add chopped veg and rest of stock and seasoning, slowly stirring, and bring to boil.

Add watercress.

Simmer for 1 hour.

- **Salmon Noodle Power Soup**

- 2 wild salmon fillets
- 1½ ltr chicken stock (made from organic carcass)
- 2 cloves garlic
- 1 tsp grated root ginger
- 1 red chilli
- 125g rice noodles
- 50g tender stem broccoli
- 50g mange tout
- 50g green beans
- 50g baby corn
- 50g sliced carrots
- 2 spring onions
- ½ red pepper
- Ground almonds
- Coconut oil
- Himalayan salt and black pepper

In a large pan, heat stock with ginger, garlic and chilli.
Bring to boil and add prepared vegetables, and cook for
about 2 mins.
Griddle salmon fillets, with coconut oil and salt and pepper.
Add noodles to veg and cook until they are soft (about
3 mins).
Spoon hot noodles into bowls and top with fish.
Garnish with the ground nuts and spring onions.

Chickpea Burgers

Copyright: Hans Geel/ shutterstock.com

Dinner Recipes

Chickpea Burgers with Salad
Sweet Potato Nachos and Turkey Mince Chilli
Wild Salmon with Chargrilled Asparagus and Carrots
Thai Fish Cakes with Baked Brown Rice and Onions
Chicken and Lentil Curry with Baked Brown Rice

- ## Chickpea Burgers

  - 1 small onion
  - 2 cloves of garlic
  - 1 cup chickpeas
  - ¾ cup cooked quinoa
  - ½ red pepper
  - Bunch of fresh coriander
  - 2 tbsps chickpea or buckwheat flour, plus 3 tbsps for coating
  - Himalayan salt and ground black pepper
  - Pinch of cayenne pepper
  - Coconut oil for cooking

In a large pan, melt coconut oil and fry the onion and garlic until slightly golden. Remove from heat and allow to cool.
Finely chop the red pepper and coriander and set aside.
In a food processor, process the chickpeas until they turn to a slightly textured paste. Transfer into a large bowl.
Add all the other ingredients to the bowl and mix; seasoning to your liking.
Take a large plate and sprinkle a few tablespoons of chickpea flour on it.
Scoop up some of the mixture, shape into a small ball, and press gently to make a patty. Drop into the chickpea flour to coat evenly

.Once you have a very light coating all over the patties/ burgers, place under a medium grill for 8 minutes on each side or until browned.

Serve with a big salad or sautéed veg.

- ### Sweet Potato Nachos and Turkey Mince Chilli

The Beans:

- 1 onion
- 1 red pepper
- 1 green chilli, finely chopped
- 1 tbsp apple cider vinegar
- 400g pinto beans (pre-cooked)
- 1 tbsp tom puree
- ½ tsp cumin

Sauté onion, chilli and pepper, and add vinegar and beans. Turn heat down and add splash of water; cover and cook for 10 mins, adding more water if required; cook for further 10 mins.

Sweet Potato Chips

- 3 large sweet potatoes
- 3 tbsp melted coconut oil
- 1 tsp Himalayan salt

To make the sweet potato chips, preheat the oven to 375°F. Peel the sweet potatoes and slice thinly, using either a mandolin or a sharp knife.

In a large bowl, toss them with coconut oil and salt.

Place the chips in a single layer on a rimmed baking sheet covered with parchment paper.

Bake them in the oven for 10 minutes, then flip them over and bake for another 10 minutes. For the final 10 minutes watch the chips closely, and pull off any that start to brown, until all of them are cooked.

The Meat

- ¼ kg organic minced turkey
- 2 medium tomatoes, blanched, peeled and seeded
- 1 medium onion, finely diced
- 1 red pepper, chopped
- 1 tbsp coconut oil
- 1 green chilli, diced
- 2 cloves garlic, minced
- ½ tsp oregano
- ½ fresh chilli, finely chopped
- 1 stick celery
- 1 carrot
- Handful of greens (spinach or kale)
- 1 tbsp tomato paste
- 1 tsp Himalayan salt
- ½ tsp pepper

While the potato chips are baking, start preparing the turkey.
Melt the coconut oil in a large pan over a medium heat. Add the onion and chilli to the pan and sauté for 3–4 minutes until softened.
Add the turkey and cook for 4–5 minutes, stirring regularly.
Add the peppers, tomato paste, and remaining spices and stir well.
Bring the mixture to a simmer and then turn the heat down to medium-low. Cover and cook for 20–25 minutes, stirring regularly.

Meanwhile, place the celery, peeled, chopped carrot, greens, tomatoes, and garlic cloves into a blender and whizz to form a thick sauce.

Add sauce at the last minute, so that the veg in the sauce is as raw as possible.

Add salt and pepper to taste.

Remove from heat.

To assemble the nachos, form a large circle with the sweet potato chips on a platter. Spoon the meat mixture into the middle of the circle and top with refried beans and sprinkle with fresh coriander.

• Salmon and Chargrilled Vegetables

- 2 pieces of wild salmon
- 12 asparagus tips
- 2 large carrots
- 2 cloves garlic
- I small red onion
- 1 lemon
- Sprig of rosemary
- Knob of butter

Lay salmon on a baking tray, lightly greased with coconut oil. Drizzle with freshly squeezed lemon juice and a little coconut oil; lay rosemary springs on top.

Placc under a medium grill.

Meanwhile, on a hot griddle melt a little butter, and throw on asparagus tips, and diagonal slices of carrot. Add chopped spring onions and garlic, and griddle until lightly charred but not burnt.

Serve with lemon wedges.

Thai Fish Cakes

- 1 large clove garlic
- 1cm fresh root ginger
- Large sprig fresh coriander
- Zest of a lime
- 1 medium red chilli
- 75g creamed coconut
- ½ small red pepper
- Fish fillets (either wild salmon or unsmoked, undyed haddock)
- Himalayan salt and black pepper

Place garlic, ginger, coriander, lime zest, chilli, coconut and red pepper into blender and process to a smooth paste. Make into flat patties and toss in a little buckwheat flour. Heat coconut oil until hot, then lower heat before cooking fishcakes to a pale golden colour (about 30 secs–1min each side).

Serve with a green salad, and baked brown rice with onions (see below).

Baked Brown Rice with Onions (serves 4)

- 1 tbsp butter or olive oil
- ½ cup chopped onion
- 2 cloves garlic
- ¼ inch of turmeric root
- garlic clove
- 1 cup brown rice
- 2 cups chicken stock
- Himalayan salt and ground black pepper

Preheat oven to 180°C.

In a medium hob-to-oven pot, melt butter or olive oil over a medium heat.

Add chopped onions and cook for 3–5 minutes, stirring until softened.

Add chopped turmeric and garlic.

Add rice and stir until well coated.

Add chicken stock, salt and pepper to taste.

Bring to the boil.

Cover and bake until the rice is tender and the stock is absorbed, about 20–25 minutes.

Let stand, covered for 5 minutes before serving.

- ### Chicken and Lentil Curry (serves 4)

  - 2 medium organic chicken fillets
  - 1 large onion
  - 2 cloves garlic
  - Sprig of fresh coriander
  - 1 med chilli
  - ½ cm fresh root ginger
  - ½ cm fresh root turmeric
  - Coconut oil
  - Tomato puree
  - 2 large tomatoes
  - 4–5 large mushrooms
  - 1 large carrot
  - Handful green veg (spinach/kale)
  - Cumin seeds
  - Organic curry paste
  - Generous handful red lentils
  - Himalayan salt and black pepper
  - Brown rice

Coat chicken in a little melted oil and place under grill and cook until tender and juices run clear.

Meanwhile, in a large, heavy-bottomed pan, sauté finely chopped onion, ginger, turmeric, chilli and cumin seeds in coconut oil. Add chopped mushrooms, pepper and carrot. In a blender, whizz blanched, peeled tomatoes with green veg, garlic, coriander, tomato puree and curry paste. Add a little water if too thick. Set aside.

In a separate pan cook lentils in a little water until soft, and add to cooked veg and spices.

Meanwhile, remove chicken from grill, and using two forks, shred meat to form "pulled chicken". Add this to cooked veg and lentils. Add the blended veg sauce at the last minute (so that the veg in the sauce is as raw as possible before serving) and heat.

Serve with cooked brown rice, and fresh coriander sprinkled on top.

Hummus

Snacks

Make sure you have a good supply of nuts, seeds, fresh fruit and vegetables for snacking.

You can also use sweet potatoes, beetroot, and carrot chips, homemade (as in chilli recipe above).

A simple homemade hummus is healthy, filling and tasty for your crudités. See recipe below.

- **Hummus**

    - 800g chickpeas (pre-cooked)
    - 4 tsps tahini
    - 2 garlic cloves, crushed
    - Pinch Himalayan salt
    - 6 tbsps quality extra virgin olive oil
    - 3½ tbsps freshly squeezed lemon juice
    - Paprika (optional)

Tip the chickpeas into the food processor. Add the tahini, crushed garlic, salt, lemon juice and seven tablespoons of water. Turn on the food processor and slowly pour in the oil while it runs.

When the mixture is fully combined and smooth, tip it into a serving dish. Drizzle with some more extra virgin olive oil and decorate with a few whole chickpeas. Sprinkle with paprika.

• Golden Paste and Golden Milk Recipe

Turmeric Paste

A most effective way to reap the nutritional benefits of this wonderful spice!

- ¼ cup turmeric powder or 2½ cm knob of fresh turmeric, finely chopped
- ½ teaspoon ground black pepper
- ½ cup filtered water
- 2 tsps coconut oil/olive oil
- Optional: 1cm piece of fresh ginger, finely chopped

Cook all ingredients together in a small saucepan on medium heat.
Stir well until the mixture thickens—it doesn't take long.
When a paste has formed, removed from heat and allow to cool.
Add to smoothies or make into golden milk!

Golden Milk

A delicious, nutritious, soothing drink.

- 1 cup milk (organic nut milk or sheep or goat's milk)
- 1 tsp raw organic coconut oil
- ¼ tsp turmeric paste (or more, to taste)
- Raw honey, to taste

Combine all ingredients except honey in a small saucepan. Cook on medium heat, stirring constantly. When completely blended and hot (but not boiling), remove from heat and add honey to taste, stirring until dissolved.

CHAPTER 2

Detoxifying Treatments

One of the most important things about strengthening the immune system is to make sure the organs of detoxification are not already overloaded. If a patient is booked in to undergo procedures of chemotherapy, radiotherapy or surgery, the body will have to cope with the toxic effects of these modalities, on top of trying to combat cancer.

I recommended detoxifying the organs as much as possible prior to treatment, alongside the detox diet plan, and then again after treatment, along with good nutrition and adequate rest, when the patient has overcome the initial effects and is starting to feel stronger.

If the patient is choosing to only have alternative therapies, then this is also a very important part of the process.

The major organs involved in detoxifying the body are the liver, the kidneys, the lungs and the skin.

There are some who will argue that the body constantly detoxifies itself through these organs without any additional intervention, and will even argue that detoxifying doesn't work. But these arguments are largely based on healthy individuals who want to "cleanse" after a heavy weekend on the alcohol, and discuss elements such as colon cleansing tablets that contain polymerising agents, or foot pads, which claim to extract toxins from your feet overnight. Most of these are marketing ploys to get good folk to part with their hard earned cash, and not sadly do very little to help the body.

Other than cleaning up our diet and the products we expose ourselves to, the best detox protocols are very simple, non-gimmicky, and can be explained in simple terms as to how they work.

I am recommending a few that I have had personal experience with, and that are well used in naturopathic medicine.

• Abdominal Massage

This helps to revitalize all the digestive organs in the body, and to physically move food that may be static through the gut. Abdominal massage can be very beneficial for those with constipation, an underactive thyroid, diabetes or poor abdominal tone. If the patient has any tumours in the abdominal region, abdominal pathologies or is pregnant, however, this treatment must be avoided or checked with the patient's doctor first.

• Castor Oil Packs

These can be beneficial to the entire intestinal tract. It is just less than 5% essential fatty acids, which will encourage photon/electron movement to take place. Castor oil packs have also been found to have a suppressive effect on some tumours[1].

Castor oil packs are said to:
- Increase and balance eliminations
- Stimulate the liver and gall bladder
- Helps to reduce nausea
- Dissolve and remove adhesions and lesions
- Relieve pain
- Release colon impaction
- Increase lymphatic circulation, thus enhancing the immune system
- Improve intestinal assimilation

1 International Journal of Toxicology. Final Report on the Safety Assessment of Ricinus Communis (Castor) Seed Oil. May 2007 vol. 26 no. 3 suppl 31–77 http://ijt.sagepub.com/content/26/3_suppl/31.short

- Reduce inflammation and flatulence
- Increase relaxation
- Co-ordinate liver and kidney function

Castor oil packs can be used anywhere on the body, but it is recommended that the liver be treated at the same time with an additional pack.

You will need:
- High quality cold-pressed castor oil – take care to check the source of the oil, and not buy one that has been treated with pesticides or chemically processed, which can damage and even contaminate the oil
- A hot water bottle or heating pad
- Two or three one-foot square pieces of wool or cotton flannel, or one piece large enough to cover the entire treatment area when folded in thirds
- Two towels, one large and one small
- Greaseproof paper cut large enough to cover the flannel.

Instructions

Fold flannel three layers thick so it is still large enough to fit over your entire upper abdomen and liver, or stack the three squares.

The oil should be at room temperature. Saturate the cloth (but not so that it's dripping).

Lie on your back on the large towel (to protect your bed/sofa, as the oil can stain) with your feet elevated (using a pillow under your knees and feet works well), placing the flannel pack directly onto the area to be treated (e.g. liver, located under right breast and right ribcage); cover oiled flannel with the greaseproof paper and then cover that with the small towel, and place the hot water bottle on top.

Pack can be left on from 20 mins (ayurvedic practice recommends this) to one and a half hours (naturopathic practice recommends this).

The same pack can be used up to 20 times before washing if stored in a glass jar and topped up with additional oil before next use. However, if you notice that the pack has become discoloured then it should be changed.

For maximum benefits, use packs for at least four consecutive days each week for one month.

NB castor oil packs can cause gastrointestinal (GI) discomfort in some people, so if the patient suffers from irritable bowel syndrome, ulcers, colitis, diverticulitis or diarrhea, or has recently undergone surgery, the packs should be avoided or check with the patient's doctor before use.

- **Ginger Packs**

These can be used on the kidneys to assist their function and to warm them. They can significantly increase circulation, and encourage movement where stagnation exists. Stagnation is usually presented by stiffness, swelling, pain or inflammation. Ginger penetrates easily into the body, stimulating local circulation.

You will need:
- **4–5oz fresh root ginger**
- **A small muslin bag or a clean cotton sock**
- **Cotton flannel cloth**

Place the ginger, grated, into the bag or sock and close at the top. Place in 1 litre of boiled water. Return to boil before turning down to simmer for 15 minutes. When the ginger-infused water is ready, soak the middle part of the cotton cloth, wring out and apply as hot *as you can safely manage* to the kidney area. Cover with folded towel and keep warm. Refresh the pack in the hot water every 5 minutes, or when it no longer feels warm, for 20–30 minutes. You will need to make fresh ginger infusions daily, but the previous water is lovely in an evening bath or as a foot soak!

Ginger packs shouldn't be used on babies or very elderly patients; during pregnancy or for those with appendicitis, pneumonia or a high fever.

• Guasha and Skin-brushing Technique

Gua sha is an ancient technique used by the Greek, Asian and Egyptian populations. "Gua" meaning to rub or scrape and "sha" is the term used to describe the hyperaemia or increase of blood flow to the skin. Traditionally it was done with a smooth-edged scraping tool, and always in the direction of the heart. However this method combines the technique with an exfoliating scrub, to detoxify the skin. These simple ingredients make a skin scrub that kills bacteria that accumulate in the skin, and helps to restore the skins pH balance. It used to open the skin and rid the body of bad bacteria and potential yeast, fungus, parasites and petrochemicals that become trapped in the seven dermal and epidermal layers.

The skin is the largest of the eliminating organs, and should eliminate up to 2kgs of material per day, but because it gets clogged up with products, sweat and airborne toxic substances, its job as an eliminatory organ becomes very difficult!

You will need:
- **1 bottle of triple-distilled alcohol**
- **Aluminum-free bicarbonate of soda**
- **Resealable jar**

Ginger Packs

Copyright: Marc Mina

Gua Sha Skin Brushing Technique

Copyright: Marc Mina

When you shower, simply rinse your whole body, then step out and add a tablespoon-sized scoop onto a scrubber, glove or loofah, and scrub each arm and leg, your mid-section and back etc, towards the heart.

Then get back in the shower and completely wash the mix off. The theory is that this technique can reduce the workload of your other organs[2].

• Epsom Salts Baths

Epsom salts are made from the mineral magnesium sulphate. When this mineral is absorbed through the skin it draws toxins from the body, sedates the nervous system, lowers blood sugar levels, decreases stress related hormones, reduces swelling and relaxes the muscles. This works because the heat of the water draws the toxins to the skin's surface and then when the water cools it pulls the toxins from the skin.

This is not recommended for patients with heart problems, high blood pressure or diabetes, or in pregnancy.

Method
Dissolve 1 cup of pure Epsom salts in hot water, and soak for 20 minutes.
Add cooler water near the end of the bath and remain in for a further few minutes (or take a cool shower).
Rest after your bath and stay warm to induce further perspiration.
Drink plenty of water.

---

2 The Ultimate Detox For Skin Conditions And To Get Glowing Skin – The Process Of Guasha. http://www.tylertolman.com/health-articles/detox-for-skin/

Variations

- Add half a cup of bicarbonate of soda and 10 drops of lavender essential oil to the Epsom salts bath. Baking soda helps to neutralize skin acidity, and promote elimination of toxins. The lavender will promote deep relaxation, further stimulating parasympathetic nervous activity, which is fundamental in reducing blood sugars, blood pressure, stress hormones and aiding muscle relaxation.
- Add half a cup of the volcanic ash sediment - bentonite clay, to assist in drawing out toxins from the body. When negatively charged bentonite clay it is mixed with water the clay swells, and acts like a porous sponge, where they draw the (positively charged) toxins, bind and neutralize them[3].

Note: bentonite clay should not come into contact with metal, as it will reduce its effectiveness. Also check the quality – it should be grey/green in colour.

Other essential oils that are useful in aiding detoxification are peppermint, lemon, frankincense and rosemary. Add a blend of up to 10 drops of your chosen oils in total.

- **Deep Breathing**

The human lung capacity is about 6l of air but typically we use so much less. Shallow breathing is allows stagnant air and pollutants to accumulate in the base of the lungs and can contribute largely to fatigue, sluggishness, diminished tissue function and poor immune health.

---

3 Bentonite Clay. https://www.mountainroseherbs.com/products/bentonite-clay/profile

Pranayama breathing, which is the practice of voluntary breath control when done slowly, has been shown to have positive effects on immune function, hypertension, asthma, autonomic nervous system imbalances, and psychological or stress-related disorders. Jerath, R. et al., 2006[4], hypothesized that voluntary slow deep breathing, functionally resets the autonomic nervous system. Investigations have demonstrated that slow pranayama breathing techniques activate the parasympathetic (inhibitory) nervous system. This type of breathing employed with deep stretching will have a combined effect on stimulating parasympathetic activity while concurrently decreasing sympathetic activity. This will lower the heart rate and blood pressure, induce relaxation and move stale air from the body.

Method

Either lie down or sit with a lengthened spine, to open the airways fully. Close your eyes and your mouth and place your hands on your belly and inhale slowly and deeply through your nose feeling your belly rise as you do. Now move your hands to the base of your ribs and continue the inhalation into the mid-section of your lungs and feel your ribcage expand laterally. Lastly move your hands to your upper chest breathe into the top of the lung and feel the chest rise. Hold that breath for a moment, before very slowly exhaling from the belly, then the middle and lastly form the top of your lungs. Do this for at least five minutes. Try to focus on this and think of nothing else; give it your full attention.

---

4 PubMed. Epub. Physiology of long pranayamic breathing: neural respiratory elements may provide a mechanism that explains how slow deep breathing shifts the autonomic nervous system. 2006;67(3):566–71. Jerath R1, Edry JW, Barnes VA, Jerath V. http://www.ncbi.nlm.nih.gov/pubmed/16624497

Deep Breathing

• Steam Inhalation

See Chapter 4 recipe for thieves' oil, to use in a wonderful detoxifying, immune boosting inhalation. Just a few drops in a bowl of hot water can really helps with congestion in the nasal cavities, ears, or chest. If you have an infection add a little colloidal silver too, to help fight it.

• Coconut Oil Pulling

Studies have shown oil pulling to be very effective as an anti-plaque and anti-gingivitis treatment, and to be a powerful cleanser for the soft tissues and mucosa of the mouth[5].

Ancient Ayurvedic health practitioners believed that oil pulling could reduce more than just diseases of the mouth and throat. Naturopathic practitioners recommend the practice for various health conditions. It is believed that this exercise may help the function of the lymphatic system of the body to remove harmful bacteria and introduce beneficial micro flora.

5 Indian Journal of Dentist Research. Mechanism of oil-pulling therapy – in vitro study. 2011 Jan–Feb;22(1):34–7. doi: 10.4103/0970-9290.79971. Asokan S1, Rathinasamy TK, Inbamani N, Menon T, Kumar SS, Emmadi P, Raghuraman R.http://www.ncbi.nlm.nih.gov/pubmed/21525674

CHAPTER 3

During/Post Treatment Diet

Choice of food is crucial during this phase for anyone undergoing treatment, who is finding eating difficult due to lack of appetite, nausea and/or physical discomfort. The options suggested in this chapter are designed to give maximal calorific and nutritional intake for someone who is struggling to eat. Meals should be taken every 2–3 hours. Main meals can be portioned into two, and eaten at intervals rather than in one hit.

Some of these recipes will inevitably suit some more than others, so select accordingly.

I advise pre-preparing some vegetable and/or chicken stock, as it/they will be very useful for many recipes. To do this: for a vegetable stock, boil up vegetable ends, e.g. beans, carrots, squash, fennel etc. with some fresh herbs, or use the vegetable pulp from a freshly made vegetable juice*; or, for a chicken stock, if you make a broth with a chicken carcass (see recipe for bone broth) you can use this.

- ***Pre-Breakfast Juice (see Chapter 1)**

Breakfast Recipes

Buckwheat porridge
Small organic yoghurt with fruit and nuts
Organic smoothies with protein powder

• Buckwheat Porridge

- ⅓ cup of pre-soaked buckwheat oats (soaked overnight)
- ⅔ cup of organic whole milk (sheep's or goat's) or organic almond milk
- 1 level tbsp ground almonds
- Fresh raspberries, chopped banana, dried cranberries and goji berries
- Sprinkle of cinnamon
- Raw local honey to sweeten

Cook in a pan until thickened. Add a little filtered water to give a thinner consistency if required. Add honey after pan is removed from heat.

• Yoghurt with Fruit

- 1 cup live organic natural whole yoghurt
- 1 level tsp chopped or ground nuts (almonds, walnuts, brazils, cashews)
- Mashed banana (or mango)

• Smoothie

See Chapter 1 for main recipe, but add in coconut oil and hemp protein powder for extra nutritionally rich calories.

Lunch Recipes

Bone broth[1]
Scrambled eggs with almonds
Chicken noodle soup
Soft poached or boiled eggs with rye bread and butter
Gazpacho soup

• Bone Broth

- • 1kg long bones from organic butchers or farmers who raise grass-fed animals (or a carcass of an organic chicken)
- • 1 onion
- • 2 carrots
- • 2 stalks of celery
- • 2 tbsps apple cider vinegar
- • 1 bunch of parsley, Himalayan salt, ground black pepper, additional herbs or spices to taste
- • 2 cloves of garlic
- • Bay leaf
- • Options: if you use cabbage, broccoli, turnips, brussels sprouts etc., the broth will have a more bitter flavour, but will still be very nutritious

Wash bones. Pat dry.
Roast the bones at 200°C for about an hour until well-browned – roasting the bones guarantees a good flavour in the broth. Drain off any fat.
Add the bones to a big pot along with your veggies.

---

1 Bone Broth – Good medicine for optimal health. Bone broths are high in calcium, magnesium and phosphorus, and also in glycine which supports the body's detoxification process and is used in the synthesis of haemoglobin. http://probodystyling.com/bone-broth-good-medicine-optimal-health/

Bone Broth

Add water to cover and bring to the boil.

Add the vinegar and bay leaves.

Turn down the heat and continue to simmer on lowest heat for *at least* 4 hours, but the longer the better, up to 24 hrs.

Throughout the cooking process, skim off any foam and add water as needed.

Option: if you are not eating straight away or have made enough to store – after filtering through a sieve, freeze in ziplock bags. The stock should set just like gelatin, and the fat should rise to the top.

The gelatin can be re-heated and served as soup, and the fat can be used forhealthy cooking.

• Scrambled Eggs with Almonds

- • 2 organic eggs
- • ⅓ cup organic whole milk (sheep's, goat's or almond)
- • 1 level tbsp ground almonds
- • Pinch of paprika, Himalayan salt and ground black pepper
- • Coconut oil

Whip the eggs, milk, ground almonds, paprika, salt and pepper together, and cook in coconut oil until you reach the desired consistency. Serve with rye bread[2] and butter.

---

2 Rye. In rye flour production, because it is difficult to separate the germ and bran from the endosperm of rye, rye flour usually retains a large quantity of nutrients compared with refined wheat flour. http://www.whfoods.com/genpage.php?tname=foodspice&dbid=65

- **Chicken Noodle Soup**

  - Organic chicken carcass with some meat left on, or chicken thighs. (If you can add chicken feet too, they are a great source of glucosamine, chondroitin, collagen and trace minerals.)
  - Apple cider vinegar
  - 2 large carrots
  - 1 large onion
  - 2 cloves of garlic
  - Himalayan salt, ground black pepper, pinch of saffron, pinch of turmeric, bay leaf
  - Angel hair or vermicelli noodles

Cover chicken with water and bring to boil.

Add all other ingredients apart from noodles, and turn down to simmer on lowest heat for at least 4 hours and a maximum of 24 hours, topping up with water as necessary and skimming off any froth. Just before you are ready to eat, boil water and cook noodles until soft. Strain and place in a large soup bowl.

Strain soup, and serve over noodles, or store in a glass jar in the fridge or freeze in ziplock bags for future use.

- **Gazpacho Soup**

  - 4 ripe tomatoes
  - ½ cucumber
  - 1 small onion
  - 1 clove garlic
  - 1 small red pepper
  - Apple cider vinegar
  - Olive oil
  - Himalayan salt, ground black pepper

Wash all vegetables, and peel onion and garlic.
Roughly chop everything and place in a good blender.
Add seasonings and oil and vinegar.
Add water if consistency is too thick.
Serve chilled, with rye bread and butter – perfect healthy lunch
for a hot day!

Gazpacho

Dinner Recipes

Wild Salmon with avocado
Chicken casserole
Mashed root vegetable hash
Lightly poached fish with creamed squash
Chickpea hotpot

• Wild Salmon with Avocado

- 1 small piece of lightly steamed and cooled wild salmon (or 1 small tin of water-packed skipjack tuna[3])
- 1 ripe avocado
- 1 small carrot
- 1 small onion
- 1 tbsp organic crème fraiche or natural yoghurt
- Apple cider vinegar
- Hemp oil
- Himalayan salt, ground black pepper, pinch cayenne pepper

Mash or blend salmon with avocado.

Grate carrot and finely chop onion and add to mixture.

Add crème fraiche, oil and vinegar, and seasonings.

Serve with jacket potato or roasted potato wedges, and salad.

---

3 What is the best tuna to buy? Water-packed is preferable to oil-packed tuna. In addition to questioning the quality of non-organic oils used in oil-packed tuna, water-packed tuna, on average, contains a slightly higher omega-3 fat content than oil-packed tuna. Plus, canned light tuna, ordinarily made from skipjack tuna, actually poses a substantially lower risk in terms of mercury exposure than fresh yellowfin or albacore tuna. http://whfoods.org/genpage. php?tname=dailytip&dbid=316

- **Chicken Casserole**

  - Organic chicken carcass with some meat on or chicken thighs.
  - 1 small butternut squash, chopped into chunks
  - 1 leek, sliced
  - Handful of green beans, cut in 1cm-lengths
  - Fennel bulb, sliced
  - 1 large carrot, cut into chunks
  - Chicken or veg stock
  - Thyme, paprika and turmeric
  - Option: you can add pearl barley for a thicker, more filling casserole

If using thighs, pan sear them first, with spices to seal flavour.
Pour stock over and add chopped veggies.
Bring to boil, then either simmer on low or place in a low-heat oven for 2–3 hrs, checking periodically.

- **Mashed Root Vegetable Hash**

  - 1 sweet potato
  - 1 small parsnip
  - 1 carrot
  - ½ suede
  - 1 onion
  - Butter
  - Whole organic milk (sheep's, goat's or almond)
  - Himalayan salt and black pepper

- For gravy: 25g butter; 1 tbsp buckwheat[4] flour; chicken or vegetable stock

Chop onion and lightly fry in coconut oil.

Peel and dice veg, and boil until soft.

While veg cooks, make gravy: melt butter in a pan and then remove from heat. Add flour and stir until blended. Now slowly add in your stock until you have a slightly thickened consistency.

Return to heat and keep stirring until it thickens further.

Mash together the veg and add the onion, butter, dash of milk and seasoning.

Pour gravy over and serve.

- **Lightly Poached Fish with Creamed Squash**

  - **White fish (well-sourced)**
  - **Butter**
  - **½ cup of whole organic milk (sheep's, goat's or almond milk)**
  - **Ground black pepper**
  - **Himalayan salt**
  - **1 small squash or piece of squash**
  - **Green peas**

Cut squash into cubes and steam until soft.

Lay the fillets flat in a large frying pan.

Pour in enough milk to cover the bottom of the pan and about half the fish; then grind black pepper and salt on top to taste.

---

4 Buckwheat Health Benefits. In studies of gluten-free buckwheat (actually not a grain but a relative of rhubarb), it was found to be more beneficial than ordinary wheat in stimulating helpful gut bacteria, lowering blood pressure and blood glucose. It also has higher levels of anti-oxidants, B vitamins, magnesium, phosphorus and potassium. http://wholegrainscouncil.org/whole-grains-101/buckwheat-health-benefits

Cover the pan and bring the milk to the boil.

Turn down quickly to simmer for about 15 minutes or until the fish is cooked.

Steam peas.

When the fish is cooked, retain the milk to mash with the squash, and add butter.

Serve the fish on top of the squash, with peas on the side.

• Chickpea Hotpot

Chickpeas preparation: soak overnight and then boil for 20 mins before use.

- 1 cupful of prepared chickpeas
- 1 onion
- 1 clove garlic
- 2 ripe tomatoes
- Handful spinach
- 1 stick of celery
- 1 large carrot
- Tomato puree
- 250ml chicken or veg stock
- Apple cider vinegar
- Himalayan rock salt and black pepper
- 1cm fresh root turmeric
- 1cm fresh root ginger
- Pinch of thyme

Lightly fry chickpeas, onion and garlic.

Add finely chopped spices and herbs, and tomato puree.

Finely chop pepper and carrot and add in.

Roughly chop tomatoes, spinach and celery, and place in a blender with the vinegar and stock.

Pour this over chickpea mix and bring to boil. Turn down to gentle simmer for 10–20 mins, or until carrots are soft enough. Serve with creamy mashed potato.

Mashed Root Vegetable Hash

Copyright: Paul Brighton/Shutterstock.com

Snacks and Desserts

• Gingersnap Biscuits

Sometimes we need a sweet treat, and although I don't advocate sugar for anyone who is being treated for or recovering from cancer, if you are struggling to eat and need the calories, this is a healthier option than most!

- 50g butter
- 50g organic brown sugar
- 50g organic maple syrup
- 113g buckwheat flour
- ½ tsp bicarbonate of soda
- ½ inch fresh root ginger
- 1 tsp ground ginger
- Pinch of cinnamon

Preheat oven to 180°C.
Line baking tray with greaseproof paper and grease with some of the butter.
Melt the rest of the butter, the syrup and sugar in a pan.
Sift in flour, ginger and bicarbonate of soda.
Form small balls and space evenly on baking tray, pressing each to about the size of a 2-pence piece.
Bake for 15–20 mins.

Gingersnap Biscuits

- **Fruit Popsicles**

These are a great way to give someone who has a poor appetite or is uncomfortable a nourishing, soothing snack. They can be enjoyed as a drink or as an ice pop.

Juice Options
  - Apple and blueberry
  - Melon and peach
  - Watermelon and strawberry

Extract the juice, pour into lolly moulds and freeze.

- **Smoothie popsicles**

  - Pineapple, banana, natural yoghurt
  - Strawberry, raspberries, natural yoghurt
  - Filtered water, coconut water or almond milk

Place your selected peeled, chopped fruit in a blender, with a generous tbsp. of natural yoghurt. Add filtered water, coconut water or almond milk to blend.
When done, enjoy as a drink or pour into lolly moulds and freeze. Eat one whenever you fancy a cool, smooth treat!

- **Avocado Chocolate Mousse**

  - 1 large avocado
  - 4–6 dates
  - ½ orange and zest
  - 1–2 tbsps coconut oil
  - 2–5 tbsps of organic cacoa or cocoa powder
  - Almond milk

Blend dates until fine.

Add the remaining ingredients, except the almond milk. Add this last, slowly, until the required consistency has been achieved.

Pour into ramekin dishes and chill in fridge.

Serve with a twist of orange peel or some sliced raspberries.

Note: if orange is too tangy for the palate or you want to add more calories, you can replace the orange for a tablespoon of natural peanut butter (either homemade or natural organic).

Avocado Chocolate Mousse

Copyright Magdalena Paluchowska/Shutterstock.com

CHAPTER 4

Non-Toxic Products

They are everywhere... in your haircare, skincare, suncare, and make-up products. They are in your laundry products, cleaning products and air fresheners. They are plentiful in your upholstery cleaner, your dry cleaners and your car fresheners.

The average person uses over 200 chemicals per day – and that's just in personal care products! They bathe in them, shower in them, rub them all over, inhale them, and most likely inadvertently ingest them too! We are literally drowning in chemicals. So, let's take a closer look at some of the more common chemicals used in most products, where to find them and what they may do, and then we can look at how we can start to make changes...

- **Common Toxins Found in Everyday Products**

Toxic chemical	Effect on the body	Product found in
Fluoride	Neurotoxin – may affect neurodevelopment[1] and cognitive function, decreased thyroid function; immune function	Toothpaste

---

1 Environmental Health Perspectives.Developmental Fluoride Neurotoxicity: A Systematic Review and Meta-Analysis. 2012 Oct; 120(10): 1362–1368. Anna L. Choi, Guifan Sun, Ying Zhang, and Philippe Grandjean. http://www.ncbi.nlm.nih.gov/pmc/articles/PMC3491930/

SLS; SLES	Contaminated with dioxane, a carcinogenic by-product[2] – may be toxic to the brain, nervous system, liver and kidneys	All emulsifiers, surfactants, and foaming products, such as toothpaste, shampoo, shower gel and soap agents
Triclosan	Bactericide – may interfere with muscle function and hormone regulation[3]	Toothpaste, deodorant, shower gel and soap
Fragrance – anything with harmful chemicals that do not legally require listing by name, e.g. synthetic musks	Contains carcinogenic phthalates which may cause decreased sperm counts, early breast development, birth defects, and liver and kidney damage[4]	Shampoo, shower gel, deodorant and perfume

2 Scrub These 15 Toxic Personal Care Ingredients Out of Your Bathroom. September 16, 2014 . http://www.gaia.com/article/scrub-these-15-toxic-personal-care-ingredients-out-your-bathroom

3 5 Toxic Chemicals in the Products You Use Every Day – The truth behind some common ingredients in your sunscreen, deodorant, lotions and make up. November 19, 2014. Sage McHugh http://www.alternet.org/personal-health/5-very-toxic-chemicals-found-your-cosmetics-bags

4 Is Your Perfume Poison? November 27, 2013. Dr Mercola http://articles.mercola.com/sites/articles/archive/2013/11/27/toxic-perfume-chemicals.aspx

All-Purpose Cleaner

Copyright: Marc Mina

Note: as yet, little is known about the effects these toxins have when they are combined in a product, because the majority of clinical trials are done on them as individual chemicals, NOT as interactive ingredients!

It's pretty scary, but the good news is that you don't have to expose yourself and your family to all of these nasties. You can very easily make most of your own products, and for a fraction of the cost that you pay for the toxic cocktails listed above.

Note: please remember these recipes are for NATURAL products, so they don't have chemicals in them to give them nice colours or fragrant aromas (add your own essential oils). Also, again, because they don't have the chemicals to prevent it, they can separate or go hard when stored, so be prepared to mix, shake and/or stir before use!

Cleaning Products

- **All-Purpose Cleaner**

A favourite of mine – so cheap to make and takes two minutes! And it works like a dream on everything from mirrors and sinks to worktops and floors – and even kills insects – without harming you or your family.

- 4 cups rubbing alcohol
- 1 cup white vinegar
- 1 large spray bottle
- 10 cups filtered water
- 1 tbsp liquid castile soap
- Essential oils of your choice

Mix vinegar and alcohol and top up with water. Add soap, and any essential oils and pour into the spray bottle.
Store any excess for top-ups. Shake well before use.

- **Castille Laundry Soap**

This one takes a bit of getting used to because it separates when stored, so needs to be shaken well before use, but it still washes clothes as well as any leading commercial product.

- 1 cup liquid castile soap
- 1 cup washing soda (sodium carbonate)
- 2 cups + 3 cups hot water (plus more to top up)
- ⅓ cup of sea salt, or other coarse-grained salt
- 1 large container (any clean jug or milk bottle works)
- Optional: essential oils

In a large jug, pour 2 cups of hot water and stir in the washing soda and salt until dissolved (it won't dissolve completely).

In a separate jug, add the castile soap to the 3 cups hot water, stirring until mixed and then pour this into the large jug slowly. Stir constantly to break up the gelling that will happen.

Fill the rest of the jug with more hot water and stir to mix. Leave to cool.

When cool, dispense into large container or smaller containers for ease of use, and leave the rest stored. Shake well before use, and add more water if necessary! Use ¼ cup of laundry soap per load.

- **Laundry tips:**

  - For fabric softener, just use white vinegar with your favourite essential oils – I like peppermint and orange – my laundry smells so fresh!
  - Using vinegar keeps your machine super-clean too – no gunk!
  - For stubborn stains: wet fabric and sprinkle with bicarbonate of soda before washing.
  - For stubborn stains on whites: soak, then spray with white vinegar and hang in direct sunlight after washing.
  - For extra-white whites: add a cupful of hydrogen peroxide to your wash.

- **Powdered dishwasher detergent**

  - 2 cups borax
  - 2 cups washing soda
  - 1 cup citric acid
  - 1 cup salt
  - Optional: essential oils for scent

Combine all ingredients and store in an airtight container.
Use 1 tablespoon per load as needed.
For an extra boost, add a few drops of dishwashing liquid (only
a few!!!) to the powder before closing the soap container in
the dishwasher.
You can also add white vinegar as the rinse agent.

Note: this mix can go hard when stored, so be sure to shake frequently.

Personal Products

- **Foaming hand soap**

This is another favourite of mine, because it's so simple to make, and cheap.

- 250ml distilled or filtered water
- 2–3 tbsps liquid castile soap
- ½ teaspoon moisturising oil, optional (Vitamin E, almond oil, or vegetable glycerin)
- Foaming soap pump dispenser (Note: if you don't use a foaming dispenser, it won't foam, as there are no artificial foaming agents!)
- Optional: essential oils of choice. Lavender, tea tree and lemon work well

Fill your soap dispenser about ¾ full with water.
Add castile soap to fill the rest of the bottle, leaving some room at the top for the pump to fit.
Add moisturising oil. Add essential oils, if using.
Cover dispenser with pump and shake well to combine the oils and soap with the water.

Foaming Hand Soap

Copyright: Marc Mina

Sunscreen

Research shows that both fixed oils and essentials oils have a natural SPF value[5]. You can select oils from here to give you an approximate value for your own recipe, or you can use my recipe!

Olive oil *	SPF 7.5
Coconut oil *	SPF 7
Peppermint oil *	SPF 6.5
Lavender oil *	SPF 5.5
Shea butter	SPF 3–6
Wheatgerm oil	SPF 20
Carrot seed oil	SPF 38–40
Red raspberry seed oil	SPF 25–50

*Pharmacognosy Res. 2010 Jan-Feb; 2(1): 22–25.

• **Sunscreen**

- ½ cup almond or olive oil
- ¼ cup coconut oil
- 2 tbsps shea butter
- 2 tbsps zinc oxide (this is a non-nano version that won't be absorbed into the skin.). This makes an SPF of 20+
- Up to 1 tspn red raspberry seed oil
- Up to 1 tspn carrot seed oil
- Up to 1 tspn Vitamin E oil (acts as a preservative too)
- Optional: essential oils: lavender and peppermint both have good SPF values.

---

5 Pharmacognosy Research. In vitro sun protection factor determination of herbal oils used in cosmetics. 2010 Jan–Feb; 2(1): 22–25. Chanchal Deep Kaur and Swarnlata Saraf http://www.ncbi.nlm.nih.gov/pmc/articles/PMC3140123/

Combine all ingredients except zinc oxide and essential oils in a saucepan, stirring continuously. When melted, add the zinc oxide. Stir well and pour into clean jar.

Stir a few times as it cools to make sure the zinc oxide is incorporated.

Add essential oils last, when cool but still liquid.

Use as you would a regular sunscreen.

Note: this sunscreen is partially, but not completely, waterproof and will need to be reapplied after excessive perspiration or swimming Make sure not to inhale the zinc oxide: use a mask if necessary! This recipe has an SPF of about 20; adding more zinc oxide will increase the SPF.

Store in a cool, dry place.

- **Deep Conditioning Moisturizer**

  - ¼ cup shea butter
  - ½ cup coconut oil
  - Essential oils of choice: up to 10 drops

Note: I love jasmine and orange in the winter, but in summertime, I use a blend of citronella, lemon, neem, catnip and lavender, so my moisturiser acts as a non-toxic insect repellent too!

In a saucepan, melt the coconut oil and the shea butter.

Allow to cool to room temperature, but still pouring consistency. Add your essential oils.

Put in blender and whip to give a lighter texture, if desired.

Pour into small jar and allow to set. Store in cool, dark place. Note: if temperature is warm, this will turn into oil, but is wonderful to use on the skin. Can be used on the face, and also on the hair as a deep conditioning treatment, and don't forget it has a natural SPF too.

• Toothpaste

Every ingredient is good for teeth and gum health!

- ¼ cup bentonite clay powder
- 2 teaspoons non-GM xylitol
- ¼ teaspoon unrefined sea salt or Himalayan salt
- ¼ tsp bicarbonate of soda
- ¾ cup filtered water
- 12 drops peppermint essential oil
- 2 tsps (melted) coconut oil
- Usnea or Vitamin E oil (as a preservative)
- Optional: 1 tsp colloidal silver

Bring water to the boil, and leave to one side. In a glass or ceramic bowl combine the bentonite clay, xylitol, bicarbonate of soda and salt.

Note: bentonite clay loses some of its beneficial properties when it comes into contact with metal, so always choose non-metallic bowls and utensils when mixing this toothpaste.

Pour the boiled water over the dry ingredients, carefully mixing until it becomes a smooth paste. Melt the coconut oil, and slowly add to toothpaste. Lastly add essential oils, usnea and colloidal silver and mix well.

Allow the mixture to cool completely before transferring some into a small glass jar or squeeze tube. Store the rest in the fridge to extend shelf life.

• Thieves Oil

This is a lovely massage oil with excellent immunity-boosting properties[6,7]. For anyone with a low-functioning immune system, who needs extra protection, massage this into the soles of the feet, the armpits (works as a deodorant too!), the backs of the knees and/or the crooks of the elbows, or onto the chest or temples (use blended with base oil for skin application; never apply undiluted). For chest infections, coughs, colds and headaches, this works wonderfully well as an inhalant. You can even add it to home soaps and cleaning products.

- **40 drops of Clove Essential Oil**
- **35 drops of Lemon Essential Oil**
- **20 drops of Cinnamon Essential Oil**
- **15 drops of Eucalyptus Essential Oil**
- **10 drops of Rosemary Essential Oil**

This should fill a 10ml bottle.

I like mine blended with either olive or avocado oil, so it can be applied direct to the skin (1 drop to 4 drops of base oil).

---

6 Journal of Essential Oil Research. Effect of a diffused essential oil blend on bacterial bioaerosols. Vol. 10, no. 5, pp. 517–523. Sep–Oct 1998. Chao, SC, Young, DG, Oberg, CJ. http://www.laborforlove.com/effect-of-a-diffused-essential-oil-blend-on-bacterial-bioaerosols.html

7 Thieves Essential Oil Benefits. Jan 27, 2015. Ellen Douglas. http://www.livestrong.com/article/129905-thieves-essential-oil-benefits/

Thieves Oil

Copyright: Marc Mina

Remedy List

During our journey, one of the most important lessons I learnt about cancer is that it's a most complex disease. Cancer cells are clever. If you take just one magic supplement, herb, pill or potion, or only go organic, or just eliminate hazardous products from your cupboards, you will neither prevent nor cure it.

There are hundreds of natural remedies available, and in our story we only touched on a few. We were lucky because the blend of treatments we chose worked for us, but they won't necessarily work for everyone.

My advice to anyone seeking a natural path, be it as a support to conventional therapy or as a standalone set of protocols, is to employ a whole selection of different practices, from clearing out your chemical cupboards to eating an organic, alkaline-forming diet, to meditation, and supplements. I know it seems like a minefield, and that's why I wanted to share our story, to give you a way to begin your journey. You will still need to do your own research on what will work for you, and on what will not interfere with any conventional treatment you are having, or have negative reactions if two treatments are had simultaneously. Always seek advice both from your medical doctors and a good naturopathic nutritionist.

I do know that every single patient who has cancer, and especially those who are having conventional treatments, will need to support their immune system – not just to fight the cancer, but also to be able to cope with the treatments and to reduce the damage done by them.

On the following pages you will find a list of other herbs, nutrients and supplements that have been beneficial in the prevention and treatment of cancer.

- ## Alpha Lipoic Acid (ALA)

ALA has been studied with positive outcomes for patients with metastatic and non-metastatic pancreatic cancer[1].

- ## Astaxanthin

An anti-oxidant with many health benefits that has been purported to help protect against the harmful effects of radiation. Krill oil is a good source of this[2].

- ## Astragalus

A traditional Chinese medicine taken from the root of the herb *Astragalus membranaceus*. Studies suggest that astragalus may improve immune system function and boost the effect of conventional immune therapy for some cancers.

- ## Ayurvedic medicine

Natural medicine practised in India: an ancient art that uses herbs, roots and minerals.

- ## Bee Propolis

You may already have the natural version of an approved colon cancer-fighting drug sitting in your kitchen. Bee Propolis –

---

1 Integrative cancer therapies. Revisiting the ALA/N (alpha-lipoic acid/low-dose naltrexone) protocol for people with metastatic and nonmetastatic pancreatic cancer: a report of 3 new cases. 2010 Jun;9(2):247 Berkson BM1, Rubin DM, Berkson AJ. http://www.ncbi.nlm.nih.gov/pubmed/20042414

2 Astaxanthin: The Most Powerful Nutrient Ever Discovered for Eye Health. November 23, 2010 Dr Mercola. http://articles.mercola.com/sites/articles/archive/2010/11/23/astaxanthin-the-eye-antioxidant-550-times-more-powerful-than-vitamin-e.aspx

along with rosemary and turmeric, and grapes – contains naturally occurring compounds with similar properties to the manufactured chemicals found in the drug Celecoxib; they work much in the same way.

- **Beetroot**

According to Jonathan Hartwell, author of *Plants Used Against Cancer*, the beautiful red beet (*Beta vulgaris*) has been used historically to treat a number of illnesses and cancerous conditions[3].

The disease-fighting and detoxifying benefits of the beet have been widely documented for health problems such as:

- **Tumours of the intestines, head, leg, genitals, and rectum;**
- **Cancers of the lung(s), prostrate, breast;**
- **Leukaemia.**

- **Black Seed Oil**

This is found to have very positive effects on the immune system, with antiviral, antibacterial and anti-inflammatory properties. The seed contains many vitamins, minerals, antioxidants and essential fatty acids.

- **Budwig Diet**

This diet comprises flaxseed oil and cottage cheese, but organic fruit, nuts, seeds etc. can be added. It is a very specific protocol

---

3 Using Vegetables for Cancer Therapy – Beetroot Fights Disease and Even Cures Cancer. Danica Collins, http://undergroundhealthreporter.com/vegetables-for-cancer-beetroot

and if being followed must be done so precisely. The purpose of this diet is to convert oil-soluble omega 3 fatty acids into water-soluble omega 3 fatty acids. As well as cancer it has been shown to be successful in treating many diseases including arthritis, asthma, fibromyalgia, diabetes, high blood pressure and MS. For cancer, the diet is recommended for 3–6 months[4]. For more information please go to http://www.budwigcenter.com/the-budwig-diet/

- **Cannibis Oil**

Although still controversial in some circles, the medical effect of this tetrahydrocannabinol (THC) has been shown to be effective in killing cancer cells, and pharmaceutical forms of this (dronabinol and nabilone) have been FDA approved and are used to treat patients for certain conditions, including the relief of pain and nausea. However, the naturally occurring THC has been shown to have considerable effect in raising melatonin, the level of which is significantly lower than normal in cancer patients, and the results of this treatment have been very promising. For more information on how to make the oil (it should be homemade for best effects)[5], please visit http://phoenixtears.ca/make-the-medicine/

- **Carrots**

Carrots are undoubtedly one of the top cancer-fighting foods. This is due to a group of pigments called carotenoids, which give the vegetable its orange colour.

---

4 The Budwig Diet, http://www.budwigcenter.com/the-budwig-diet/#.Vbn05kVA8u

5 PRODUCING THE OIL . http://phoenixtears.ca/producing-the-oil/

- **Castor Oil Packs**

Castor oil is of potentially high therapeutic value, with low odour, and a low-side effect, low-risk profile, and is highly underutilised in today's modern medical world.

Its main component is ricinoleic acid (RA), which exerts analgesic and anti-inflammatory effects. A leading theory of how it positively affects the immune system is via T-cells (a type of white blood cell that acts as an anti-body) in the skin and an increase of prostaglandins. The respective cell increase represents a general boost in the body's specific defence status[6,7]. To use this soothing, healing practice, either over the liver for a general detox, or over a specific area, please see Chapter 2.

- **Chilli Pepper**

A substance found in chilli peppers (e.g. sweet, cayenne), called capsaicin, has been found to kill cancer by starving the cells of oxygen. Humans would, however, have to eat a huge number of peppers to achieve the needed dose, so the compound would instead need to be taken in concentrated drug form.

- **Coenzyme Q10**

An amazing anti-oxidant that treats cancer. This supplement can also be found in its more biologically active form, Ubiquinol, which is especially important if you are an older person or someone whose immune system is compromised.

6 Born Naturopathic Associates.inc. The Forgotten Therapeutic Applications of Castor Oil. Dr Todd Adam http://www.bornnaturopathic.com/blog/health-articles/forgotten-therapeutic-applications-castor-oil/

7 Castor Oil Packs – How to Make & Use Them. http://wellnessmama.com/35671/castor-oil-packs/

- **Colloidal Silver**

Naturopathic medicine regards cancer as a viral and fungal process. Colloidal silver is antiviral, antibacterial and antifungal. Unlike conventional antibiotics it does not destroy beneficial enzymes, and is very safe to use.

- **Cucurmin (Turmeric)**

This is a powerful root spice that is able to recognise cancer cells and kill them. It also treats inflammation, inhibits metastases, prevents growth of stem cells, and can increase the effectiveness of certain cancer drugs while inhibiting their toxicity! For best results and absorption it should be taken with a good quality oil, such as olive or coconut, and black pepper (see recipe for golden paste, Chapter 1: Detox Diet Plan).

- **Digestive Enzyme Therapy**

In 1906, Dr John Beard proposed that pancreatic enzymes represent the body's defence system against cancer, and would work as a cancer treatment.

- **Echinacea**

Echinacea is a herb that stimulates the white blood cells that help fight infections in the body. Research has shown that echinacea enhances the activity of a particular type of white blood cell called a macrophage (these engulf and digest cellular debris, foreign substances, microbes, cancer cells, and anything else that does not have the types of proteins specific of healthy body cells). A particular glycoprotein in echinacea was found to significantly increase the killing effect of macrophages on tumour cells.

- **Flaxseed Oil/Linseed Oil (see Budwig)**

- **Frankincense Essential Oil**

In 2011, the journal *Cancer* published the results of a 44-person clinical trial showing how brain swelling was affected by frankincense. 60% of the patients displayed a 75% or greater reduction in cerebral swelling after being treated with 4200mg daily of frankincense[8].

- **Gerson Therapy**

Developed by Dr Max Gerson in the 1930s, initially for migraines but eventually also as a treatment for other degenerative diseases and most famously cancer – the therapy is based on the theory that it's the cause rather than the symptoms that should be treated: the approach being to target toxicity and nutritional deficiency. Copious quantities of fresh, organic juices are consumed daily, up to a glass an hour, 13 times a day, along with 3 plant-based meals, and fresh fruit and vegetables for snacking. This diet oxygenates the body and the metabolism is stimulated[9].

- **Grape Seed Extract and Grape Skin Extract (see Resveratrol)**

These supplements contain several cancer-killing nutrients, such as resveratrol and oligomeric proanthocyanidin complexes (OPCs).

8 Dr Axe Food is Medicine. Frankincense Oil: A Natural Treatment for Cancer? http://draxe.com/frankincense-oil-cancer/
9 The Gerson Institute. The Gerson Therapy. Friday, September 16, 2011. http://gerson.org/gerpress/the-gerson-therapy/

- ## Green Tea

Green, white and, to a lesser extent, black tea contain polyphenols, particularly epigallocatechin-gallate (EGCG), which not only inhibits an enzyme required for cancer cell growth, but also kills cancer. Consumption of black tea or its polyphenolic compounds has also been shown to be beneficial in the prevention of cancer cells[10].

- ## Inositol/Inositol Hexaphosphate (IP-6/IP6)

The B vitamin inositol and its derivative IP6 are a naturally occurring polyphosphorylated carbohydrates that are present in substantial amounts in almost all plant seeds, particularly rice, corn, soy, wheat and sesame, and in mammalian cells.
Inositol possesses moderate anti-cancer activity. IP6 reduces cell proliferation and increases differentiation of malignant cells[11]. The best anti-cancer results were obtained from a combination of IP6 and inositol.

- ## Melatonin

Melatonin is a cancer-killing hormone that can enhance the human immune system, protect against the toxic side-effects of chemotherapy, and radiation therapy, and improve wound

---

10 Food Science and Human Wellness. Black tea in chemo-prevention of cancer and other human diseases. Volume 2, Issue 1, March 2013, Pages 12–21. Min-Hsiung Pana, Ching-Shu Laia, Hong Wangb, Chih-Yu Loc, Chi-Tang Hod, Shiming Lie. http://www.sciencedirect.com/science/article/pii/S2213453013000153

11 The Journal of Nutrition. Cancer inhibition by inositol hexaphosphate (IP6) and inositol: from laboratory to clinic. 2003 Nov;133(11 Suppl 1): 3778S-3784S. Vucenik I1, Shamsuddin AM. http://www.ncbi.nlm.nih.gov/pubmed/14608114

healing after cancer surgery. To naturally optimise melatonin levels, do not expose yourself to light sources for at least an hour before bed (including TV, phone, electronic devices,etc.). Get plenty of safe sun exposure. Sleep in complete darkness. Keep your bedroom temperature at no higher than 70°F. Avoid electromagnetic field (EMF) exposure, e.g. from lamps, power outlets, cables and extension leads, especially in the bedroom[12]. Supplement dose recommendations for cancer management: high dose of 20mg per day (some practitioners recommend starting at a low dose (0.3mg) and increase the dose over 1–4 weeks to 20mg to minimise side-effects (vivid dreams and/or drowsiness). Take 20 minutes to 3 hours before sleep.

There can be contraindications to taking it as a supplement so check with your doctor first,[13]

• **Milk Thistle (Silymarin)**

A spiky plant known for its "liver-cleansing" properties, milk thistle has been shown to have powerful cancer-suppressing activity. In 2013, researchers uncovered the chemo-preventive and anti-cancer activity of milk thistle when used alone and along with other medicinal agents against lung cancer[14].

---

12 Exposing Yourself to Light at Night Shuts Down Your Melatonin and Raises Your Cancer Risk. March 19, 2013 Dr Mercola. http://articles.mercola.com/sites/articles/archive/2013/03/19/melatonin-benefits.aspx

13 Oncology Association of Naturopathic Physicians. Just Got Back From A Great Naturopathic Cancer Conference (OncANP): Update on Melatonin and Cancer Treatment. Feb 18, 2013 Brian D. Lawenda, M.D. http://www.integrativeoncology-essentials.com/2013/02/just-got-back-from-a-great-naturopathic-cancer-conference-oncanp-update-on-melatonin-and-cancer-treatment/

14 Natural Cancer Treatments. The anticancer effects of milk thistle . September 21, 2014 Christine M. Dionese, LAc, MSTOM. http://www.naturalhealth365.com/milk-thistle-anticancer-effects-1149.html

- ## Oil of Oregano

Oregano, as part of the Mediterranean diet, and in its whole extract form, may have significant cytotoxic effects. Oregano extract has been shown to "lead to growth arrest and cell death in a dose- and time-dependent manner" in colon cancer cells[15].

- ## Pau d'Arco Tea

A South American tea containing selenium, that if taken regularly can have powerful anti-tumour and anti-oxidant effects[16].

- ## Reishi Mushroom (*Ganoderma lucidum*)

Among the 400 bioactive compounds found in Reishi mushrooms, 5 compounds in particular have been highlighted as the major components that contribute to most of its active pharmacological properties. They are the polysaccharides, triterpenoids, adenosine, organic germanium and ganoderic essence. These compounds have many benefits, including strengthening the immune system, and anti-cancer properties[17].

---

15 Nutrition and cancer. Origanum vulgare induces apoptosis in human colon cancer caco2 cells. 2009;61(3):381–9. Savini I1, Arnone R, Catani MV, Avigliano L. http://www.ncbi.nlm.nih.gov/pubmed/19373612

16 Health Benefits of Pau d'arco Tea. Mar 5, 2013 Loretta Lanphier, NP. http://www.exhibithealth.com/natural-knowledge-base/health-benefits-of-pau-darco-tea-516/

17 Reishi, the Mushroom of Immortality: Miraculous Health Benefits! Heal Cancer, Slow Aging, Regrow Hair, Control Diabetes, Strengthen Immunity. JB Bardot. http://www.jbbardot.com/reishi-the-mushroom-of-immortality-miraculous-health-benefits-heal-cancer-slow-aging-regrow-hair-control-diabetes-strengthen-immunity/

- **Resveratrol**

A COX-inhibitor found particularly in the skin of red grapes and in cucurmin – this anti-oxidant has tumour-inhibiting qualities[18].

- **Selenium**

This essential trace mineral is a cancer-fighting powerhouse. It functions to increase the activity of glutathione, the body's master anti-oxidant. It enhances immunity and may suppress tumour growth[19].

- **Spirulina**

Spirulina, an edible freshwater algae used as a dietary supplement, has been impressing researchers for years with its high levels of beneficial nutrients and phytochemicals. The plant pigment-protein phycocyanin, which gives spirulina its characteristic colour, is a strong anti-inflammatory and anti-oxidant, and has a role in apoptosis (cell death) when used with other enzymes such as cucurmin, resveratrol, isoflavones and quercetin[20].

- **Vitamin C therapy**

Over 40 years ago, twice Nobel prize-winner Linus Pauling, and Ewan Cameron MD, a Scottish cancer surgeon, demonstrated the effectiveness of 10,000mg of vitamin C per day to reverse

18 Foods That Heal. http://www.curezone.org/foods/default.asp

19 The Proceedings of the Nutrition Society. Selenium in cancer prevention: a review of the evidence and mechanism of action. 2005 Nov;64(4):527–42. Rayman MP. http://www.ncbi.nlm.nih.gov/pubmed/16313696

20 Nutrition News. Spirulina extract 100 per cent effective against breast cancer cells. August 19, 2014 Karen Sanders. http://www.naturalhealth365.com/nutrition_news/spirulina-kill-breast-cancer-cells-1114.html

cancer in 13 patients – who were left by conventional medicine to die. Overall, the research to date strongly supports the importance of eating a diet rich in vitamin C.

While supplementing 1–5g vitamin C may help prevent some cancers, cancer patients are most likely to benefit from 10g or more a day. These higher levels are best taken with the guidance of your health practitioner[21,22].

- ## Vitamin D therapy

Researchers have pointed out that increasing levels of vitamin D3 among the general population could prevent chronic diseases that claim nearly one million lives throughout the world each year; and incidence of several types of cancer could be slashed in half.

The best way to optimise levels of vitamin D is appropriate sun exposure.

However, this must be on unprotected or at most moderately protected skin, as one of the leading vitamin D researchers, Dr. Michael Hollick suggests: "sunscreen on with a sun protection factor of 30, reduces your ability to make vitamin D in your skin by about 95 to 98 per cent." For some protection with no toxin exposure, use a natural, low-SPF sun product or an oil with a natural SPF (see Chapter 4).

According to www.vitamindcouncil.org: "You don't need to tan or burn your skin to get vitamin D. You only need to expose your skin for around half the time it takes for your skin to turn pink and begin to burn."

---

21 Vitamin C Benefits. IV Vitamin C Therapy: a Cancer Perspective. April 15, 2015 Jonathan Landsman. http://www.naturalhealth365.com/western-medicine-riordan-clinic-irwin-stone-1387.html

22 The Truth About Vitamin C and Cancer. 5 Jan 2010 Patrick Holford. https://www.patrickholford.com/advice/the-truth-about-vitamin-c-and-cancer

Optimum levels for disease prevention are 50–70 ng/ml, but for treating disease such as cancer, the levels are suggested at 70–100ng/ml.

NB To maintain prevention levels of 50–70 ng/ml, the recommended dose is 1,500 – 2,000 IUs per day, for patients of normal bodyweight (to be increased if patient is obese). Also, it's important to remember that high dose Vitamin D requires supplementation of Vitamin K2 to ensure correct placement of calcium in the body[23].

• Wheatgrass

If we look at oxygen as a bullet to kill cancer cells, then we should look at wheatgrass[24,25] as a shotgun blast at treating cancer. The number of ways in which it deals with cancer is incredible. First of all it contains chlorophyll, which has almost the same molecular structure as haemoglobin. Chlorophyll increases haemoglobin production, meaning more oxygen gets to the cancer. Selenium and laetrile are also in wheatgrass, both are anticancer. Chlorophyll and selenium also help build the immune system. Furthermore, wheatgrass is one of the most alkaline foods known to mankind.

As you will know by now, this was a huge part of our therapy! For more information, visit: http://www.livewheatgrass.com

---

23 Vitamin D—One of the Simplest Solutions to Wide-Ranging Health Problems. December 22, 2013 Dr Mercola. http://articles.mercola.com/sites/articles/archive/2013/12/22/dr-holick-vitamin-d-benefits.aspx

24 Why Wheatgrass? http://hippocratesinst.org/benefits-of-wheatgrass-2

25 WHEATGRASS JUICE BENEFITS. livewheatgrass.com/our-story/health-benefits/wheatgrass/

A Final Word...

To go through an experience such as we did, for anyone, be it yourself or in supporting a loved one, is one of the most difficult challenges life can lay at your door. Often, upon finding out that terrible diagnosis, we ask ourselves, "why me?" and wonder if somehow maybe we have brought it on ourselves as some type of retribution for an imagined sin, or through making poor choices in earlier life, or maybe it is just a cruel twist of fate.

But although it is a terrible ordeal, for us, in one way, I discovered it had a silver lining. Before this happened to us, we lived a relatively healthy life, or so I thought – but when we were faced with the verdict that suggested otherwise, it made us literally turn our lives around. We have learned so much about how we treat our bodies, and the consequences of what we do to ourselves. It could be argued that it is unjust that we had to go through this to find out what we should have known all along, but sometimes it takes something so shattering to make you sit up and take note of what really matters and of how you are living your life.

The point I am trying to make here is that the life you live matters, so much. If you treat your body with the love and respect it deserves, you stand the best chances of good health and happiness – but you must treat it so for life. Coping with cancer and its devastating treatments was not just about getting through it: it's been an awakening, a revelation. You must take care of your body every day, always. Feed it the right nutrients; and don't allow it to become poisoned by toxins. Keep your immune system in good shape, just as you might your muscles in the gym. Invest in your health and you will reap the benefits.

I wish you good health, happiness, and a long and fulfilling life.

Why Wheatgrass Played Such a Key Role in Our Journey

There are of course many factors involved when it comes to supporting and healing the body through a journey such as ours. It is not enough to rely on one ingredient, one protocol or one supplement. Combining healing practices and nutritional support is a complex but fundamental strategy in any cancer patient's experience if they are to have the best recovery possible.

In our case, Saul was dependent on the feeding tube throughout his treatment. This posed huge limitations on what we could do nutritionally, and for this reason having something that packed a huge nutritional punch in one small liquid form was invaluable. Saul was able to have a plentiful source of vitamins, minerals, amino acids and enzymes.

Wheatgrass juice has been highly regarded for its nourishing properties for many years amongst health professionals. It is exceptionally rich in nutrients and chlorophyll.

To summarise, here is what giving Saul just one ounce of live wheatgrass juice per day provided him with:

- All vitamins (except Vitamin D)
- 91 minerals
- 20 amino acids (out of a possible 24)
- Over 80 beneficial enzymes

1oz wheatgrass juice contains:

- As much Vitamin E as 700g of broccoli; that is 12 times more Vitamin E than is in broccoli! 100g wheatgrass contains, weight for weight, 270% more Vitamin A than broccoli
- 1600% RDA of B12 – that is almost as much as in shellfish!
- 17 times more Vitamin B5 than is in a banana
- 7.5 times the amount of precious green chlorophyll that is in broccoli[1]

Not only does wheatgrass contain all these bountiful nutrients, it also has a very similar chemical structure to haemoglobin (our red blood cells, which are responsible for transporting oxygen in the blood). Wheatgrass helps to cleanse our blood, improving its oxygen supply[2] which prevents anaemia, and it strengthens our immune system by increasing the levels of white blood cells (leukocytes) and antioxidants[3] . For patients who have to undergo radiotherapy, the treatment is likely to be more effective in those with good haemoglobin levels, meaning that if a patient becomes anaemic, survival rates are lower[4]. Patients undergoing radiotherapy and chemotherapy are highly likely to experience anaemia and a weakened immune system, so prevention is key.

The chlorophyll in wheatgrass not only oxygenates the blood, it also helps to remove toxins and heavy metals, helping

---

1 http://livewheatgrass.com/health-benefits/wheatgrass/

2 Indian Pediatr. 2004 Jul;41(7):716–20. Wheatgrass juice reduces transfusion requirement in patients with thalassaemia major: a pilot study.

3 A Novel Antioxidant Isolated from Young Green Barley Leaves. Agric. and Food Chem. 1992; 40: 1135–1138

4 Radiotherapy-Associated Anemia: The Scope of the Problem. http://theoncologist.alphamedpress.org/content/5/suppl_2/1.full

to detoxify the body of all the harsh chemicals that a patient has to receive during conventional treatments.

For example, it has been found in a preliminary scientific study of 60 patients with breast cancer that wheatgrass juice taken during chemotherapy may reduce the side effect known as myelotoxicity (the slowdown of bone marrow function to produce white blood cells, red blood cells and plasma cells) and the need for medication (granulocyte-colony stimulating factor [G-CSF] support) without reducing the effectiveness of chemotherapy[5].

5　Wheat grass juice may improve hematological toxicity related to chemotherapy in breast cancer patients: a pilot study. Nutr Cancer. 2007;58(1):43–8.

About the Author

Lorraine Ereira began her journey into natural health during the pregnancy of her first child over 20 years ago, when she studied aromatherapy. Not realising at the time just how powerful plant-based medicine was, although she enjoyed it, she put the profession aside and went on to study for a degree in Sports Therapy, which she has now practised for many years and continues to do so as part of the natural health therapy she offers her patients.

It wasn't until her husband received his diagnosis of cancer that Lorraine turned her focus back to natural medicine– this time to the magic of plant-based nutrition. Throughout her husband's journey she studied more and more and finally embarked on a nutritional therapy diploma to consolidate her knowledge and continue to put it to good use.

Since her husband's experience, she has begun to work with other cancer patients who realise the importance of supporting their bodies through cancer and the treatment for it: whether they choose the all-natural approach which Lorraine favours, or conventional medicine, Lorraine has been able to help them with nutritional therapy and supportive healing.

Lorraine felt it was her calling both as a writer and a therapist to share her story to help as many people as she can.

Lorraine lives most of the year in southern Spain with her husband, younger son, and dog; her elder son has flown the nest to build his life in the UK.

Housing Management

A guide to quality and creativity

by
Anne Power
with PEP Associates

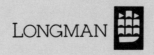

LONGMAN

Published by Longman Industry and
Public Service Management, Longman Group UK Ltd,
Westgate House, The High, Essex CM20 1YR, UK.
Telephone: (0279) 442601
Fax: (0279) 444501

First published 1991

British Library Cataloguing in Publication Data
Power, Anne
  Housing management: a guide to quality and creativity.
  1. Great Britain. Local authority housing.   Planning I. Title
  711.580941

ISBN 0-582-08001-0

Produced by Longman Group (FE) Ltd
Printed in Hong Kong

Cover photographs: © Paul Herrmann/Profile

CONTENTS

LIST OF DIAGRAMS

Chapter IV

Chapter V

Chapter VI

Chapter VII

Chapter VIII

Chapter IX

Chapter X

LIST OF PLATES

1. Tenant participation. Neighbourhood Committee, Thorpes Estate, Hull
2. Tenant consultation. Broadwater Farm Estate, Haringey
3. Support for tenants. A tenant management co-operative flat in Islington
4. Estate management board election campaign. Bacup & Stackstead's Estates, Rossendale
5. Tenant management co-operative committee. Regina Road Co-operative, Islington
6. Tenants and staff working through decisions. Cloverhall Management Co-operative, Rochdale
7. Local office in the high street. Bacup, Rossendale
8. Estate team at St. John's Estate, Isle of Dogs
9. Making offices friendly, welcoming and helpful is the best way to prevent violence, Chelheath Estate, Stoke-on-Trent
10. Enforcement of tenancy conditions involves a great deal of co-operation. St. Paul's Gardens, Bristol
11. 'Allocating housing is far from a mathematical task.' Cloverhall Estate, Rochdale
12. A multiracial team is vital in a multiracial community. Broadwater Farm Estate, Haringey
13. Efficient day-to-day repairs help to prevent long-term damage. Bacup Estate, Rossendale
14. All housing requires constant renewal
15. Capital work. Stoops and Hargher Clough Estate, Burnley
16. Major renovation. Bloomsbury Estate, Birmingham
17. The quality of caretaking makes or breaks estate conditions. Thorpes Estate, Hull
18. Estate wardens help the elderly with their gardens. Kirkholt Estate, Rochdale
19. Controlling budgets locally helps residents understand what is possible. Cloverhall Estate, Rochdale
20. Direct contact with tenants is the best rent system. Norley Hall Estate, Wigan
21. Staff need to understand why they are collecting information. Monitoring at the Bacup Estate, Rossendale
22. Holding training events with tenants and housing staff helps. PEP National Conference, Liverpool 1988
23. Induction course for tenants' representatives. St Paul's Gardens, Bristol
24. Local training programme at Shadsworth Estate, Blackburn
25. Liaising with key services makes estate living work. Pensioners' lunch club, Broadwater Farm Estate, Haringey
26. Estates need a wide variety of inputs. Bloomsbury Estate, Birmingham
27. Employing resident to carry out environmental work. Digmoor Estate, Skelmersdale, Lancashire

LIST OF ABBREVIATIONS

BWFYA	Broadwater Farm Youth Association
CRE	Commission for Racial Equality
DLO	Direct Labour Organisation
DoE	Department of the Environment
DSS	Department of Social Security
EMB	Estate Management Board
ESF	European Social Fund
HA	Housing association
HAK	Housing Appraisal Kit
HC	Housing co-operative
HRA	Housing Revenue Account
GLC	Greater London Council
LA	Local authority
LMO	Local management organisation
LSE	London School of Economics

NACRO	National Association for the Care and Resettlement of Offenders
NFHA	National Federation of Housing Associations
NFHC	National Federation of Housing Co-operatives
NMC	Neighbourhood Management Committee
OAP	Old Age Pensioner
PEP	Priority Estates Project
RFS	Registrar of Friendly Societies
SI	Statutory Instrument
SNU	Safe Neighbourhoods Unit
TA	Tenants' association
TMC	Tenant management co-operative
TPAS	Tenant Participation Advisory Service

PREFACE BY HIS ROYAL HIGHNESS, THE PRINCE OF WALES

I am delighted to introduce a book which will help tenants to take a lead in the management of their housing estates.

Many densely-built inner city estates must be hard to live in and hard to manage. Large overspill estates outside our major cities such as Glasgow, Liverpool, Newcastle and Leeds are equally depressing. They have an atmosphere of desolation and abandonment with few shops or buses; they show visible disrepair and neglect of properties, the environment is poor and there are disproportionate levels of unemployment – although you will find quite often that residents say there is a good spirit amongst those who live in such estates.

Large numbers of families live on these estates, around one million households. The problems facing them and facing the Councils which own the estates are enormous, yet there are ways of improving things quite dramatically.

The Priority Estates Project has pioneered a new approach to housing management and resident involvement, often reversing the fortunes of the most deprived housing areas in Britain.

The Project has two main strategies. The first is to bring services to local areas through small-scale, locally controlled projects. The second is to discover and support local leaders who always exist in every community.

The Project has found talented and energetic people, working long hours – often completely voluntarily – to reverse sometimes appalling conditions on estates throughout Britain. They offer inspiration for this guide to local management which sets out in clear, simple language how to go about the task of managing rented housing with the full involvement of residents. It will be an invaluable aid to all those concerned with the future of the 2,000 or more rundown estates in this country that desperately need new inspiration.

Charles

Kensington Palace
London
1990

FOREWORD

Housing management is a complex and demanding job. It is also a big business. Housing management is an activity which has been much neglected throughout its history with neither central nor local government, neither education nor training establishments paying sufficient attention to it. For too long tenants and the users of housing services have borne the cost of this neglect.

This book, prepared by a group from within the Priority Estates Project, sets down the basic principles of housing practice. Concern with tenants and the views of tenants are the heart of this volume and they are seen as critical to the success of estate-based management. For it is at the estate level that many will judge the success or failure of housing management. The tenants themselves are seen as central rather than being a footnote or a chapter at the end after the management position has been laid down.

The book has not been written to sit symbolically on the shelf. It has been produced to generate action by tenants and housing staff, by councillors and committee members, by local authorities and housing associations. As housing organisations across the United Kingdom emphasise their commitment to services for the tenant rather than to the tenant, so here we have a guide which in its own way can help make the rhetoric of change into a reality. Please read on.

Peter Williams,
Professor of Housing Management,
University of Wales, Cardiff

May 1990

CONTRIBUTORS

The following PEP Associates contributed to the following sections of this publication:

Trevor Bell – Tenant consultation and Estate Management Boards

Sarah Gregory – Budgets, rents, capital works, monitoring and evaluation

Chris Holmes – Tenant consultation and organisation

Caroline Keightley – Setting up a local office and staffing

Roger Saunders – Caretaking, training, dealing with the public

George Varughese – Race and housing

Mary White – Repairs and planned maintenance

Tricia Zipfel – Estate Management Boards

Caroline Hunter of Arden Chambers and the London School of Economics wrote the chapter on the legal implications of estate-based housing management.

ACKNOWLEDGEMENTS

We would like to thank all those local authorities who have helped us by providing information and examples through the development of their own priority estates projects.

Michael Hatchett has advised PEP on repairs and heavily influenced our thinking.

Michael Burbidge offered continual and meticulous advice on the approach. Other DoE officials, including David Martin, Ed McHugh, Keith Kirby, Paul Fletcher, Philip Burns and Steven Marshall-Camm, offered useful advice and suggestions.

Richard Zipfel, Cleonie Eccleston, Tim Oshodi and Ron Belgrave gave invaluable advice on the racial issues in housing management.

The housing management practice guidelines, developed at the London School of Economics by Margaret Brown, provided detailed information which has been drawn on.

Gavin McCairns prepared an outline of lettings issues.

Mike Bradley, David Carmichael and Roger Hull of Rhondda Borough Council have since 1984 debated the ideas and techniques presented in this volume, illuminating many of the points.

Thanks are also due to Gill Beckett and Bob Brett of Tower Hamlets Council, Don Simpson of TPAS (formerly of Rochdale Metropolitan Council), Paul Mugnaioni of Quality Street (formerly Glasgow District Council), Neale Coleman (formerly of Haringey Council), Steven Lister, Peter Williams of Cardiff University, Margaret Hodge of Islington Council, David Piachaud, Howard Glennerster and John Hills of the London School of Economics, with whom I have discussed the main direction of local housing management.

The PEP team at a Workshop in Buxton, Derbyshire, organised by Sally Phillips in May 1988, devised the outline for these guidelines.

The views expressed in this book reflect the views of the author, and not those of advisers or the Department of the Environment.

Hilda Gage kept continual track of the information, worked through many drafts, incorporated suggestions and corrections, designed diagrams, checked information, liaised with 15 PEP Associates and generally held the information together till they became a book. Lindsey Olliver helped with word-processing and drew new plates. Philippa O'Neill and Monika Zulauf hunted down references and other information.

Deborah Georgiou and Chris Holmes checked the work page by page. Margy Knutson and Mary White helped to edit the manual.

The manual is a result of many years' work by council staff and tenants who have pioneered local housing management projects on their difficult-to-manage estates. The material in these volumes is drawn from their experience. Without the co-operation of many local authorities, it would not have been possible to produce it.

The Department of the Environment sponsored the Priority Estates Project from 1979. The Welsh Office supported PEP in Wales. Without that support, PEP's work on rundown estates would not have been possible.

I accept full responsibility for any mistakes and for the limitations of this volume – the impetus of the Housing Acts 1988 and 1989 made urgent the task of going to print.

INTRODUCTION: WHY MANAGE ESTATES?

Many people slip into housing work through a series of accidents. They apply for an administrative job in the council; they become a rent collector; they join a graduate training scheme; they switch from welfare or social work to a housing job in the hope that it may produce more immediate help for low-income people; they start work as a book-keeper in the finance department and find that rents are taken over by the housing department; they want to do something useful and practical.

The vast bulk of housing staff have little or no direct training in housing management. The majority have little experience of dealing with members of the public. Very few have any knowledge of building or repair work. Only a small minority would be prepared to take on full responsibility for running rents, lettings, repairs, finance and welfare for a group of properties.

Many are afraid of the idea of being based in an estate office, close to the tenants and far from the Town Hall, at the beck and call of whoever walks in through the office door. Yet this is precisely the job this manual sets out to promote. It is an exciting, challenging and rewarding one.

Why is the housing world being encouraged to move many of its 200,000 employees out to estates by the Department of the Environment?
Why are tenants increasingly being asked what they think?
Why are council landlords either breaking up their own services into small, responsive units, or being threatened with break-up by outside pressure?
Why are tenants showing greater interest in influencing decisions?
Why are universities and polytechnics in England, Scotland, Northern Ireland and Wales, funded by the Government, to train postgraduates for housing work?

– because running estates is a complicated task that requires training;

– because tenants have voiced their dissatisfaction with housing management, and in particular repairs, more and more vociferously;

– because the valuable housing stock of five million homes built by councils mostly since the war has been fast running down;

– because millions of pounds and thousands of workers have been tied up in vast bureaucracies;

– because rent arrears have been rising, better-off households have been moving away from council housing and the poorest communities are becoming more vulnerable;

– because housing problems are at the root of many other problems;

– because early local estate initiatives offered promise of happier tenants, better conditions and more motivated staff;

– because innovative local authorities and groups of tenants up and down the country are showing new and more exciting ways of doing things – **on the estates;**

– because local management could save money by providing a better and more efficient service and by rescuing estates that otherwise threaten to become obsolete.

This manual is a guide for tenants' organisations, housing organisations, unions, and estate-based staff in **how** to run an estate. The PEP Guide to Local Housing Management (1987) presented the case for local estate-based organisation. This manual attempts to give a step-by-step outline of each element necessary for a successful estate-based management project.

We put residents first because we think it is self-evident that without them, no aspect of housing management will work.

Who the residents are, is largely dependent on how lettings are done. Therefore we discuss lettings straight after the role of residents and the setting up and staffing of the office. We discuss race and housing issues here because the access by minorities to housing, the causes and consequences of discrimination, are closely linked to housing; and because relations between different racial groups are often most intense, most extensive and most fraught in the poorest housing areas. It is crucial that the worst estates in major cities do not become racial ghettos.

Repairs come next because they are pivotal to the survival of estates. They are one of the areas where local management has been most successful. Caretaking is closely linked with repairs.

The other sections follow logically. Budgets, accounting, rents and benefits, are closely associated with and underpin other aspects of management.

Links with the outside world keep enthusiasm, energy and standards alive. Monitoring, support, training and co-ordination with other services help staff and tenants alike to achieve the 'impossible'. Wider links and the promotion of good practice help convince Government, local authorities, housing organisations, and the public that effort pays.

Housing organisations can combine a dynamic, forward-looking central role in a fast-changing world, with a meticulous and detailed delivery of day-to-day management services.

USING THE MANUAL

The manual is not a blueprint. It describes a local approach to housing management that is meant to be used flexibly and adapted to the very different situations on each estate and in each housing organisation and local area. Readers should be able to dip into the sections that interest them and are useful at a particular time. They should skip sections they are already familiar with. The manual does not offer a series of detailed and comprehensive procedures. Rather it gives guidelines to be interpreted widely and applied variably according to local circumstances.

The 10 key ingredients of local housing management are examined in five parts:

Part 1: People and place – the priority for local management – residents; the local office and staff; local lettings, access and racial issues.

Part 2: The buildings and environment – repairs and capital works; caretaking and caring for the environment

Part 3: Money for local management – estate budgets and ring-fenced housing revenue accounts; rents, arrears and benefits

Part 4: Working with the outside world – monitoring and support; co-ordination with other services; training for staff and tenants

Part 5: The legal aspects of estate management

There are many aspects of housing management that are barely touched upon in the manual – for example, the right to buy; design modification; the resources required to meet the capital and revenue costs of major repair and renovation. Where possible, we alert readers to other sources of information.

Practice in individual estates varies hugely and rarely matches the ideal. Therefore the manual can only serve as a guide and not a blueprint. Housing management is about responding to infinite variations in problem-solving around people and property. Their constant interaction makes neat and fixed prescriptions impossible. However, the basic approach adopted by the Priority Estates Project from numerous different sources should be relevant to most socially rented housing areas.

A manual dealing with current and live issues is almost bound to be overtaken by events. Certain ideas are highly experimental, such as the Estate Management Boards and estate budgets. Others are profoundly influenced by new legislation affecting caretaking, cleaning and repairs. The whole future of local authorities as direct landlords is clouded with uncertainty following the Housing Acts of 1988 and 1989.

The manual is based on five guiding principles:

– the housing service is operating in an uncertain climate of rapid change that requires flexibility, quick wits and the confidence to innovate and adapt;

– the style of service, the way buildings are maintained and the way residents are consulted and involved will largely determine the outcome of local projects;

– the obsession with size, with economies of scale and with uniform provision is giving way to a more varied, more flexible and more localised approach to problems and solutions;

– the inevitable fragmentation of housing into much smaller and more local units of organisation will create the need for co-operation, exchange and support as well as creating an atmosphere of competition and suspicion;

– the advent of the European Community and 1992, as well as the greater movement of people and ideas around the world, will take us out of our sometimes insular approach to housing ownership and tenure, housing management and housing futures. Where we find ourselves in great difficulty, we should look for ideas to countries that are more successful in their approach to housing management.

A final word – the manual draws on ten years of intensive experimentation with local housing management on rundown council estates in England and Wales. But we hope that the practical experience on which the manual is based will be of use for a wide range of housing organisations, including local authorities, housing associations, co-operatives, government and private bodies, as well as our counterparts in other countries with whom many of these ideas have been developed. We believe that the lessons can be applied to almost any size and type of housing organisation and estate. Whilst we refer throughout to estates, areas of mixed housing and traditional streets and neighbourhoods have many of the same needs if they are rented from a landlord.

Local housing management should fit into a wider structure; local organisations require wider support; and tenants' organisations require nurturing. The exact division of responsibilities will need to be brokered in each situation.

This all leaves a big role for central housing organisations. But it may be a very different one from that conceived in the past. It is important to seize the opportunity to change and adapt while there is a head of steam behind new initiatives. The local authorities and associations that succeed in adapting to a more flexible and bottom-up approach to housing management, that reduce the red-tape and improve the quality of service, that encourage tenants to take on responsibility and get involved in their estates, are likely to be the organisations of the future.

Starting points for housing management

Contents

*'Creative thought –
the precursor to invention
– requires an act of faith'*

George Gilder

1. SUMMARY

The four priorities in setting up local housing management are:

- to set up direct face to face dealings between landlords and tenants.

- to provide a simple, accessible local housing organisation for tenants and management staff.

- to give the local housing manager full responsibility

for managing the housing, under the direction of the landlord.

- to give residents a say in areas where traditionally they have had none

The local housing management organisation is responsible to the landlord for a good service and an efficient business. It has 10 key elements illustrated in Diagram S.1.

Diagram S.1   Running an estate with links to the outside world

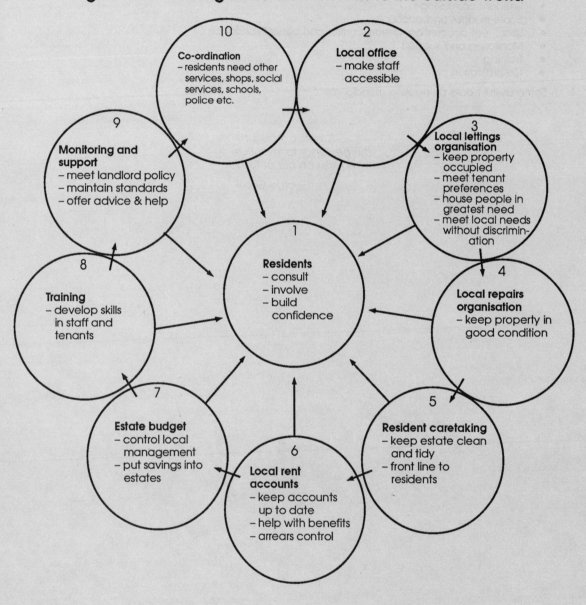

2. KEYWORDS: TENANTS; LANDLORDS; REWARDS

Housing management is about relations between **tenants** and **landlords.** If tenants cannot reach their landlord quickly and easily and vice versa, the relationship will swiftly deteriorate. When things go wrong, it is important to act quickly, fairly and with good sense. A local office, with local staff, local knowledge and open to all tenants, makes this possible. Most rented housing run by local authorities is built on estates, many of them with over 500 dwellings. Any estate of 200 or more rented homes needs its own manager to take care of day to day management and repairs.

Many housing bodies, including the Priority Estates Project, have shown that it is no more expensive to run housing this way (Power, April 1987, Vol. 2). It is certainly more attractive to tenants and more rewarding to housing staff. Often it saves money, particularly if the landlord is large and far from the estates, with a big central bureaucracy. It also brings many non-cash **rewards.**

3. TEN KEY PRIORITIES FOR RUNNING ESTATES

Resident participation

Only residents experience directly and fully the problems of a particular estate. They have a strong vested interest in making things work. Without them it is impossible to sort out many social as well as physical and management problems that affect estates. The Priority Estates Project aims to set up elected Committees, Estate Management Boards or Tenant Management Co-operatives to give residents a controlling say in the running of their estates.

Residents on their own cannot solve the complex, interacting problems of management and economic viability, unless they themselves become the landlord. Therefore, a partnership between tenants and the landlord is usually the best way forward. Within the **partnership,** tenants are **active** partners, not passive supporters or recipients.

The local estate office

The local estate office is the vital base for running areas of rented housing. Local offices are set up in a variety of situations – covering scattered dwellings; serving a big estate; covering two or three smaller adjoining estates; serving intensively a small estate that is either isolated or has major problems.

Local lettings

Local lettings mean that the local office plays an important role in controlling empty property and having an input into lettings. All lettings should be within the policies laid down by the local authority. Applicants can be nominated by the local authority; they should be in need of housing, and eligible for rehousing. In areas of low housing demand, the local office could recruit applicants directly to a local waiting list. In areas of high demand, priority applications should be forwarded from the centre to the local office. In the case of co-operatives or other housing organisations, a system of nominations can be devised. Lettings should be carefully monitored and the lettings system should be open to scrutiny and widely publicised.

Repairs and capital works

Repairs and capital works require a major input from the local office.

A **local repairs organisation** should be based in a depot on the estate with a core team of workers responsible for all day to day and empty property repairs. This team is paid under contract to carry out repairs out of a local repairs budget. Repairs may be done through a Direct Labour Organisation (DLO) or through other local contractors. The choice should rest on the quality of work, level of service, efficiency and responsiveness, and the cost. The work of the repairs team, whether private or DLO, should include cyclical and some planned maintenance. A local budget is vital to the organisation of repairs.

Capital works to the estate should be under the day-to-day supervision of the estate manager. They require detailed local liaison and tenant contact. They also require technical support.

Resident caretaking

Resident caretaking makes a vital difference on flatted estates. Wardens or caretakers are also important on all large, rundown, communally-built estates of houses. Cleaning and upkeep of the environment are central tasks. Caretakers are the front line of the local housing organisation. They have a most crucial role in the management of estates. They can only work well with the support of residents and an efficient local housing office. Caretakers should be resident in order to provide supervision and support. They in turn need local supervision and support from the estate manager, if they are to perform well. They also need to be part of the team, answerable to the estate manager.

Estate budget and accounts

An estate budget and accounts should be identified through a management and maintenance allowance per dwelling per year under the direct control of the estate manager or local management organisation. It should be enough to meet the cost of day-to-day management and maintenance. The local repairs team should be paid for from the local budget. Without a local budget a local manager cannot manage properly. With a local budget, tenants can see realistically what they are getting and what is possible. Any savings made through better management performance should be ploughed back into the estate.

Diagram S.2   The role of landlord in setting up and supporting local housing management

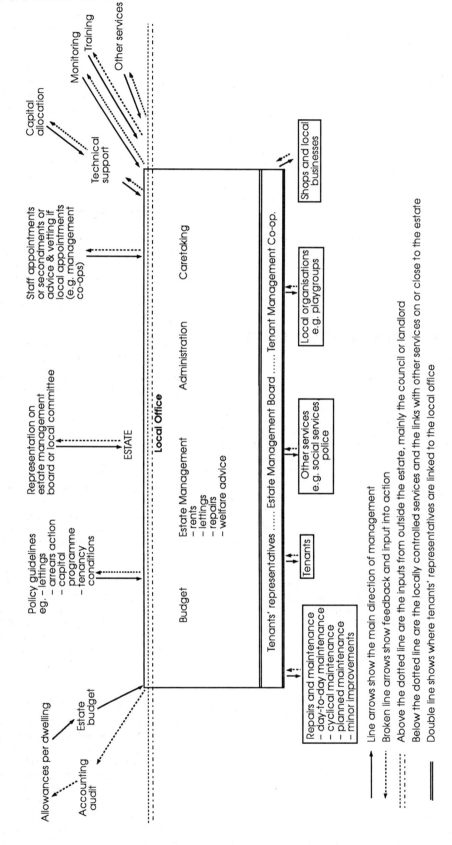

Line arrows show the main direction of management

Broken line arrows show feedback and input into action

Above the dotted line are the inputs from outside the estate, mainly the council or landlord

Below the dotted line are the locally controlled services and the links with other services on or close to the estate

Double line shows where tenants' representatives are linked to the local office

Local rent accounting, arrears control and benefit assistance

Tenants have a legal duty to pay rent, even if it is often with the help of benefits. They need a direct and local service to stay out of debt. Local responsibility makes it possible for estate-based staff to tackle arrears swiftly and provide welfare advice directly to tenants. Regular rent accounts should be available locally so that the local office can decide quickly what to do. Control of arrears is easier and more rewarding if local managers have direct access to rent account information. Cash transactions need not take place locally, though it can be arranged safely and successfully. It should be possible to do local benefit calculations.

Monitoring and support

Monitoring and support are essential to ensure that local organisations keep up their quality. Local progress in rents, lettings, repairs and spending should be shown on wallcharts in the local office. Monitoring helps to set realistic targets for improvements in the service. Local organisations require outside support if they are to perform well, to adapt to changes, to develop and retain the incentive to provide a good service. The landlord must be involved in monitoring and support, even if other agencies are also called upon to help.

Training

Training in the basic ingredients of housing management helps staff and tenants to develop their understanding and skills as they gain experience and confidence. Start-up team training for local staff, training for residents' groups and tenants' representatives, local management courses are examples of what is needed.

Co-ordination

Co-ordination with other services and organisations such as architects, parks, cleansing, social services, economic development, schools, the police, voluntary bodies, tenants' organisations, shops, businesses, etc., needs to be built up on the estate. Housing alone cannot reverse bad conditions. The existence of a local base can greatly facilitate this co-ordination.

Making a success of running rented housing is not an easy task, especially where the property is rundown and built on large estates, where a majority of the tenants are on low incomes, where housing staff are used to administering housing from central or district offices, and the estate itself has a bad name. Setting up a local office with control over the ten ingredients flies in the face of much previous practice. There are hundreds of objections to it, especially when tenants and housing staff see change as a threat to their homes or jobs, a threat to the very survival of council housing.

There is now solid evidence that local housing management involving tenants directly and basing staff in local offices works best (DoE, 1989). Here we attempt to explain **what** we need to do and **how** to do it. Diagram S.2 shows the role of landlords in setting up and supporting local housing management.

Running rented housing is like running a household. It is a day-in, day-out task. It requires single-minded attention to detail. Above all, it requires a **combined** approach (Burbidge, 1981). You have to do a number of things at once to make it work, **and go on working.**

The ten sections of this manual explain in more detail each of the ten priorities.

4. SOME USEFUL BOOKS ON HOUSING MANAGEMENT

AUDIT COMMISSION (1989): Managing the Crisis in Council Housing. HMSO

DEPARTMENT OF THE ENVIRONMENT (1989): The Nature and Effectiveness of Housing Management in England. HMSO

INSTITUTE OF HOUSING (1987): Effective Management; Effective Management Workbooks 4 and 5; Effective Management Self-Assessment Pack 4 and 5. London

NATIONAL FEDERATION OF HOUSING ASSOCIATIONS (1987): Standards for Housing Management. London

STEWART J (1988): A new management for housing departments. Local Government Training Board, Luton

Part 1
The People

I. Tenants and housing management

A A role for tenants in the management of estates — how to achieve it

B Local management organisations — Estate Management Boards

C Tenant management co-operatives

A A role for tenants in the management of estates – how to achieve it

Contents

"I can't exactly put my finger on it and say to you it happened at one particular time because it didn't. It was more a gradual sort of thing. But people did – they became more and more separate. A lot of early comers moved away ... nobody knew anybody any more, and nobody had the same amount of pride in living on the estate that the first people who came here had ...

I suppose the other major way in which I've changed since I came here is that I've set my sights a lot lower."

Tony Parker
(People of Providence)

1. SUMMARY

The four main priorities for involving tenants in housing management are:

- organising informal, small group meetings to give all tenants a chance to have a say;

- recruiting tenant representatives to help with decision-making;

- establishing an estate-based decision-making body involving tenants and the landlord;

- providing support and training for tenants' representatives.

The ten basic stages in supporting tenant involvement are shown in Diagram 1.1.

Diagram 1.1 Supporting tenant involvement

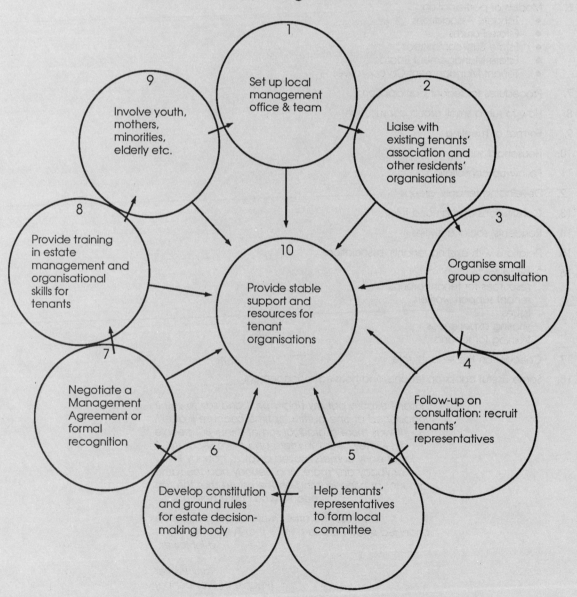

1 Set up local management office & team

2 Liaise with existing tenants' association and other residents' organisations

3 Organise small group consultation

4 Follow-up on consultation: recruit tenants' representatives

5 Help tenants' representatives to form local committee

6 Develop constitution and ground rules for estate decision-making body

7 Negotiate a Management Agreement or formal recognition

8 Provide training in estate management and organisational skills for tenants

9 Involve youth, mothers, minorities, elderly etc.

10 Provide stable support and resources for tenant organisations

2. KEYWORDS: LISTENING; DIALOGUE; RESPONSIBILITY; SHARING; CONTROLLING

Persuading tenants that they have a vital role to play and that their views count, is not a quick or easy task. The residents of each area will have their own, often strongly held and, sometimes, divided views on problems and on how consultations should be organised.

Our approach stresses the importance of **listening** always to what people have to say. On that basis, it may then be possible to create a constructive **dialogue.** From there, a willingness to take **responsibility** for certain areas of development may grow. The result may be a greatly strengthened sense of **sharing** and **controlling** the future of the estate.

Consultation is particularly important where:

– an area has become rundown and unpopular;

– a local housing office will be or has been established;

– residents are not yet actively involved in the running of the estate.

Consultation has three main purposes:

– to give information in a factual and unbiased way;

– to learn from tenants what their views are;

– to encourage the formation of tenants' organisations that are fair, open and responsible, so that as many residents as possible can influence the future of the estate.

The ideas and methods described here may be applied to other housing situations and not just large or unpopular council estates.

Under the Housing Acts of 1988 and 1989, tenants will need to register their views and respond in ways that have not previously been tried. Tenants need to feel confident that they are being consulted in an open and fair way with a real chance to shape the outcome. Tenants themselves play the most crucial role in sorting out an estate.

3. DEFINITIONS

'Participation' means 'tenants have a share in housing decisions'. This can take different forms: **'Consultation'** means 'to seek the opinion of' – where the council puts forward a proposal and seeks a response from the tenants. **'Involvement'** means 'to include' – where tenants are members of bodies which take decisions. **'Control'** means 'to have under command' – where tenants have control of facilities, resources and decisions. (See TPAS/IOH report on tenant participation for detailed discussion, 1990)

4. TARGETS FOR PARTICIPATION

– Hold small group consultations within six weeks of the office opening.

– Organise priorities based on residents' views.

– Organise feedback on service, e.g. repair satisfaction cards.

– Work out ways of reaching special groups, such as isolated mothers, young people, housebound residents, and members of ethnic groups.

– Hold regular meetings between estate staff and tenants' representatives.

– Aim for a formally constituted body.

– Find a budget to support tenants' initiatives.

– Develop a training programme for tenants.

5. WHY TENANT PARTICIPATION IS ESSENTIAL

Tenant participation is essential because:

a) It leads to **better decision-making.** Tenants have a bigger reservoir of knowledge and experience about their estate than any outsider.

b) Where tenants have been involved in the design of improvements or the organisation of services, they are more committed to them and therefore are **more likely to defend them.**

c) Tenants **develop skills and talents** which have previously lain dormant.

d) Decline can only be reversed by a **partnership.** Local authorities can bring skills and expertise, but this needs to be matched by a commitment from residents.

e) Estates need **local effort:** tenants on a particular estate cannot identify with, control or even influence many of the wider issues but they can make things **work** better at a local level if there is a small-scale, locally responsive organisation.

6. MODELS OF PARTICIPATION

Programmes should be tailored to suit the particular needs of the estate.

The five main levels of involvement discussed in this publication are shown in Diagram 1.2. Others are being developed.

Tenant's Associations often exist or have existed at some time on priority estates. They are voluntary groups of residents often with a double aim of providing social and community events and facilities, and acting as a pressure group on the council on behalf of the tenants of the estate. They do not normally control any decisions on how the estate is managed. Any tenants' association will want to have a say in a new initiative and will probably want to play a part in organising consultations.

Estate Forums or liaison meetings are the most common structures to emerge on priority estates, allowing **tenants' representatives and local staff** a fairly informal means of discussing problems and resolving on action. Increasingly estate forums are developing into or being replaced by more formal bodies with more local control.

Diagram 1.2
Five levels of involvement

Tenants' Association	Estate Forum	Estate Sub-committee	Estate Management Boards	Tenant Management Co-operatives
residents	residents & staff	residents staff and local councillors	residents & staff	residents
dialogue	joint discussion	decision-making power	decision-making power	delegated authority to run the housing fully
lobbying	consultations over decisions	some decisions referred to Housing Committee		
representations				
		control over budget	control over budget	
influence	influence	some control	control	control

1. *Tenant participation. Neighbourhood Committee, Thorpes Estate, Hull*

Estate Sub-committees are a local sub-group of the main Council Housing Committee which delegates some decision-making power and control over a budget to a committee comprising residents and councillors.

Estate Management Boards are legally constituted, local bodies with delegated management powers and control (Zipfel, 1989). Estate Management Boards with a team of locally based staff will take responsibility for all (or as many as possible) day-to-day management functions. The local authority is a corporate member of the Estate Management Board and nominates representatives to it.

Tenant Management Co-operatives are organisations where **residents** make up the membership. They **take over** responsibility from the council for the running of the estate and usually employ their own staff to help them to do so. In a tenant management co-operative, the landlord retains the ownership of the housing. The role of landlord and tenant comes together in ownership co-operatives and in some community-based housing associations.

7. PROCEDURES FOR TENANT PARTICIPATION

Consultations should take place shortly before or as soon as possible after a local office is opened. Consultation programmes should seek to establish residents' views about the estate where they live and priorities

for tackling major problems. If they take place before the office is set up, then tenants' views on conditions and problems can influence how the team is recruited and what jobs are given priority.

Small informal **consultation meetings** early on in a local project give tenants a chance to air their views. These meetings should have three objectives:

* to provide a clear picture of **residents' priorities;**

* to encourage **tenants' representatives** to play a part in future activities, e.g. an Estate Management Board or Estate Forum;

* to develop **direct relations** between the Council and tenants.

8. HOW TO RUN A SMALL GROUP CONSULTATION

Running a consultation programme requires a person from the housing organisation with communication and organising skills to set up the meetings, arrange publicity, visit, convene, write up and follow up. Often outside bodies such as the Tenant Participation Advisory Service, Safe Neighbourhoods Unit, secondary co-operatives or the Priority Estates Project (PEP) are taken on to run consultations.

The meetings should be organised as follows:

– Each group meeting should be led by a **convenor.** All convenors should be properly briefed and work to a

2. *Tenant consultation. Broadwater Farm Estate, Haringey*

Priority Estates Project

structured agenda. PEP staff, local community workers or volunteers can play this role. It is better to have a non-resident.

– Between 50 and 100 households – the number depending on the types of dwellings and layout of the estate – should be invited to each meeting. Between 10 and 25 households are likely to attend.

– Personal invitations should be sent to every tenant, followed by visiting door-to-door, followed up by a reminder notice on the day of the meeting.

– The meetings should be held at **a time and place** which is convenient and accessible for tenants (on the estate or adjacent to it). The meetings should **not last too long.** A meeting starting at 7 p.m. and lasting for 1½ hours is often the most sensible, although afternoon meetings may be better for blocks of older tenants and on estates where there is very high unemployment.

– Special arrangements for children may be necessary for people with young children. Special meetings to consult young people in a place where they feel at home may also be necessary.

– Meetings should take place in **a pleasant venue easily reached** from the block or street involved. Usually a church, school, local office, community hall or a flat can be found. Displays at the meeting showing the estate area and the work of other PEPs help to break the ice and create interest. It helps to serve tea or coffee.

– The **agenda** should be sufficiently **'open'** for tenants to be able to voice their main concerns and bring up their own issues. Individual problems, e.g. a particular repair, should **not** be dealt with in the meetings. These should be followed up **after** the meetings. The general atmosphere should be informal but people's ideas and problems must be recorded.

It may take two or three months to work right round a large estate holding two consultation meetings a week. The procedure is shown in Diagram 1.3.

9. FORMAT OF MEETING

Meetings should cover a number of basic points as exemplified in Diagram 1.4.

Role of the convenor

There are several basic but important functions that the convenor must fulfil in running consultation meetings:

a) A list of **people's ideas** under each of the agenda headings should be written up on large sheets of paper so that everyone can read it. Flip charts are excellent.

Diagram 1.3
Plan for initial consultation

- Identify different groups on the estate, e.g. ethnic minorities, make sure translations/interpreters are available.
- Split estate into small areas (50–100 dwellings).
- Find convenient time and place for meetings (several different meeting places may be needed for a very large estate).
- Leaflet whole estate announcing programme of meetings.
- Door knock and leaflet one week before each meeting.
- Find neutral convenor for each meeting.
- Send out reminder notices on day of meeting.
- Do extra visits to households needing special encouragement.
- Draw up agenda under 3 main headings:
    problems on estate,
    assets of estate,
    ways of tackling problems.
- Recruit volunteers for future activities.
- Establish agreement on way forward.
- Send notes on the main points of meeting to participants.
- Call follow-up meeting of representatives.

Diagram 1.4   Format of meeting

A short explanation of the purpose of the meeting and of any plans for the estate

↓

Introduction of each group member saying something about him/herself, e.g. how long he/she has lived on the estate

↓

Features about the estate or council services which present problems for residents – each participant contributing one idea

↓

A discussion to get residents to agree on the worst problems, making sure that everyone has a chance to speak

↓

Good features of the estate – each participant contributing one idea

↓

Ideas for tackling those problems ranked 1, 2, 3. Participants should feel free to discuss the ideas and explore solutions further

↓

A round-up of what happens next

Otherwise old wallpaper, bluetack and felt pens will do. These sheets provide the basis for the report to the estate after the consultations.

b) Convenors should encourage **everyone to contribute** to a debate.

c) **Notes of the meeting** should be circulated as soon as possible afterwards to all those who attended, and include **points for action** to be taken.

d) Before the end of the meeting, the convenor should ask for **volunteers.** Volunteers are needed to become members of an estate steering group to plan future action. They can form the nucleus for a Tenants' Association, an Estate Forum, an Estate Management Board, or Tenant Management Co-operative.

e) Racial minorities, young people, single mothers, the elderly and other special groups can often feel left out or be shy of volunteering. They need to be represented in any body that develops.

Consultations are very labour-intensive. Some staff feel that such lengths should not be necessary and are 'over the top'. But it requires a lot of effort to overcome apathy, cynicism, ignorance and even despair, and it is the only sure way of making housing management work.

10. HOUSEHOLD SURVEYS

Some projects carry out a household survey as a means of getting residents' views. (See Chapter 9, Monitoring, for fuller discussion of surveys.) Usually forms are delivered to each household and collected later after tenants have had a chance to fill them in.

The form asks residents:

− what they like and dislike about the dwelling and the estate;

− what are the particular problems of the dwelling and the estate;

− what are their priorities for improvements to the dwelling and the estate;

− how well or badly different services work;

− what they think about security on the estate;

− how many people live in the house;

− how many children (under 16), young people (16−21), and elderly (over 65) there are.

The replies provide projects with basic information about the estate which can be used by estate managers in developing management plans and planning capital programmes.

The survey organiser should be recruited on a temporary contract. A typical timescale for an estate survey of 800−1,000 dwellings from starting the work to the report writing would be three months.

A survey organiser needs to recruit, train and supervise volunteer helpers to deliver and collect survey forms. The survey organiser and volunteer helpers should also be able to help residents to complete forms if required.

All survey forms should be coded and a simple computer analysis undertaken. A clear and simple report should be prepared on the basis of the survey findings. These findings should be presented so that they provide the local team with basic information that can be used in setting work priorities and targets.

Tenant surveys are very useful where: information on households and needs is lacking; information on conditions is critical to get capital resources; and/or a follow-up survey is planned to show progress.

11. FOLLOW-UP CONSULTATION

Report

The report of the small group consultations or door to door survey should be simple and short; it should make clear the most important issues which staff and residents need to tackle on that estate. The results can help work out better management practices and can make the case for capital investment in improvements or major repair. The report should be available to all residents, the council and to other concerned bodies.

Back-up

Residents will stay involved if things happen. Some ideas for helping are:

− provide meeting space for the use of the residents' association and other community groups in the estate office

− deliver regular newsletters to every household

− do follow-up surveys on specific topics, e.g. tenant satisfaction with repairs

− present findings from the consultation at a public meeting

− call-back on residents who were interested

− put up displays in the office

− organise special exhibitions, e.g. on house modernisation work

− set up a suggestion box

− call area meetings to discuss the report − follow-up reports

− set up an estate forum to which all volunteer representatives are invited.

12. DEVELOPING TENANTS' GROUPS

The number of residents' representatives may range from as few as 5 to as many as 25. It is helpful to draw representatives from each area of the estate; also from existing tenants' organisations and from ethnic minority groups in addition.

Diagrams 1.5 to 1.8 illustrate the different structures that may be used.

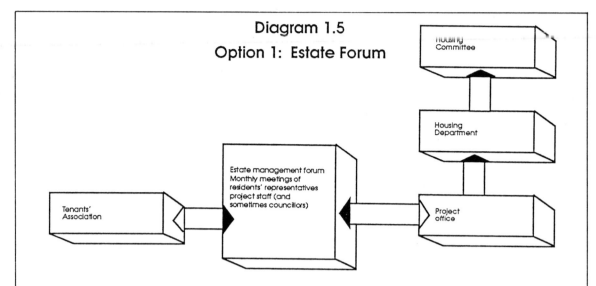

Diagram 1.5
Option 1: Estate Forum

- Ward councillors may be involved.

- Any tenants' association should be represented.

- The management forum receives information about performance on key management areas, on spending from the revenue budget and about capital programmes.

- The management forum has no executive power but can influence management decisions.

- The forum can initiate and support community ventures such as play schemes and small environmental improvement projects. It may be allocated a budget for this purpose.

- The forum may set up working parties to look at particular problem areas.

- A forum sometimes has the drawback that it can be bypassed or overridden by the council.

Examples: Isle of Dogs Estate Committees; Wigan Neighbourhood Forum; Ocean Estate, Tower Hamlets

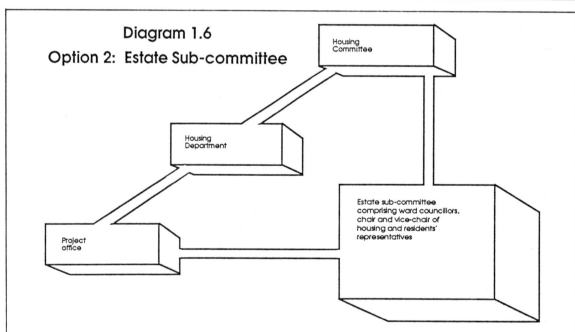

Diagram 1.6
Option 2: Estate Sub-committee

- The sub-committee makes recommendations to the main housing committee.

- Agendas and minutes are formal and the committee is serviced by a council committee clerk.

- Smaller and less formal working parties look at particular problem areas and report to the sub-committee.

- A sub-committee operates like an official council structure.

- It may have significant delegated powers.

- It can have control over the estate budget.

Examples: Broadwater Farm, Haringey; Thorpes and Danes Projects on Orchard Park Estate, Hull

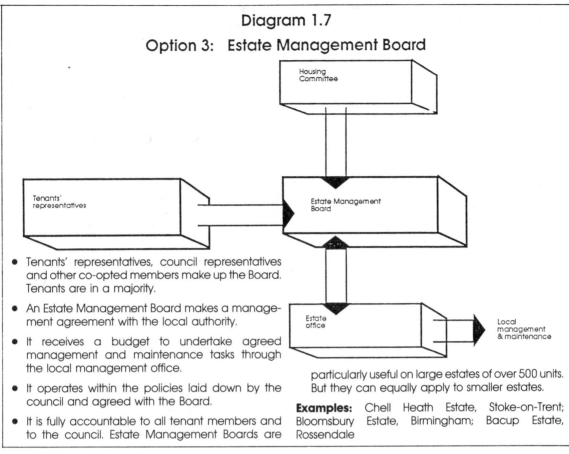

Diagram 1.7

Option 3:   Estate Management Board

- Tenants' representatives, council representatives and other co-opted members make up the Board. Tenants are in a majority.

- An Estate Management Board makes a management agreement with the local authority.

- It receives a budget to undertake agreed management and maintenance tasks through the local management office.

- It operates within the policies laid down by the council and agreed with the Board.

- It is fully accountable to all tenant members and to the council. Estate Management Boards are particularly useful on large estates of over 500 units. But they can equally apply to smaller estates.

Examples: Chell Heath Estate, Stoke-on-Trent; Bloomsbury   Estate,   Birmingham;   Bacup Estate, Rossendale

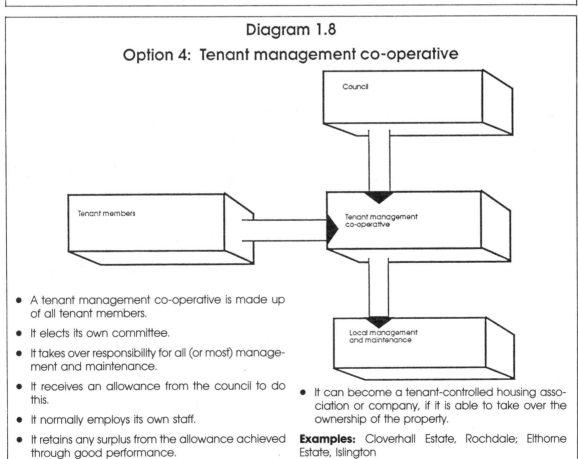

Diagram 1.8

Option 4: Tenant management co-operative

- A tenant management co-operative is made up of all tenant members.

- It elects its own committee.

- It takes over responsibility for all (or most) management and maintenance.

- It receives an allowance from the council to do this.

- It normally employs its own staff.

- It retains any surplus from the allowance achieved through good performance.

- It can become a tenant-controlled housing association or company, if it is able to take over the ownership of the property.

Examples: Cloverhall Estate, Rochdale; Elthorne Estate, Islington

13. CONSTITUTIONS AND GROUND RULES

Rules for membership of tenants' organisations, meetings, representation and control need to be as fair and open as possible. Model rules for tenants' associations, co-operatives and other tenants' bodies are available from the Registrar of Friendly Societies, the National Federation of Housing Associations, the National Federation of Housing Co-operatives, the Tenant Participation Advisory Service and often from local authorities.

Important features to consider are:

a) All sections of the community need to be represented on any decision-making body, with co-options of ethnic minority representatives where necessary.

b) It is important to agree at the outset that no religious, political or ethnic prejudice or exclusion should be allowed in any organisation.

c) Equally, it should be agreed that the local forum, association or Board should not be used for political or religious propaganda purposes.

d) Ground rules for the conduct of members and of meetings should be adopted and enforced with the sanction of exclusion from meetings or membership where these are broken. Inexperience, rivalry and prejudice can make it difficult for newly formed groups to run the business of participation fairly, openly and efficiently. Participation and democracy require practice and clear rules. The problems of participation are as common to elected politicians as to groups of low-income tenants, as the radio and television broadcasts of parliamentary proceedings show. (See Appendix on Code of Conduct.)

Rules

The following are some of the basic rules: formal agendas and minutes; courteous conduct of business; speaking through the chair; no threatening language or behaviour; careful book-keeping and accounting; and open membership, within agreed rules of behaviour.

Order

It is vital to strike a balance between openness to as wide a group as possible and the ability to control developments so that disruptive intruders can be excluded. Some residents' groups have failed either because they are too narrow and exclusive or because they have been taken over by destructive personalities. Getting the balance right is the most difficult and most important part.

Experience

It is important to discuss these ground rules fully where a new group is being formed that may be inexperienced. The power that is devolved to estate level can help create factions, divisions and conflicts. It can also generate ambition and a desire to wield power. Established institutions regulate such problems through convention and agreed procedures but often only after struggles and long practice.

Development

New organisations will little experience need to develop ways of coping with some of the pressures that will certainly mount as tenants, often for the first time, see a chance of taking control. The support offered at the beginning will help establish the organisation on a stable basis.

14. RESIDENTS' SOCIAL ACTIVITIES

It is important to support and encourage many types of activity. For example, tenants may want to join together to organise events or services for the community or to provide facilities. They can play a leading role in establishing estate organisations. The following are some of the activities which tenants have established:

• community centre	• Gingerbread
• youth club	• art club
• cafe	• summer fete or festival
• social club	• 'bring & buy' and jumble sales
• pensioners' lunch club	
• day nursery	• advice centre
• playgroup	• credit union
• mothers' & toddlers' group	• workshop (mending & making)
• gardens	• crime prevention
• play area	• women's group
• after-school club	• camping holidays
	• community business

Tenants' groups setting up and running these organisations and activities need: training; help with fund-raising; and support and advice from experienced bodies (e.g. Under-Fives Asssociation, Pre-School Playgroups Association).

Community facilities should be as open as possible to encourage maximum use.

Tenants can also form pressure groups and organise campaigns on particular issues, such as damp, repairs, security, rubbish-dumping and clean-ups, dog control, facilities for play, health, bus routes etc. These can be useful in involving more tenants and in informing the local office and the elected representatives of problems.

15. RELATIONS WITH EXISTING TENANTS' ASSOCIATIONS

It is important to work as closely as possible with existing tenants' associations. However, this may not be the sole vehicle for tenant involvement.

On some estates, tenants' associations are not representative of all the areas of a large estate; or all the racial groups or age groups. At worst they can be composed of a small clique (sometimes all male, sometimes all white) which entirely excludes other people. In such situations, a more broadly-based representative organisation is needed. If at all possible, this should work alongside the existing group. In some cases, it may incorporate or supersede it. As a result of consultations, there are many new people who usually come forward.

16. SUPPORT FOR TENANTS

Resources for tenant groups

To work well, tenants need access to resources which can help them to organise effectively, such as: an office 'base' or at the least a regular meeting room; access to a telephone, photocopier and other equipment; and funds for producing newsletters and other publicity material for tenants.

Some local authorities provide funding for recognised Tenants' Associations – in a few cases through a Tenants' Levy. Sheffield and Glasgow do this. Organisations like PEP can help on a very limited basis. However, many tenant groups have little access to resources. Projects may have to raise money independently. They need some help from the landlord and the landlord should be willing to provide resources. Where an estate budget is developed, an annual sum of £5 per household can be set aside for local initiatives and for pump-priming tenants' activities.

Tenant support workers

Tenant support workers help to develop stronger, more representative groups of tenants, who can then play a more active role in making decisions about their estates. PEP appoints project assistants or tenant support workers on many estates.

It is best for the worker to be employed by an independent organisation such as PEP or a secondary co-operative, recognised by both the council and tenants. The worker needs a clear agreement with the tenants on his or her role and the extent and limitations of the support that he/she can give. The support worker's role in local management initiatives is primarily to promote good local management **with the involvement of tenants.**

Tenant support workers usually do the following jobs: convening meetings; organising consultations; preparing agendas and minutes; servicing and supporting tenants' activities; liaising with the local office; helping involve ethnic minorities; helping organise and support children's and youth activities; helping to raise money; and preparing ground rules, constitutions, registration, management agreements and other formal procedures.

It is vital that tenant support workers produce results in the eyes of the tenants. This requires resourcefulness, energy and tact.

3. *Support for tenants. A tenant management co-operative flat in Islington*

Paul Herrmann/Profile

Issues to be resolved in employing tenant support and community workers

On some estates community workers employed by either the local authority or independent community agencies have been appointed to carry out similar tasks. There are some cases where workers have been employed directly by the tenants' group.

a) Workers employed directly by the Council can face a **conflict of interests,** where there is disagreement between the tenants' group and the local authority.

b) Independently employed community workers can be **resented** by tenants' groups, not least because they are often paid well for what tenants do voluntarily; and yet they are neither part of the project nor the council.

c) During the period when tenant participation is evolving and developing, there can be problems in having a worker employed directly by the tenants' group because the group is **at an early stage** (often there is no single representative association that could take on that role).

d) It is important for the tenant support worker to maintain some **independence.**

e) Valuable support for tenants can come from groups with **specialist or professional skills,** such as Technical Aid Centres, Community Architects or Law Centres. Those 'experts' are particularly valuable who are prepared to use their knowledge as a resource to help tenants develop their own proposals or solutions. 'On tap, not on top', as the Weller Street tenants have put it (McDonald, 1986).

Sharing experiences

Visits

'Study visits' to other estates teach volumes. Seeing the success of a project at first hand is perhaps the most effective argument in convincing people that changes can actually be achieved. It is often specially stimulating to meet members of Tenant Management or Community Ownership Co-operatives and to visit particular experiments on different estates – for example, schemes for landscaping and environmental improvements; plans for improving access and security in tower blocks; special initiatives involving youth; or caretaking experiments.

Some residents' groups on estates have been so successful that they are constantly welcoming streams of visitors, e.g. Broadwater Farm, Haringey; Hornsey Lane Estate, Islington; Penrhys Estate, Rhondda; Calvay Co-operative, Glasgow; Cloverhall Co-operative, Rochdale. They may need help with the cost of hosting visits. The visiting group needs to be well prepared to make maximum use of the visit. They need to understand the purpose of the exercise, be well briefed and know what they are looking for.

Conferences

PEP organises one-day Tenant Conferences, bringing together tenants from projects in different areas of the country; these are very popular. The conferences are chaired by an experienced tenant. Many of the workshops are led by tenants. The main talks are usually given by tenants. The agendas of the conferences are prepared by tenants' representatives from different estates who meet in London for a planning meeting. Whilst housing professionals have many opportunities for learning about initiatives in other areas, most tenants have practically no opportunity for such experiences. Tenants' conferences and study visits are ways of starting to redress this imbalance.

Training for tenants

Many tenants who become active will have had no previous experience of groups of this type. Although they know a lot about the needs and problems of their estate, many may have little knowledge of the policies, structures and procedures of the Council and the way it organises its services.

Offering well-prepared training to tenants' representatives is a key way of developing tenants' organisations. It is especially important where tenants are preparing to take on major management responsibilities, through an Estate Management Board or Tenant Management Co-operative.

Other aspects of training for tenants follow:

a) Training needs to be based on the **tasks** being taken on by residents, and their need for **information and skills.**

b) Training needs tenants to be **committed** to new initiatives or responsibilities and to want the **knowledge** that will help them to achieve their goals.

c) 'Training' is not an activity confined to formal training sessions. It should be seen as a continuous **day-to-day** activity, where knowledge and skills are developed, shared and transferred.

d) Council staff, experienced tenant activists, PEP workers and other **resource people** from the community can all play a crucial part in the training process.

e) The most important training is **'action training,'** simply the direct involvement of people in setting up and running their own organisations, as well as participating in the local management effort.

f) **Formal training** has an important place and should be closely allied to the development and running of a tenant-led organisation.

g) Formal training gives people **enthusiasm** and **confidence** to get involved, building on the 'learning by doing' approach.

Tenants who become representatives on Estate Management Boards, Tenant Management Co-operatives, or other forms of local management organisation need training in order to:

– understand **tenants' rights and responsibilities,** for example under a local management agreement;

– acquire the **skills and responsibilities** to play an effective role in the organisations on the estate;

– learn about **housing management;**

– understand **budgets** and basic accounts;

– win the support of and keep in touch with the wider body of tenants and **build up participation;**

– understand **staffing** matters and **employment issues;**

– understand the **problems of organisations;**

– learn about **constitutions,** council structures;

– develop skills in **working as a team;**

– learn how to **run meetings;**

– develop **procedures** for Estate Management Boards, co-operative forums etc;

– learn to cope with **conflicting interests** and to contain actual conflicts.

An induction course for tenants is needed once representatives have volunteered or been elected to a management steering group or actual Estate Management Board (EMB) or Tenant Management Co-operative. Different courses are needed, depending on how far the group has gone.

The course should include the following:

– **Housing finance:** where the rents/housing benefits go; capital funding; estate budgets.

– **Basic housing management:** what is involved in running an estate – rents, lettings, caretaking, repairs and welfare.

– The **tenant's role** in management.

– Developing and running a **representative organisation: running meetings; links** between the team, tenant representatives and the rest of the tenants; how to consult/inform.

– **Review** session; planning ahead.

– A **study visit** to another estate where tenants play a major role in management.

Residential training for 2–3 days is **very** useful, particularly if tenants from several estates join in.

Diagram 1.9

A weekend residential course for a newly elected EMB

FRIDAY EVENING

Introduction
Background to the EMB and the principles behind it.

Discussion
Members' hopes and aims for the EMB. Potential difficulties and how they might be overcome.

SATURDAY

The Management Agreement
What will the EMB's duties and responsibilities be?
What sort of decisions will the EMB have to take?
What information and other support/resources will the EMB need to enable them to fulfil their responsibilities?

Running a Budget
What will the estate budget cover?
How much discretion will the EMB have over how it is spent?
What information on the budget should the EMB receive, and when? How should information be presented?

Meetings skills
What skills do EMB members need, for meetings to run well?
How will conflicts be resolved?
How will the organisational matters be managed? (e.g. chairing; agendas; minutes; notices)

Involving other tenants
How can EMB tenant reps be truly representative and accountable?
How can the interest of non-EMB tenant activists be encouraged and sustained?

SUNDAY

Responsibility for staff
What are the EMB's reponsibilities towards staff working on the estate, and how should they be fulfilled?

Communication skills
What type of skills do EMB members need to be able to communicate effectively with other Board members, with Council officers, with tenants? What different skills are needed for small meetings, for large meetings, or for conferences?

Planning session
The EMB's Aims and Objectives for its first year, together with an Action Plan.

Ongoing training is needed once EMBs or co-operatives are established – to help tenant representatives with the realities of control, to encourage new tenant activists to get involved and to prepare new representatives after each election.

If tenants are going to take on major tasks that local authorities and housing associations have found dauntingly difficult, they should get all the support, information, training and development skills that imagination and talent can devise. IT WILL BE NO EASIER FOR THEM!

The programmes shown in Diagrams 1.9 and 1.10, give examples of tenant training sessions.

17. CHECKLIST ON THE TENANTS' ROLE

- How many tenants are involved in the tenants' association, the estate forum, Estate Management Board, Tenant Management Co-operative or in other activities?

- What proportion of the tenants on the estate came to consultation meetings?
  - completed the survey forms?
  - volunteered to help in the follow-up?

- Do the tenants who are active represent all the different groups on the estate (e.g. ethnic groups, young, elderly, male, female, large families, young single people), types of dwellings (e.g. tower blocks), areas of the estate?

- Are tenants able to influence day-to-day management and repairs services?

- Do tenants have an input into the planning of capital improvements?

- Do tenants make decisions that count (as distinct from just taking part in meetings) e.g. is there a budget that tenants' representatives can control?

- On what terms do they exercise control?

- Is there a range of different types of activity which make it possible for people with different interests and aptitudes to take part (e.g. committees and

---

Diagram 1.10

PEP residential training course for potential resident members of Estate Management Boards

Day 1

10.30 am	Registration
11.00 am	Coffee
11.30 am	Introduction – Roger Saunders, PEP Training
11.40 am	Short presentations from each participating estate
1.15 pm	Lunch
2.00 pm	Introducing housing management – Sarah Gregory – PEP Associate (including an exercise on the tenants' role in management)
3.30 pm	Tea
4.00–5.30 pm	Tenant participation & control – Trevor Bell, Chris Holmes, PEP Associates (including group discussions)
6.00 pm	Dinner
7.00 pm	'The Great Debate'
8.30 pm	Finish

Day 2

9.30 am	'The Jargon Quiz'
10.00 am	How councils work (or sometimes don't) – Caroline Keightley, PEP Associate
11.00 am	Coffee
11.30 am	What is the Management Agreement? – Steve Sharples, PEP Associate
12.30 pm	Lunch
1.30 pm	Role play exercise – working as an Estate Management Board
3.00 pm	Discussion
3.30 pm	Tea and free time
6.00 pm	Dinner
7.00 pm	Team exercise – feedback on afternoon role play
8.30 pm	Finish

Day 3

9.30 am	The procedures manual – Roger Saunders, PEP training
10.15 am	Being a resident representative – Chris Holmes, PEP Associate
10.45 am	Coffee
11.00 am	Planning the way forward
12.00 pm	Presentation of certificates
12.30 pm	Lunch and finish

working parties, social and community activities, practical tasks)?

- Have tenants' representatives been given enough training to help them carry out their responsibilities?

- **Litmus test**: Would the council go ahead with a new policy for estate repairs or lettings **without** consulting residents?

18. SOME USEFUL BOOKS ON TENANTS AND HOUSING MANAGEMENT

ALDBOURNE ASSOCIATES (1986): Household Survey for PEP – Forms and Guidance. Ulmus Ogbourne, Marlborough

CAIRNCROSS L, CLAPHAM D, GOODLAD R (1990): Participation – A Tenant Handbook. TPAS England, Salford

DEPARTMENT OF THE ENVIRONMENT (1983): Housing Appraisal Kit 2 – H.A.K. for Improvement Work (survey methods on tenant satisfaction)

FOWLER F J (1984): Survey Research Methods. Applied Social Research Methods Series, Vol 1. Sage Publications, London

GARDNER G (1978): Social Surveys for Social Planners. The Open University

INSTITUTE OF HOUSING & TENANT PARTICIPATION ADVISORY SERVICE ENGLAND (1989): Tenant Participation in Housing Management. London/Salford

LOCAL GOVERNMENT TRAINING BOARD (undated): Whose Home is it Anyway? Making Decisions with Tenants. Luton

NATIONAL FEDERATION OF HOUSING ASSOCIATIONS (1987): Standards for Housing Management. London

PLATT S, PIEPE R, SMYTH J (1987): Heard or Ignored? Tenant Involvement in Housing Associations. NFHA, London

PHILLIPS D (1981): Do-It-Yourself Social Surveys – A Handbook for Beginners. Research Report No. 4, Polytechnic of North London, Survey Research Unit, School of Applied Social Studies and Sociology

RIBA & INSTITUTE OF HOUSING (1988): Tenant Participation in Housing Design – A Guide for Action. London

ROSEHAUGH PUBLIC LIMITED COMPANY (1988): The Rosehaugh Self-Build Housing Initiative

TENANT PARTICIPATION ADVISORY SERVICE ENGLAND (1988): Tenant Participation in Cambridge: An Analysis of the Possibilities for Developing Tenant Participation within the Housing Service (also available for Bury, Calderdale, Eastleigh, Southend-on-Sea, Gloucester). TPAS, Salford

TENANT PARTICIPATION ADVISORY SERVICE ENGLAND AND NATIONAL CONSUMER COUNCIL (1990): The Tenants' Guide to Tenants' Choice. Salford

TENANT PARTICIPATION ADVISORY SERVICE SCOTLAND (1986): But Will it Fly Mr Wright? Tenant Participation in Practice. Glasgow

B Local management organisations – Estate Management Boards

Contents

*"Power tends to corrupt and absolute power
corrupts absolutely"*

Lord Acton

1. SUMMARY

If tenants are to influence decisions about their homes, they need a formal structure in which they and the landlord are partners. Estate Management Boards offer four basic conditions:

- a legal structure for local housing management

- open membership to all residents within agreed rules with a majority of tenants on an elected board

- full partnership with the landlord involving a negotiated management agreement between tenants' representatives and landlord

- local staff, answerable to the Estate Management Board, carry out all day-to-day management functions.

Diagram 1.11 illustrates the four parts.

Diagram 1.11   Four parts of an Estate Management Board

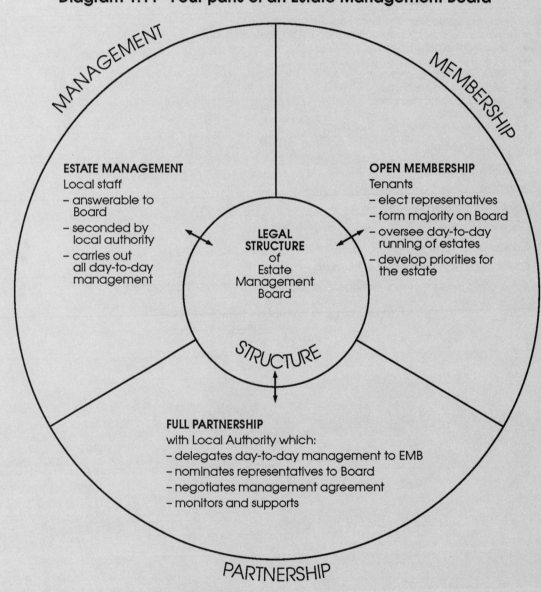

MANAGEMENT

MEMBERSHIP

ESTATE MANAGEMENT
Local staff
– answerable to Board
– seconded by local authority
– carries out all day-to-day management

LEGAL STRUCTURE
of
Estate
Management
Board

OPEN MEMBERSHIP
Tenants
– elect representatives
– form majority on Board
– oversee day-to-day running of estates
– develop priorities for the estate

STRUCTURE

FULL PARTNERSHIP
with Local Authority which:
– delegates day-to-day management to EMB
– nominates representatives to Board
– negotiates management agreement
– monitors and supports

PARTNERSHIP

2. KEYWORDS: OBSTACLES; POWERS; ELECTED

Estate-based management only works with the involvement of tenants. But even where a local estate-based office has been set up, there are major **obstacles** in the path of resident control and efficient management:

– on most estates, decision-making **powers** and the level of tenant involvement are often limited.

– very few projects manage to identify and establish estate revenue **budgets.**

– **Control** over services such as cleaning or open area maintenance and over capital work continues to be problematic.

– the local management organisation is vulnerable to changes dictated from the **centre,** e.g. frozen posts; staff reorganisation.

Estate Management Boards and Tenant Management Co-operatives have both arisen with the aim of giving tenants control over the day-to-day management and maintenance of their housing. However, many tenants do not want to form co-operatives, particularly on larger, already tenanted estates under the present conditions of uncertainty and financial stringency:

– Tenants are often wary of taking on the **complex tasks** which landlords have been unable to deal with, particularly on large rundown estates.

– Most estates are large involving several hundred dwellings.

– Estates require a large number of full-time staff, including professional housing managers. The **employment** of an estate team is a complex area for tenants to embark on.

– PEP estates have many serious, **long-term problems** requiring outside help.

For these reasons, the idea of an **elected** Estate Management Board to run an estate has emerged.

3. DEFINITION OF AN ESTATE MANAGEMENT BOARD

The Estate Management Board is an independent, locally based body, involving a partnership between the council and the tenants of one estate or area. The Board becomes the managing agent for the council in all day-to-day management and maintenance services.

An Estate Management Board (EMB) creates a new framework for the management of council estates. It separates the local authority's responsibilities for housing policy from the day-to-day management and maintenance of an estate. The local authority delegates management and maintenance responsibility to a local organisation (in this case an EMB) under Section 27 of the Housing Act 1985, as inserted by Section 10 of the Housing and Planning Act 1986. The local authority negotiates a management agreement with resident representatives who are organised and registered as a legal organisation, which must be approved by the Secretary of State. The Estate Management Board becomes the agent of the council. Both the council and the tenants are represented on the Board, although the tenants are in the majority.

An EMB **must** register as an Industrial and Provident Society (acting for the benefit of the community) or as a company. The Rules are registered with the Registrar of Friendly Societies or at Companies House.

The Estate Management Board is the decision-making body of the local management organisation which **must** be a membership organisation open to all households on the estate. All members are eligible to vote. Elected tenant representatives, who comprise the majority on the Board, **must** be members and be elected by members. Other representatives will be nominated by the council or co-opted by the Board.

The Estate Management Board has four aims:

– estate-based management and maintenance,

– tenant control of local services,

– long-term council commitment to the estate,

– partnership between local residents and the council.

An Estate Management Board involves the local authority as partner with clear responsibilities under the new management arrangements, but it also provides a level of autonomy and independence for an estate which is not possible within ordinary local authority structures.

Diagram 1.12 illustrates these characteristics clearly.

4. TARGETS

– Establish support for tenant representatives by employing a development worker.

– Devise a budget that builds a **better** caretaking and repairs service and includes comprehensive cyclical maintenance.

– Make the estate manager answerable to the Board for the full management service.

– Put the budget under the control of the estate manager (but answerable to the Board).

– Work out with staff a training and development programme that makes an EMB attractive to tenants and council.

– Establish an EMB within 18 months.

5. STAGES IN THE DEVELOPMENT OF AN ESTATE MANAGEMENT BOARD

The establishment of the Board involves seven stages:

Stage 1: Preliminary consultation

Before residents can appreciate the opportunities and obstacles offered by an Estate Management Board, initial consultations must be run, using street or block meetings as outlined in the previous section on resident participation. The consultations will **inform** residents of

Diagram 1.12
Estate Management Board

- The council has corporate membership of the Board.
- A majority of tenants must support the formation of the Board but do not need to become members, although all residents are eligible for membership.
- The management structure is in partnership with the local authority.

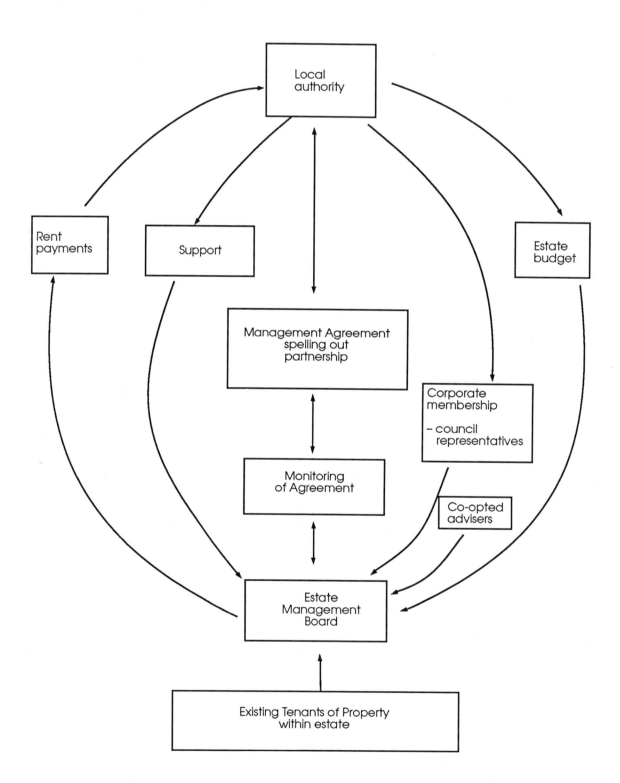

the proposals, **recruit** representatives, **identify** problems, and **discuss** proposals.

If the proposals are supported, then a steering group of 20–30 residents can be set up to progress the idea with the Council.

Stage 2: The steering group

The Steering Group can begin to consider issues raised during the initial consultations, opening a dialogue between the residents, housing officers and local councillors.

The Steering Group should also consider the **rules** of the proposed local management organisation and the content of a draft **management agreement.** The residents in the steering group will also be the focus of an intensive training programme as they are likely to form the nucleus of the Estate Management Board when formed.

Stage 3: Legal structure

The local management organisation needs to be a legally constituted organisation with an Estate Management Board as its governing body. The two main options are:

a) An Industrial and Provident Society registered under the Industrial & Provident Societies Act 1965. The Industrial and Provident Society rules require the local organisation to operate in a way which is open, democratic and publicly accountable. Membership must be open to all households with a formal tenancy on the estate.

b) A Company limited by guarantee which would also have membership open to all households and which would be registered at the Companies Registration Office under Company rules.

In either case, the members elect tenant representatives to the Estate Management Board; the council is entitled to nominate representatives; other individuals may be co-opted, for example additional tenants representing minority groups within the community, or professionals such as an accountant or lawyer, or representatives from other community organisations. Since the right to buy, many residents of council estates are now owner-occupiers or leaseholders. They can most easily be involved through co-opted representatives or they can be full members of the Society. Or they could be associate members with voting rights on issues that affect them. A Board covering an estate of 1,000 dwellings might have about twenty members as follows:

12 elected tenant representatives ⎱
4 council representatives ⎰ – voting

4 co-opted members ⎫
(to include advisers such as PEP, ⎬ – non-voting
a secondary co-operative or ⎪
other body) ⎭

Stage 4: Management Agreement

The Steering Group will negotiate a Management Agreement with the local authority clearly defining the powers and obligations of each party (see below).

Stages 3 and 4 will usually take place alongside each other.

Stage 5: Official consultation prior to formal approval

Section 27 of the 1985 Housing Act as inserted by Section 10 of the Housing and Planning Act, 1986, requires that all the tenants on an estate must be formally consulted about the proposals by the local authority. It may be necessary to involve a secondary co-operative or other development body at this stage to work with the tenants. The Secretary of State will not approve the Management Agreement if there is a clear majority of tenants against the proposal. The council and tenant activists will need the positive support of the majority of tenants for the proposal. A formal ballot may be desirable but is not required by the law.

As part of these consultations, the residents on the steering group should run a publicity campaign on the estate to explain the proposals and call for support.

Stage 6: Interim Estate Management Board

If the Steering Group and the council are satisfied that the consultations have shown sufficient support for an EMB, but there are delays in finalising the Agreement, it may be helpful to set up an **Interim Board.** Councils can only delegate their management responsibilities with the approval of the Secretary of State. Therefore the interim board has no decision-making powers.

Stage 7: Approval of the Estate Management Board

The Management Agreement and the consultation process and outcome require formal approval by the local authority and the Secretary of State.

6. THE MANAGEMENT AGREEMENT

The Management Agreement is the contract between the local authority and the Estate Management Board. It spells out the detailed responsibilities of both parties and defines the geographical area of activity. It details the financial arrangements, such as the treatment of rents collected by the Estate Management Board on behalf of the local authority, and the setting up of an estate budget to be under the supervision of the Estate Management Board. The contract will apply for a specific period of time. On expiry there must be a fresh agreement if the delegated management is to continue, unless the agreement has no termination date, i.e. is a 'rolling' agreement.

The Rules of the EMB are also included as part of the agreement, building in the requirement that the Estate Management Board be open, democratic and accountable to its members.

The management agreement involves the council as a partner with the tenants and the management agreement must reflect this.

The content of the Management Agreement

The agreement at the same time guarantees the Estate Management Board the autonomy it will require to manage effectively, yet provides the council with checks and safeguards that will ensure its more general housing and employment policies are followed.

The Estate Management Board management agreement breaks new ground and should therefore provide for regular and detailed monitoring and also for opportunities to review the arrangements. These should be ongoing.

The format will vary but the Estate Management Board management agreement will normally include:

– a statement of the aims of the agreement;

– the actual agreement to delegate management responsibilities;

– the Rules of the Estate Management Board;

– termination and variation arrangements; disputes and arbitration procedures;

– the division of responsibilities between the council and the Estate Management Board;

– financial arrangements; service charges;

– code of conduct for Board members;

– detailed arrangements for: allocations; rent collection and arrears recovery; maintenance and repair; services charges for leaseholders; cleaning and care-taking, including open space maintenance; capital works; resident consultation; staffing; monitoring; training for staff and tenants; procedures to deal with Right to Buy, Right to Repair and Right to Improve Notices; enforcement of tenancy conditions; and a Code of Practice for Board members.

It should also include:

– the tenancy agreement;

– the list of properties covered by the agreement;

– a plan showing open space and other facilities within the Estate Management Board area, marking those the Estate Management Board will be responsible for.

7. COUNCIL AND ESTATE MANAGEMENT BOARD RESPONSIBILITIES

Within the Agreement, **the council** retains important responsibilities:

i) **corporate membership** of the local management organisation. The right to nominate representatives to the Estate Management Board can be inscribed into the rules of the local management organisation.

ii) **ownership** of the dwellings which means that the tenants remain tenants of the local authority.

4. *Estate management board election campaign. Bacup & Stacksteads Estates, Rossendale*

Priority Estates Project

iii) power to fix **rents** (although there may be scope for the Estate Management Board to vary these in return for additional services).

iv) responsibility for setting **overall policy and standards** and for monitoring performance.

v) responsibility for **nominating applicants** and for overall policy concerning **access.**

vi) responsibility for **determining** an annual **estate budget,** subject to consultation with the Board, and for allocating resources for **capital improvements.**

The Estate Management Board takes on the following areas of responsibility, as specified in the Agreement:

i) **The control and management of an estate revenue budget** The budget will be an amount extracted from the Housing Revenue Account (HRA) sufficient to provide for the proper management and maintenance of the estate. In the first year, it is likely to be based partly on average costs across the particular local authority and partly on known expenditure on the particular estate (see section on Estate Budgets). Thereafter, it will be negotiated on an annual basis, taking into account the actual costs which the Estate Management Board will be able to identify in detail. In most EMBs, the account will be held by the Director of Finance in a separate named account. All payments from that account will have to be authorised by the Board although in practice staff will often have delegated authority in order to allow budgetary decisions to proceed. With the council acting as banker in this way, the Estate Management Board will avoid having to handle directly the large sums of money involved. The budget will include performance targets for voids and rent arrears, providing financial incentives to encourage better management. The Estate Management Board will be allowed to use any surplus resulting directly from improved performance for the benefit of the whole estate.

It is possible for a totally independent bank account to be established in the name of the Estate Management Board and for the management and maintenance allowances to be paid by the council into that account. This is the normal procedure with management co-operatives. However, typical Estate Management Board estates are large and so are the corresponding budgets. Staff often continue as employees of the local authority although they are wholly accountable to the Estate Management Board for their management performance. It therefore makes more sense to establish an account within the local authority structure. It has the added advantage of continued local authority responsibility and interest in ensuring the proper conduct of affairs, while delegating day to day control.

ii) **Running the estate office** The Estate Management Board will be responsible for all the management and maintenance services delivered by the estate team based at the local office.

iii) **Staff** In some of the pioneer EMBs, the estate-based team, including housing management staff, caretakers and cleaners is made wholly accountable to the Estate Management Board for its performance. In this way the staff remain employees of the local authority with the same conditions of employment and retain access to promotion or other jobs outside the Estate Management Board. But as secondees to the

Estate Management Boards, they are accountable directly to the Board for the running of the estate and for their own performance.

The Estate Management Board, through the manager and the budget, should have direct control over all repairs.

The management agreement will need to spell out arrangements for recruitment of staff into the estate teams, disciplinary and grievance procedures, opportunities for promotion and training. The Estate Management Board is required to comply with local authority equal opportunities policies.

iv) **Rent collection and arrears** The management agreement will require the Estate Management Board to 'pay over' to the council 100% collectable rent on a regular basis minus an agreed allowance for losses, or a percentage of the total rent due to allow for arrears and voids. The method of collection will be up to the Estate Management Board and many will elect to continue using the council facilities for payment of rent. If so, an agreed charge will be made against the Estate Management Board budget.

The management agreement will specify the point at which the local authority should become involved in arrears recovery. The Estate Management Board may be responsible for arrears recovery up to and including the point at which a Notice Seeking Possession is issued. Any evictions would be carried out by the council and within their existing policy guidelines.

The Estate Management Board should provide effective housing benefit advice linked to arrears recovery. If possible, this should be locally administered.

Rents will be in line with other council rents but the Estate Management Board could, if it had a clear mandate from tenants, require the council to vary the rents, and at the same time the allowances to reflect a change in the level of service.

v) **Allocation and lettings** The Estate Management Board will be responsible for all lettings on the estate, including internal transfers, within policies agreed with the council and set out in the management agreement. The policies will reflect council priorities but may vary for the estate with the agreement of the council e.g. proportion of single people; numbers of children etc. All lettings will be closely monitored by the local authority.

The Estate Management Board may maintain a waiting list of applicants, which is drawn in whole or part from the local authority's central waiting list. The EMB may be required to allocate to priority homeless applicants and to other priority groups as agreed in the policy guidelines.

The administration of the lettings system should be carried out by the local housing staff under the general direction of the Estate Management Board, not by Board members directly. Confidentiality will be essential at all times.

vi) **Repairs and maintenance** The Estate Management Board will be responsible for all aspects of routine estate maintenance including emergencies, day to day repairs, cyclical maintenance and repairs to voids. It will also be responsible for identifying planned maintenance requirements and bidding to the local authority for capital resources. As with tenant management co-operatives, the Estate Management Board would be required to set aside a portion of the revenue budget to cover cyclical and planned maintenance.

A separate contract for repairs will usually be let by the manager or by the landlord with the approval of the EMB with respect to the Estate Management Board area which the Estate Management Board must approve. The Estate Management Board will be in control, authorising work and approving payments.

Thus the Estate Management Board will be directly responsible for organising the repairs service either with the Direct Labour Organisation and/or other contractors, and for meeting agreed standards and performance targets within the budget.

vii) **Capital works** The Estate Management Board will be responsible for identifying and planning any programme of capital works to the estate and will bid to the council for an appropriate allocation of capital resources. The local authority or other landlord would provide expert technical advice and would retain final responsibility for the work if the contract is between the local authority and the contractor. The management agreement will spell out the responsibilities.

The Estate Management Board may then oversee the improvement works, being directly responsible for ensuring that technical staff and contractors carry out their work properly. It will also ensure that proper liaison with tenants take place. The Estate Management Board will oversee the various stages: drawing up specifications; the right to ask that individual contractors be excluded from the approved tender list on the basis of bad experience; finalising design briefs; liaising with technical staff; confirmation of chosen tender; tenant liaison; and authorisation of payments.

viii) **Other management responsibilities** Other key areas of the management agreement where responsibilities will be defined and the Estate Management Board will have a direct role include:

– all estate management and tenancy matters including cleaning, nuisance, dogs, etc.

– open space maintenance (as funded by the HRA);

– cleaning and caretaking (as funded by the HRA);

– staff and tenant training, resident consultation and community development;

– monitoring of performance and maintenance of standards.

The management agreement may also set out guidelines for the co-ordination of other local authority and non-local authority services on the estate. The management agreement will spell out arrangements for a systematic review by the council to ensure that the management agreement is being adhered to and that performance is satisfactory.

The Estate Management Board may seek a contract with the council to carry out some non-housing services, e.g. management of community facilities, maintenance of open spaces. It will be important for the EMB to encourage and help the development of other services to the estate and local voluntary initiatives to tackle wider social and economic problems (see section on Co-ordination).

The division of responsibility between the council and the Estate Management Board can vary but must be clear. Diagram 1.13 gives a typical outline.

8. TENANCY AGREEMENT

In addition to the respective rights and responsibilities of the council and the Estate Management Board, the management agreement will set out the terms of the tenancy agreement between the Estate Management Board, acting as agent for the council, and individual tenants on the estate. Neither the Estate Management Board nor the council can make any changes without consulting tenants and gaining their agreement. The council remains the landlord under all arrangements for the Estate Management Board. The Estate Management Board will have the responsibility for enforcing conditions of tenancy on all individual tenants up to the point of court action.

Diagram 1.13

Proposed division of responsibility between the council and Estate Management Board	
Council responsibilities	Estate Management Board responsibilities
Overall responsibility as landlord	Day-to-day management responsibility
Corporate membership	Revenue budget and accounts
Ownership	Running office
Rent fixing and rent collection (where agreed)	Staff
Policy and standards	Rents and arrears chasing (and collection where agreed)
Monitoring and support	Allocations and lettings
Nominations and access policy	Repairs and maintenance
Allocation of budget and capital	Capital works
	Other management

9. VARIATIONS

Each management agreement will be drawn up with a particular local authority and will reflect very different local circumstances. The division of responsibilities outlined here does not reflect all these differences. It is important to remember that there is no one model.

10. THE TIMETABLE

The minimum timescale (see Diagram 1.14) for setting up an Estate Management Board would normally be 18 months. It may be less where there is already a local estate office, an active tenants' organisation,

and strong Council support. Diagram 1.14 suggests the targets. These stages sometimes run alongside each other. In all cases there must be a catalyst and a supporting organisation, recognised by the tenants and local authority to achieve these targets. An EMB will not just 'happen'.

11. TRAINING FOR STAFF AND TENANTS

Through the early estate-wide consultations, PEP identifies a core group of tenants (usually between 20–35) who are willing to take the Estate Management Board proposals forward. Training is initially concentrated on this core group but continuing consultation with tenants

Diagram 1.14
Timetable for setting up an Estate Management Board

Month	Activity	Month	Activity
1	Identify possible estate	9–12	Draw up with council draft management agreement
1	Find **someone** to work with tenants – voluntary organisation, a council officer, a secondary co-op or other development agency	9–12	Establish local budget
2–3	Conduct feasibility study and produce proposal for council	13–14	Recruit local staff
2–3	Contact existing tenants' association and other local bodies about proposals	15	Plan training for tenants
4	Seek formal agreement in principle from council for proposal	15–16	Carry out formal consultation
5–7	Carry out initial estate-wide consultations – recruit representatives to Steering Committee	17	Hold elections for Interim Board
7	Decide on legal structure	18	Seek formal approval of council and Secretary of State
8	Register organisation	20	Sign management agreement
9	Plan training for tenants	21	Hold elections for Board; Co-opt additional members

across the estate is also vital if the new proposals are to win majority support.

Training will cover:

– legal status of the Estate Management Board;

– constitution and rules of the Industrial and Provident Society or Company;

– membership of the Estate Management Board;

– organisation, composition and conduct of the Board;

– budgetary matters;

– staffing;

– relations with other council staff;

– basic housing management including repairs, rents, lettings, tenants' welfare, caretaking;

– capital works;

– tenancy conditions and enforcement;

– equal opportunities;

– consultation, answerability and representativeness;

– the role of tenants' representatives;

– teamwork;

– running meetings;

– code of conduct and good practice;

– standards for service.

The negotiation of the management agreement is a process combining training with discussion and development. A typical session on lettings might involve training on how the council's allocations system works followed by discussion about what local arrangements might go into the agreement.

Training is also necessary for local staff and for council members, both of whom will be required to operate very differently within the Estate Management Board framework. For them, a shift of power to tenants can be threatening and it is important that they understand the procedures, policies and safeguards built into the new arrangements and feel genuinely a part of the EMB initiative. They should also receive basic training in estate-based management which in itself is radically different from central or even most officially decentralised housing structures.

PEP has organised residential training courses for tenants actively planning the development of an EMB. These provide an opportunity to look in more depth at some of the issues – including opportunities for role-playing exercises, mock debates and small group discussions. They help to build confidence and strong group and inter-group relations. They can bring together several groups of tenants. Study visits to other estates where an EMB is being set up can also be an inspiration.

12. CODE OF PRACTICE

It may be helpful to agree a Code of Practice for EMB members which would provide guidelines or rules on issues such as confidentiality, dealings with staff, and conflict of interest. The Code of Practice might evolve from training sessions on these matters and would be developed on a voluntary basis by the Board. Once agreed, however, the Board must ensure that its members act in a responsible way in accordance with the Code of Practice. Any abuse of their power by Board members will quickly bring the EMB into disrepute (see Appendix 3). The Code of Practice needs to cover:

– the conduct of meetings,

– relations between staff and the Board,

– confidentiality,

– arrangements for the conduct of business,

– correct procedures for handling finance.

13. CONCLUSION

Estate Management Boards are a new and experimental form of local management and tenant control. They may throw up as yet unseen problems. The Estate Management Boards seem to offer tenants and local authorities the following advantages:

– They establish a **formal partnership** between the tenants and the local authority, separate from the council's political and bureaucratic structures, but part of the council's overall responsibility.

– The management agreement guarantees a degree of **local autonomy** over estate management.

– They **empower the tenants** without loading sole responsibility onto them.

– They provide for good estate-based management from a team of **well-trained staff** who themselves have greater freedom to manage within the terms of the agreement.

– Although the Estate Management Board should be supported by a clear majority of tenants, **it does not depend on high levels of direct tenant participation** for its success.

– The tenants retain their **status as council tenants.**

– The Estate Management Board ensures that **decisions are made locally** for the benefit of residents.

– The Estate Management Board is attractive to local authorities and to tenants who have a common interest in a more local, more efficient and more responsive service.

14. CHECKLIST ON ESTATE MANAGEMENT BOARDS

– Have consultations been organised by an independent body?

– Is there a development worker or tenant support worker?

– Is the local authority helping with:
  * the legal structure?
  * the financial arrangements?
  * the management agreement?

– Does the budget cover all the extra costs of running a difficult estate, including better caretaking, repairs and planned maintenance?

– Will any budget saving be retained locally to spend on improvements?

– What activities have been organised to ensure all residents know about plans for the EMB?

– What arrangements are there for reporting back regularly to residents on the estate?

– Are ethnic minority groups represented?

– Are women fairly represented?

– Do a majority of tenants clearly support the proposals?

– Is there a full training programme for tenants' representatives and estate-based staff, including repairs workers and caretakers?

– Will central staff involved in the EMB and councillors attend any relevant training sessions?

15. SOME USEFUL BOOKS ON LOCAL MANAGEMENT ORGANISATIONS – ESTATE MANAGEMENT BOARDS

BARBER S (1985): 'Heseltown Goes Local' – A case study in the management and politics of the decentralisation of a large housing department. Ref. No. HS 0029 Local Government Training Board, Luton

HAMBLETON R & HOGGETT P (undated): The Politics of Decentralisation: Theory and Practice of a Radical Local Government Initiative. Working Paper 46, University of Bristol, School for Advanced Urban Studies

HANDY C B (1985): Understanding Organisations. Penguin Books, Harmondsworth

JACOBS J (1968): The Economy of Cities. (on city developments). Vintage Books, New York

ZIPFEL T (1989): Estate Management Boards – An Introduction. Priority Estates Project, London

Note: The first three references on this list are about changing the way organisations operate and outline new approaches to management

C Tenant management co-operatives

Contents

"No man is an Island, entire of itself. Any man's death diminishes me, because I am involved in Mankind; and therefore never send to know for whom the bell tolls; it tolls for thee."

John Donne

1. SUMMARY

Co-operatives allow tenants to take over the running of their own housing. Successful tenant co-operatives have six requirements:

- a strong group of determined and well organised tenants

- a landlord willing to give up direct control

- adequate financial resources

- property in reasonable condition or with good potential

- full training for tenants

- solid outside support

Diagram 1.15 shows the ten elements of a co-operative.

Diagram 1.15
Ten elements of a co-operative

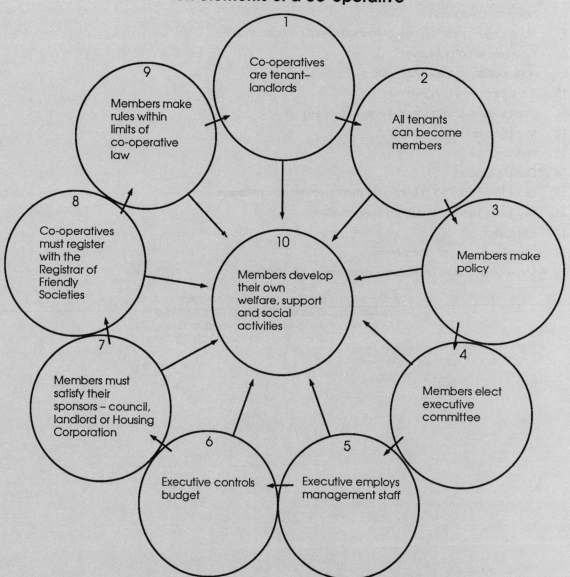

2. KEYWORDS: EXPLOITATION; EXPERIMENT

Co-operatives became popular in the 1970s, in London, Liverpool and Glasgow. Some were member-owned co-operatives which had first emerged in the mid-nineteenth century among groups of working people trying to escape the tyrannies of a harsh industrial **exploitation.** Management co-operatives are different from ownership co-operatives in that the property remains with the landlord who retains significant responsibilities. The tenant-members take over as many management responsibilities as they feel able to handle. For some councils and tenants, the shared responsibility makes management co-operatives more attractive, although in some circumstances ownership co-operatives may make more sense. Management co-operatives provide the basic structure and experience on which the Estate Management Board **experiments** have been based. Much of the detail already known about management co-operatives may eventually apply to Estate Management Boards as they evolve.

3. DEFINITIONS

A **housing co-operative** is an organisation owning and/or managing rented housing for the benefit of its tenant members. A co-operative usually registers with the Registrar of Friendly Societies under co-operative rules in order to become a legally recognised body.

The tenants buy a £1 share in the co-operative in order to become members and agree to abide by the co-operative rules and participate in its decision-making.

The co-operative **members** form the final decision-making body of the co-operative through general meetings, but usually elect an executive committee to represent them in dealing with the business of the co-operative. All residents in co-operative property are eligible for membership and normally it is a condition of becoming a tenant of the co-operative that an applicant becomes a co-operative member.

There are two principal types of housing co-operative: par-value, fully mutual co-operatives; and tenant management co-operatives.

A **par-value co-operative** is a registered co-operative organisation which owns its own property and lets it exclusively to members. Members do not individually own any part of the co-operative property. In a **fully mutual co-operative,** all tenants are members and all members are tenants. Par-value co-operatives depend on funding from the Housing Corporation, local authorities or, in some cases, private loans.

A tenant **management co-operative** is organised on the same principles of member control and responsibility, but the property is usually owned by a local authority or by a housing association. The co-operative is the managing agent, responsible for the regular management and maintenance of the property on behalf of the landlord. All tenants of co-operatively managed property normally become members of the co-operative.[1] Where a local authority is willing to delegate management responsibility to a co-operative, the approval of

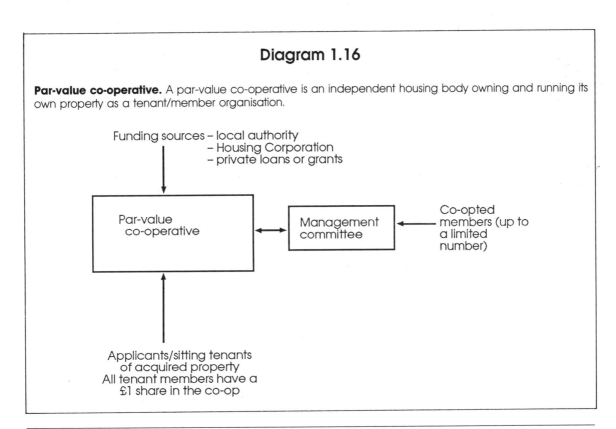

Diagram 1.16

Par-value co-operative. A par-value co-operative is an independent housing body owning and running its own property as a tenant/member organisation.

Funding sources – local authority
– Housing Corporation
– private loans or grants

Par-value co-operative

Management committee

Co-opted members (up to a limited number)

Applicants/sitting tenants of acquired property
All tenant members have a £1 share in the co-op

---

[1] There are exceptions where individual tenants do not wish to become co-operative members. These are usually households living in the area before the co-operative was formed.

Diagram 1.17

Tenant Management Co-operative wherein: (a) the landlord nominates representatives to advise and support the co-operative; (b) a majority of tenants must become members of the co-operative; (c) the management structure is independent of the local authority or housing association, but subject to a management agreement.

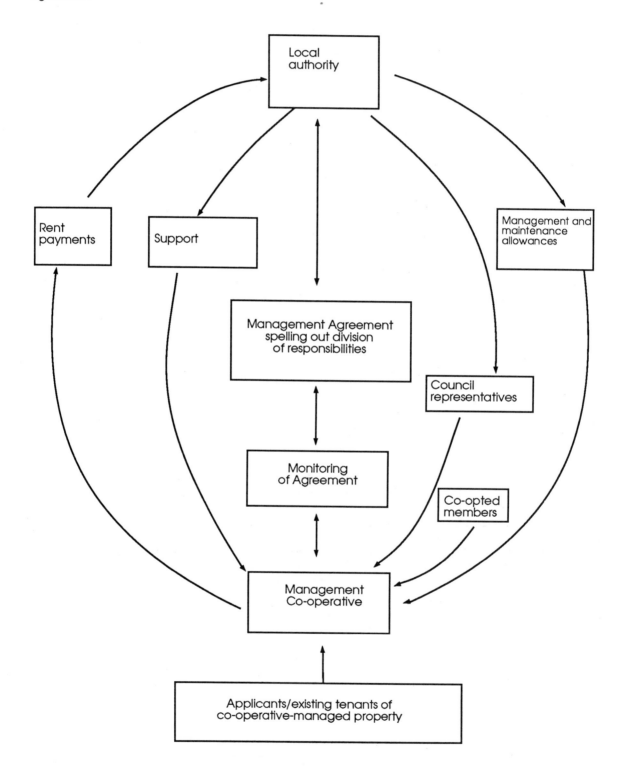

the Secretary of State is required. In the case of housing associations, it is not.

In a tenant management co-operative, the co-operative reaches a formal **management agreement** with the council or other landlord over the areas of management and maintenance that the co-operative will take responsibility for. The council generally retains responsibility for the upkeep of the basic structure of the buildings and for major repair such as roofs. All management co-operatives take on direct responsibility for day-to-day repairs and usually cyclical maintenance too. General management, such as rents, lettings and office records, is also usually done by the co-operative.

All management co-operatives receive an **allowance** from the owner in payment for the duties carried out. In some co-operatives it is deducted directly from the rent income.

The co-operative has a budget made up of management and maintenance allowances from which it pays directly for services. To the extent that it performs well (e.g. quick reletting, access for repairs, efficient rent collection), it will be able to save on day-to-day spending and invest any surplus in improvements and long-term maintenance. This gives co-operatives a strong and direct incentive to perform well. Of course this incentive should also be built into EMBs. But the cut-off is not so complete.

Diagrams 1.16 and 1.17 show the structures of par-value co-operatives and management co-operatives, respectively.

4. TARGETS

– A negotiated management agreement with the landlord.

– At least 20 % of members active in the co-operative.

– At least 75 % of tenants within the area as paid-up members.

– A local office, repairs organisation, rent collection and waiting list.

– A representative committee, e.g. with ethnic minority members in a multi-racial area.

– A budget to cover all management and maintenance and a surplus in the budget for small improvements.

– Regular open meetings.

– Proper systems and programmes for monitoring, training and support.

– Social and welfare activities.

5. *Tenant management co-operative committee. Regina Road Co-operative, Islington*

Priority Estates Project

5. HOW MANAGEMENT CO-OPERATIVES ARE DIFFERENT FROM ESTATE MANAGEMENT BOARDS

Management co-operatives offer a simple structure for councils willing to hand over management and maintenance responsibility to groups of tenants, and for organised tenants' bodies determined to take over the running of their housing. Resident leaseholders and owner-occupiers on the estate can become members if the co-operative wants this.

In most respects, a Tenant Management Co-operative operates like an Estate Management Board (see Diagrams 1.18 and 1.19). However, it has several important and unique characteristics:

– The co-operative is an **entirely separate body** with **only tenants as members** and only members with voting rights. Outsiders can be co-opted in an advisory role.

– The co-operative sets up and runs its **own bank account.** It has its own budget made up of allowances from the landlord.

– Most management co-operatives employ **their own workers.**

– Although co-operatives operate within council or Housing Association guidelines, members take **full responsibility for their organisation.**

Diagram 1.18

Main similarities between an EMB and a TMC
• Local authority or housing association retains the ownership of the property.
• Tenants representatives negotiate a management agreement with the landlord.
• Both take on only part of the landlord responsibility, though to varying degrees.
• A management and maintenance allowance covers all day-to-day running costs.
• The landlord monitors the agreement and supports the local organisation.
• The co-operative or local management organisation is open to all residents.
• Tenants have the majority in the decision-making body.
• Both TMCs and EMBs depend in the end for their success on the willingness of a group of tenants to take on significant management responsibility.
• They both also depend on the willingness of the landlord to hand over management responsibility including a budget.

Diagram 1.19

Main differences between an EMB and a TMC. Note that only the first of these five main differences is intrinsic to the organisation of EMBs or TMCs. The others apply to varying degrees.	
Estate Management Board	Tenant Management Co-operative
1. The landlord is a corporate member with full voting rights. Therefore tenants *share* responsibility.	1. The landlord is supporting an *independent tenant* organisation. Therefore, tenants shoulder *more* responsibility.
2. Estates are normally larger.	2. Estates are normally smaller.
3. Staff are *seconded* from the council and retain council terms and conditions of employment.	3. Staff are usually directly *employed* by the co-operative.
4. The management and maintenance allowance is held by the local authority in a separately identified account.	4. The management and maintenance allowance is paid into a separate co-operative bank account.
5. The local authority or housing association retains a significant role in the EMB.	5. The local authority or housing association plays an important but less dominant role.

6. NEED FOR CO-OPERATIVES

Co-operatives offer tenants an alternative means of control where:

− the tenants are organised and want to exercise more **direct control** over their area.

− **social conditions** are so bad that a tenant body is able to achieve a lot more than an outside body − this often applies in very unstable and deteriorated conditions.

− the tenants are organised so strongly that only by taking over will they be able to **satisfy their ambitions** for their neighbourhood and exercise sufficient influence over events that affect them directly.

− the backlog of poor repair and management is so serious that tenants **no longer have faith** in the landlord, even where the landlord shows goodwill.

− the landlord has **virtually abandoned the attempt** to manage the estate because of previous failure or difficulties.

− the landlord has such wide-ranging property and responsibilities that the estate will not receive **intensive management and full repair.**

− the estate has such a strong **sense of identity** and community that residents want to preserve it.

− the landlord is prepared to make **sufficient resources** available for a co-operative to be able to rescue the estate.

7. ADVANTAGES AND PROBLEMS OF MANAGEMENT CO-OPERATIVES

For both tenants and council, there can be many advantages in management co-operatives:

− co-operatives offer the opportunity for **tenant control;**

− co-operatives usually achieve a **good standard** of performance;

− the landlord can lay down **guidelines** and enforce standards;

− the council or housing association can provide the **back-up** and support for often inexperienced tenants;

− tenants know that they can **turn to** the local authority or housing association if they need to;

− although management co-operatives carry more responsibility than EMBs, they carry **less than ownership.**

There are problems too:

− Co-operatives are sometimes slow to develop and require a lot of **nurturing.**

− Internal **tensions** and conflicts can grow in a small group of tenants.

− The **load** carried by the few activists can become a serious burden for them.

− It is hard to **sustain** the initial enthusiasm over a long period.

− **Money** can go missing unless tight procedures and safeguards are built in.

− There are dangers of **élitism** and favouritism.

− **Employing members** in co-operative jobs can create tensions and jealousy.

8. WHO LIVES IN CO-OPERATIVES

All residents of the area run by the co-operative are eligible for membership. Normally co-operatives cover discrete areas or blocks and all homes within that area form part of the co-operative. The aim should be 100 per cent membership of the co-operative by all households; at least a clear majority should belong for the co-operative to be viable. The majority of those who do not join should not actively oppose the co-operative, even if they do not become members, otherwise the co-operative will fail. This could apply where a co-operative is formed on an existing estate. Where the co-operative recruits members as applicants for empty property, then it can insist on eligible applicants becoming members before they can be rehoused. Membership is normally indefinite so you only have to join once.

9. PARTICIPATION AND VOLUNTARY ACTION

Participation

A driving aim of enthusiasts for co-operatives is participation. There are different levels and types of participation, active and passive, formal and informal. The small group of leaders will participate in active and formal ways such as committee membership. The large group of general members will participate passively and informally, only making their views known at critical points.

The extent to which people like to be asked to have a say seems greater than their actual willingness to shoulder direct responsibility. This explains tenants' willingness to be members and their support for co-operative ideas alongside their reluctance to assume active roles, which is the common experience of most co-operatives.

A major issue in co-operatives is that only a minority of tenants tend to carry the biggest burden of responsibility, unless the co-operative is very small (under 50 units), in which case it will be easier to keep a majority involved at some level.

Any group larger than six will rarely keep all members fully involved. Small groups of leaders and activists will emerge and tenant co-operatives will depend on a small élite in the same way as **all other organisations.** They will sometimes have to take hard decisions; they will make mistakes; and they will not always be popular. However, taking an active role in a co-operative does offer rewards, otherwise people would not do it:

− it offers local power and influence;

− it offers the chance of experience in matters normally remote from tenants;

- it offers a sense of control;

- it offers responsibility and therefore recognition;

- it offers the chance to achieve results;

- it offers better environmental and social conditions;

- it offers greater sense of neighbourhood and belonging;

- it offers better housing.

In a co-operative all members participate in some way, more often passively rather than actively:

- The decision-makers are answerable to the full membership.

- The local scale and organisation allows informal participation.

- The controls, both internal and external, help to prevent abuse.

- The underlying aims of the co-operative are to help weaker members and to provide a useful service.

- The possibility to become involved and participate is always there, should a member wish to.

- The final sanction of one member, one vote, can be used.

- An unrepresentative clique can be removed through the wider membership.

It is important to remember that passive participation is in itself valuable. If tenants look after their patch, worry about litter or damage, have generally good relations with the staff and manual workers, enjoy going to the office and paying their rent (as tenants have actually said), and turn out to meetings occasionally, that is all 'grist to the mill' and represents significant progress within a small community.

Voluntary Action

Co-operative members carry out a huge range of voluntary duties and at least one fifth of members usually play a part in some small way. The following activities go on with the support of members in addition to basic housing management:

- running meetings

- helping needy members

- fund-raising

- providing community facilities and activities

- helping tenants with small repairs

- helping with cleaning and maintaining the co-operative in good order

- visiting for arrears

- holding arrears meetings

- helping with selection

- recruiting members, introducing new members

- producing publicity

- encouraging non-active members to join in

- visiting where serious disputes arise

- meeting with the council

- attending events, e.g. conferences

- sharing experience with other co-operatives

- organising a credit union.

10. THE MANAGEMENT AGREEMENT

The Management Agreement is drawn up between the landlord and the co-operative. Both parties must sign it; and the Secretary of State must approve it, in the case of local authorities.

The Management Agreement between tenant management co-operatives and landlords has served as a model for EMBs because it makes the delegation of responsibility workable.

The Management Agreement aims to clarify the relationship between the landlord and the co-operative, to maximise support and minimise conflict and potential breakdown. It aims to spell out clearly the exact division of duties and responsibilities.

Management co-operatives operate within agreed policy guidelines. Allocations of tenancies will usually be carefully negotiated with the landlord and, where the landlord is the council, it will normally have nomination rights to a majority of dwellings. In the case of housing associations, guidelines for allocations need to be agreed.

The co-operative need not take on the full range of management responsibilities. There are co-operatives which do not accept responsibility for rent collection. Management co-operatives do not carry out evictions.

Although management co-operatives rely on the landlord as a partner, a co-operative succeeds by virtue of its independence. There should therefore be as clear a dividing line as possible between the co-operative and the landlord. However, **proper support and monitoring** must be built in, with clearly stated mechanisms for addressing grievances, disputes and failure to carry out the Agreement by either side. The landlord also needs to assure itself that the co-operative is helping to meet the landlord's policy objectives. There should be an independent arbiter in the case of irreconcilable breakdown in the agreement. The landlord and support bodies must be ready to respond to crises in the co-operative and to help with problems so that the local organisation stays on track or gets back in control as quickly and smoothly as possible. However, in the final analysis, the landlord may have to face terminating the management agreement. This has happened in a small number of co-operatives.

Diagram 1.20 shows the typical division of responsibilities.

11. STEPS IN SETTING UP A MANAGEMENT CO-OPERATIVE

The steps in establishing a management co-operative are outlined below and in Diagram 1.21.

1.   A group of tenants expresses an interest in forming a co-operative.

Diagram 1.20

Typical division of duties between councils and management co-operative	
Council landlord	Co-operative
* ownership of properties * maintenance of structure * major repairs * payment of allowance for management and maintenance * nominations for lettings * receipt of rent and payment of allowances for management and maintenance * the council will make an allowance for an agreed proportion of empty property and for an agreed level of arrears (e.g. 4%) * eviction proceedings * authorisation of Housing Benefit * advice and support to the co-operative * monitoring of Agreement including inspection of property and of records * monitoring of co-operative performance * allocation of capital resources for improvements and major repairs	* collection of rent * calculation of Housing Benefit * procedures for recovering arrears * operation of waiting list * selection of members and tenants (within agreed policies and priorities) * operation of internal transfers * running of day to day repairs * running of cyclical maintenance * minor improvements * negotiation with council over major repairs and structural elements * overseeing of any contractual work on behalf of the members, whether undertaken by the council or by the co-operative itself * repair and reletting of empty property * maintenance of common areas * negotiation with the council over services the council is responsible for * enforcement of the tenancy agreement * maintenance of the co-operative agreement * operation under the co-operative rules * publishing of annual accounts * holding of AGMs * election of a management committee * employment of staff

2. Tenants contact the landlord or outside body for information and advice.

3. Tenants apply to the landlord for support in principle for the idea of forming a co-operative. At this point most co-operatives contact secondary co-operatives, which are support and development agencies set up to help develop tenant co-operatives. They may provide a development worker. Or the local authority may support the tenants through a co-operative worker.

4. The worker helps tenants to find out more and helps with education and training.

5. Tenants discuss the model rules and establish the basis on which they want to work.

6. Tenants register as a management co-operative with the Registrar of Friendly Societies. (At this point there must be seven founding members.) A bank account is opened in the name of the co-operative.

7. The founding group of co-operative members recruit as many members as possible from existing tenants on the estate or area.

8. The co-operative negotiates a Management Agreement with the landlord, covering all areas of responsibility, spelling out in detail the responsibilities of each party.

9. The co-operative holds an A.G.M., elects an executive committee and sets up its own structure for managing co-operative affairs. The co-operative keeps members informed through open meetings, newsletters, visits and social events. It also keeps the landlord informed of progress. Training for new **committee** members should be provided at this point.

10. A method of landlord representation and support to the co-operative is agreed between the landlord and the co-operative.

11. A period of joint management begins in which

Diagram 1.21
Steps in setting up a Management Co-operative

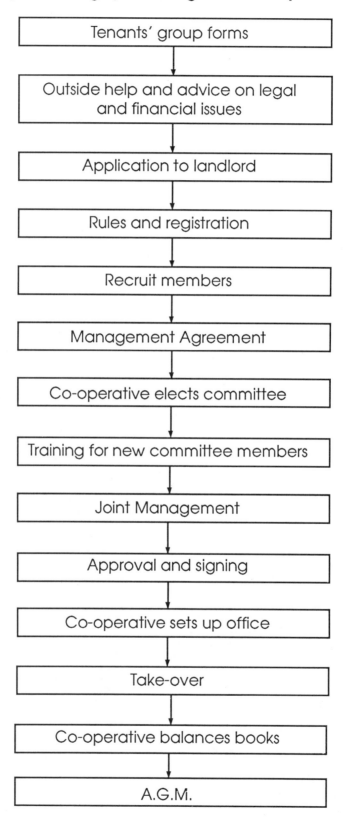

the co-operative takes on some responsibilities under supervision of the landlord, and without final decision-making powers.

12. The Management Agreement is formally approved by the Secretary of State in the case of local authorities. The Agreement is signed between the co-operative and the landlord.

13. The landlord carries out his duties, attending meetings as agreed, receiving reports and management information, ensuring proper standards are met.

14. The co-operative sets up an office where required, takes on staff to run the office, carry out cleaning and caretaking duties and perform repairs.

15. The co-operative takes over full management responsibility within the Agreement.

16. Co-operative continues to carry out many tasks on a voluntary basis.

17. The co-operative balances its books on a monthly basis with an annual audit.

18. The co-operative holds next A.G.M. at which one-third (or all) of committee members may stand down so that new people can seek election. (Many co-operatives have this system to ensure continuity of experience.)

12. MANAGEMENT RESPONSIBILITIES

Co-operative members are free to carry out all management and maintenance tasks on a voluntary basis. However, in co-operatives of over 50 units, this is likely to prove unworkable in the long run. Councils have often failed their tenants through lack of locally based competent staff, so co-operatives might fail, after the initial enthusiasm, unless they take on capable staff to run the business side, i.e. rents, repairs and lettings. Tenants, as members, form the controlling body; but they usually need to employ staff to deal with management, repairs and caretaking responsibilities. Often there may be just a co-ordinator or just a handyperson.

Co-operatives need information and training, both in the basic management responsibilities they are taking on and in the employment of workers. It is not at all simple to set up an office, handle a large budget – around £30,000 a year for a co-operative of 50 dwellings – and employ staff. Protecting the co-operative's

6. *Tenants and staff working through decisions. Cloverhall Management Co-operative, Rochdale*
Paul Herrmann/Profile

interests, making the staff effective, guarding against dishonesty and incompetence, producing better services, all require understanding, stamina and skill.

13. PERFORMANCE

The first year's performance and accounts will show:

– whether the co-operative can manage

– whether the Agreement and allowances are workable

– whether the co-operative can carry out improvements from any surplus

– what areas are best and worst in the co-operative's performance

– what can be more efficiently run.

Co-operatives are small, responsible, self-contained organisations. They can usually react swiftly, clearly and sensitively to problems. As a result, they usually run cheaper, faster repairs; they relet property more quickly; they have lower arrears; they keep common areas cleaner; they have more tenant involvement; they help those in need.

There is now significant evidence that co-operatives are generally efficient managers as well as helping households which otherwise would have to be housed by the council or suffer great hardship (Power, Nov. 1988).

14. OUTSIDE SUPPORT

It is very difficult for a management co-operative to become established without outside support. At the very least it will require a sympathetic landlord, willing to negotiate new arrangements. However, even where the council becomes the **promoter** and active supporter of co-operatives (as has happened in Glasgow and Islington) there is almost always a need for local development support to help the organisation, to keep the co-operative informed, to facilitate training, to help with negotiating the Agreement, to advise on staffing matters, to help with technical, legal and financial

matters, if only getting access to expert and impartial advice. In recognition of the fact that co-operatives do not simply emerge, the Government set up the Co-operatives Review in order to examine (amongst other things) the way in which co-operatives, EMBs and other forms of tenant involvement could be encouraged and supported. An important outcome was the proposal to provide grants from the Government to support agencies and to tenants' organisations directly in the promotion, development, support and training of tenants. This grant regime is known as Section 16 'Tenant participation grants' (see Appendix). Tenants' groups and support agencies, like secondaries and PEP, will have to apply direct to DoE for funds. For Housing Associations Section 87 grants are available from the Housing Corporation.

Development support often comes through secondary co-operatives (organisations which offer a range of services to, and whose membership is open to, tenant co-operatives), other independent agencies such as PEP, TPAS, NFHC, or through directly employed workers. For any local authority, housing association or tenants' group considering a tenant management co-operative proposal, it is important to establish early on where such outside support can come from. It can also come from a special co-operative development unit, such as Islington, Wandsworth, Brent, Camden, Lewisham, Birmingham and Glasgow Councils have set up. Many other councils are now following this model.

All bodies interested in promoting co-operatives should expect to offer a great deal of help to an embryonic tenants' group in order for it to reach the point of taking over. After the initial stages, contact needs to be regularly available but much less intense.

15. ISSUES TO BE TACKLED IN SETTING UP MANAGEMENT CO-OPERATIVES

– An immense **amount of work** has to be done by **some** tenants, almost inevitably a small minority. This can cause frustration and resentment.

– The establishment of a co-operative depends on the **local authority's willingness** and continuing support.

Diagram 1.22
Issues in setting up and running co-operatives

Issues in setting up co-operatives	Issues in running co-operatives
– Amount of work	– Training in employment and other skills
– Local authority support	– Involvement of members
– Relationship between landlord and tenant	– Need for outside agencies
– Size of co-operative	– Procedures for problem-solving and decision-making
– Employment of staff	– Maintaining social networks
– Resources needed	– Support for sensible behaviour

The more sympathetic the council, the more likely co-operatives are to flourish.

– Support for co-operatives is a **new role for local authorities** involving monitoring, setting standards, enforcing cyclical maintenance and allocations policies, while allowing freedom to manage to the tenants. A growing number of local authorities are encouraging and setting up tenant management co-operatives.

– **'Small'** has tended to be the rule for co-operatives. They work well **because** they are small. Larger co-operatives are possible – up to 500 has proved viable and some even bigger ones are now being developed. This is still a **small** management unit in council terms. If an estate is very large, sub-divisions may be necessary. Co-operatives formed on parts of the estates may have greater organisational and development needs, at least in the early stages. The four Elthorne co-operatives in Islington are good examples of this. So are the Summerston co-operatives in Glasgow.

– For tenant management co-operatives to take on full-time staff, they need to have more than about 50 units. **Taking on staff** is the most difficult and one of the most important jobs a co-operative has to do.

– Co-operatives cannot on their own address the **need for capital** on rundown estates or poorly renovated housing. They look to their council or housing association landlords to make capital allocations.

Diagram 1.22 displays the issues in setting up and running co-operatives.

16. KEY ISSUES INVOLVED IN RUNNING CO-OPERATIVES

– Staff relations/conditions are a fraught area. Co-operatives need proper training in **employment** practices. Councils or other agencies can provide this.

– Maintaining **involvement of members** and landlord over a long period requires imagination and determination. It is only necessary to have a small group directly involved, maybe 20 % of members. However, elections should be lively and if possible involve a choice of candidates. Meetings should be short and businesslike so **many** tenants feel able to come along.

– Sustaining activists and nurturing potential participants may be easier with the help of **outside agencies.** Conferences, visits and involvement in wider issues can help sustain a co-operative.

– Continuous **training** is needed so that tenants keep abreast of changes and so that new members are not excluded through ignorance.

– Activists are sometimes **'bad tenants',** e.g. in arrears. **Procedures** need to be laid down in the rules of membership to avoid later trouble.

– Transition from **conflict to co-operation** with the landlord is often difficult and co-operative leaders often adopt a hostile and beleaguered stance. Support and training can give people confidence to talk problems over without being 'on the attack' unnecessarily.

– Tenants **'policing' neighbours** can be a delicate job. Many co-operatives take on this role gladly. Others find it very difficult. In most cases co-operatives are better at providing social cohesion and support, thereby 'policing' informally, than more distant landlords. A carefully worded Code of Conduct should avoid the charge of 'nosey parker' (see Appendix).

– Certain individual members can take advantage of co-operative structures to **bully** others, to throw their weight around, or to act unjustly. General meetings, committees and the management office need to be carefully developed in the early stages so that they can support sensible, responsible and reasonable behaviour.

17. CONCLUSION

It is the style, the scale and the responsiveness of co-operatives, led by members rather than outsiders, that make them a unique form of housing provision. The level of participation is important; sufficient participation is vital for a member-based organisation to survive. Co-operatives require far more tenant participation than any other form of housing. But they can run efficiently with only about a fifth of members participating actively, bringing significant social benefits as well as better housing management.

18. CHECKLIST ON TENANT CO-OPERATIVES

– Does the co-operative have regular, open, well chaired meetings?

– Does the council take up issues with the co-operative and check on performances in a supportive way?

– Do members from minority groups join the co-operative, attend meetings, stand for committees?

– Does the co-operative help households in difficulty, e.g. over rent arrears, access?

– Does the co-operative run a proper cyclical maintenance programme?

– Does the co-operative listen to members' complaints?

– How does the co-operative handle disruptive behaviour?

– Are all households in the co-operative area paid-up members?

– Does the co-operative organise social and welfare activities?

– What training is organised for elected tenants?

– What methods are used for reporting back to members – by staff, by committees?

– Do staff enjoy working for the co-operative?

19. SOME USEFUL BOOKS ON TENANT MANAGEMENT CO-OPERATIVES

BIRCHALL J (1988): Building Communities the Co-operative Way. Routledge, London

CO-OPERATIVE DEVELOPMENT SERVICES LIVERPOOL (1987): Building Democracy – Housing Co-operatives on Merseyside

DEPARTMENT OF THE ENVIRONMENT (1989): Tenants in the Lead: The Housing Co-operatives Review. HMSO

HOUSING CORPORATION (undated): Co-op Outlines. London

NATIONAL FEDERATION OF HOUSING ASSOCIATIONS (1984): Co-ops Information Guide. London

—— (1984): Managing Housing Co-ops' Money

NFHC (1990): Model Management Agreement, London

OSPINA J (1987): Housing Ourselves. Hilary Shipman, London

POWER A (1988): Under New Management. PEP, London

II. The local office and staff

A The local office

B Staff for the local office

C Security in local offices and violence against staff

D Social conditions and tenancy agreements

A The local office

Contents

"Buildings do not work unless they are managed properly."

Richards Rogers
at L.S.E.

1. SUMMARY

The local office is the focus for running the estate:

- It brings together all the staff needed to manage the estate.
- It takes action on local housing management problems.
- It provides the link for other services needed on the estate.
- It provides an open door to tenants.

Diagram 1.23 illustrates the role of the local office.

Diagram 1.23
Role of local office

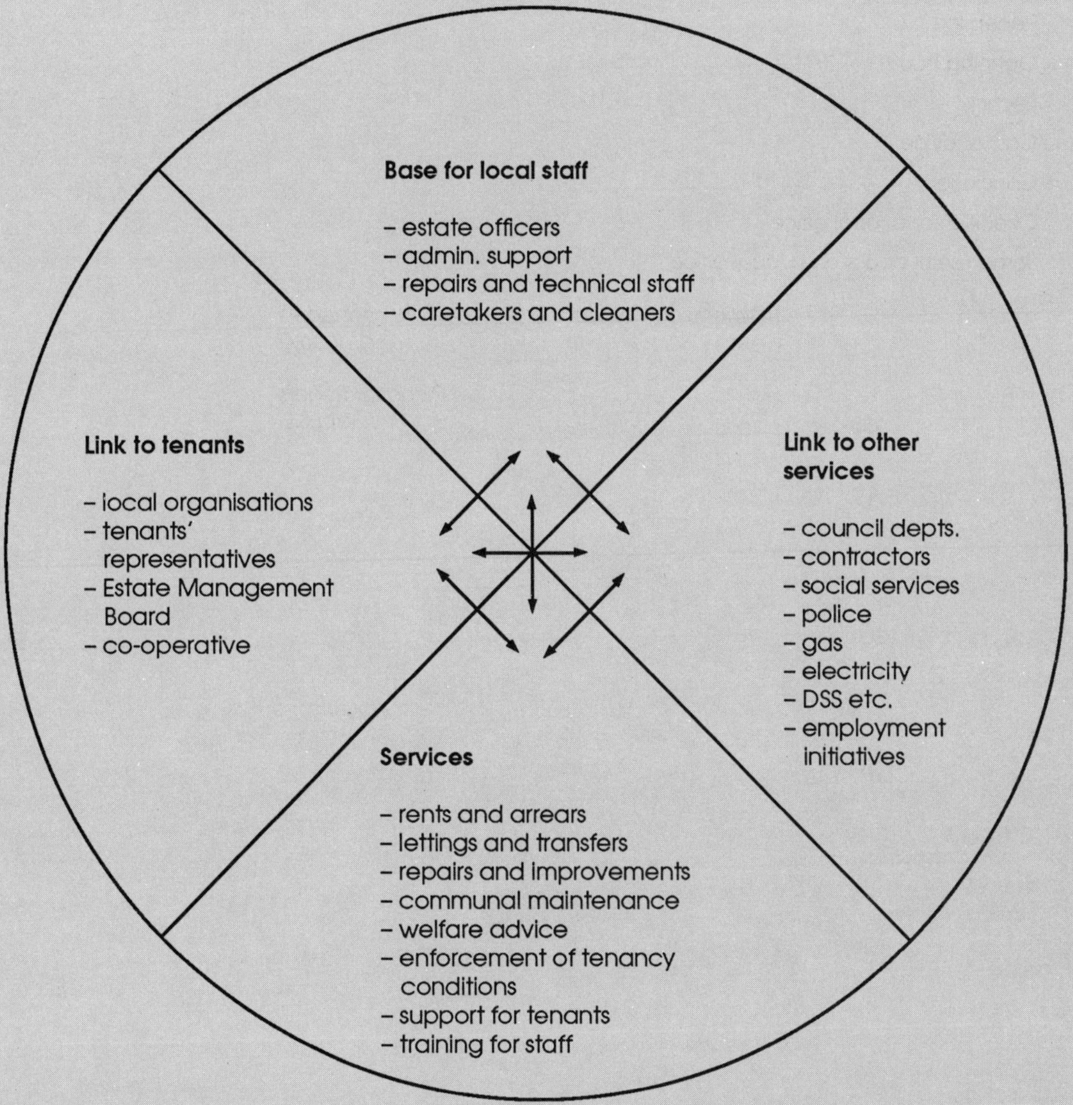

Base for local staff

- estate officers
- admin. support
- repairs and technical staff
- caretakers and cleaners

Link to tenants

- local organisations
- tenants' representatives
- Estate Management Board
- co-operative

Link to other services

- council depts.
- contractors
- social services
- police
- gas
- electricity
- DSS etc.
- employment initiatives

Services

- rents and arrears
- lettings and transfers
- repairs and improvements
- communal maintenance
- welfare advice
- enforcement of tenancy conditions
- support for tenants
- training for staff

2. KEYWORDS: WELCOME; SECURITY; ISOLATION; LINKS; LOCAL

The office is the most basic ingredient of local management. Tenants everywhere have welcomed the idea of a local office.

It is important to win the early support of residents for the **location and style** of the local office. They must **like** the office and identify with it.

A local management office needs to be:

– well located;

– **welcoming;**

– sufficiently large for staff and tenants;

– cheap enough to be provided within limited budgets, but **secure** and comfortable enough to be attractive to staff and tenants.

The area to be covered by the local office is hugely variable. Ideally the local office should cover a single estate or identifiable area. Normally 500–1,000 dwellings provide a workable size.

Estates of 200 or more can support a local office.

But very small offices have problems of **isolation,** adequate staff cover and safety. It is also harder to justify a very small office in budgetary terms. The decision on size and location will depend very much on a range of local circumstances, including tenants' views, the intensity of problems, the type of landlord, the **links** between the estate and neighbouring areas, the distance from the main office and so on. Some small estates support highly successful small offices. Some appear not to need them. Most co-operatives of 50 dwellings or more have their own **local** office.

Large offices covering more than one large estate recreate many of the bureaucratic problems of centralised systems. Estates of more than 1,500 dwellings can sometimes be divided. They are very difficult to run through one office although tenants and staff of a densely built large estate may oppose breaking up the estate into smaller units. Each estate has to be looked at carefully to work out the best local solution.

3. TARGETS

– Find an existing building and convert it within six months.

7. Local office in the high street. Bacup, Rossendale

– Make the office look attractive for staff and provide good conditions.

– Question the use of screens.

– Work out a proper security scheme.

– Get good kitchen and toilet facilities.

– Make room for babies and children.

– Put up good displays in reception.

– Find money for paint and plants.

– Make the outside as well as the inside attractive.

– Employ a local cleaner.

– Aim to have all tenants coming in within three months.

– Do not keep people waiting.

4. LOCATION

The office should be easy to get to from all over the estate. Location in relation to shops, transport, other agencies and the layout of the estate is important. Tenants need to identify with the office and as far as possible see the office as a focus – for example: by the main bus stop; on the main road; in the centre of the estate; at a major converging point for pedestrian routes; or in the local shopping centre.

One important factor to be considered in setting up a local office is the sense of 'community identity' that exists amongst the residents. Lumping two or more totally different communities together for administrative reasons does not work well. But often adjacent or nearby estates 'run into each other' and form part of the same local area, particularly in densely built-up city areas. The boundaries that exist and those that residents identify with should be considered and respected as far as possible. For this reason estate bases have been very popular. In villages or areas where there are scattered groups of property and small estates, it may be best to locate the office in the centre of the main village or town (e.g. Bacup, Rossendale and Rhondda).

Diagram 1.24 showing the layout of the Barnfield Estate, Greenwich, indicates the location of the local office on the thoroughfare near shops and transport, but within the estate.

5. TYPE OF BUILDING

Wherever possible, the office should be an **empty dwelling, shop** or other available premises, requiring a minimum of conversion work. This will be cheaper and quicker than new building and more permanent than a portakabin.

It is sometimes difficult to justify using an **existing dwelling** in areas of acute need but for local management an economic and accessible local base must be found. It is often of more use to needy households to sacrifice an existing dwelling in the short-term to provide a local office if, as a result, repairs get done

more quickly and empty dwellings can be let within days rather than weeks or months.

Offices can be built at the **base of blocks,** under decks and within garages if there is sufficient ceiling height. This type of conversion is more expensive than a shop or dwelling but can be spacious and welcoming.

Portakabins or prefabricated offices can be used where no existing building is available. These can provide well-laid-out, accessible office facilities. However, they look **temporary;** they are expensive to hire; and they can be damaged if placed on isolated land. They should be solid and able to withstand wear and tear. They should also be reasonably soundproof. It should be possible to guard them and prevent vandalism. The Isle of Dogs, with eight local offices, has used all four: dwellings, shops, garages and prefabricated offices.

Expensive **'purpose-built'** offices often draw the antagonism of tenants whose conditions have been poor and neglected. They take much longer to produce. They take money away from urgent repairs. On the other hand, local authorities sometimes want to show tenants and staff their commitment to a new style of management by building attractive new offices or converting existing premises to very high standards. This can be positive as long as it is done with care to win public support.

6. LAYOUT; REPAIRS AND CARETAKING BASES; EQUIPMENT

Layout

– The local office should provide **sufficient space** for all staff.

– There should be at least one **quiet room** where staff can hold small meetings and where 'thinking is possible'.

– It is helpful if the **tenants'** organisation has a **base** nearby or adjacent with easy access to the office. Where there is an Estate Management Board or other formal tenants' committee involved in management, space for their meetings is essential.

Repairs and Caretaking Bases

Caretakers and repairs organisations also require a base, which can be in part of the same building as the local management office or close by. Space to sit, washing facilities, storage, equipment, tea-making and other needs for caretakers and a repairs team should all be provided for (see later sections). Repairs workers should have independent access to stores and to the chargehand (see Diagram 1.25). Repairs workers need workshop space too.

It works well to have all the estate-based staff working from the same base as long as co-ordination is good, space and location are suitable, and the manager is directly responsible for all staff. Otherwise, a separate but **adjacent** base should be provided. It is important that the noise of sawing, hammering and moving equipment and materials does not intrude too much into the office.

Diagram 1.24
Layout of the Barnfield Estate
and location of Barnfield housing office

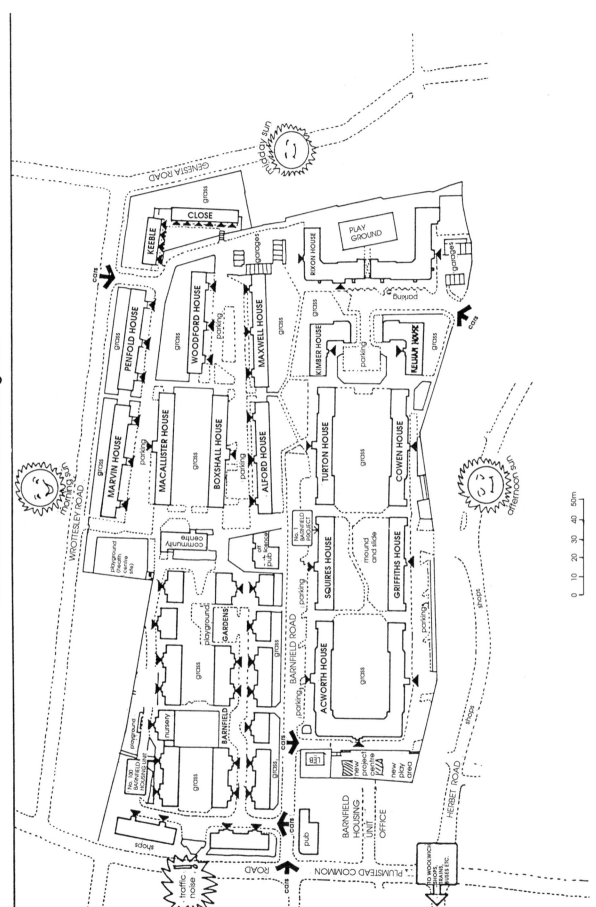

Diagram 1.25

Diagrammatic Layout for estate housing office for estate of 500 or more dwellings

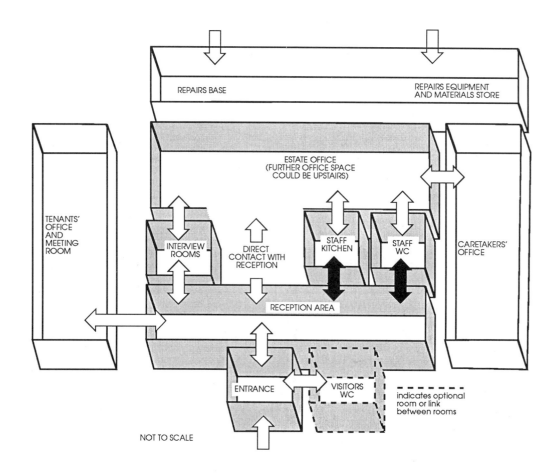

REPAIRS BASE

REPAIRS EQUIPMENT AND MATERIALS STORE

ESTATE OFFICE (FURTHER OFFICE SPACE COULD BE UPSTAIRS)

TENANTS' OFFICE AND MEETING ROOM

INTERVIEW ROOMS

DIRECT CONTACT WITH RECEPTION

STAFF KITCHEN

STAFF WC

CARETAKERS' OFFICE

RECEPTION AREA

ENTRANCE

VISITORS WC

- - - - indicates optional room or link between rooms

NOT TO SCALE

Diagrams 1.25 and 1.26 illustrate some points about layout and location.

Equipment

The office should have adequate basic furniture and equipment for each member of staff and for reception. In addition, shelves, files and other storage systems should be up-to-date and attractive. There should be tea and coffee making facilities. These can be shared with caretakers. A good **telephone** system with outgoing and incoming direct lines is very important. It is also necessary to be able to transfer calls to lines on other desks. There should be an answerphone if the office phone is sometimes not manned.

7. COMPUTERS

In most offices and repair bases there will be a computerised information system. The cost of purchasing the equipment and software will range from approximately £6,000 to £13,000. Stand-alone micro-

computer systems are often more effective than extensions of existing main frame authority-wide systems where these cannot serve the management needs of local offices. Stand-alone micros can be compatible with central computer systems and with other local offices.

8. RECEPTION

- The **reception area** should be spacious, clean, comfortable and welcoming to tenants. Staff should let tenants know how they will be dealt with and in what order.

- **Leaflets** about services provided by the office and by other council services, posters, photographs of the office team with responsibilities, and newsletters should be on display in the reception area.

- Publicity should be in clear **basic English** and in **ethnic minority languages** used by residents.

- Activities for **young children** should always be provided – a rocking horse, comics, picture books, soft toys,

Diagram 1.26
Sketch Plan of Bacup Neighbourhood Office, Rossendale

Ground Floor

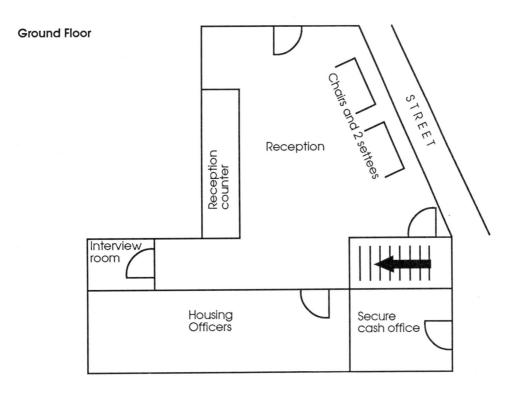

First Floor

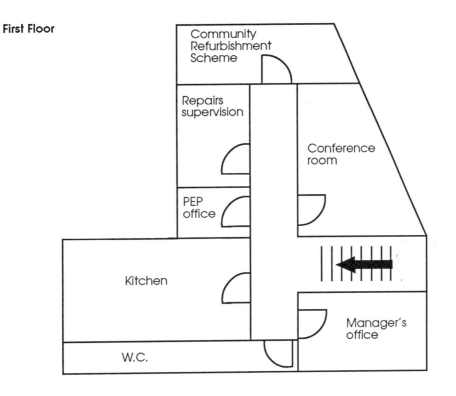

Notes
1) This office is in the shopping street of a small Lancashire town.
2) The repairs workers have their own depot outside the office but the supervisor is in the estate office.
3) The estates are small and in scattered groups around the area. Caretakers are not needed for the houses. There is no caretaking base within the office. Estate cleaners work on the estates.

scrap paper and crayons. Staff and tenants can often contribute items. A few toys, presented attractively, are better than a large unsupervised 'junk box'.

– There should be access to **toilets** for callers at the office.

– **Screens** to separate staff running the reception from tenants are not a good idea and have not been used in most PEP offices (see Section on violence against staff for a more detailed discussion). If a secure cash collection point is essential, it can be provided in a separate part of the reception area (see Bacup plan). However, there should be an easy method for counter staff to call for help if necessary e.g. alarm buttons, back-up staff. Where there are serious worries about violence, then the root cause of the problem should be found and special measures taken. The vast majority of tenants, no matter how bad their conditions or how great their frustrations, are reasonable, patient and understanding. They should **not** be greeted with security bars or screens in anticipation of violence. On the other hand, there are some disturbed, aggressive people and great care should be taken to make sure that staff are not exposed to these exceptional people in situations they cannot handle. There must always be an agreed method for calling for help in emergencies.

– Housing staff should be close to reception to give **back-up and support** to the person on reception and to make reception part of the general office. It often works best to have all staff helping at the counter on a rota basis. No one person should ever be left alone in an open office.

– **An open atmosphere** in the office helps overcome tenants' suspicions and fears. It also makes it easier for staff to identify with local people.

– There should be a separate room for **confidential interviews.**

– Housing staff should be **out on the estate** and seeing tenants in their home as far as possible, reducing the demands on reception.

– There should be access for the **disabled.**

9. OPENING HOURS

The office should be open five days a week. Where necessary, the office should open one evening a week for the benefit of working tenants. It can close one half-day to make up for the evening. Late opening should **only** be introduced where a significant proportion of tenants work during the day and where staff are able to work evenings.

Many offices close one half-day a week to allow for team meetings, staff training and paperwork. This is very important as it gives all staff a chance to catch up. But training sessions and meetings need to be formally structured and agreed so that they actually happen.

There may need to be lunch-hour closing, unless there are sufficient staff to allow staggered lunches. There may also be some times when the office needs to be closed so that staff can work uninterrupted, be free to make visits or hold meetings.

In larger teams, it should be possible to stay open most of the day with the possible exception of a half day for training. There should be definite times each week when tenants can be sure to see the estate officer responsible for their area or patch.

Diagram 1.27 illustrates the hours that a local office opens to residents.

10. SECURITY

The office should be made secure against break-ins and vandalism. Alarms, strong locks, strengthened glass, fixed equipment, night watchmen, neighbours, use of the office for evening meetings and other measures make break-ins and damage to local offices rare where these measures are linked to a reliable and friendly service. Security measures should be backed up by team agreement on security procedures. Offices on PEP estates have usually survived with very few attacks, break-ins or other security problems (see Section on violence against staff).

Diagram 1.27
Example of office opening hours

	9–10 am	10–12 am	12–2 pm	2–4 pm	4–5 pm	5–7 pm
Monday	Office hour	Open to callers	Lunch and visits	Open to callers	Office hour	Closed
Tuesday	"	"	"	"	"	"
Wednesday	"	"	"	Closed - training etc.	"	"
Thursday	"	"	"	Closed in lieu of evening opening	"	Late opening
Friday	"	"	"	Open to callers	"	Closed

11. COST OF AN OFFICE

It will normally cost between £15,000 and £50,000 to convert and equip an existing building as an estate office. Minimal conversion work to two adjacent maisonettes, one for use as an office and the other for use as a repairs base, may cost £15,000. Diagram 1.28 shows example costs.

These costs represent the bottom end of the range. Conversion of an abandoned shop-front and upper dwelling into offices may cost up to £100,000. A balance needs to be struck between economy and providing adequate working conditions with reasonable privacy for staff and tenants alike.

Local authorities that have decentralised several services to one area office have spent up to £250,000 on each office.

12. CONCLUSION

The local office should if possible form part of the estate or be very close to it, e.g. the local shopping centre. Staff and tenants should feel comfortable and secure in it. It should offer good working conditions and an attractive and welcoming reception area.

13. CHECKLIST FOR A LOCAL OFFICE

1. Is the office accessible?
2. Is is big enough for staff and tenants?
3. Is it attractive and welcoming?
4. Is the reception room open and friendly?
5. Is there an interviewing room?
6. Is there a quiet room?
7. Is there a meeting room?
8. Is there a toilet callers can use?
9. Is there something for children to do while waiting?
10. Are there safety precautions, such as an alarm bell in reception, for emergencies?
11. Is the cost of the office reasonable (i.e. repeatable)?
12. Can the office cause a nuisance, e.g. noise?
13. Can elderly, frail, disabled people and people with pushchairs and prams get in and out easily?
14. Does the phone line work efficiently?
15. Can rents be collected securely if necessary?

Diagram 1.28

Example costs of converting existing dwellings to an office for an estate of 500

Minimal conversion works	£6,500
Secondary glazing	£2,117
Burglar alarm system	£ 530
Fire extinguishers	£ 182
Carpets & other floor coverings	£2,315
Venetian blinds	£ 370
Furniture and furnishings	£3,281
Wallpapers	£ 400
Telephone system	£1,200
Total	£16,895

16. Is the office clean and well organised?
17. Are there posters, photos, charts and other signs of activity?
18. Do tenants like the office?
19. Is the information on display useful, attractive, up-to-date and in languages used by residents on estate?

14. SOME USEFUL BOOKS ON A LOCAL OFFICE

BARBER S (1985): 'Heseltown Goes Local' – A case study in the management and politics of the decentralisation of a large housing department. Ref. No. HS 0029. Local Government Training Board, Luton

DEPARTMENT OF THE ENVIRONMENT (1989): Nature and Effectiveness of Local Housing Management. HMSO

HAMBLETON R & HOGGETT P (undated): The Politics of Decentralisation: Theory and Practice of a Radical Local Government Initiative. Working Paper 46, University of Bristol, School for Advanced Urban Studies

INSTITUTE OF HOUSING & NATIONAL FEDERATION OF HOUSING ASSOCIATIONS (1990): Tackling Violence against Housing Staff. A Guide for Employers and Employees. London

MAINWARING R (1988): The Walsall Experience – A Study of the Decentralisation of Walsall's Housing Service. Department of the Environment. HMSO

NALGO: Health and Safety at Work Act: a NALGO Guide. Centurion Press 77, London

B Staff for the local office

Contents

*"A problem shared is a problem halved. If you share
a problem six times, you end up with only one
sixty-fourth of the problem you started with."*

1. Summary

Staff provide the key to success in managing estates:

- **Locally-based staff** are needed for all estates of 200 or more rented homes.

- Local staff need to be responsible for the maximum number of housing management functions at the local level, with **real control** and ability to deliver.

- Local staff need to **work flexibly** with the emphasis on responding to tenants, solving problems and reducing bureaucracy.

- Local staff need outside support, training, a solid **team** and a sense of purpose and achievement.

Diagram 1.29 shows how the four aspects of staffing interlock.

Diagram 1.29
Four aspects of staffing

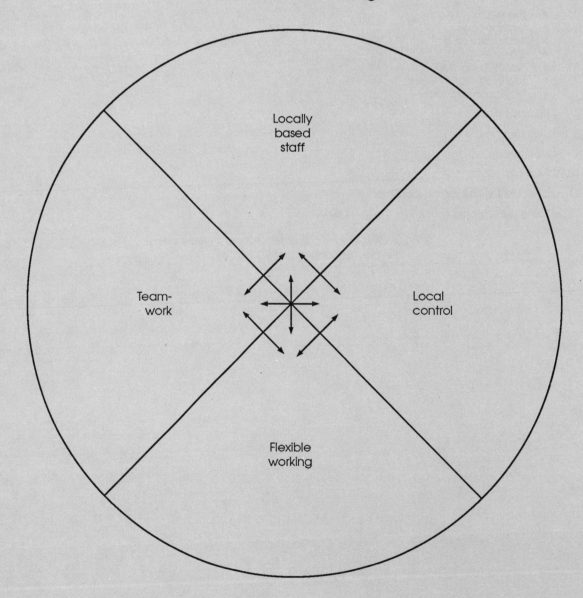

2. KEYWORDS: NEW SKILLS; IMAGINATIVE; INDEPENDENCE

The style, location, size, age and popularity of the estate will shape staff needs; the style of the local authority will shape the ethos of existing staff. **New skills,** different approaches, and **imaginative** and flexible procedures will be developed by the local team. The team itself will need energy, resourcefulness, **independence** and co-operation to overcome the difficulties of developing a working local office.

3. TARGETS

- Recruit able staff
- Check if staff want to work with tenants
- Reduce staff turnover and sickness level
- Provide a staff induction course and ongoing training
- Integrate all levels of local staff
- Check if people enjoy their jobs
- Make each person's job satisfying

4. STAFFING NEEDS

- The Estate Manager will be central to an effective local office.

- All locally based staff should be answerable to the Estate Manager. This includes caretakers and cleaners. Repairs staff will have a contractual relationship to the local management organisation through the Estate Manager.

- There should be at least one estate officer for every 350 dwellings. An estate officer may need to cover fewer dwellings where there are more management difficulties. For example, on Broadwater Farm each estate officer covers 250 dwellings. Even on popular estates with few problems, it is hard for one manager to cover more than 400 properties.

- Estates with communal areas and a difficult environment need resident caretakers. One caretaker/warden is recommended for an area of 500 houses, depending on the layout and conditions. Flatted estates require one resident caretaker to about 120 dwellings. Cleaning of common parts must be provided either by the caretakers, or by additional cleaners where there are many communal areas.

- Some administrative/secretarial/book-keeping support is essential in offices covering 200 dwellings or more.

- Local teams can only work effectively if staff agree **in advance** to cover for each other and work flexibly.

- Staff must work as a **team.** It is worth devoting as much time as necessary to develop a strong collaborative team. Team meetings are vital for this.

- The size of the local team depends on the size of the estate and on its structure. Flatted estates generally require more staff. Small estates of about 250 dwellings may require four or five staff, depending on conditions. Cloverhall Co-operative in Rochdale employs this number, with 240 dwellings. If there is a fully autonomous local management organisation, there will be about one member for 60 dwellings including caretakers. On a cottage estate of 1,000 dwellings, there would be 10–15 staff. On a flatted estate of 1,000 dwellings, there would be about 16 staff. This would include about 8 caretakers, 3 estate officers, a cleaner, an administrative worker, some book-keeping support, and a manager, based on the experience of local offices (Power, April 1987, Vols. 1 and 2; see Diagram 1.30). It is difficult to co-ordinate much larger groups of staff than this on an estate without developing a more hierarchical structure.

- The local repairs organisation will need approximately one repairs worker to every 150 dwellings, depending on conditions. At least carpentry and plumbing should be locally based. The chargehand, local contractor or head of the local repairs team will take orders from and have work completions approved by the Estate Manager. The local repairs organisation will be working under contract to the landlord but the landlord can use the local management organisation as agent. In some cases it may be cheaper or more efficient to 'buy in' repairs services on a flexible basis. The local control of the budget is the key to control over the quality of repairs (see section on Repairs).

5. FUNCTIONS OF ESTATE STAFF

Estate-based staff should be responsible for all day-to-day estate management functions. The main functions of the local office and the central housing organisation are divided as shown in Diagram 1.31.

6. ROLES OF ESTATE STAFF

The Estate Manager co-ordinates the team and takes responsibility for the staff. The manager's job includes:

- overall effectiveness of the office

- staff management including recruitment and disciplinary matters

- team support, regular team meetings (at least fortnightly)

- training needs of staff

- budgetary control, authorisation, annual accounts

- forward planning

- liaison with tenants' associations or representatives (regular formal meetings at least monthly)

- liaison with other departments

- servicing the local Board or Committee (where the manager is locally answerable to a Board, estate committee or co-operative)

- maintaining caretaking standards

- developing and co-ordinating planned maintenance, improvements and capital programmes

Diagram 1.30

Examples of staffing structure for a local office
a)   Team for Estate with 1,000 Dwellings. Total staff = 15 ****

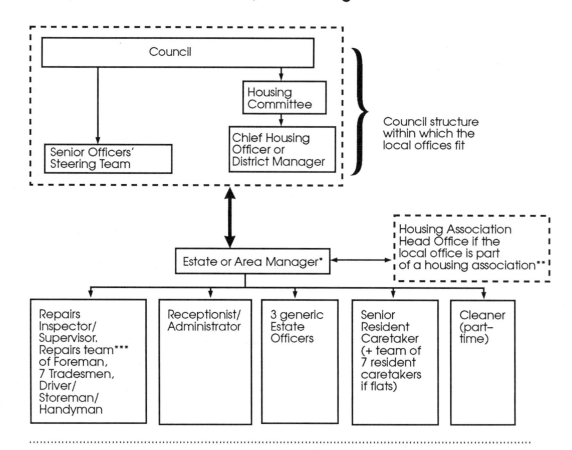

b)   Team for estate with 350 dwellings.   Total staff = 7 ****

(Council structure as above)

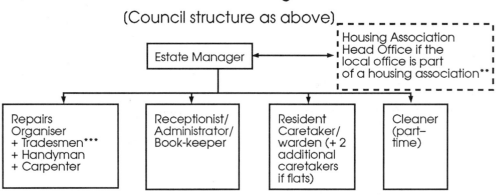

* Sometimes a Project Co-ordinator is in this position (see p.72)

** Similar structures and staffing ratios may apply in Housing Association local offices.

*** The repairs teams will work on a contractual basis with the local office.

**** Total does not include repairs team.

Diagram 1.31
Local office and central housing organisation responsibilities

Local office responsibilities	Central housing responsibilities
1 Advice and information	**1** Policy
2 Rent accounts and arrears control	**2** Overall financial control
3 Control of local payments	**3** Allocation of resources
4 Local allocations and lettings administration	**4** Allocations policy and priorities
5 Control of empty dwellings	**5** Specialist services (legal, financial, technical)
6 Day to day repairs	**6** Central monitoring
7 Planned maintenance	– checking budget & accounts
8 Co-ordination of improvements & capital works	– checking performance
9 Tenancy conditions and benefits advice. Housing benefit assessment (where possible)	– audit
10 Tenant consultation	**7** Management support & supervision
11 Caretaking & cleaning	**8** Housing benefit approval
12 Communal maintenance	**9** Right to buy
13 Local staff co-ordination	**10** Wider training
14 Office organisation	**11** Employment of local office staff
15 Local procedures & record-keeping	
16 Liaison with other services	
17 Monitoring of performance	
18 Staff training and development	

– back-up in issues unresolved by estate officers, e.g. neighbour disputes

– members' enquiries

– liaison with outside agencies

– sharing in work of team

Estate Officers are the front-line housing managers. Tenants are often dependent upon the Estate Officer, particularly for the ordering of repairs and also for initiating and following through a whole range of management services. The estate officer's job includes:

– repair ordering and monitoring, including some inspections

– transfer applications

– investigation of tenants' complaints, neighbour disputes, etc.

– welfare benefits advice

– arrears action, monitoring and control

– accompanied viewing

– ensuring empty property is relet quickly

– void property inspection

– control of voids

– action against squatters

– ensuring upkeep of common areas, garages, car parking, estate lighting, lifts etc.

– supervision of cleaning and caretaking staff

– rota duty to cover availability times in the office

– contact point for tenants

– developing improvements for the patch

– helping with tenants' activities and interests

– attending meetings

– helping with reception duties.

Administrative staff can make the difference between a chaotic, inefficient, beleaguered service, and a smooth-running, efficient, calm and pleasant work environment. Administrative responsibilities usually include:

– reception and telephone duties

– typing and word-processing

– office supplies and equipment

– servicing meetings

– ordering basic repairs

– logging completed repairs

– monitoring

– maintaining filing and records systems

8. Estate team at St. John's Estate, Isle of Dogs
Priority Estates Project

- book-keeping

- handling callers and enquiries

- operating and updating computers where used.

Caretakers (*see separate section*)   It is important in this section to underline the central role played by caretakers, cleaners and estate wardens. They form a vital part of the local team. They should be directly answerable to the estate manager. They should enjoy status and recognition for their important and demanding job of maintaining the environment and communal areas. Only by liaising well with other estate staff and becoming an integral part of local management, can they succeed. The success of the local office often hinges on good caretaking. Caretakers need a good, strong and supportive manager. They need good relations with estate officers on their patch. They also need to have good relations with residents. The manager should make their job viable with equipment, training etc. They should attend team meetings.

The main caretaking duties are:

- maintaining common areas

- checking lighting, refuse, lifts, entrances etc.

- keeping contact with tenants

- doing small and immediate repairs

- helping with voids, viewings, incoming tenants

- chasing repairs to common areas.

Staff employed by other departments also work on the estate and should liaise with the local office: repairs workers; street cleaners; parks and gardens staff; environmental health; social services. Some non-housing staff may be based in the local office such as social workers, advice workers, community workers, and technical staff. Other services to the estate make a huge difference to the viability of the local management organisation (see chapter on Co-ordination with Other Services).

Technical staff (see section on Repairs and Capital Works for more detail), e.g. architects, surveyors, should

wherever practical be based in a local office where major works are in process. There may be a permanent repairs inspector or supervisor in the local management team, particularly where there are many major repairs, a big backlog or complex structural issues. A repairs inspector is particularly desirable on difficult, flatted estates.

Project co-ordinator   Where an estate has a great range of social and management problems, the council may need a project co-ordinator to set up and develop the local office. The role of a project co-ordinator is often very important in the early years of attempting to reverse very bad conditions – maybe two to five years depending on the size of the estate and level of problems. Many PEP estates need a project co-ordinator to pull together the different services, work closely with the tenants, have direct access to senior management and sort out a realistic capital programme. The Ocean Estate, Tower Hamlets, Kelvin Estate, Sheffield, Bloomsbury Estate, Birmingham and Stoops & Hargher Clough Estate, Burnley, all have project co-ordinators, partly funded for a limited period by PEP. (See Appendix on the Role of the Project Co-ordinator).

7. RESIDENT STAFF

Staff should as far as possible be in sympathy with the local community. Caretakers and wardens should normally be resident as a requirement of their job. But other staff can be resident or be drawn from the surrounding area. Local recruitment should be attempted for as many jobs as possible. Residents are often keen to take up employment but must be encouraged to apply for relevant jobs. Some jobs are better done by outsiders because of particular internal tensions. This can apply to community workers for example. Difficulty in recruiting resident staff sometimes makes the appointment of non-residents unavoidable. However, the general consensus is that at least for caretaking services, residents work best in most situations. In very difficult cases where the existing resident caretaking service has all but ceased to function, it may be necessary to start from scratch with a totally different system involving some non-resident staff including cleaners.

8. STAFF RECRUITMENT

Local offices are almost invariably set up with existing local authority or housing association staff. However, staff should want to work in a local office with a much more varied and flexible job description than is traditional. They should also have the right approach to dealing with the public. Therefore jobs should be advertised in order to recruit the best people. Equal opportunities should be offered to all, regardless of race, sex or belief, and particularly disadvantaged groups, such as members of ethnic minorities, or local residents, should be encouraged and helped to apply. Where there are **no** suitable internal staff, jobs should be externally advertised. Getting the RIGHT staff is much the most important consideration. Where a new office is being set up, staff should have a two- or three-day induction course (see Training).

Diagram 1.32

Staffing structure for Stoops & Hargher Clough Estate, Burnley, Lancs (1989). Includes 8 staff.

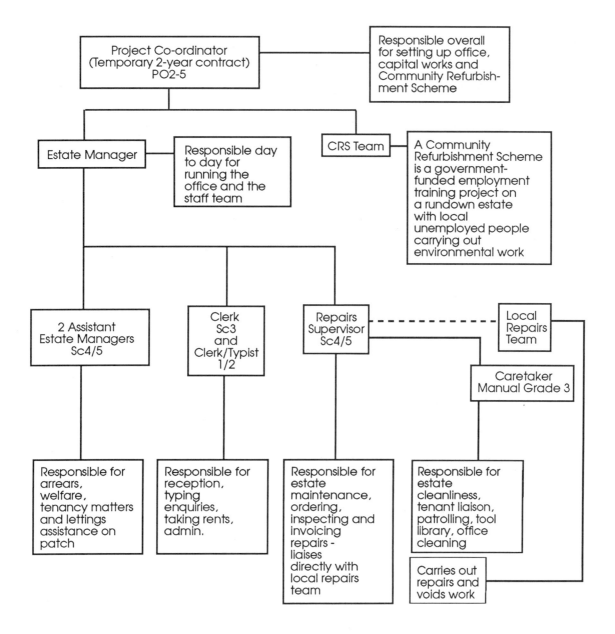

9. STAFF NEEDS

There are many difficulties and problems in estate teams:

– Staff may feel isolated.

– The team may be small and sometimes too intense as a result. Tensions and frictions can arise.

– Staff can feel under a lot of pressure from tenants because the office is **on** the estate.

– Things can go wrong and staff are very exposed when they do.

– Local councillors can interfere and give staff a hard time; or they can be indifferent and unsupportive.

– Tenants' representatives can be demanding, aggressive, impatient and accusatory. The 'them and us' stance often dies hard.

But these problems can be successfully overcome with proper discussion and support. Local staff need good training, strong leadership and confident backing if they are to cope with local management problems. Where they do, there is a sense of achievement as a reward. Team morale and greater tenant satisfaction will also be important rewards.

10. EXAMPLE

The actual staffing structure, employing eight staff, for Stoops & Hargher Clough Estate, Burnley, Lancs. (shown in Diagram 1.32) – 900 pre-war houses, bungalows and flats, two miles from the town centre – gives a live example. It also helps illustrate why local management organisations are able to tackle problems.

11. CHECKLIST FOR LOCAL STAFF

1.   Is the estate manager senior enough/experienced enough/paid enough to make a go of the local office?

2.   Are there sufficient estate officers?

3.   Are there sufficient caretakers?

4.   Is there sufficient administrative support?

5.   Are posts externally advertised?

6.   Is some flexibility written into all job descriptions?

7.   Do salaries reflect local autonomy and responsibility?

8.   Are duties and priorities simple and clear?

9.   Are all local staff made directly answerable to the estate manager?

10. Is there enough space for staff to have meetings, to take breaks, and to have necessary equipment?

11. Is staff training planned/provided?

12. Is decision-making authority and budgetary control given to the estate manager?

13. Are there strong links between office staff, caretakers, cleaners and repairs workers?

14. What are relations like between staff and resident representatives? Are there clear links? Do staff enjoy working with tenants? Do staff accept the need for tenants to be involved? Do staff support a formal structure for tenant representation?

15. Are there links with other staff concerned with the estate e.g. technical staff?

16. Are there good relations with local politicians?

17. What is staff morale like?

18. Is sickness and absenteeism a problem?

19. Do staff cover for each other?

20. Are there regular team meetings for **all** local staff – at least fortnightly?

21. Do staff participate fully in team meetings? Are all staff willing to attend?

22. What are the rewards of the job?

12. SOME USEFUL BOOKS ON STAFF FOR THE LOCAL OFFICE

AUDIT COMMISSION (1985): Good Management in Local Government. Local Government Training Board, Luton

MAINWARING R (1988): The Walsall Experience – A Study of the Decentralisation of Walsall's Housing Service. Department of the Environment. HMSO

NATIONAL FEDERATION OF HOUSING ASSOCIATIONS (1989): Race & Housing: Employment and Training Guide. London

OFFICE OF THE MINISTER FOR THE CIVIL SERVICE (1987): Getting the Best Out of People. HMSO

PETERS T (1987): Thriving on Chaos – A Handbook for a Management Revolution. MacMillan, London

PETERS T & WATERMAN R (1982): In Search of Excellence. Harper & Row, New York

STEWART J (1988): A new management for housing departments. Local Government Training Board, Luton

Note: There is very little published material on this subject. The publications listed here have some ideas about how to treat staff.

C Security in local offices and violence against staff

Contents

"The conditions and machinery seemed right for polarisation to increase. We certainly found instances where it had occurred to an alarming degree."

Difficult to Let Investigation, DoE, 1983

1. SUMMARY

Staff in local offices may be worried about security and the threat of violence.

- Efficient, informal, friendly service is the best deterrent.

- Basic security precautions and procedures are essential.

- In emergencies, calling for help is vital.

- Screens are not normally necessary and may be counter-productive in estate-based housing offices.

- Front-line reception staff need confidence, back-up and training.

- Techniques can be learnt, but calm, patience and competence are the essentials.

The whole team needs to agree on a strategy to cope with violence and security problems.

Diagram 1.33 shows how security and insecurity can be generated.

Diagram 1.33 The vicious circle that often leads to violence and the counter-circle that generally averts it

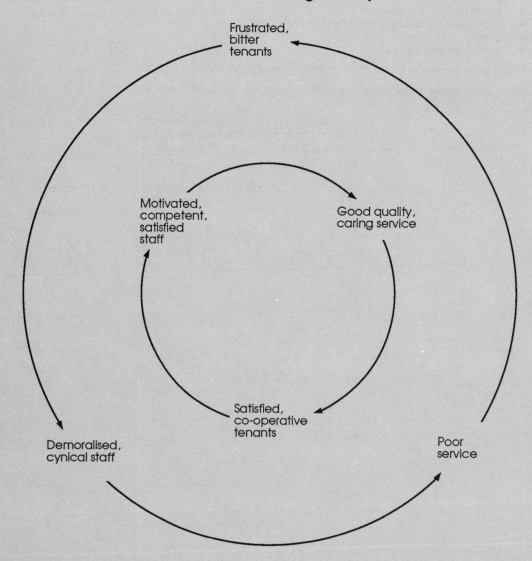

2. KEYWORDS: GRIEVANCE; ENFORCEMENT; ATTACK; DEFUSING

– Tenants with a **grievance** must know the **procedure** for getting satisfaction. They should be helped to follow that procedure.

– Tenants' **representatives** should be involved in drawing up plans for security and for dealing with the public. They will then identify with their **enforcement.**

– **Enforcement** is all-important. Any **attack** on a member of staff, any illegal action, any 'breach of the peace' must evoke a clear response with legal action if necessary to enforce safe conditions.

– **Prevention** is better than cure – try to avoid or divert conflict.

– Women are generally less aggressive than men and are often supposed to be better at resolving conflict and **defusing** difficult situations. This controversial point needs to be discussed by staff.

3. CONDITIONS

– Changes in behaviour and organisation are raising the issue of violence and security.

– Police and public are increasingly security conscious. Police riot shields and guns have appeared with growing frequency since 1981. This has raised public consciousness of the threat of violence. There is a new image of a violent society that undermines public confidence in the non-violent resolution of conflict.

– There is a significant increase in reported crime. Fear of attack, particularly among women and girls, is now prevalent, and in cities and other high crime areas, particularly the poorest housing estates, there is even greater fear than elsewhere. The crime rate in these areas for certain crimes is four times higher than the average (Hough & Mayhew, 1983).

– Dealings between public employees and the public are often noticeably rude or hostile. Most people have witnessed insulting and aggressive exchanges – on buses, in council offices, in waiting rooms, at train barriers, etc. It is, however, extremely rare in shops. Sometimes the official adopts an aggressive or offensive stance; often it is the member of the public dissatisfied with the official response who first 'loses his cool'.

– Many organisations are putting up protective screens, behind which staff work, especially where cash is involved – banks, DSS, post offices. These institutions handle money and are particularly vulnerable. Interestingly, banks are now moving the other way by expecting staff to step out from behind the counter to talk to customers. DSS is seriously considering a change in its policy of using screens.

– Many staff are refusing to work without proper

9. Making offices friendly, welcoming and helpful is the best way to prevent violence, Chelheath Estate, Stoke-on-Trent

Paul Herrmann/Profile

security – London housing departments have closed down sections of their service (e.g. Brent homeless unit) for this reason.

– The proliferation of local offices has made some staff feel more vulnerable. The access to tenants **without** the corresponding ability to deliver has left staff exposed to abuse, hostility and sometimes attack. Incidents have most often occurred where a single member of staff has tried to deal with a member of the public without proper back-up or a procedure for getting help.

– At the same time, many local housing offices are working well without screens. Staff are confident and cope well even on estates with many difficult problems.

4. TARGETS

– Establish strong links with residents and with other local services, e.g. police.

– Establish basic security measures.

– Develop training in handling violence and abuse.

– Avoid screens by introducing other strong measures.

– Develop a friendly, informal style of service.

– Make sure staff are competent, confident and polite.

– Make sure that delivery is possible.

5. THE SITUATION OF UNPOPULAR ESTATES

– There is general agreement that attacks are exceptional and usually happen because a disturbed or upset person cannot be given the help s/he wants or thinks s/he deserves. Attacks have taken place in a number of housing offices, some of them serious. Refusal to do a repair, to rehouse or to arrange a transfer could provoke violence. So could an eviction order. Women staff often feel more vulnerable than men, even though they may be involved in violent situations less often (see Islington Crime Survey, Jones, Maclean & Young; also *Observer*. Sept. 1989).

– On a rundown estate that has for many years been used by the local authority as a place to 'dump difficult households' or households ejected for 'unneighbourly behaviour' from elsewhere, there will often be a higher level of crime and fear. This will affect staff working there as well as residents. It will tend to create a beleaguered and distressing atmosphere, where no one has the confidence to contain disturbing behaviour. Sometimes the police, resident leaders, estate managers and housing caretakers have given up their attempt to 'hold' the situation. A spiral of disorder can set in (Power, 9 December 1987).

– In a small local office on an unpopular estate, staff can feel unsure of the community they are there to serve, feeling unprotected by the council they represent and therefore vulnerable.

– The closure of hostels and psychiatric institutions appears to make the situation more difficult to handle, especially in poorer areas and on estates where transient, vulnerable households can be readily

accommodated and where there are already a lot of pressures.

– On large estates with a high turnover of tenants, it is harder to maintain close personal links and easier for strangers to pass unnoticed. Everyone becomes more vulnerable in this situation.

6. STEPS TO AVOID VIOLENCE

Diagram 1.34 shows the type of response that will help to overcome some of the basic problems.

Precautions

A number of basic steps are essential:

a) Young and inexperienced staff should not run a reception area alone. Back-up staff should be present whenever the office is open to the public.

b) Even experienced and confident officers should not open an office to the public without other staff being available to help, should it prove necessary, within the building or near enough to be called on immediately.

c) The reception area should be immediately adjacent to the main office, not cut off at the bottom of stairs or at the end of a corridor.

d) There should be direct access from the reception area to the main office through an open door. In some cases the reception area and main office are in one open-plan space. The reception area should be clearly visible to other staff.

e) Rent-taking in the local office requires proper precautions and contingency plans if there should be an incident. It is possible to do this while creating a general atmosphere of openness and accessibility.

f) Staff should have a clear understanding of what constitutes 'abusive' behaviour and, in those instances when abuse or violence does occur, be clear what steps should be taken to follow up incidents, including keeping a record of what happened, assessing why it happened, contacting the offender, taking steps to make sure it does not recur, contacting the police and reporting the incident to a senior manager if necessary.

g) There should be an out-of-sight alarm bell within immediate reach of the receptionist (sometimes called a panic button).

h) Two staff should run reception if necessary, to prevent a build-up of pressure from large numbers of tenant-callers. It is important not to have long queues, to avoid overcrowding, and to let people coming in know that someone will deal with their problem quickly.

i) All staff should be trained in dealing with the public. Basic courtesies should be rigorously observed. Dealing with a regularly difficult customer politely over time is incredibly stressful, but essential to survival. It is this core technique that will most assist front-line staff (see training section).

Diagram 1.34

Situations in which violence against staff is likely to arise and how those problems can be overcome

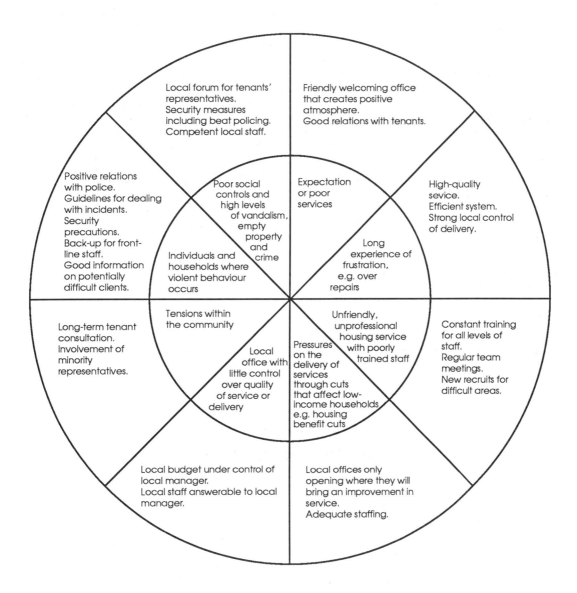

j) Staff who provoke or worsen tense encounters should **not** deal with the public. Staff who are easily upset or become tense or aggressive under provocation should not do reception. Staff who are afraid should be encouraged to overcome their fears, but if they cannot, they should not work on the counter.

k) Men as well as women should be involved in reception and expected to help with back-up as needed. It is not right to leave counter duty to the most junior female staff. However, contrary to much popular belief, women are not more prone to attack than men. On the contrary, they are probably less likely to provoke attack and therefore be victimised (*Observer*, September 1989).

l) As much information as possible should be made public, e.g. allocation method, repairs priority, arrears procedure. The more open the management system, the less likely grievances are to arise.

m) Senior staff should sometimes work on the counter. This ensures that they understand the problems and pressures, that they show their concern for junior staff who are often doing the most difficult job; they can then constantly review office and team arrangements in the light of what they learn.

n) Staff must receive proper training in defusing conflict, in responding to crises, in handling awkward cases, and in taking emergency steps where a situation explodes. Telling people the truth about their situation is likely to help rather than hinder.

Service

The right staff must be **available** to see callers, otherwise there is **no** point in having an open local office. In many offices, the receptionist receives callers.

– **Estate officers** should be available during opening hours to see tenants from their patch.

– **Estate officers** should work out a proper cover system between them.

– Offices where estate officers are only rarely available do not work nearly as well as offices where tenants can normally expect to see **their** estate officer at definite times.

– For **estate officers** who find this idea difficult, it is important to remember the stress caused to themselves, the receptionist and tenants by a build-up of unsatisfied customers.

Attacks are unlikely under the following conditions:

a) an efficient local repairs service;

b) a competent, locally-supervised caretaking workforce;

c) good direct liaison between the office and tenants' representatives;

d) full and clear records so that tenants' queries can be easily answered;

e) a calm and level-headed project manager who gives confidence to staff;

f) an open, friendly, welcoming reception area that does **not** have the appearance of a remote, uncaring office;

g) a style of receptionist who answers politely, who shows care and concern, who is efficient and clear, who immediately acknowledges tenants.

h) immediate interview facilities for any visitor to the office who is upset – the receptionist should not have to take on board complex problems or handle more difficult cases. People should sit down to discuss problems.

Estate-based management

Attacks are extremely rare in estate-based offices, compared with offices covering wider areas (G. De Max, 1988), because of the ready identification of staff and residents and the accessibility of local management. Only two serious incidents have been experienced in 35 Priority Estates Project offices in 10 years. Neither caused long-term injury, though both were potentially serious. In both cases the open office was retained at the request of staff. Precautions were taken. Better training and clearer procedures were introduced. No further incidents have occurred. It is important to remember how rare incidents are; otherwise we may be tempted to organise the housing service to accommodate the unusual, awkward customer, and thus inject fear and suspicion into normal relationships with the vast majority of tenants visiting local offices.

Attacks have occurred in local offices where:

a) the receptionist acts as the buffer, without proper information, back-up or a working management system;

b) tenants cannot see relevant officers without formal and pre-arranged appointments – this can happen

Diagram 1.35
Security in estate offices

DO	DON'T
– organise an efficient service	– use screens
– provide back-up	– open the office alone
– aim to prevent 'dumping'	– put inexperienced staff on the counter
– consult residents over security measures	– put aggressive or tense staff on the counter
– arrange proper security for cash collection	– close the office unexpectedly, if at all possible
– provide alarm bell	– refuse tenants access to estate officers
– expect senior staff to help	– use the receptionist as a buffer
– provide good information	– leave phones ringing
– keep good records	– let long queues build up
– provide training sessions in 'dealing with the public'	– allow empty properties to build up
– run competent repairs	– allow 'dumping'
– run high standard caretaking	
– make the office attractive	
– have good links with local beat police	
– make sure people can sit down	

with estate officers and causes more problems than any other single issue;

c) there is no local repairs team and therefore response times cannot be guaranteed;

d) the area covered is large – 1,500 or more – and not a single estate entity;

e) the office closes frequently and opens unpredictably. This can be unavoidable, due to staffing problems, but it is the beginning of the 'slippery slope';

f) the phone is left ringing with no proper system for answering it;

g) staff do not cover for each other or work flexibly;

h) tenants have to queue for hours;

i) the waiting area is crowded and unwelcoming;

j) the central organisation fails to give front-line staff sufficient authority, back-up or ability to deliver;

k) the police are not available locally to help, on the basis of good liaison and detailed local knowledge;

l) people with serious personal problems, who cannot cope with normal pressures and normal living are 'dumped' on the worst estates;

m) there is no clear procedure for handling aggressive or disturbed customers;

n) squatting becomes common. Some violent incidents in London have been a consequence of letting squatting get out of hand;

o) a single staff member decides to open up the office without back-up, or out of hours.

Measures should be built in to prevent these circumstances.

Diagram 1.35 suggests some basic hints.

Techniques for handling difficult encounters

1. **Keep calm** – use tactics you feel most comfortable with to calm the other person down.

2. **Call for help** – but do not show you are worried or afraid.

3. Persuade the person as early on in the encounter as possible to come to a quiet room or somewhere away from the public and **sit down** if you think this will help.

4. Make sure you have the right forms and **information** to hand.

5. Refuse to do reception or open the office if proper **back-up** is not available.

6. If an argument or trouble seems likely, call your **senior manager** to see the person.

7. Don't pull **rank** – let seniors do that.

8. Talk **quietly.**

9. **Listen.** Try not to respond defensively to an aggressive encounter.

10. Don't hesitate to call the **police** in a threatening situation which might get out of hand.

Action

Where an incident takes place:

1. Get help for the staff involved – call a doctor, ambulance, police if necessary. Provide maximum support for the victim.

2. Inform the senior manager immediately.

3. Make sure the person (people) responsible for the incident is (are) taken away from the immediate scene.

4. Inform other staff and discuss follow-up to prevent the spread of rumours and panic.

5. Inform tenants' representatives and enlist their help and support.

6. Decide on action to help those involved and affected and to prevent further incidents – follow through carefully. Adopt decisions as events develop.

7. Keep proper records of the incident and the circumstances around it.

8. Make sure legal help and advice are available if legal action is appropriate.

9. Make it absolutely clear that attacks on staff cannot be tolerated under any circumstances.

10. Enhance staff training and team support on the basis of the incident.

11. Develop new procedures if necessary.

12. Take precautions to enhance staff confidence – training, office layout, back-up.

13. Try to avoid creating a 'fortress' mentality. But all serious incidents should be reported and sanctions applied to the offender.

Central housing offices

The central organisation determines the way local offices are able to function to a large extent. Very often the wider organisation provides essential information, resources and back-up. It invariably determines overall policy and to some extent procedures for implementing decisions. Central offices therefore have a major influence on the functioning of a local office.

Central offices have been subject to violent incidents under a number of circumstances. Lettings, homelessness, repairs and court evictions are prime triggers. Central offices have often erected screens to protect counter staff. Incidents have happened, certainly in inner city offices, in spite of screens.

The more remote and unresponsive the service, the more likely attacks are. It is hard for the central housing department to be responsive on all fronts. Hence decentralisation.

Good advice, good back-up, short waits, ability to reach the right person, get an answer, all help the situation. It is important for central offices to develop the right techniques and strategy too as this will create a more supportive and positive climate for local management. It is really important that local offices have the power and flexibility to sort out management difficulties rather than simply replicate the same problems.

7. CHECKLIST ON SECURITY IN LOCAL OFFICES AND VIOLENCE AGAINST STAFF

– Is security discussed regularly with staff and tenants' representatives?

– Are staff trained in dealing with the public?

– Are there security procedures that everyone knows how to follow?

– Is the office welcoming and relaxing rather than forbidding?

– Is the office able to deliver basic housing services?

– Do staff know of particular difficult cases?

– Does the central housing department support local staff?

8. SOME USEFUL BOOKS ON SECURITY IN LOCAL OFFICES AND VIOLENCE AGAINST STAFF

DEICKE I (1989): Violence against Housing Staff: A Case Study of Paddington Churches Housing Association. Long Essay, London School of Economics, LSE Housing

NATIONAL FEDERATION OF HOUSING ASSOCIATIONS & INSTITUTE OF HOUSING (1990): Tackling Violence against Housing Staff. A guide for employers and employees. London

NALGO (1977): Health & Safety at Work Act. A Nalgo Guide. Centurion Press 77. London

NALGO (1985): Coping with Violence at Work. Nalgo News, 27-9-85. London.

POYNER B & WARNE C (1988): Preventing Violence to Staff. Health & Safety Executive. HMSO

D Social conditions and tenancy agreements

Contents

"There is an optimum size beyond which each further increment of inhabitants creates difficulties out of all proportion to the benefits. There is also an optimum area of expansion beyond which further urban growth tends to paralyse rather than to further important social relations."

Lewis Mumford,
The Culture of Cities, 1938

1. SUMMARY

- For rented housing to work, there must be a contract or agreement between the landlord and tenant concerning: the amount of rent; when and how it should be paid; the conditions under which the tenant is allowed to occupy the property; and the services which the landlord will provide in exchange for rent.

- The tenancy agreement must be enforced by the landlord if social conditions are to be reasonably stable.

- Social conditions on rented housing estates are often very poor. The level of the landlord services is often insufficient to maintain the property or environment in good condition.

- Tenants in poor areas often have problems with payment of rent and are also vulnerable to other social and economic pressures, such as unemployment, ill-health and family break-up.

Diagram 1.36 shows the interaction of four factors: social conditions, need for enforcement, the landlord responsibilities, and the tenant responsibilities.

Diagram 1.36

Interaction of social conditions, need for enforcement, the landlord and tenant responsibilities

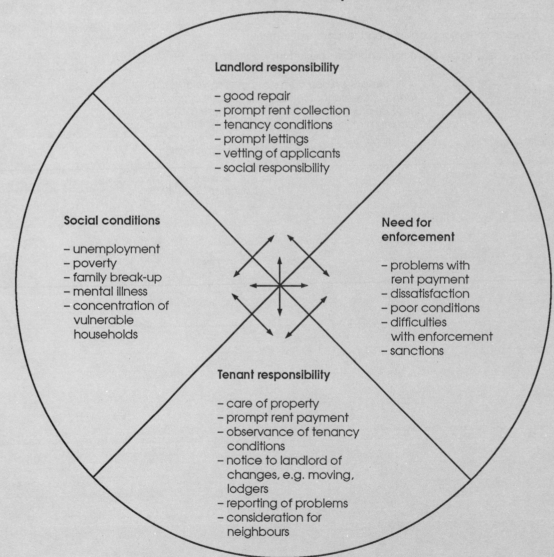

Landlord responsibility

– good repair
– prompt rent collection
– tenancy conditions
– prompt lettings
– vetting of applicants
– social responsibility

Social conditions

– unemployment
– poverty
– family break-up
– mental illness
– concentration of
  vulnerable
  households

Need for
enforcement

– problems with
  rent payment
– dissatisfaction
– poor conditions
– difficulties
  with enforcement
– sanctions

Tenant responsibility

– care of property
– prompt rent payment
– observance of tenancy
  conditions
– notice to landlord of
  changes, e.g. moving,
  lodgers
– reporting of problems
– consideration for
  neighbours

2. KEYWORDS: INTERLOCKING; SPIRAL; ALIENATED; WEAK; STRESSFUL

There are many **interlocking** elements that create poor communities in rich societies like Britain. Social conditions in these areas are often very bad, with high unemployment, poor educational attainment, a high incidence of one-parent families, often a higher than average level of crime and many other problems (Downes, 1989).

People in rented housing areas have much lower incomes than most other areas and tend to have many more social and economic problems, linked to this fact (Bonnerjea, 1987). Social and physical conditions can interact with each other, creating a downward **spiral**. Tenants on poor estates often aspire to better conditions but do not believe this can be achieved where they are, and are therefore **alienated** from their surroundings.

In this situation, the social controls that bind people together are not strong enough to contain behaviour. Some individuals and groups take advantage of **weak** controls to act out their problems or to breach the rules of neighbourliness and common courtesy that make life on our crowded island bearable.

People's private lives are their own affair. But when private action affects neighbours badly, or spills over into public areas, something must be done. The breakdown of informal social controls makes the task of the landlord in maintaining reasonable conditions doubly difficult. It also makes the lives of tenants more **stressful.**

Landlords and tenants have to work together to keep rented housing functioning. The legal contract between them gives tenants the right to make a home in the landlord's property under certain conditions. The landlord has the legal right to enforce those conditions of tenancy in order both to maintain the property in usable condition and in order to ensure that tenants in neighbouring property can enjoy their right to peace, privacy and reasonable conditions.

Landlords of estates of rented housing do not have enough income from rents to make the task of providing high quality services under difficult social conditions easy. This makes enforcement even more difficult.

3. DEFINITIONS

Social conditions describe those aspects of our lives that relate to our dealings with other people, including family, friends, neighbours, residents in the wider community. It includes hard-to-define areas of contact between people which lead to both co-operation and conflict. Social conditions are directly affected by wider influences, such as the closure of a factory, changes in policing, cuts in a bus service, and many other seemingly disconnected events. Social conditions interact with each other, intensifying particular problems – for example, bad schools, truancy and vandalism. There is also a ripple effect outwards to the wider society of poor social conditions, such as the cost of unemployment in terms of state benefit or the impact of crime on the level and type of policing. Social conditions escape precise definition but are part of the fabric of all our individual lives.

Tenancy agreements are contracts between landlords and tenants that spell out the rights and obligations of both landlords and tenants on the basis of which tenants occupy the property and landlords let it. There must be a way of enforcing a tenancy agreement; otherwise rented housing quickly deteriorates. The ultimate sanction for breaching the tenancy agreement is eviction, although this is very much a last resort and can only be done legally with the sanction of the courts. Action under Public Health laws for nuisance is another sanction (Arden, 1989).

4. TARGETS

– Find out about the social problems on the estate.

– Go through the tenancy agreement with residents' representatives.

– Check whether it can be enforced.

– Identify the weak areas.

– Work out step by step how to stop breaches of tenancy conditions.

– See if residents will back these steps.

– Find out what other services will be needed to help, e.g. legal, environmental health.

– Run staff training sessions on reporting and enforcement.

– Work out sanctions – informal and formal – can they be used?

– Work out a timetable for getting estate conditions back to a level that satisfies resident representatives.

– Get the support of the central housing department for enforcement of tenancy conditions.

5. EXAMPLES OF NUISANCE AND UNNEIGHBOURLY BEHAVIOUR

The following problems, if sufficiently serious, usually constitute a breach of the tenancy agreement, an infringement of a neighbour's legal right to peaceful occupation of the home or a statutory nuisance under the Public Health Acts. Sometimes they can also constitute a criminal offence:

– noise;

– rubbish dumping:

– verbal abuse;

– intimidation and harassment, including racial harassment;

– domestic violence;

– lack of control over dogs;

– drug abuse and alcohol abuse;

– lack of control over children.

There are many other actions that make life more difficult but may not constitute an offence or breach.

To the extent that the behaviour of a particular resident or household disrupts estate conditions and services, the landlord must intervene. Hence the need for a tenancy agreement that spells out conditions of occupation.

6. WHAT TO DO

Enforcement of basic tenancy conditions and the strengthening of social controls come to the top of the agenda when a local office with strong local powers is set up, resident involvement grows, and an estate forum or board to sort out estate problems develops.

Without some improvement in social conditions, the local office cannot deliver proper management services and residents' representatives will be embittered by the failure of their voluntary efforts to restore estate conditions. The following steps will help bring about change:

− list all the social problems among residents, in partnership with residents − this can be done at the initial consultations if social problems are very dominant;

− list the tenancy conditions that are most often broken and work out why − see if any of them are redundant − work out how to simplify the tenancy agreement and include only those basic conditions of tenancy that are essential and enforceable;

− agree to take action on particular cases of social breakdown, but only if particular individuals can be identified. Names and addresses will be necessary, but the identity of reporters and witnesses may need to be kept confidential. General 'hot air' about 'young people today', 'problem families', 'those awful so'n'sos' will get enforcement nowhere;

− find out as much as possible about the cases which seem to be causing recurrent social problems and complaints;

− work out what to do to help in as practical a way as possible by discussing the problem with the tenants affected;

− visit the case(s) if they live on the estate and try to find out more about the problem and the different sides of the story;

− make sure that residents' representatives support the approach. Without support, enforcement will be impossible;

− keep up support, combined with pressure to abide by basic courtesies, so that the household causing problems has a real incentive to try and respond to neighbours' needs and reactions;

− resort to legal action only if all else fails − the Courts are blunt instruments, but may be necessary in extreme cases;

− complaints by tenants about neighbours must be verified, and be dealt with even-handedly;

− where conditions become serious, other agencies

10. *Enforcement of tenancy conditions involves a great deal of co-operation. St. Paul's Gardens, Bristol*
Priority Estates Project

(e.g. social services, environmental health) may need to be involved. Higher authority (e.g. senior officials, lawyers, Courts) may be needed if local attempts at enforcement fail;

– close liaison with social services, schools, the probation service and the police will pay dividends (see Section X on co-ordination and the development of other services).

– economic development could provide the key to solving many problems.

– a local office should have the power to prevent households that absolutely cannot cope with estate conditions or have a history of seriously disruptive behaviour from moving onto the estate unless there are proper structures and supports for helping such households. At an early stage in the development of local management, it will be important to stop the 'dumping' of unhappy, reluctant and NEEDY households in areas where disproportionate numbers of disadvantaged, dissatisfied and vulnerable households already live (see Section III on Allocations).

There is a limit to how many households with multiple problems an area can house. It is very important to remember, however, that only a tiny minority of households have problems of this severity. This needs to be recognised (Power, 1987).

The problem of what to do with rejected households is part of a much wider set of problems in our urban society and is far beyond the scope of this manual. But unpopular, rundown estates must not be seen as the **catch-all** for society's problems; rather they are too often the product of them, and must begin to exert a higher level of local control if they are to begin to work. Some of the responsibility for the most intractable problems must therefore be taken by the wider society.

There are several golden rules:

– if residents complain about poor social conditions and call out for enforcement, that is the cue on which the local housing office should act;

– residents are acutely conscious of social breakdown and will help to restore conditions if they have any hope of success;

– the police are needed to back enforcement where crime and nuisance are involved;

– pressure combined with understanding makes more impact than a woolly and softly-softly approach that people with tough problems may not notice. We are all both selfish and social animals and therefore respond to the right kind of pressure;

– most tenants on estates are reasonable and responsible, and will work with housing staff if approached in the right way;

– business should be run in a business-like way and tenants will respect a landlord that knows how to enforce basic conditions;

– liberal outsiders often make the mistake of regarding the strict enforcement of tenancy conditions as the imposition of 'middle-class standards'. This is rarely the case as residents themselves are usually the most vigorous critics of the failure to enforce tenancy agreements.

7. In Practice

– The Tenancy Agreement needs to be written in plain English.

– Rules should be basic and few.

– There should be sanctions against those who break basic conditions.

– The link between local housing management, resident organisations and other services needs to be strong (see Section X on Co-ordination).

– There is a fine line between order and disorder; between enforcement and imposition; between social responsibility and scapegoating; between private and public issues.

– The framework of local housing management needs to be benign, service- and customer-oriented, courteous and tolerant. But clear targets and terms for the landlord-tenant relationship need to be set. And the approach to problems needs to be firm, confident and backed by knowledge and understanding.

(See Appendix on Model Tenancy Agreements).

8. Conclusion

Proving that actions constitute a breach of the tenancy agreement, a nuisance or a criminal offence, is extremely difficult, and there are many unclear areas. The matter of degree or limits is almost indefinable. Therefore, enforcement works much better through informal, local networks than through legal action.

The interrelation of social conditions, social controls and social breakdown is extremely complex. Here we can only indicate a way forward, based on resident involvement, firm and fair management, enforcement through local means if possible, and better local services.

The tenancy agreement provides a framework for landlord–tenant relations and cannot start to deal with all the wider social and economic problems we have touched on. It is, however, an important basic tool for estate management.

9. Checklist on Social Conditions and Tenancy Agreements

– Does the area have a bad reputation?

– What problems put off applicants?

– How many residents find difficulties with neighbours?

– What do they complain about?

– Can they quote chapter and verse?

– Do you check upon reports of nuisance?

– Do you visit before taking action?

– What action do you take?

– What central departments are helpful?

– What is the attitude of residents' representatives?

– Is the tenancy agreement clear and simple?

– Is it explained to new tenants when they move in?

10. SOME USEFUL BOOKS ON SOCIAL CONDITIONS AND TENANCY AGREEMENTS

ARDEN A & PARTINGTON M (1983): Housing Law. Sweet & Maxwell, London
—— (1985): Housing Law – First Supplement. Sweet & Maxwell, London

DOWNES D (ed) (1989): Crime and the City. MacMillan, London (particularly concluding chapter)
LONDON BOROUGH OF ISLINGTON (undated): Tenancy Agreement
PARKER T (1983): The People of Providence. Hutchinson, London
REYNOLDS F (1986): The Problem Housing Estate: An Account of Omega and its People. Gower, Aldershot
SCARMAN, LORD (1986): The Scarman Report – The Brixton Disorders. Pelican Books, Harmondsworth
SOUTH LONDON FAMILY HOUSING ASSOCIATION (CO-OPS UNIT) (undated): A Sample of a Tenancy Agreement for Housing Co-operatives

III. Lettings

A Allocations and lettings

B Racial issues and rented housing estates

A Allocations and lettings

Contents

"We should try to introduce in our modern villages and towns what was always a lovely feature of English and Welsh villages, where the doctor, the grocer, the butcher and the farm labourer all lived in the same street. I believe that is essential for the full life of a citizen ... to see the living tapestry of a mixed community."

Aneurin Bevan

1. SUMMARY

Allocations have four key elements:

- Getting those in greatest need into housing that matches their need.
- Keeping property filled and reletting empty property quickly.
- Keeping the administration of lettings to a minimum to avoid delay and to respond to individual and local needs.
- Avoiding the creation of isolated, impoverished ghettos with a high turnover of tenants and constant empty property.

To do this requires a simple localised system and strong policy guidelines from central and local government. To do it fairly requires skilled housing management.

Diagram 1.37 illustrates lettings pressures and problems.

Diagram 1.37
Lettings pressures and problems

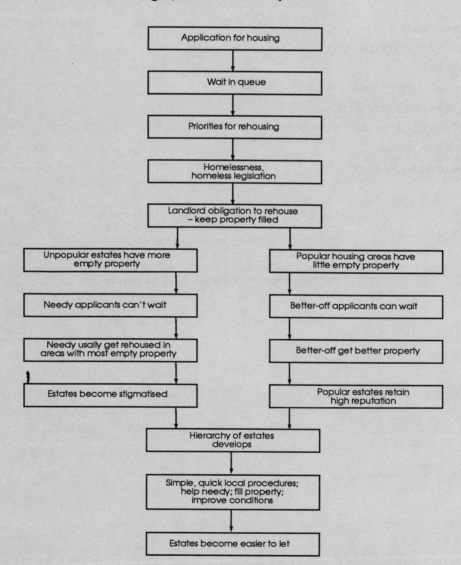

2. KEYWORDS: HUMAN TASK; CHOICE; HIERARCHY; VICIOUS CIRCLE; LOW DEMAND; FAIRNESS

Human task Keeping all dwellings let on a large estate requires a lot of detailed work and local knowledge. The success of estate-based management depends on being able to match available dwellings with needy and eligible households. It is **not** a mathematical task. It is a **human task.** It is the most sensitive and delicate job, that is easily open to abuse. Whatever system is used should be set up with care, should be operated with scrupulous fairness and should be open to scrutiny by all concerned.

Choice Applicants often have ideas of where they would like to live. Almost always it is the places where lots of other people want to go too. In popular areas there are very few empty dwellings, a very low turnover of households and lots of applicants queuing and often pushing hard to get rehoused there. With private housing these would be the expensive areas – most people would be excluded simply by cost. With council or housing association housing, they are the areas where better-off tenants and less needy households tend to live because they can wait longer, because they know how to push harder, and because traditionally councils have tended to house better-off people in better-off areas (Reade, 1982).

Hierarchy of estates The council rehousing system has followed a social hierarchy similar to the wider society. With the right to buy now guaranteed to all council tenants, the more popular areas are harder than ever to get into – each letting is potentially worth thousands of pounds to the successful applicants. People living in such areas now hold on until they can afford to buy. They are also far more likely to want to buy. This situation makes any lettings system very difficult to operate fairly. It means that there are lots of frustrated and disappointed applicants pushed, through lack of choice, into less popular housing areas.

Vicious circle The worse the housing area, the more serious the problem of empty dwellings and lack of demand becomes. It is hard to get enough applicants to want to live on unpopular and run-down estates. It takes longer to relet each dwelling. Turnover is higher than in other areas. Households living there tend to be poorer and in greater need. There are more empty dwellings. There is more desire to move off the estates. This combination – low demand, high turnover, slow re-letting, reluctance to move in – creates a loss of confidence, a poor image, weakening social controls, and a sense of alienation or apathy. Vandalism, theft and squatting in empty dwellings lead to high repairs costs and greater appearance of decline and decay. A vicious circle of unpopularity, low demand, high turnover, slow re-letting, empty dwellings, damage, delay, further unpopularity sets in. A lettings policy giving little sense of choice is almost bound to fail.

Low demand In inner London, where there is very high housing demand generally, but low demand for very rundown estates, an unpopular flat can be refused many times; it also happens on rundown estates in the Midlands and the North, where there is a surplus of family-sized units in some areas and where there is lower demand generally. The result in both cases is that only households with very little or no choice live in the least popular estates.

The problems of low demand for unpopular estates should be tackled through a many-sided approach to the management problems. The first step is to try and make the estate acceptable to a range of potential occupants, not just to those who are so desperate that they would accept anything.

Involving the residents in management issues, tackling the repairs, opening up the local office, setting up proper cleaning and caretaking are all obvious ways of making the estate more attractive and therefore easing lettings problems (see other sections). But the lettings process itself will make or break the other management efforts and must be fully integrated with it. The least successful strategy is to use the surplus of empty dwellings on the worst estates for "dumping" powerless and desperate households. Deciding to target homeless families with one offer only to the least popular estates, as some London boroughs have done, tends to make the situation worse, creating resentment, the sense of imprisonment and the sole ambition of moving out. As a result there is very little commitment to home or estate.

Fairness Lettings can be carried out within council policy, *and* at a local level, to maximise the chances of fairness, efficiency and resident support. The aim is to attract more applicants than there are empty dwellings to a particular estate; to reduce turnover; to shorten the time taken to re-let; to cut vandalism, squatting and repairs to empty dwellings; to improve management performance.

All lettings systems must take account of the two inherent problems: assessing need fairly, and allocating dwellings fairly. It is probably true that neither of these goals can be achieved perfectly.

3. DEFINITIONS

Lettings describe the process of allocating empty property to a particular household and selecting the most suitable eligible applicant for a particular available dwelling. Lettings involve matching people with property. It involves deciding **who** should be considered, e.g. the first household of the right size on the list for a particular area; or the most needy household of the right size, regardless of time on the waiting list or preference for that area. Local authorities and housing associations registered with the Housing Corporation must make available to the public their lettings system.

An applicant is a person who wants to gain access to rented housing.

A waiting list is the queue of people registered for rehousing by the council, a housing association or other housing body. Most housing organisations have a waiting list and will only consider those who have registered on the waiting list.

A transfer is the movement of a household from an existing tenancy into another more suitable or appropriate dwelling. Many housing organisations do not give transfers to households in arrears with rent. In some circumstances a transfer may be to a worse dwelling, as some authorities evict families for arrears and rehouse them in worse property. Transfers do not require an additional **number** of units but movement within existing units.

The points system is a method of assessing applicants according to their need for rehousing. Points are given for different aspects of **need** – overcrowding (lack of bedrooms), lack of basic amenities (indoor toilet, running hot water, bath or shower, hand-basin), medical needs, disability and other special circumstances. Points can also be given for length of time spent on the waiting list, length of time spent in bad conditions and length of residence in a particular area.

The aim of a points system is to assess the priority of different applicants for rehousing according to need.

The main problem with the points system is that while it attempts to be fair, it is always open to discretion and abuse. **Assessment** of need, however seemingly objective, often leads to discrimination against those least favoured, very often black people (Henderson & Karn, 1987; Parker & Dugmore, 1976; CRE, 1984; 1988).

The points system, while it may attempt to measure need, does not help with matching dwelling and applicant or vice versa. It is therefore only one part of the lettings process.

Date order describes the order in which applicants register on the waiting list and become eligible for rehousing. Under this arrangement, the household that has been registered for longest will normally be the first in the queue for rehousing. Many local authorities have operated this system and still do.

It is possible to combine a date-order system and a points system, which some local authorities are now doing.

The problem with date order is that it does not accurately reflect the particular housing conditions or special needs of a household. Increasingly, local authorities are using date order to rehouse priority homeless households.

Targets. Local authorities can establish targets for rehousing different groups, with a share of the likely empty property in any one year being allocated to match the needs of different types of applicants. This is done to try and ensure some chance for all the groups in need.

Several local authorities are now adopting this system because points systems have become over-complex and unworkable, given the shortage of property in high demand areas and the pressure of urgent cases.

There are five main **rehousing routes** which require targetting if a target system is adopted: decanting (rehousing), emergency (flood, violence, fire, etc), priority homelessness, health (medical priority), and waiting list (and transfers).

Rehousing routes. When someone applies for rehousing, whether the housing organisation uses date order, points, targets or some combination to rank applicants, there will be factors affecting their eligibility for rehousing more directly:

i) Decant. If a household is a tenant in a property which the landlord needs for some other purpose,

e.g. demolition or total renovation, the landlord has a direct obligation to secure satisfactory comparable housing for the household. This is an overriding duty and households requiring decanting will take priority over all other rehousing obligations. However, **the time** taken to decant is very variable. A household may wait for years for suitable rehousing.

The families awaiting rehousing may be very choosy because the local authorities' obligation to them gives them a powerful lever in getting the best that is available.

ii) Homeless. Since 1977, local authorities have had an overriding duty to help unintentionally homeless households in priority need with a local connection or without any other local connection.

They must give priority to three main groups of homeless people – families with dependent children under 16; pregnant women; vulnerable households, e.g. elderly, mentally or physically ill; young adults discharged from care. Only the local authority has this duty and, therefore, especially in areas of high need, high demand and high levels of homelessness, particularly London, the local authority tries to keep control of the stock, admissions under homelessness and other lettings.

However, because homeless households are by definition **in crisis** and require immediate help, local authorities can give them the worst property and rehouse them in temporary or emergency accommodation. This they tend to do. Nonetheless, homelessness and threatened homelessness have become an important rehousing route, overriding the waiting list and the points system. The local authority has no obligation to offer housing if it can be shown that the family has become intentionally homeless.

Emergencies are treated in a similar way to homeless households.

iii) Medical priority. Where a household has an acute medical problem linked directly to housing (e.g. wheelchair disability in a household occupying a dwelling on a high floor with no lift), the local authority accepts responsibility for attempting to help. Many cases with **extremely** high medical priority often wait years for help. This is sometimes because their requirements are so special; sometimes because the local authority is over-bureaucratic. Many medical priority cases are "marginal" and not clear-cut; many are elderly so that the need is for sheltered accommodation. Many need ground floor accommodation and in London this can be difficult.

iv) Special needs. Increasingly, local authorities and housing associations are providing for special needs:
– sheltered accommodation for elderly or disabled households that cannot cope with full independence;
– hostel accommodation, usually for either homeless single people or people discharged from institutions (prisons, hospitals, children's homes);
– adapted accommodation, usually providing wheelchair access, where there is no additional service;
– young single accommodation, equivalent to student accommodation.

In all these cases only people fitting the categories for which the accommodation is designed will be eligible. Because of the policy of rehousing more and more people with special needs in the community, there is growing demand for special housing.

v) Sons and daughters. There is **no** obligation on local authorities to give priority to the children of existing tenants. However, there are some situations where this is done; for example, in areas where virtually the only rented housing is owned by the council, there may be no other possibility for rehousing low-income, newly formed households. If they compete with homeless families and decant cases, they will **never** get rehoused other than by becoming homeless themselves. It can apply in rural areas such as Devon and Cornwall where retirement homes and the right to buy have reduced the supply of rented accommodation and pushed up prices. It also applies in boroughs like Tower Hamlets where 80 per cent of the total stock is owned by the local authority and prices are very high because of pressures from the city. It is also sometimes introduced on very unpopular estates to increase community stability. The waiting list should include adult children of tenants.

An offer involves the landlord telling an applicant that accommodation believed to be suitable is available for the applicant's household and that he/she can become the tenant of that property if he/she wants.

In the private market, the principle of first come, first served, is combined with a judgement on the suitability, however defined, of the applicant. A ban on children, proven ability to pay rent, are common criteria. Local authorities have other criteria for eligibility, such as need, statutory homelessness or living in the local authority area. Offers are made on the basis of administrative systems geared to these often complex criteria.

Refusals. Most housing organisations accept the right of applicants to refuse an offer of accommodation without disqualifying them from further offers. However, a growing number of local authorities restrict the number of offers they are prepared to make, commonly to two or three offers. Homeless households are often made one offer only. If they refuse that offer, they can be disqualified from further chances of rehousing, at least for a time. The reason for restricting the number of offers an applicant gets is to prevent time being wasted on offers which will be turned down as the applicant holds out for the offer he/she really wants. Because popular and readily acceptable offers are in short supply, applicants rarely receive the offers that they want or have expressed a choice for. Better-off tenants can often afford to wait, following a council appeal system in an attempt to outmanoeuvre the lettings system. Desperate tenants often accept from fear that later offers may be worse (a practice adopted by some councils in an attempt to reduce refusal rates).

The system of refusals causes havoc in the already complex lettings system. A major cause of refusals is the remoteness of many lettings systems that give individual applicants very little sense of choice and that lead to frequent mismatches of dwellings and people.

Nominations. Local authorities, housing associations and co-operatives may agree that applicants can be "nominated" for rehousing. An organisation with units agrees to take nominated applicants in exchange for support from the local authority. This system can help all parties, as long as the rehousing organisation

retains the right to match an individual with a particular property. The use of nominations is likely to increase as ownership of "social" housing becomes more diverse.

Because the different rehousing routes are often in conflict with each other and local authorities are forced to select between conflicting and equally deserving needs, the whole question of lettings and selection is fraught with pitfalls and injustice.

4. TARGETS

– Create a social mix on the estate as close to the wider community as possible. This should apply to income levels, proportions of children, racial minorities, young single people etc.

– Make lettings information available in the different languages spoken on the estate and in the area.

– Keep the waiting list up to date by requiring re-registration at least once a year.

– Give written confirmation of all applications, dated.

– Make the allocations system available at the local office to all callers.

– Control empty property locally – the aim should be to re-let within four weeks maximum.

– Keep down the cost of repair of empty property by giving incentives to outgoing tenants and giving repair and decoration allowances to incoming tenants.

– Visit all new tenants within two weeks of moving in.

– Keep the number of empty properties at any one time below 2 per cent.

– Introduce as much flexibility as possible with internal transfers.

– Keep turnover to below 20 per cent – use imaginative ways of reducing turnover – internal transfers are very successful.

– Localise as many procedures as possible.

– Keep a constant check on refusals – adopt whatever strategy minimises them.

– Produce monthly lettings information for the centre.

5. ESSENTIAL STEPS IN THE LETTINGS PROCESS

1. An applicant registers with a housing organisation.

2. A lettings officer assesses the application – are they eligible?

3. The applicant is visited to verify the application and to determine priority, target group and points.

4. The size of unit needed is established.

5. The area the applicant wishes to live in is established – in relation to available property.

6. The applicant joins the queue for an offer. The queue (or waiting list) is normally broken down

in four ways: – rehousing route, e.g. health, homeless, decant, waiting list, transfer; – level or priority· – area required; and – bedroom size.

7. Unintentional priority homeless cases are helped immediately but may then queue for permanent rehousing in temporary accommodation.

8. An empty dwelling is found.

9. The property is checked for the right size in roughly the right area.

10. An offer is made to the most eligible applicant (i.e. with highest points or at the head of a target queue, such as decant).

11. The applicant is asked to come and collect the keys for a viewing. The applicant does one of three things: – collects the key and goes to see the property; or – does not answer within the time limit, e.g. two weeks; or – informs the lettings officer that the offer is in the wrong area, in the wrong estate, the wrong storey height, or the wrong size.

12. The applicant decides to accept or reject the offer.

13. If the applicant accepts, a date for moving in is agreed. If the applicant refuses, a new offer is made to the next highest priority case, and so on until accepted.

14. The tenancy agreement is signed.

15. The rent-paying arrangements with the issue of a rent book are agreed.

Diagram 1.38 shows the steps in simplified form.

6. THE THREE MAIN ELEMENTS OF REHOUSING

The three elements that most strongly influence lettings are the lettings policies, the administrative method and the level of discretion:

– **the policies** within which lettings are operated should be laid down centrally by the council or other housing organisation;

– **the administration** of lettings involves largely routine operations that are best conducted locally to avoid delay and to improve matching;

– **discretion** comes in under whatever system is adopted, when applicants are visited, when applicants say which is their preferred area, and when offers are made, considered and accepted or refused. A more local and more personal system is regarded by tenants as more likely to be fair (Maclennan, 1989). It is important to limit discretion in lettings to the matching of applicants and property, and not to the rules of access.

If lettings policies and priorities are clear, *lettings officers can be trained and trusted* to carry out their duties directly at a local level, in direct contact with applicants. There is no need to make the system remote and impersonal. They should be encouraged to sort out the best solution to the lettings jigsaw. And they should be **clearly answerable** to the council, through their manager, for all decisions.

Central lettings systems do not address the problems of the worst estates or the most disadvantaged households since they tend to push the two together and create stigmatised housing areas (Burbidge et al., 1981).

Local lettings systems have been shown to work effectively for low-income households and for the least popular housing areas, as long as they operate within agreed wider policies and as long as they are carefully monitored (Power, April 1987; 1987; November 1988).

Having a single queue for many thousands of dwellings is neither efficient nor equitable. People in housing need will always be at a disadvantage. They want some sense of control over their own destiny, however limited; by creating many smaller, more local queues, rather than pushing all applicants through a central and bureaucratic machine, there is some chance of this being achieved.

7. CENTRAL LETTINGS

Usually the allocation of housing is organised through the Town Hall or central housing department. Applicants are allocated points based on agreed measures of need or are registered in date order. Normally applicants are asked to state their preference for areas of rehousing, maybe up to three estates or areas from the total stock. Applicants then wait in a queue for an offer.

The wait in the queue

Depending on general housing demand in the area, and also the level of priority an applicant has, it may take anything from a few weeks to several years between registering need for a home and moving in. Sometimes family circumstances will have changed in the time between applying for housing and receiving an offer. For this reason many councils only visit to assess and verify circumstances when it looks likely that the household might be nearing an offer. However, this means that neither the housing body nor the applicant knows the position they are in accurately. It also means that the queue or waiting list does not accurately reflect demand for housing or need (Prescott-Clarke, Allen and Morrissey, 1988). The most obvious way to overcome this problem is to require annual re-registration and constant updating of the waiting list. L. B. Greenwich does this very effectively.

A major problem with the wait in the queue is that a household may never quite make it to the top of the queue because cases of more extreme need "jump the queue" each time. An elderly disabled person, an overcrowded family or a couple without children in insecure accommodation may never be more needy at a particular point in time than an emergency homeless case. This is one of the intractable lettings problems.

Diagram 1.38 Essential steps in the lettings process

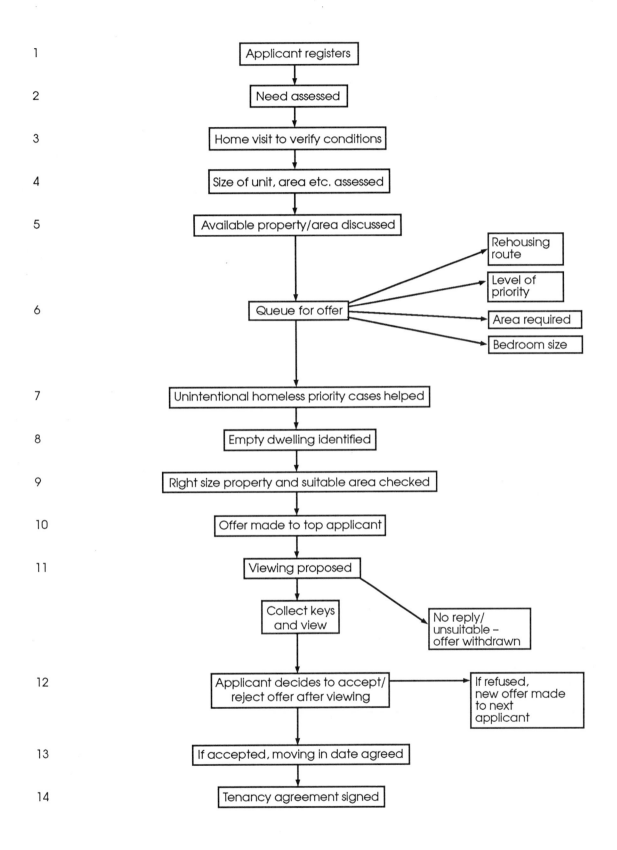

Personal circumstances

There are many variables involved in each person's cir cumstances and their need for housing. The following are a few:

- size of household

- composition of household

- children (under five/school age)

- young adults

- elderly (single, couple)

- single parent

- any disability

- relationships within household

- sex of children, young people and adults.

It is extremely hard to devise a system that gives weight to different types of need objectively, e.g. the needs of the elderly against the needs of a lone mother or a teenager leaving a children's home.

Choice of area

Area preferences may be influenced by:

- work (possible needs of more than one member of household)

- transport

- family ties – informal support network and caring obligations, e.g. a dependent relative

- schools

- health needs – hospital or other treatment needs

- special needs, e.g. access to day care for small children; access to support for elderly or lone parents.

The need to live in a particular area may be overriding or it may reflect simply a preference for a particular estate. It is hard to devise points that measure such things as existing employment or attendance at a particular school. The factors influencing choice of area are separate from dwelling preferences, e.g. house and garden, flat on lower floor, small block etc.

Problems with central lettings

It is unrealistic to expect a central allocations system to allow for such highly personal variations in need or desire. It is impossible to judge between two equally deserving but different cases in an impersonal way. The systems that have evolved to cope with these difficulties are more and more complex to cover a wider and wider range of possible variations in circumstance. As a result discretion has constantly crept in. Black households have been consistently discriminated against as a result.

A central system raises other problems too:

- incorrect information in the application process

- difficulty in matching dwellings with applicants

- little contact between the applicant and the lettings officer

- lengthy paperwork

- slow re-letting of empty property.

- difficulty in gaining access to housing for certain groups

- potential abuse of the lettings system by applicants

The council's central role

There is a vital role for the local authority that no one else can adequately cover:

- laying down **priorities**;

- developing the lettings **system**, e.g. points, targets, date order, waiting list;

- **nominating** the most needy families to the local list;

- **checking** on each case that is to be rehoused.

Local authorities have a statutory duty to give priority to helping:

- overcrowded and large households;

- unintentionally homeless households;

- vulnerable households;

- households in inadequate housing, particularly if it is unfit;

- people made homeless through emergency disasters, e.g. flood, fire, earthquake;

- people made homeless through the authorities' own action such as demolition, slum clearance, closing orders, public building, e.g. schools or road building.

The council should:

- establish policies;

- determine priorities and criteria for rehousing;

- hold a central waiting list in order to measure demand;

- keep track of problems, e.g. unpopular estates, needs of elderly or single people, shortage of large family units, homelessness problems, etc.;

- determine the method of ordering priorities, involving some combination of date order, targets and points (Parker & Barrilea, 1989).

8. LOCAL LETTINGS

Within that broad policy framework, each estate office or housing organisation can operate a fair and efficient local lettings system, with all applicants being nominated or approved by the council. For no method of allocation works smoothly over a large number of properties, unless some of the steps are handled locally.

Local lettings involve the administration and control of the lettings process at a local office or through a local housing organisation, rather than through the Town Hall. The aim of local lettings is first and foremost to get empty dwellings in unpopular areas let quickly and to get needy households into dwellings through a local system that will make them feel welcome, rather than feeling pushed into accepting an offer through an impersonal system.

The main requirements of a local lettings system are as follows:

– **a local waiting list** made up of applicants nominated by the council or of people who apply direct to the local office and are eligible for rehousing. Their registration and eligibility should be approved by the local authority (or housing association or co-operative);

– a system for **ranking applicants** according to need, using date order, points or a targets system (L.S.E. Housing, 1990). The priority system should be guided by the centre or can be precisely laid down by the centre;

– **administrative procedures** for handling enquiries, applications and nominations, making offers, viewing and signing up.

Most local authorities are moving towards **local administration of lettings** – where they are also decentralising other functions. The major rehousing steps that can best be carried out locally follow.

Local inquiries

Local inquiries about lettings are bound to happen if a local office is doing its job properly and is open to tenants. At the very least, the adult children of tenants will need to find somewhere to live when they get married or have children themselves or simply mature to the point of independence. There may also be homeless or other very needy people who hear about the local office and come and inquire. A good local office should be a lot more accessible than a large Town Hall or central department.

The local office should be able to refer these potential applicants to the right place and advise them on the best possible routes to housing. Ideally, the local office should have application forms for the central waiting list. If there are computerised lettings, the inquirer may be able to register locally. This already happens in places like Walsall and Islington.

Local registration

It is very helpful if all households wanting to be rehoused in the local office area register at the local office either before they have been visited and checked, where there is a local waiting list, or after, where there is a nominations system or a central allocation system.

The local registration ensures that everyone being considered for rehousing actually wants to live there and also that there is face to face contact. It reduces the refusals, it simplifies administration and monitoring and it speeds up the process of matching.

The most important reason for local registration is that it allows the applicants, however little choice they have and however desperate they are for housing, to take some steps themselves towards solving their housing problem. It increases their control over the process, even if it does not expand their choice. It is rather like being poor and controlling your small income rather

than being forced to depend on an institution **because** you are poor.

Local waiting lists

All registered local applicants, whether nominated from the centre or simply applying through the local office, constitute the local waiting list. Where there is low demand and a problem in letting the available dwellings, it makes sense to have a local waiting list, not just of nominations but also of local applicants – anyone living in the local area (or local authority area) interested in living on the estate. A waiting list at the local office of people wanting to live in the area makes the process of letting immediately simpler and more manageable.

Local applicants can be assessed in the same way as nominated applicants. Where there is such low demand that there are permanently empty dwellings, then applicants can simply register and be rehoused straight off the list. This already happens in parts of the North-West, North-East and South Wales.

Internal transfers

This is the part of lettings that is most commonly handed down to a local area. Where there is a local office handling any other areas of management, but not the lettings process, the local office will often be the first point of contact for households on the estate not wanting to move away but needing another type or size of dwelling, for example a larger or smaller unit, or one nearer the ground floor.

Internal transfers do **not** reduce the number of available dwellings but they do:

a) change **which** dwellings are available;

b) **reduce** pressure for transfers away from the estate;

c) help to **stabilise** the community by satisfying local demand first;

d) help the local office to make best use of the stock through local **knowledge**;

e) give the local office some **control** and some ability to respond directly to local needs.

By reducing the turnover of households, internal transfers make a major contribution to **reversing** decline.

There is an objection to internal transfers in that they sometimes lead to the most desirable local dwellings being taken by local people rather than outsiders. But as long as rules of eligibility are followed and as long as internal transfers are monitored to ensure fairness, they can greatly help to stabilise the estate, reduce the demand to move off, and therefore enhance the chances of the success of local management. This in turn helps the lettings performance.

Because an internal transfer case is vacating an existing local dwelling in order to occupy another already empty dwelling, there is no net loss and another household can move in. The fine arguments about **who** deserves **which** dwelling on an estate are almost impossible to answer.

There is a strong practical advantage in locally controlled internal transfers: it enables the local office to insist that the existing dwelling is left clean and in good condition. This makes re-letting easier, cheaper and quicker.

Nominations

A simple nominations system is the most effective way for a local authority to ensure that the households it gives priority to (e.g. homeless) get rehoused first within local areas. In the case of homeless families, as long as all empty property is notified immediately to the centre, the centre can nominate to the local office where property is available, either after a visit to the applicant by the Homeless Persons Unit or with a request for the local office to visit.

Assuming that only eligible applicants are forwarded from the central waiting list to the local office for home visits, the local office should be able, following the visit, to hold those applicants in readiness for rehousing offers. Their eligibility will have been determined through the points or target system. If necessary, there can be formal approval from the centre of each applicant visited.

Home visits

The need for visiting is created by the points system. If households know that rehousing is according to certain rules, then they will want to put forward as strong a case as possible according to the rules. If there is no checking, then people have a strong incentive to "bend" the facts, e.g. give the address of a relative in the correct area, turn a bedroom into a "cupboard", "share" a bathroom or kitchen. It makes no sense to put forward the literal facts if distorted facts will help you get a home!

Therefore, home visits to applicants have become an essential means of assessment. Visits are best carried out by the local office to which applicants have been referred. In low demand areas, many local authorities only visit a sample of applicants or applicants with particular needs.

Visiting applicants should be done by trained, experienced and trusted staff, as visiting is the area where discrimination most easily creeps in. The manager, committee, or senior housing officer should check rigorously. And visits should have the **sole** purpose of establishing the **facts**, e.g. number of rooms, floor measurements, basic amenities, household size, special needs (e.g. disability).

In areas where ethnic minorities are concentrated, it is essential to keep records in order to ensure fair policies and practices (see section on racial issues).

The home visit should not be used for purposes such as establishing the area of choice, pressuring the applicant to accept an unsuitable offer, assessing housekeeping standards or other subjective assessments. (The GLC found that 80 per cent of all visited

11. 'Allocating housing is far from a mathematical task.' Cloverhall Estate, Rochdale

Paul Herrmann/Profile

Diagram 1.39
Control of empty properties

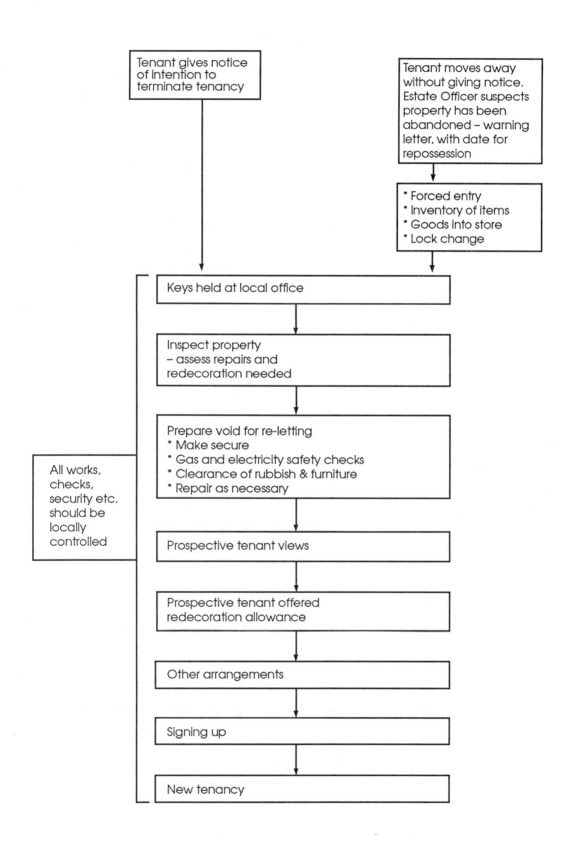

applicants had good housekeeping standards – so what!). It should, however, be used to uncover any unusual circumstances that **directly** influence the applicant's position, e.g. a handicapped child and level of handicap – wheelchair, special schooling; chronic mental or physical illness, requiring supported housing; domestic violence, requiring urgent rehousing in a different area; harrassment of a serious nature, including racial harassment; serious debt or other financial crisis requiring legal or other advice, e.g. court proceedings for recovery of the existing tenancy. None of these factors act as a bar to rehousing but they dictate the need for speed, the problem of location and access, and the need for other support (medical, social services etc).

Where the home visit is done by staff at a local office with a view to local rehousing, it is important for the visitor to be able to refer applicants to other areas or other avenues for rehousing if there is nothing suitable available locally. It is also important to be able to tell people how likely they are to be rehoused and when. Better to give **bad** news than total uncertainty. Facts, not opinions, are needed.

Viewing

Viewing is one of the most important steps in lettings, where an applicant goes to look at the prospective property and decides whether or not to accept. If there is only the central lettings system, where the keys are picked up from a central or district base and the applicant goes alone to the property, there are scores of possible snags in the system – lost keys, unrepaired or newly vandalised property, wrong date, failure to show up – all of which cause delay and **often** cause refusals or a simple failure ever to get to the right place. Also the impersonal nature of it and the lack of any positive "marketing" of the dwelling or estate means that the applicant often refuses to view dwellings on estates with a bad reputation.

Accompanied viewing, where an estate officer or caretaker arranges to **meet** the applicant and **go with** them to the property, not only leads to greater acceptance, it helps the applicant who can ask questions, agree a date to move in, get a better feel for the place and the organisation, feel more **"at home"**. All this will apply particularly to a large estate, an estate in an unfamiliar area, a flatted estate with blocks and numbers which are often hard to locate, or an estate which has a reputation as "rough", "unpopular" or "bad".

Accompanied viewings are far easier to organise and a lot more successful if the local office arranges them. There is then the double advantage that the prospective tenant knows the office and is even more likely to want to accept an offer as a result.

Signing up

Signing up is the process of becoming a tenant, agreeing to the rent, getting a rent book, agreeing to the tenancy conditions, and actually signing up for the dwelling.

If these administrative tasks are controlled through a local office, there is a clear link between the person responsible for management of a tenancy and the person who becomes the tenant. To do it anywhere else is cumbersome and reduces the direct sense of responsibility of both parties. To complete the letting locally maximises the mutual sense of responsibility and therefore the chances of the tenancy working well.

Local control of empty dwellings

The local control of empty dwellings is a most important step in ensuring efficient lettings. If empty dwellings are repaired through a local office, and keys are held locally, then there will be far fewer hiccups in the lettings system.

Most of the delays in lettings are caused through delays in handling voids. Most delays in voids are caused through administrative mistakes or through the complex chain of decisions and paper processes over which no one person has proper control.

If the local office is in full control, then it should be possible to get most property ready within a few days, and even property needing repair within 2–4 weeks (Power, November 1988). Diagram 1.39 shows the different stages involved in controlling empty property. Very few of these steps can be executed efficiently except through the local office **on the spot**.

Squatting

One of the most serious consequences of **empty property** is squatting or illegal occupation. When once property is occupied illegally, other things follow:

a) There is no rent income.

b) The property cannot be let.

c) Eviction proceedings are costly.

d) Squatters are unknown to the landlord and cannot be dealt with as official tenants, e.g. for repairs – as a result, relations with squatters are often fraught because access is refused.

e) Squatters operate outside the law and often attract other illegal activities; particularly notorious is drug abuse and drug dealing. This brings them ill repute and stigmatises the estate.

f) There are many squatters who are simply desperate for somewhere to live. If empty property is inefficiently controlled and left empty for long periods and if the lettings system does not work, then it makes sense to those in need to occupy the unused property anyway.

The simple and obvious way to overcome squatting is to let quickly, fairly and efficiently and to control empty property carefully. This has been done on Broadwater Farm, the Isle of Dogs, and the Ocean Estate, all in areas of London, where there is high demand, through local control of empty property.

In practice, squatting is a much bigger problem in London than elsewhere because of housing pressures and also because re-letting is slower and there is more empty property. Many problems in London are compounded by a higher level of turnover. On unpopular estates, squatting can probably only be overcome through concentrated localised effort.

Diagram 1.40
The operation of local lettings

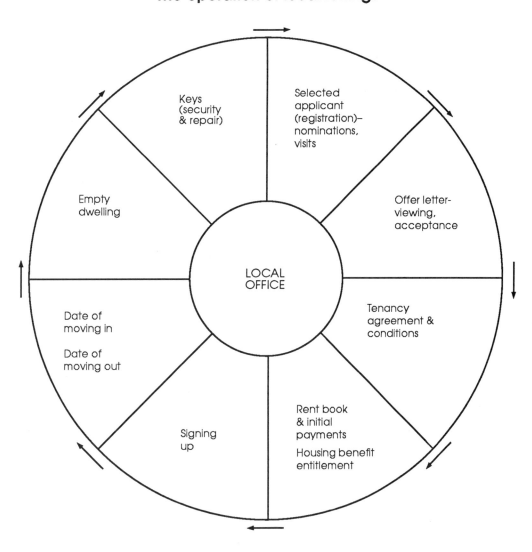

Diagram 1.40 illustrates the operation of local lettings. It is easy to see the logic for handling all segments of the circular process within a simple self-contained local organisation. The more bits of this process are taken on by separate or remote parts of the organisation, the more likely it is to break down. In unpopular areas, it is **only** likely to work if they are all co-ordinated through a local office.

9. LOCAL MONITORING AND TRAINING

The most important lettings targets are full occupancy and rehousing those in need. There should be simple wall charts in the local office, showing month by month the number of empty dwellings, re-letting time and squatted dwellings. Also the number of new applicants and cases rehoused should be shown. It will be important to monitor the rehousing routes to prevent "dumping" and to make sure needs are being met.

Targets and priorities should be shown, with actual lettings set against them, e.g. homeless rehousing target for 1989 in one local office – 50; actual rehousing – 47. The local authority or housing association should require monthly monitoring returns on lettings from all local offices, management co-operatives, Estate Management Boards.

Proper training for staff and residents' representatives is an essential prerequisite for a good rehousing system. This means training in allocations procedures, policies and implementation. Training in interviewing skills, dealing with the public, ethnic monitoring, equal opportunities, customer care, legislation, marketing, presentation and report writing, telephone behaviour etc. are all areas that affect allocations and require careful skilled preparation. Local responsibility will **only** work if local skills are developed. Lettings and transfers are primary causes of friction and upset. Training staff in handling the lettings process and the public is crucial.

10. COMPUTERS

Until recently, most lettings systems were run with written manual records. However, increasingly computers are used. Computers make a number of things possible:

a) a simple method for ordering the queue according to bedroom size needed, area of choice, priority (or target) group, points level;

b) a link between the centre and local offices. This makes local registration, local waiting lists and nominations far simpler. It facilitates local administration with central supervision;

c) where there is a computer at the centre but not in the local offices, it still helps the centre to monitor **as long as** the local office supplies information regularly to the centre. A local microcomputer (even without a direct link but that is compatible with the centre) can make the transfer of information much simpler and quicker.

The disadvantages of computers are:

– snags in the system can cause it to break down;

– many complex human variables cannot be handled by computer;

– the matching and prioritising is mechanical and any defect in the information fed in immediately causes a miscalculation or mismatch;

– constant changes in circumstance require constant updating;

– the actual offer, viewing, signing up, etc. all require **personal** contact.

Computers are **most** useful in combination with a local and **personal** lettings procedure.

11. EXAMPLES OF LETTINGS SYSTEMS LINKED TO LOCAL OFFICES

In high demand areas, local offices can play a major part in the administration of lettings, while following council priorities and allocating on the basis of need. Broadwater Farm, Haringey and Bethnal Green, Tower Hamlets are two examples of this.

In low demand areas, local offices need to play a highly active role in recruiting applicants, controlling empty property and attempting to reverse the intense decline of the least popular areas. Cloverhall, Rochdale; Kelvin Estate, Sheffield and Penrhys Estate, Rhondda all have localised lettings.

12. ROLE OF TENANTS IN REHOUSING

Where tenants take on management responsibility within a local organisation, responsible tenants' representatives should have a role in lettings processes. Tenants' representatives should discuss and be informed about:

a) the lettings system

b) priorities for rehousing

c) targets, e.g. rehousing special groups

d) racial discrimination

e) monitoring.

This will help them to understand the complexities of lettings.

Some roles that tenants have played successfully include:

– taking prospective tenants to view property;

– interviewing applicants about living on the estate (co-operatives);

– producing a handbook for new tenants;

– visiting new tenants after they have moved in;

– helping to develop policies for special needs e.g. furnished lettings;

– helping to prevent "dumping";

– supporting the transfer of households who desperately need different accommodation.

The actual matching of individual properties to those with highest priority is best done by paid staff who are directly accountable either to the Tenant Board or Co-operative Executive Committee or to the Council for how they carry out allocations procedures. The Estate Management Board or Co-operative Agreements spell out the division of responsibility between local management organisations and the local authority or housing association (Zipfel, 1989).

Tenants' organisations with a direct role in rehousing should follow council and Government policy, be supervised and monitored in exactly the same way as anyone else. No tenant who has a direct interest in a particular applicant or property (e.g. is a relative or lives in adjacent property) should have any role in selection.

Where there is a local housing office, locally-based staff and a local management organisation, local lettings need to be carefully controlled. It is vital for clear safeguards to be built into all aspects of the lettings process so that the role of both tenants' representatives and local staff is clear, open to scrutiny and supported by the local authority. A number of local authorities, such as Glasgow and Islington, have developed mechanisms for devolving significant responsibility to tenant co-operatives and to locally-based housing staff.

In areas where rehousing is a fraught issue and the local authority cannot agree to tenants having a direct role in selection, tenants can play an advisory role in developing policies (this can arise on estates where there have been incidents of racial harassment for example). They are entitled to full information on the lettings system and they can be allowed to make representations on issues that affect them directly, such as internal transfers.

The level of responsibility of tenants in lettings should match their involvement in other management areas such as repairs and budgets.

They may play an advisory role where there is an Estate Committee. They may have a more direct input, some responsibility and shared control where there is an

Estate Management Board. They may take on much fuller responsibility and control where there is a tenant management co-operative.

In all cases, the landlord retains final responsibility for lettings policies and priorities, for ensuring that these are carried out fairly and without discrimination, and for delegating direct responsibility only within a formal legal framework approved by the Secretary of State.

13. COMBINING A CENTRAL AND LOCAL SYSTEM

Priority for those in need. However limited or extensive the role of the local office in running local lettings, the role of the central organisation is **all**-important in ensuring that those in need get housed.

Nominations. Local authorities gain tremendous advantages by agreeing nominations with local housing organisations. It helps access for the most needy but it leaves the local management organisation with the responsibility for matching and also all the administrative headaches of viewing, signing up, etc. As local authorities move towards greater decentralisation and as co-operatives, housing associations and Estate Management Boards grow, nominations to other bodies will become an important route to rehousing. In Europe it is already the main method of rehousing used by local authorities.

Homelessness and local offices. Local authorities need to liaise closely with local offices over rehousing homeless families.

Homeless households can be asked to apply direct to local offices. Islington already does this. Or they can be referred to local offices, for rehousing in a particular empty property. Either way, local offices can help the local authority to carry out its legal obligations to the homeless more effectively. The Isle of Dogs, Bethnal Green and other decentralised neighbourhoods in Tower Hamlets are examples of this approach, significantly reducing the numbers in bed and breakfast (L.S.E. Housing, 1990).

Other priorities for rehousing. The centre needs to lay down wider rehousing priorities. For example, in areas of inner London where prices are high, a priority might be to rehouse local "key" workers such as teachers, transport workers, young employed, newcomers with jobs, etc. These groups might be given priority on the grounds that without them the area would decline economically; with them it will thrive (vis. shortage of London teachers and London nurses). Another priority may be the adult children of existing residents who are being "priced" out by gentrifiers or, in desirable rural areas, by second-home buyers. Another priority may be housing for the elderly.

Supervision. Local authorities have direct responsibility for ensuring that their own (very large) stock of housing is properly managed. They must therefore supervise lettings and access, no matter how far they decentralise.

There are a number of obvious ways of checking (see Section on Monitoring) e.g. are the numbers of black people getting rehoused as great as in the area as a whole? Are the numbers of households on housing benefit comparable with other similar areas? Are the numbers of homeless in bed-and-breakfast rising and if so why?

It is sometimes easier for local authorities to check on once-removed, small organisations than on their own internal bureaucracy. In a large, complex bureaucracy, the distance between decision-makers and implementers is very great. There are strong vested interests in concealing faults in the system and disguising blame. As a result, those at the top rarely have a very accurate picture of what is happening on the ground (Peters, 1987).

Conversely, small local organisations find it hard to conceal their practices. If the local authority exercises its supervisory and monitoring role thoroughly, the local organisation is likely to perform according to the rules. There is nowhere to hide (Power, November 1988).

Government. Local government provides the essential bridge between national (central) government and local needs. Diagram 1.41 illustrates the respective roles of central and local government and local housing organisations in the allocation of housing.

14. CHECKLIST ON LETTINGS

1. How many empty dwellings a month are there? Are there fewer empty dwellings now than when the local office opened? Is the turnover of households going up or down?

2. Is there a waiting list of people wanting to move to the estate? Is it growing? Are there families wanting to live there? How long do people wait before being rehoused?

3. How long does it take to repair empty dwellings? How much does it cost? How long does it take to fill an empty dwelling? How much rent is lost each month on empty property?

4. Do you make unsuitable lettings (e.g. a single young person in a 3-bedroom house) simply to fill the voids?

5. Are there many young single lettings? Does this create special management needs? Problems?

6. Are there ghost tenancies – "Giro drops" – or unauthorised tenancies?

7. Do adult children of existing residents want to stay on the estate? Do you have any policies that facilitate this **fairly**?

8. How many right to buy applications are there? What impact do they have?

9. How many tenants are on housing benefit (full/partial)? Are there more low-income tenants than in other estates?

10. Is the estate used for "dumping" difficult households?

Diagram 1.41

**The roles of central and local government
and local housing organisations in the
allocation of housing**

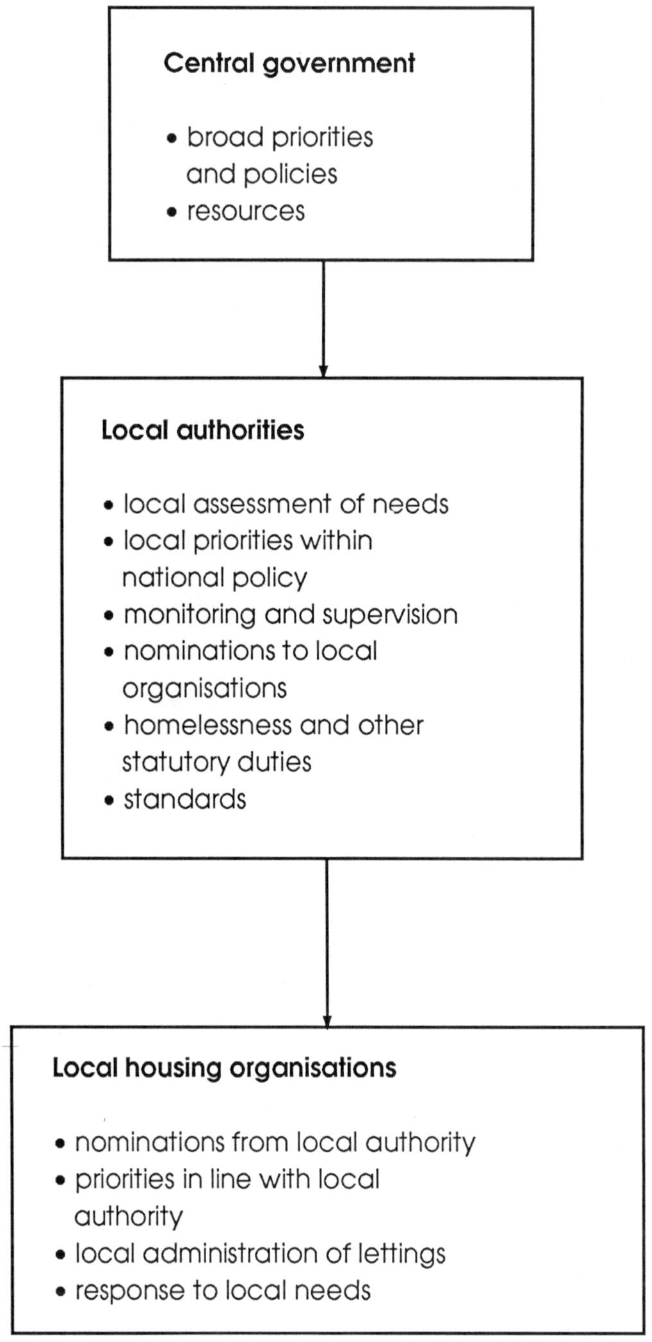

Central government

- broad priorities
  and policies
- resources

Local authorities

- local assessment of needs
- local priorities within
  national policy
- monitoring and supervision
- nominations to local
  organisations
- homelessness and other
  statutory duties
- standards

Local housing organisations

- nominations from local authority
- priorities in line with local
  authority
- local administration of lettings
- response to local needs

11. Does the council allow the local office to promote the estate?

12. Are tenants' representatives negative/positive about the estate?
And about incoming tenants?

13. Does the local office have any say in allocations? Or play any part in the lettings process?
Do tenants' representatives have an input into lettings?

14. Does the local office control internal transfers?

15. How many applicants refuse offers?

16. Are viewings accompanied?

17. Are flats cleared out/cleaned/redecorated, and to what standards?

18. Are there squatters on the estate?
How are they dealt with?

19. Are there particular areas or blocks on the estate that are harder to let?

20. What reasons do people give for refusing offers?

21. Does the office monitor lettings, e.g. ethnic monitoring; rehousing route (homeless, transfer, etc); time on waiting list; reletting time; cost of each relet, etc?
Does the local authority monitor lettings?

15. SOME USEFUL BOOKS ON LETTINGS

ALA, LHAC, LBA (1989): Partners in Meeting Housing Need. Local Authority Nominations to Housing Associations in London – Good Practice Guide, NFHA, London

Association of Metropolitan Authorities (1988): Allocations. Local Authority Housing and Racial Equality Working Party. London

Burbidge M et al (1981): An Investigation of Difficult-to-Let Housing, Vol 1: General Findings. HMSO

Commission for Racial Equality (1984): Race and Council Housing in Hackney – Report of a Formal Investigation. London

—— (1988): Homelessness is Discrimination – Report of a Formal Investigation into the London Borough of Tower Hamlets

—— (1989): Racial Discrimination in Liverpool City Council – Report of a Formal Investigation into the Housing Department

Cullingworth (1969): Council Housing, Purposes, Procedures and Priorities. 9th Report CHAC, HMSO

Department of the Environment (1988): Queuing for Housing: A Study of Council Housing Waiting Lists. HMSO

Housing Corporation (1989): Access to Housing Association Homes: A Guide to Tenant Selection. HC 48/89. London

London Research Centre (1988): Access to Housing in London – A Report Based on the Results of the London Housing Survey 1986–87. London

National Federation of Housing Associations (1982): Race & Housing: A Guide for Housing Associations. London

—— (1985): Race & Housing: Ethnic Record-Keeping & Monitoring

—— (1989): Tackling Homelessness: A Good Practice Guide for Housing Associations

—— (1989): The Core System: A manual for the continuous recording of new lettings and sales

Scottish Housing Advisory Committee (1980): The Allocation and Transfer of Council Houses. SDD Edinburgh, HMSO

B Racial issues and rented housing estates

Contents

> "Civilizations have risen upon the face of the earth ... Almost all of them have descended into the junk heaps of destruction. The decline and fall of these civilizations ... was not caused by external invasions but by internal decay. They failed to respond creatively to the challenges impinging upon them."
>
> Martin Luther King

1. SUMMARY

It is impossible to do justice to the complex and distressing origins and impact of racial discrimination in housing. Members of minority ethnic groups not only suffer the disadvantage of worse economic conditions, which are reflected directly in housing conditions; they also experience discrimination at many levels of society. This discrimination, whether direct or indirect, is often illegal under the Race Relations Act, 1976.

Four things seem true:

- discrimination hurts vulnerable communities;

- black people are under-represented in local organisations of all kinds;

- a multi-racial, locally based housing team will help overcome discrimination and will give minority representatives the confidence to come forward;

- delivering quality services on an equal basis in stigmatised estates will reduce racial tensions and encourage better community relations.

Diagram 1.42 illustrates the interplay of discrimination and service.

Diagram 1.42
The interplay of discrimination and service

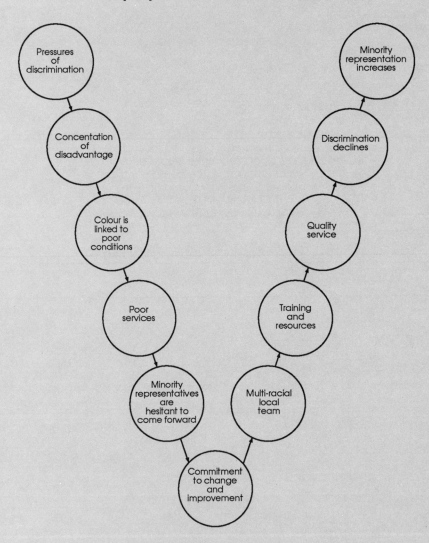

2. KEYWORDS: DISCRIMINATION; DISADVANTAGE; ACCESS; REPRESENTATION; EQUALITY OF SERVICES

Several important studies have been made of racial discrimination in housing in Britain (see Appendix). They all point to the fact that racial minorities often end up in worse housing than people who are white, even after allowing for other factors such as homelessness, income level, numbers of children and so on, as a result of **discrimination**.

Households belonging to racial minorities often have lower incomes, larger families, and come from worse housing conditions than many white households. This makes many of them more needy and gives them less choice when they apply for rehousing by the council or a housing association. Because vacancies occur more often on the least popular estates, they are pushed into accepting poor housing in disproportionate numbers. Lord Scarman called attention to racial **disadvantage** as a serious threat to society (Scarman, 1986). If, in addition, people are discriminated against because of their racial origins, they are doubly disadvantaged.

There is consistent evidence that racial minorities suffer both discrimination and disadvantage in **access** to housing, including council housing.

Ensuring that people do not suffer unnecessary disadvantage and are treated fairly and equally, without regard to colour, is an underlying principle of democracy which affects housing particularly sharply. Access to housing is only one part of the process. Ensuring that services, as far as possible, are open, available and accessible to all racial groups on an **equal** footing is a vital requirement (DoE, 1989). Involving members of all racial groups in tenants' organisations and in **representative** management bodies is equally important. In this section, we will consider briefly the racial aspects of these three important areas of housing management: access and allocations; accessible services; tenant representation and involvement.

3. DEFINITIONS

Definitions of race and racial terms are often ambiguous and sometimes offensive to one or other party. It is important, therefore, that people be allowed to identify themselves. The terms often overlap, for example Black, Asian, Black British, Muslim, Turkish.

a) **Racial minorities** include people distinguishable from the white majority by the colour of their skin. This would include people of various backgrounds.

b) **Racial Discrimination** means that an individual or group has experienced differential treatment or judgement by someone on grounds of colour or race (see Legal Section for legal definitions). Direct discrimination arises from the prejudices or bias that exist against particular groups.

c) **Indirect discrimination** results from the de facto exclusion of certain groups from the benefits or services available to other groups through the way in which those services are provided. For example, indirect discrimination may result from the fact that home-less households are offered the worst accommodation and that racial minorities are disproportionately represented among homeless families. It is illegal to discriminate directly or indirectly (Race Relations Act, 1976).

d) **Disadvantage** reflects the handicap or greater difficulties faced by certain individuals or groups which does **not** result from providing services or benefits purely on the basis of group identification. For example, rundown housing areas have more available accommodation and are cheaper. Newcomers on low incomes are likely to find housing there and experience disadvantages as a result.

e) **Prejudice** or **bias** is not based on fact or on objective criteria, but on subjective and often untrue or distorted views about the person(s) being discriminated against. Prejudice leads to exaggerated and derogatory stereotypes which can be taken by many people as reflecting the truth. Prejudice also leads to scapegoating, "blaming others for your troubles" without solid reasons. Prejudice is not normally influenced by rational argument or by evidence, since it is often based on fear, rumour and exaggerated impressions of reality. Prejudice exists in many societies against groups that are distinct from the majority, against individuals who can be readily distinguished by looks or behaviour, and against newcomers and those considered as outsiders.

4. TARGETS

– Monitor lettings carefully to ensure fairness and prevent "dumping".

– Organise representation from racial minority groups in the estate organisation, e.g. estate forum or Estate Management Board.

– Provide information in the languages most common to the estate.

– Recruit a multi-racial team in multi-racial areas.

– Provide training in quality service.

– Provide training in diffusing tensions, resolving conflict and building communication.

– Build links with local youth clubs, schools and other services.

– Build up a dialogue on racially sensitive issues with the police.

– Work out clear strategies for responding to racially motivated incidents.

5. RACIAL ISSUES

Isolation

Everybody needs to feel they belong. Family, friends, neighbourhood, cultural or religious ties, class, region, country, are all important points of identity and belonging. But the world is becoming more mobile, families and neighbourhoods more fragmented and less close-knit. This change can create feelings of insecurity as people strive to retain their identity and keep ties.

Sometimes this can lead to people excluding from their community those who do not seem to belong or who are seen to threaten continuity by looking or behaving differently.

Migration

At the same time, people move thousands of miles to find new opportunities. They loosen their old ties in order to build a new life. The British for many centuries have migrated across continents, settling in almost every corner of the globe. It is not surprising that people from distant countries have come to Britain to seek new opportunities. For many decades, more white British people emigrated than immigrants arrived to settle here. Canada, Australia, Hong Kong, South Africa have all been long "colonised" by British emigrants who, in some areas, still dominate them. Until the Second World War, most immigrants into Britain were white, apart from the relatively small settlements of distinct racial groups that grew up around the ports. The majority of immigrants came from Ireland and the Irish still make up the largest immigrant group in Britain.

After the Second World War, with Britain's economy booming and a chronic labour shortage, hundreds of thousands of New Commonwealth immigrants came year by year from the Caribbean, West Africa, India, and Pakistan. This was part of a larger worldwide migration after the war. Many were actively recruited. The process was long and complex. Here it is only necessary to highlight the fact that two million people of New Commonwealth origin have settled between 1950 and 1980 in Britain.

They were often forced into the oldest and most decayed Victorian terraced housing in the areas of settlement, doubling up into grossly overcrowded homes as public policy and discrimination debarred them from council housing; and economic necessity forced them to stay in major urban centres where work was plentiful. Their presence was often resented by the local communities they moved into.

Many issues connected with equality of treatment and the acceptance of minority groups remain unresolved, as racial minorities are increasingly concentrated in areas where facilities and opportunities are generally poor (Scarman, 1986).

Three housing targets can be identified as a response to the fact of racial disadvantage and the impact of racial discrimination:

– Households from racial minorities should gain access to housing on equal terms with the white majority households.

– Public services, private business, the police and all the bodies making up our social and economic system should be equally available and accessible to all residents without discrimination or exclusion.

– Tenants on housing estates who are from minority backgrounds are needed as full and active members of their community and should be represented directly if they are to play a full role.

Failure to meet these three targets will frustrate the need for being part of a common weal, the need for belonging. In failure and frustration, conflict will erupt. Signs of rupture have already been visible in racial disturbances in 1981, 1985 and, more sporadically, up to 1989.

Fairness, bridge-building, communication and equal opportunities are all-important, with people free to move to better housing and wider areas as the opportunity arises.

Council housing faces growing social problems because increasingly it houses those in greatest need. Some racial minorities are becoming disproportionately concentrated in council housing. Nearly half of all households of Afro-Caribbean origin live in council housing, compared with one quarter of white households, and these are concentrated in inner city areas, often on the least popular estates.

How access to housing is arranged, how services are provided and how representation is ensured are vital issues. The elimination of discrimination of any kind on any grounds must be a target at all times. Here we focus the discussion on estate-level organisation but it has far-reaching implications for housing services generally.

Diagram 1.43 illustrates the dichotomy.

The white minority

It is important in discussing racial issues and considering the needs of racial minorities to understand the difficulties faced by white residents sharing similar circumstances. They are acutely aware of having been left behind in the general affluence and progress; they often suffer an acute sense of inferiority if not outright failure; and they have far fewer resources than the society at large which have to be shared with competing groups. They feel aggrieved for a number of concrete reasons:

i)   They have suffered poor conditions for a long time.

ii)   They often cannot see a way out of their present situation, however much they want to move on.

iii)   They feel very little sense of control over their lives and conditions.

iv)   They see minority groups jostling with them for the same small resources.

v)   Their sense of identity is weakened by failure.

Of course they share many of these feelings with members of minority groups.

Any efforts to improve conditions and opportunities for racial minorities need to incorporate equally sensitive and vigorous efforts on behalf of the large white minority that has been left behind economically through industrial change. There is a serious danger that this group will be increasingly marginalised and there could be ugly racial conflict unless the issue of "poor whites", alongside issues of racial discrimination, is addressed. To avoid deep bitterness, efforts for one group must help all groups in similar circumstances, regardless of race.

Diagram 1.43
Showing negative and positive experiences and their impact

disadvantage and
poor conditions

positive
representation,
access to services,
access to housing

reduction in
discrimination
and disadvantage,
better race
relations,
better services

discrimination
stigma
racial tensions
conflict

6. ACCESS

In the section on lettings, we discuss the question of access to housing, fairness and competition for scarce accommodation. All these issues apply particularly in high demand areas where members of racial minorities often live. In this section, we aim only to highlight the particular racial aspects of access to housing and equality of treatment.

The two extremes of racial discrimination in access are:

Exclusion where minority racial groups have less access to more popular housing areas or previously all-white areas either directly on grounds of colour or indirectly on other grounds which lead to racial minorities suffering disproportionately;

Concentration where policies are introduced which lead to racial minorities being disproportionately concentrated in unpopular estates or areas and having less choice than white people over where they live.

Homeless policies illustrate these problems best.

In areas of high demand and high need, the most vulnerable and disadvantaged households have poor access to housing. They are often discriminated against particularly on grounds of colour, but also for economic and social reasons. They disproportionately end up either homeless or threatened with homelessness. A high proportion of those who become "priority" homeless are from racial minorities, up to four times more often than white households (Greve, 1990).

Homeless households, because of the urgency of their situation, must be rehoused quickly. They are not allowed, in most local authorities, to compete for the most popular property because that is reserved for families with more choice and higher priority, such as urgent rehousing out of property the council requires or transfers of existing tenants. A very few local authorities have targeted a proportion of their new and more popular property at homeless families. But most have reserved offers of least popular or hard-to-let property for homeless families. In any case, very little **new** popular property now becomes available because of the virtual halt in building programmes and the impact of the right to buy.

As a result, the homeless are usually offered the lowest quality property for which there is lowest demand. In addition, they often have no choice and have to accept the first offer.

This system is ostensibly an attempt to ensure: that the most needy get housed as quickly as possible; and that available property is filled quickly.

One result has been the rehousing of racial minorities (and other homeless households) in disproportionate numbers in unpopular estates. Some local authorities have been found to discriminate by the Commission for Racial Equality in contravention of the Law (CRE, 1987, 1988, 1989). A second result is that racial minorities feel forced by the rehousing system into the worst housing areas that are commonly rejected by more favoured households. A third consequence is that existing remaining residents on the least popular estates see their area as stigmatised by decline, by the exodus of more stable households and by the impact of racial discrimination. The population comes to identify poor housing and colour together.

Therefore to resolve problems of access in relation to racial minorities, homelessness and acute need, a **number of steps** should be taken:

a) All categories of applicants should be able to queue for all types of available housing. Restricting eligibility and access is almost bound to cause discrimination.

b) Local waiting lists should be created for local areas as this will quickly show applicants the likely waiting time for more popular areas. They then have to decide whether they can wait. This puts some of the decision-making onto the applicant, rather than setting up the allocations department as a gate-keeper.

c) The homeless, who under the best circumstances have very limited choice, should receive offers across all types of property. This will **not** remove concentrations of available property in the least popular areas but it will ensure an opening up of previously all-white areas on however limited a scale. It will also help to break down the racial stereotype which associates minorities with poor conditions. It begins the process of bridging

divides as some black households from poor conditions spread out into more popular areas.

d) Conditions on the least popular estates should be tackled so that those who live there feel less excluded and disadvantaged and so that a wider group of better-off applicants can be attracted in. The higher incidence of right to buy on more popular estates has enhanced the poverty of the worst estates (Forrest and Murie, 1984). If it happened on the less popular estates to a greater extent, it could enhance their stability and reputation.

Access to the widest range of housing for minority groups is vital. Leaders of minority organisations have consistently argued for the right of minorities to gain access to better housing **of their choice**; and equally, the right of minorities to stay together and not be "dispersed" **against their will**. There is evidence that many minority households would **choose** to move to better housing areas, given the opportunity. Many more of them are dissatisfied with existing conditions than in the population at large (Parker and Dugmore, 1976). Housing associations could, and in some areas increasingly do, play a bigger role. Nominations by local authorities can help very disadvantaged households. Those responsible for managing unpopular estates need to prevent "forced rehousing". The main alternative to "dumping and ghettoisation" is giving people the right to **refuse** unacceptable offers; and setting up a lettings **process** that enhances the chances of acceptance, through applicants deciding for themselves (see Local Lettings section). Dealing firmly with the threat

12. *A multiracial team is vital in a multiracial community. Broadwater Farm Estate, Haringey*

Priority Estates Project

of harassment makes a big difference to lettings and refusals.

Local authorities could monitor lettings and access more carefully, as the surest way of eliminating discrimination. Monitoring of course only works to counter discrimination where it is used as part of an effective management **strategy**. Statistics of themselves do nothing to change the fact of disadvantage or discrimination. Housing managers must have incentives to make things work if monitoring is to provoke a response (see Section on Monitoring).

Where allocations targets are drawn up to ensure fair access for all groups, these targets should reflect the needs of different racial groups in the population (LSE Housing, 1990). Targets should also be used to ensure that minorities get offered better quality housing in outer, more suburban areas. Lambeth followed this policy successfully. Such policies enhance opportunities for minorities and over time reduce prejudice, even if they can only operate on a very small scale because of the shortage of good quality property.

Policies which simply state equal opportunities objectives are insufficient. A fair and balanced allocation system, with clear and simple policies and locally sensitive administration procedures, provides the best combination. The Law must be used where necessary to ensure equal treatment.

At the same time, all parties will gradually learn the complexities of inter-communal relations and, rather than tolerate in helplessness or condemn in naked outrage the injustice of discrimination, work at every point of contact towards a fairer system. It has to be said that this requires the judgement of Solomon, the patience of Job and the passionate belief in justice and compassion of international leaders like Martin Luther King. But we must remember that "justice too long delayed is justice denied" (King, 1963).

To summarise the basic rules of rehousing for racial minorities:

– Make a proportion of better housing available to all eligible groups including racial minorities.

– Organise local waiting lists, local signing up and local administration of lettings to avoid a sense of coercion and to maximise people's sense of doing things for themselves; also to increase the chances of acceptance in previously unpopular areas.

– Avoid direct "one offer only" policies.

– Avoid targeting or "dumping" homeless or other vulnerable households (e.g. single parents) on the least popular estates.

– Do **not** allow particular estates to be earmarked for black or minority households – the GLC did this in the mid-seventies in the E1 area of Tower Hamlets, indirectly causing many of the rehousing problems there today (Power, 19 April 1979).

– Involve minority representatives at all levels of the letting process – policy, monitoring, viewing, local management. As with policing, it is impossible to be seen to be fair if those who control the service are all white and those who experience discrimination are not represented.

– Ensure that the lettings and access system is open

and above board and defendable – people should know where they stand and what their chances are.

– Monitor lettings as part of the management process
– use the information carefully and consistently.

– Review policy regularly.

– Train staff to carry out policies effectively and with commitment.

7. EQUALITY IN THE PROVISION OF SERVICES

In this section we are only considering the housing service and local housing management, but racial issues affect the provision of all services in multi-racial areas. Jobs, schools, police, social services, shops can intensify, or can help overcome, the problems of discrimination and racial disadvantage. In fact, all are needed to play a positive role in the striving for equality. Otherwise housing offices, at the blunt end of a range of pressures, can only respond on a limited front or simply sink into a spiral (Scarman, 1986).

A multi-racial workforce

A most important step will be taken in equality of service and access to service for minorities if the housing team includes staff from minorities who live in the area. A multi-racial team, providing a good service and working well together, will do much to reduce prejudice, discrimination, fear and intolerance.

Recruiting competent staff from minorities in itself requires commitment and skill. There is no point in adopting an "Uncle Tom" approach where, as a mere token, an isolated black person is included in a team. The fact is that many able and ambitious members of minority groups have had only limited opportunities in the past. Therefore, positive efforts at recruitment, careful selection and training may be necessary. Efforts to recruit and train will be successful as long as they are made thoroughly and with due care to involve and help all concerned parties. Strong support for new staff from minority backgrounds may be necessary, if there are only a few and if there is resistance to such change. Prejudice often dies hard.

Linguistic and cultural barriers

People from different backgrounds often have differing family patterns, religious beliefs, language and cultural traditions. These can be barriers to understanding and can generate prejudice.

It is important to try firstly to break down such barriers by increasing education, training and understanding on all sides. The schools, churches and adult education institutes have tremendous scope and power in this respect – often grossly underused and sometimes misused. Local housing offices can play their role. The multi-racial team will have an impact. Encouraging multi-racial activity, particularly among children; supporting self-help groups; providing information in various languages; putting over an ethos of respect, courtesy and tolerance, will all help to reduce tension and break down barriers.

Discrimination

Where there is evidence of discrimination, victimisation or unfair treatment, the local manager should investigate, attempt to resolve and chase through the system if no local resolution is possible. Politicians, senior managers, the police and specialist agencies such as the Commission for Racial Equality may be needed. Wider patterns of indirect discrimination need to be addressed through strong political leadership which, in turn, often depends on the climate of opinion. However, it is important to understand that resolving problems locally, while not always possible, is far more satisfactory.

Harassment

On some estates in some areas, individuals or families have been attacked or harassed because of their racial origins. Each incident should be considered separately. Blanket solutions are unlikely to work. Abrupt policy changes, with major ramifications that have not been thought through, can evoke a destabilising response, e.g. "all racial harassment cases should become top priority transfers." What about the harassers? What about those left behind? What if several transfer cases all have top priority? What if the racial harassment is between two minority groups? What other steps could be taken? What evidence is there? Clearly there are emergencies – cases of arson are the most extreme. Not all harassment involves violence. Some harassment stems from potentially soluble causes such as noise disturbance which seems to be a major factor. Each case must be carefully investigated and tackled individually.

Some conflicts defy obvious resolution. Cases of racial abuse and attack are always menacing and ugly but require carefully planned action. Documented evidence, eye witnesses, police co-operation, prosecution in the courts all have their place. Legal action should be used reservedly; but where all else fails, determinedly. The most important steps are the combination of high quality service, fair access, solid tenant representation and clear, well-publicised procedures including procedures to deal with racial harassment so that opportunities and occasions for conflict are minimised. Harassment develops and flourishes in a wider atmosphere of intolerance or of inaction on the part of the authorities.

It is important for housing officers not to be used as an informal police force or to be asked to resolve deep-set community tensions. At the same time, they can play a positive role, simply by upgrading the efficiency and quality of service. Community tensions are bound to decline where services work well and to rise where many things work badly. The staff therefore need training in:

– the different backgrounds of groups they are serving;

– racial issues, discrimination and prejudice, including the law;

– methods of overcoming racial disadvantage;

– techniques for reaching and supporting groups with different needs;

– monitoring racial aspects of housing access and delivery – how to use monitoring information for management (see Section on Co-ordination);

– working as a multi-racial team;

– liaising with schools, community groups, police, social services (see Section on liaison).

In order to ensure that the local office reaches all sections of the community, and offers an equal service to all, the following basic steps may help:

– Aim for excellent local management services, particularly in repairs, caretaking and cleaning, thereby ensuring generally satisfactory conditions on the estate.

– Aim for a multi-racial housing team. This should always prove possible in multi-racial areas and should be encouraged in as many places as possible.

– Make information available in the main languages spoken on the estate besides English, where particular groups would otherwise be excluded.

– Make the office particularly welcoming to minorities as they will often hold back e.g. by displaying multi-racial pictures and by making it explicit that **all** racial groups are welcome.

– Encourage tenants' representatives and organisations to include minorities, **without** being judgemental, patronising or overbearing, **as this will backfire**.

– Support ethnic minority initiatives, e.g. youth clubs, religious meetings, and ensure that they are represented. Tenant support workers are an important resource for this type of initiative.

– Do **not** allow exclusive facilities or activities. This, however, must **not** be interpreted as meaning that people cannot organise themselves or represent themselves. It is a fine line to draw and a difficult path to tread. Legal advice should be sought where conflict over provision cannot be resolved. (NB. Special services, e.g. "girls only" nights in youth clubs can be offered as part of a local facility).

– Build up positive relations with residents' representatives to encourage communication and discussion of these issues.

– Develop strategies for rectifying discrimination, for investigating grievances and for clarifying procedures.

– Discuss any incidents of reported racial discrimination, abuse or conflict within the team and develop, over time, a strategy for coping with the stress it creates, responding to the needs of those aggrieved, and bridging the gap in information and understanding that often causes the trouble.

– Take a strong stand against the expression in writing or verbally of racial prejudice or abuse. This last point should not require mention but it is not uncommon to find abusive graffiti, to hear racially directed swearing among young people or to hear white tenants' representatives in areas of racial tension articulate stereotyped and derogatory views about race. These actions can be curbed, if necessary by suspending the conduct of a meeting or by debarring individuals from entrance to housing or community facilities as long as such behaviour continues. Racial prejudice is commonly expressed among staff too. This should be treated in the same way.

– Set up a reporting and complaints procedure for issues of discrimination so that residents feel confident that policies and statements can be matched by performance and so that minority residents feel protected and able to report trouble.

At the end of the day, a strong and positive lead by public officials and politicians will help divided communities to cope and eventually to discover a common interest. Where there is no lead, racial tensions and abuse may grow and be exploited by certain interests. It must be stressed, however, that those with least resources and educational advantages will find it hardest to escape from the common defence of scapegoating. That is why better quality and more equally provided services are important and why better housing services can have a disproportionately important impact.

Where bullying and violent or threatening behaviour cannot be stopped by local staff and residents, the police, the press, local and national politicians should be involved. Such hideous waves as "Paki-bashing" and "skinhead" violence cannot grow unchecked. Again, it must be stressed that the best place to combat it is right in the area where it happens. Local leaders need all the support they can get to establish and retain control against abuse.

8. TENANT REPRESENTATION

In multi-racial areas, it is all too common to find that established tenants' associations are all-white. Where tenants' associations or other local organisations are multi-racial, a number of positive outcomes ensue.

The open expression of hostility and abuse decline. Previously acceptable discriminatory behaviour is no longer possible. People's understanding of each other greatly increases and judgements are more likely to be based on understanding than on prejudice. Minority interests can be brought out into the open and related to the sometimes different interests of the white residents. For example, on many estates a majority of white residents are middle-aged or elderly, while a majority of children and young people may be black. This has implications for the way different groups see their needs or depend on services and support. When groups sit together and discuss these issues in common, they are more likely to recognise each others' needs. Viewed from separate, non-communicating vantage points, people are more likely to be narrowly self-interested or bigoted. The meals-on-wheels service run by the Broadwater Farm Youth Association, which is mainly black, for elderly residents, many of whom are white, is one example (Gifford, 1986) The Holloway Tenant Co-operative in Islington which houses elderly white sitting tenants and young black homeless families together is another (Power, 1979).

Most importantly, an example of shared leadership is offered to the wider community by the presence of racial minority members in positions of leadership.

At the most basic level, tenant representation on an estate is only useful if it **actually** represents different racial groups fairly. Therefore, positive steps must be taken to ensure that this happens. This should **not** involve preaching at white representatives who may have struggled for many years to help their estates. But it should involve directing energies and support at:

a) encouraging minority members to get **involved**;

b) supporting minority **initiatives**;

c) opening up existing organisations to a **wider body** of tenants;

d) developing new and more broadly based forms of **representation**;

e) using **secret ballots** for elections to ensure that people feel free in the exercise of their vote – intimidation can be a problem in some situations;

f) **co-opting** minority representatives in situations where they cannot otherwise be represented (this should be a last resort but it can be important to ensure minority representation, as Northern Ireland amply demonstrates).

The section on resident involvement has discussed some of these approaches in more detail. Here we will pinpoint a few basic measures that may help members of racial minorities to become involved:

– **Employ support** workers from minority backgrounds.

– Use **interpreters** in meetings where language barriers are significant.

– Produce leaflets, publicity etc. in **different languages**.

– **Door-knock** before meetings to ensure that members of racial minorities receive a personal invitation to meetings and events.

– **Co-opt or invite** minority representatives to meeting, but make sure that they do represent a broad range of interests within the minority community. This may be particularly relevant for women, young people.

– Make sure that everyone **speaks** at small meetings and **representatives** of different groups get to speak at larger meetings.

– **Ban** any racially derogatory statements or references at meetings.

– Make meetings small, short and very local wherever possible. **Accessibility** is all-important.

– Make arrangements to **accompany people** who feel nervous, to and from meetings – this may apply equally to elderly women or young single mothers.

– Offer tea, biscuits and other welcoming forms of **hospitality** so that people who are used to informal social gatherings feel at ease in meetings.

– Make meetings **unintimidating and unbureaucratic** with a minimum of formality and paperwork, but enough to get decisions made and the business done.

– Offer **training** to tenants' representatives of different backgrounds. Sharing an intensive experience is likely to be positive and reinforcing.

9. CONCLUSION

The issues surrounding race, discrimination and disadvantage are far more complex and painful than this brief summary of experiences and ideas indicates. Tackling the problem requires changes far beyond those discussed here. It is essential not to belittle the problem or to imply that solutions are easy. But if estate managers and tenants' representatives are to start somewhere, the three issues we have raised – access, services and resident representation – offer beginning points on the long road to unravelling a part of our development that we often prefer to forget.

10. CHECKLIST ON RACIAL ISSUES

1. Are minority groups represented on the local management organisation?

2. Is the estate team multi-racial if located in a multi-racial area?

3. Are incidents of racial harassment reported to the office?

    Do you have clear procedures for dealing with them?

4. Are there training sessions in racial issues?

5. Do you know the law on racial discrimination?

6. Do you know the racial composition of your estate?

7. Do you know something of the background to the different racial groups?

8. Do you feel you can sympathise with the different groups caught up in racially tense situations – white as well as non-white?

9. Do you know your housing organisation's lettings policies?

    Are they fair?

    Do minority households consistently end up in the worst housing?

How could they be made to work better?

10. Does your office carry out ethnic monitoring?

    What is done with the information that is collected?

11. Do you liaise with other organisations to overcome problems of racial disadvantage and discrimination?

11. SOME USEFUL BOOKS ON RACIAL ISSUES IN HOUSING

ASSOCIATION OF METROPOLITAN AUTHORITIES (London) (1987): Reports of the Local Authority Housing & Racial Equality Working Party on:
  Allocations
  Homelessness
  Local Housing Strategies
  Racial Harassment

BELL W S (1988): Put in Your Place – Race & Council Housing in Enfield. LB of Enfield Community Relations Council

COMMISSION FOR RACIAL EQUALITY (1987): Living in Terror – A report on racial violence & harassment in housing. London

—— (1989): Race Relations Code of Practice. For the elimination of racial discrimination and the promotion of equal opportunity in the field of rented housing

—— (1989): Race, Housing and Immigration. A Guide

DEPARTMENT OF THE ENVIRONMENT (1989): Tackling Racial Violence & Harassment in Local Authority Housing: A Guide to Good Practice for Local Authorities. HMSO

FORBES D (1988): Action on Racial Harassment – Legal Remedies & Local Authorities. Institute of Housing, London

KING M L (1963): Why we can't wait. Harper & Row, New York

NATIONAL FEDERATION OF HOUSING ASSOCIATIONS (1982): Race & Housing: A Guide for Housing Associations. London

Part 2
The Buildings

IV. Repairs and maintenance

V. Caretaking, cleaning and environmental maintenance

IV. Repairs and maintenance

A The organisation of repairs and maintenance on PEP estates

B Estate-based capital repairs and improvements

A The organisation of repairs and maintenance on PEP estates

Contents

> "People who run Government activities the
> world over, tend to seek sweeping answers to
> problems; that is answers capable of being applied
> wholesale the instant they are adopted. People in
> government do not seem to bring their minds to
> bear on a particular and often seemingly small
> problem in one particular place."
>
> Jane Jacobs,
> Economy of Cities

1. SUMMARY

Repairing property has six main characteristics:

- It is endlessly varied and detailed work.
- It changes according to who owns and who lives in the housing.
- It relates in a particular way to each housing unit and housing area.
- It requires constant on-the-spot supervision.
- It can be very expensive and inefficient; its management requires meticulous business skills.
- Locally based and controlled repairs are often more efficient, cheaper and more popular than centrally based repairs.

Diagram 2.1
Features of repairing property

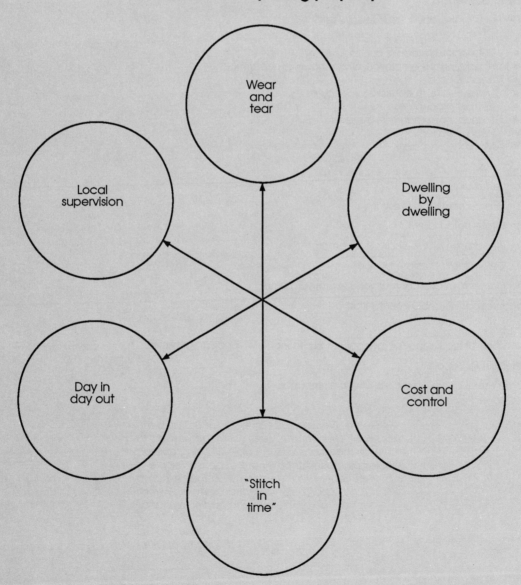

13. *Efficient day-to-day repairs help to prevent long-term damage. Bacup Estate, Rossendale*
Paul Herrmann/Profile

2. KEYWORDS: SERVICE; LOCAL; CONTROL; ORGANISATION

Repairs are the most important **service** provided by a **local** housing office. This service is an integral part of housing management. Sixty per cent of all tenants' enquiries to a local office will be concerned with repairs. A local office with no direct control over the repairs operation is powerless to deliver a proper housing service. It merely becomes another link in the chain of bureaucracy that leads to increased frustration for both tenants and staff. Local **control** of repairs is therefore **the** key to success for any local housing office. The local service will obviously vary greatly with the size of the estate – a small co-operative covering 50 units will operate very differently from a large estate of 1,000 units.

The main purpose of this section is to offer answers to 3 basic questions about repairs and maintenance:

– What do we include in repairs?

– Who should do it?

– How should it be **organised** and carried out?

3. DEFINITION – WHAT DO WE MEAN BY REPAIRS?

In the local management context, repairs cover most of the work to buildings carried out on the estate:

– **day-to-day repairs** including empty property and emergencies;

– **planned and cyclical maintenance**;

– **some capital and environmental works**.

It is common practice to separate day-to-day repairs from planned maintenance and major improvements[1], with different council departments or sections of the Housing Department controlling different aspects of the work. However, all three are part of the overall repair and maintenance of the estate. **The physical needs of the estate should be viewed as a whole**. Information obtained from the day-to-day repairs operation should feed directly into the planned maintenance

[1]Improvements are now sometimes referred to as enhancements.

programme and the capital programme and vice versa. Artificial divisions lead to duplication and mistakes. Stories about newly installed window frames and bathroom fittings being ripped out in the course of a capital improvement programme are all too common. Most mistakes are due to poor co-ordination between different sections that control different pots of money. Local co-ordination and control of **all** aspects of the repair and maintenance of an estate is the best way to ensure that such mistakes do not happen. It is also the best way of ensuring that all repair and maintenance work reflects the needs of the estate, and the priorities of the people who live and work there. There is evidence that it reflects the best value for money (Power, April 1987; DoE, 1989).

4. TARGETS

– Establish a local budget to cover all repairs.

– Establish local repairs organisation.

– Set up local property files, repairs ordering, costing and completions.

– Make technical back-up locally available.

– Set repairs priorities with staff and tenants' representatives.

– Organise repairs training for staff and tenants.

– Set aside cyclical maintenance budget.

– Arrange external repainting cycle.

– Carry out estate condition survey.

– Get communal maintenance up to standard, e.g. lighting entrances, fencing, paths, drains.

5. THE LOCAL MANAGEMENT OF REPAIRS – TECHNICAL NEEDS AND A ROLE FOR RESIDENTS

The Estate Manager should be firmly in charge of repairs and should carry full responsibility. **Nothing** should be done on the estate without his/her prior knowledge, involvement and support. In turn, it is the responsibility of the Estate Manager to ensure that the tenants are fully consulted and informed about all repairs and maintenance work on the estate.

All estate based housing staff should be competent in the following repairs skills:

– repairs ordering, completions and payment systems and procedures

– taking a repairs request

– office computer systems

– using the schedule of rates.

In other words, they must know how to get repairs done properly. They may need regular ongoing training where they do not have long experience of handling repairs. Non-technical staff can become competent at managing repairs.

A role for residents?

Residents should participate in repairs as it is usually the issue that most affects their housing. Repairs will provide employment and training opportunities for residents.

Voluntary services and local firms can also help sometimes and local employment initiatives can take off around repairs. (See later in Chapter; also Section X, Co-ordination).

Technical back-up

In order to help the estate staff carry out their repairs responsibilities efficiently, the local management team should include technically qualified staff (or have direct access to technical advice if the estate is small and/or in such good condition that it does not need full-time technical support).

Technical staff can assist in the following ways:

– pre- and post-inspection of more difficult, **expensive** jobs

– specification of jobs not covered by the schedule of rates

– monitoring of standards of work

– programmed inspections of specialist areas, e.g. electrical components, gas fittings

– help in drawing up and costing major repairs and environmental works programmes for the estate.

Technical officers require building and repair skills but do not need to be fully qualified surveyors. Competent and experienced chargehands would often be ideal people to fulfil this role.

It is vital that technical officers act as advisers to the Estate Officers and be directly answerable to the Estate Manager. One technical officer can be expected to serve an estate of up to 1,000 dwellings. However, this will depend on the condition, the level of spending etc. Qualified surveyors will be needed to supervise major capital works.

Qualified surveyors, where not estate-based, should provide back-up at the centre and work closely with the estate-based teams on all repairs and maintenance issues, acting as technical advisers in the same way as the technical officers. The role and degree of involvement of qualified surveyors will depend on the nature of the estate, the type of building problems and the volume of major work.

Contractors

The law now requires that repairs work must be carried out by contracts let through a process of competitive tendering. The estate manager should be the client's formal representative for all repairs contracts to the estate. He/she will need technical advice to do this competently.

6. DAY-TO-DAY REPAIRS

For an efficient repairs service, the local office needs to make clear the following:

– which repairs are the landlord's responsibility and which are the tenants', e.g. broken windows in a dwelling

– the methods by which repairs should be reported to the local office

– priority times for different types of repair with a majority of jobs being done within an agreed period of (say) four weeks

– the budget for repairs expenditure

– a schedule of rates by which repairs will be costed

– the procedure tenants should follow in the event of dissatisfaction or grievance

– how the local repairs team will be organised, including its size and line of command

– where it will be based

– how cyclical maintenance and capital works fit in with day-to-day repairs.

Many of these areas will be covered by council policy, but if a policy is unsuitable for the estate, new local policies should be worked out in consultation with the tenants and the council.

The majority of day-to-day repairs carried out by the on-site team are quite small, typically taking 1–2 hours and costing around £50 per job. including labour and materials. Where there is full local control, the costs can be as low as £30 per job (Power, November 1988).

Repairs should be categorised as: emergencies (dangerous); urgent jobs (damaging the property); and all other eligible jobs.

Emergencies should be made safe within 24 hours. Urgent jobs should be completed within seven days. All job orders should be completed within a maximum of six weeks, unless major works are involved (e.g. roof replacement). The **average** completion time for all jobs, excluding emergencies should be around three weeks.

There should be a simple method for checking that jobs are completed within agreed times, modelled on a library lending system. If all outstanding job orders are moved forward daily, the target date will be clear. Overdue jobs (like overdue library books!) should have a penalty attached. Diagram 2.2 illustrates a local repairs organisation.

14. *All housing requires constant renewal*

Paul Herrmann/Profile

Diagram 2.2
A local repairs organisation

```
┌─────────────────────────┐
│ Tenant reports repair   │
│ request to local office │
└─────────────────────────┘
            │
            ▼
┌─────────────────────────┐        ┌─────────────┐
│ Local office checks     │◄───────│ Checks      │
│ request                 │        │ cost and    │
└─────────────────────────┘        │ priority    │
            │                      └─────────────┘
            ▼
┌─────────────────────────┐
│ Orders repair           │
└─────────────────────────┘
            │
            ▼
┌─────────────────────────┐        ┌─────────────┐
│ Local repairs team      │        │ Access is   │
│ (or other contractor)   │◄──────►│ arranged,   │
│ is commissioned to do   │        │ materials   │
│ repair                  │        │ delivered   │
└─────────────────────────┘        └─────────────┘
            │
            ▼
┌─────────────────────────┐
│ Repair is carried out   │
└─────────────────────────┘
            │
            ▼
┌─────────────────────────┐
│ Local office checks work│
└─────────────────────────┘
            │
            ▼
┌─────────────────────────┐
│ Local office authorises │
│ payments                │
└─────────────────────────┘
```

Elements of the day-to-day repairs service

The local repairs team

A locally based repairs[1] team is essential to enable the housing office to deliver a fast and efficient repairs service and to do the many small, fiddling, but important jobs easily and cheaply. This applies to small as well as big estates, though the actual arrangements will vary (Power, November 1988). Each estate organisation should have a repairs contract that includes a local base for the contractor. Local repairs contracts are subject to compulsory tendering.

---

[1]Traditionally most local authorities have used direct labour organisations for repairs and maintenance work. Since compulsory competitive tendering has been introduced, local authorities have had to think through their repair and maintenance contract arrangements more carefully. Local repairs teams are now usually provided as part of measured term contracts which cover specific geographical areas, are based on Schedules of Rates and last for between one and three years. The repairs work may be done by the Direct Labour Organisation or by private contractors.

Most local authorities use private contractors for some repairs, and it is likely that in the future this will become more common. Private contractors carrying out the bulk of day to day repairs on an estate need a local base in the same way as DLO teams do.

The repairs team should be located at a base on the estate, adjacent to or as near as possible to the estate management office. A small repairs team could use a room in the estate office. Facilities and working conditions for repairs workers should equal those provided for other staff. A small store for materials should always be provided; an office for the chargehand or supervisor is needed; and the workers need to be able to wash, change and take breaks.

Materials can sometimes be ordered via a central store. However, if the central council suppliers are inefficient, inflexible, slow at delivery, or expensive, other local suppliers should be used. In most cases stores will come from more than one source anyway. It is usually quicker, easier and therefore more efficient to buy supplies direct or to make an ongoing arrangement with a supplier who can deliver quickly, cheaply and efficiently.

An estate of 1,000 dwellings should support a core team of 6–10 workers.

A team for this size of estate would probably include: 1 supervisor/chargehand (multi-trade and working), 2 joiners, 2 plumbers, 1 plasterer/bricklayer (depending on estate), 1 electrician (depending on estate), 1 storekeeper, and 1 general labourer

The precise trades will depend on the type of estate and the nature of repairs problems. All estates require plumbing and carpentry. Electrical and other work is very variable.

It is important to cart away rubbish and deliver supplies on time. On many estates a van and driver are essential.

On average in PEP estates, five jobs are completed per dwelling per annum with a local repairs team. On an estate of 1,000 dwellings, about 5,000 jobs a year would normally be done – about 12–14 jobs per week per repairs worker. Some of these jobs will in practice be carried out by specialist sub-contractors or by centrally-based specialist repair teams.

It is important for the contract for local repairs to cover some planned maintenance so that in quiet periods, e.g. August, the local team can be used to carry out routine planned maintenance.

A local team should carry out:

– all emergencies reported in office hours

– all jobbing repairs

– all work to empty dwellings (unless this will delay reletting because of a "bulge" in empty property)

– minor improvements and small planned works.

The central DLO or other contractors should be used for:

– out of hours emergencies

– specialist jobs, e.g. roofing, drains and sewers

– some planned maintenance.

Relations with repairs contractors

Maintenance or repair work issued to private contractors through lump sum contracts should also be the responsibility of the estate management team. They should inspect the job, specify the work, issue instructions to the contractors, monitor progress, post-inspect as necessary and authorise payment. Either each estate officer will be responsible for repairs on his/her patch or the team as a whole will run repairs from the estate office.

The number of contractors used at any one time on an estate should be kept to a minimum necessary for efficiency, to enable the local office to build up good working relationships with the firms and the operatives, without sacrificing the ability to go elsewhere if the service is unsatisfactory. A large number of contractors makes it difficult for the local office to manage the contracts efficiently. Either a private contractor or a DLO can be the sole repairs contractor for an estate. In either case, the repairs team must operate from a local base.

Handypersons employed by the Housing Department

On some PEP estates, particularly smaller estates, caretakers are employed who also act as 'handypersons' and are able to carry out minor repairs and deal with many emergencies. This system has proved very popular with tenants and can also be cost-effective.

Repairs costs

All local offices must have an agreed repairs and maintenance budget to cover all necessary day-to-day work, voids and planned maintenance. This should be under the direct control of the estate manager. About two-thirds of spending on management and maintenance goes on repairs.

Any savings from increased efficiency should be fed back into the estate budget as a 'reward' for success. This gives residents and staff an incentive to target resources effectively. Local repairs teams usually manage to increase productivity significantly (Power, April 1987). Estates generally have been so starved of planned maintenance and renewal that the incentive to plough back savings into improvements can be very great.

Local repairs budgets and costs need to be carefully monitored and audited. The requirements of auditors must be met in order to protect the interests of staff and tenants, as well as to ensure the best possible use of public resources (see Budget section).

All repairs costs should be estimated when a job ticket is issued so that accurate records can be kept of committed costs as against actual costs. Where measured term contracts are used, this is done according to a schedule of rates, but there are some cases where work is costed on a day work basis. Many schedules of rates are over-complex, over-technical and therefore unsuitable for use by non-technical housing staff who are responsible for ordering repairs.

It is vital that the schedule of rates:

– is written in simple, intelligible language

– is related to the specific needs of the estate

– covers as many as possible of the areas of work required.

Measured term contract procedures

All contracts contain procedures which should be followed if a contractor fails to perform adequately. The estate manager should follow these procedures carefully, taking legal advice where necessary.

Inadequate contractors can be removed from the approved list of contractors. Failure to comply with the contract terms can lead to termination of the contract.

Repairs procedures

– There must be a property file for each tenancy.

– All repairs orders and completions must be logged for the property and filed in the property file.

Diagram 2.3
How job tickets for repairs can be processed in an estate-based team.

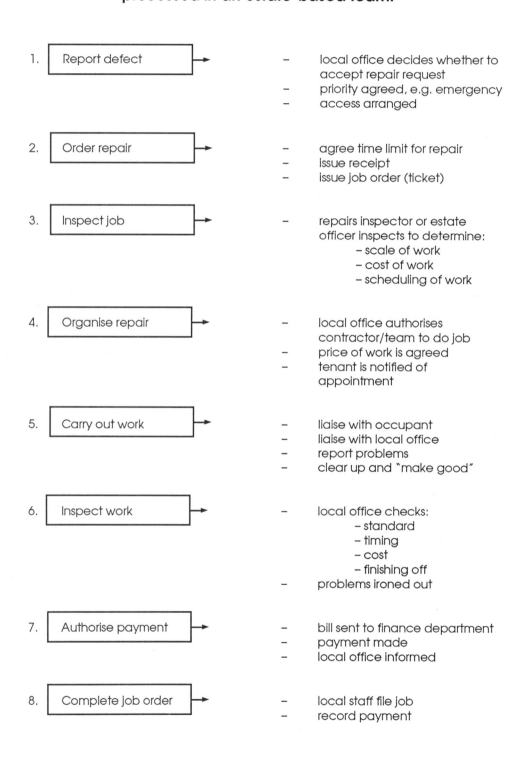

1. | Report defect |
   - local office decides whether to accept repair request
   - priority agreed, e.g. emergency
   - access arranged

2. | Order repair |
   - agree time limit for repair
   - issue receipt
   - issue job order (ticket)

3. | Inspect job |
   - repairs inspector or estate officer inspects to determine:
     - scale of work
     - cost of work
     - scheduling of work

4. | Organise repair |
   - local office authorises contractor/team to do job
   - price of work is agreed
   - tenant is notified of appointment

5. | Carry out work |
   - liaise with occupant
   - liaise with local office
   - report problems
   - clear up and "make good"

6. | Inspect work |
   - local office checks:
     - standard
     - timing
     - cost
     - finishing off
   - problems ironed out

7. | Authorise payment |
   - bill sent to finance department
   - payment made
   - local office informed

8. | Complete job order |
   - local staff file job
   - record payment

– There needs to be 'direct dealing' between the housing office and all contractors, including the local repairs team, in order to make sure that the local housing office has full control over the repairs service.

– All job tickets should be ordered and printed at the local office and passed directly to the supervisor of the local DLO or the local contractor.

– The local office should have direct responsibility for authorising payment to contractors for repairs work.

– Payment must be sanctioned by the local office.

Only in this way can the local office effectively monitor progress and keep control over the quality of service.

On an estate without computerised repairs, a logbook and manual job tickets can be used.

The central housing organisation can receive **duplicates** of all orders and completions for monitoring and for central accounting where necessary.

Diagram 2.3 illustrates the local repairs procedure.

Manual or computerised systems?

The local systems and procedures, whether manual or computerised, should:

– enable accurate and detailed reporting of repairs;

– give tenants a dated receipt of the order;

– keep a record of jobs requested;

– establish target times and priorities;

– give the repairs supervisor, contractor, chargehand a clear instruction within the terms of the contract;

– print job tickets clearly;

– keep a record of jobs completed;

– keep a record of jobs outstanding/overdue;

– keep track of committed/actual costs;

– include post-inspection of jobs as required to monitor performance and standards of work;

– include feedback from tenants on levels of satisfaction;

– maintain a property file on each dwelling.

An estate-based manual repairs system should provide a foolproof, easily understood, easily checked job ordering system. Job tickets should pass through the minimum number of transactions (see Diagram 2.3).

On a small estate where the number of jobs requested per week is below 50 (approximately 500 dwellings), a manual system is adequate. However, once the number of jobs per week exceeds 50, then some form of computerised system becomes more attractive. Usually, estate offices covering more than 500 dwellings benefit from local computerised repairs systems.

A computerised repairs system should provide:

– a VDU (screen) on the reception desk operated by the reception staff – this usually includes estate officers working on a rota;

– the ready conversion of valid requests to job orders;

– the ability to track all requests;

– a schedule of rates built into the system to provide a costing for all jobs;

– on-site printing of job tickets on demand with duplicates retained in case of breakdown;

– on-line information on job progress, jobs due and overdue, job histories and statistical information on requests, completions and cancellations;

– reports of expenditure by repair type, by budget heading and by property:

e.g. (**repair type**) Carpentry to June 30th: £12,320

e.g. (**budget head**) Emergencies to June 30th: £5,860

e.g. (**property**) 45 Allendale House to June 30th: £47

– a property file for each dwelling;

– computerised systems should use plain, simple English wherever possible; the use of codes should be kept to an absolute minimum as these will confuse staff and limit the number of people who understand the records.

Central computer systems sometimes offer these facilities but attempts to modify central systems are expensive and often difficult. They are not always suited to the needs of a local management office. They often break down.

Stand-alone microcomputers have more flexibility and are already in use in some local offices. They can be compatible with central systems, giving maximum local control and enabling central monitoring. However, different housing organisations have hugely different computer systems and the decision should rest on the best local service for the most reasonable price. Local housing staff will need regular training in the use of computerised systems.*

Repairs inspection

The local housing office, through the manager, estate officers or repairs inspector (who should be part of the housing team, where there is such a post) takes responsibility for pre-inspecting, post-inspecting, monitoring the schedule of rates or other method of costing and charging jobs, and monitoring the repairs contracts and repairs budget. At least 10 % of jobs should be pre-inspected and post-inspected.

Logically, as many repairs as possible should be inspected **after** works are completed. Any empty unit with more than minor repairs should be inspected after repair work is done and **before** payment. There needs to be a locally agreed and understood policy for pre- and post-inspections. Post-inspections may be based on a random selection of all completed job tickets, may include **all** jobs costing more than a pre-determined amount, may include **all** jobs where the final cost of the work exceeds the committed sum by more than a pre-determined amount.

Monitoring repairs is extremely important. It is one of the areas most open to abuse.

*Footnote: Local systems and microcomputers also break down. But it is easier to get help, arrange servicing and repair, and operate a local system. Technical back-up is needed for all computer systems.

Conclusion

Day to day repairs carried out efficiently transform an estate. If tenants can come into a local office and reasonably expect repairs to be made for the defects they report, their attitude will be transformed.

If local housing staff can actually control the ordering and execution of repairs against an agreed local budget, they can confidently assure tenants that the repairs that are ordered will be carried out. Their jobs are made far more rewarding through this.

If a local repairs team works well with the local office and satisfies tenants, producing a cheap and efficient service, there will be an incentive to do more work and to do it better.

7. PLANNED MAINTENANCE

The immediate priority for a local housing office is usually to establish a fast and efficient day to day repairs service. But the needs of an estate as a whole can only be met if the day to day repairs service is accompanied by a rolling programme of planned and cyclical maintenance.

The rolling maintenance programme should be prepared locally and should take local needs and interests into account.

Response maintenance is not enough. The medium and long term maintenance needs of an estate are as important.

The **process** of arriving at a planned maintenance strategy for an estate involves a number of key stages:

Stage 1: Carry out a detailed estate condition survey

Stage 2: Set up an estate data base

Stage 3: Prepare a five-year rolling programme

Stage 4: Determine the budget.

The budget should include both capital- and revenue-funded work. Funding for an estate should be set within the context of the authority as a whole and should cover such areas as HIP and Estate Action funding, capital receipts and revenue funding. However small and inadequate the capital, it should be broken down to estate level (see Section IV.B for capital work).

15. *Capital work. Stoops and Hargher Clough Estate, Burnley*

Paul Herrmann/Profile

Stage 1: Estate condition survey

This can be carried out in two principal ways:

– employ specialist consultants to do a 'big bang' condition survey;

– carry out the survey locally on an ongoing basis through the work of the estate-based team with support from technical staff in central departments where necessary. Additional paid help may be needed to record information.

The '**big-bang**' method can be expensive, unwieldy, unlikely to involve the estate team or the tenants, and impossible to arrange through lack of cash.

The most likely outcome is a long report which is read (possibly), filed and forgotten. Most housing organisations, particularly local authorities, say that they cannot afford condition surveys anyway.

The **local** method is ongoing/long term, involves the local team and the tenants and is better able to 'tap' local knowledge, and can be related to local priorities.

It is therefore more likely to be built into the estate maintenance operation and feed into capital and day-to-day repairs programmes.

It is of course important that local staff are not simply expected to add this extra task to their existing workload. It cannot be done without adequate staff.

Stage 2: Estate Data Base

The estate survey will provide information for the estate Data Base.

Basic information should be collected about:

– **the estate**, e.g. landscaping, play areas, rubbish problems, car parking areas;

– **individual blocks** (if flatted), e.g. date and form of construction, lifts, staircases, rubbish chutes, water tanks, entrances;

– **individual dwellings**, e.g. gas and electrical appliances, kitchen and bathroom fittings, window condition, damp penetration and condensation, heating problems.

On larger estates of more than 500 dwellings, a computer can simplify this task, as long as staff understand how to collect, record and use the information. Extra clerical help will definitely be required to record data and input it into a computer. Technical staff will be needed to help organise a local survey.

Stage 3: Preparation of five-year rolling programme

The first local condition survey should help to identify the main problems that need to be put right and the urgency of different jobs. Many of the priorities for work uncovered in the local condition survey will need to be tackled in a capital programme. The capital works must be integrated with revenue works. This will apply to all structural repairs (see Section IV.B). A five-year rolling programme should be agreed which might include:

– **servicing** central heating boilers, lifts, and door entry phones

– **emergency repairs**, e.g. broken stairs, balcony railings, bulging walls through wall tie failures, and persistent roof leaks

– **structural repairs**, e.g. main roof overhaul, outer walls, spalling concrete, etc., and drains

– **improvements to dwellings** and blocks to meet new standards and reflect new needs and priorities, e.g. better thermal insulation, fire- and smoke-stopping, stairwell and entrance improvements, internal modernisation, and relief of overcrowding of large families through adapting dwellings

– **regular overhaul**, e.g. drainage, plumbing, rainwater pipes, water tanks, electrics, gas supply, paths and fences, and lift maintenance

– **external repainting**, e.g. one fifth of the estate to have external woodwork repainted each year

Diagram 2.4 shows the need for a plan to cover the different elements of planned maintenance. Apart from improvements, which may take several years to complete, all other aspects need to be covered each year over part of the estate so that over five years all elements are repaired or maintained in safe working condition.

Diagram 2.4
Plan for planned maintenance

	Year 1	Year 2	Year 3	Year 4	Year 5
Emergencies	L	M	S	S	S
Structure	–	L	L	S	S
Improvements	–	M	L	M	M
Regular overhaul	M	M	M	M	M
External repainting	M	M	M	M	M

L, large programme;   M, medium programme;   S, small programme.

During each year, as a consequence of the feedback available from the previous annual maintenance programme, the five-year rolling plan can be modified.

Stage 4: Determine the estate budget

A day-to-day and planned maintenance budget should be prepared to cover a five-year period. It can be updated each year from the five-year rolling programme.

There should be an allocated capital budget (on however small a scale). There should be a reserve fund from the revenue budget to pay for cyclical maintenance. This should normally be at least one quarter of the total repairs budget. The more comprehensive the cyclical maintenance programme, the more money will be saved on the day to day budget and the more repairs money will be available for improvements (Power, November 1988). Proper planned and cyclical maintenance of an estate should extend the life of major elements of the dwellings, increase tenant satisfaction, reduce emergencies and make the demands on the office and repairs team more manageable.

Contents of cyclical maintenance programme

All renewable building parts should be included in the cyclical maintenance programme. External repainting is the most obvious and important item in **preventing** major costs. But checking roofs, electrical and gas services, external piping, drains and fencing, all make a great difference to the preservation of the property. In high-rise blocks, proper door and lift maintenance are crucial but specialist contracts may cover these.

Internal redecoration for old age pensioners and a general overhaul of communal facilities such as bin chambers, underground garages, entrances, stairways and balconies, make a great qualitative difference to an estate.

8. LOCAL RESIDENTS' EMPLOYMENT INITIATIVES

Repairs are labour-intensive and involve many jobs. On some PEP estates, in areas of high local unemployment, local residents have set up businesses or co-operatives and tendered for small repairs and maintenance contracts. These have so far involved mainly environmental improvements. But increasingly, residents are getting involved in other aspects of the maintenance of their estates including day-to-day repairs and planned and cyclical maintenance, if they form locally based organisations like sub-committees, Estate Management Boards or co-operatives. In order to identify potential in this area, it would be important for the residents to carry out a skills survey and get advice and support from organisations offering financial and management expertise to community businesses (Bootstrap Enterprises and McFarlane, October 1989). It is also true that in co-operatives and other estate initiatives, tenants get increasingly involved in doing self-help repairs and in helping maintain the environment.

9. TRAINING

Training for repairs and maintenance should be built into local management. It should be provided for the surveyors, architects, maintenance staff, the local management team, and residents' representatives. It should cover all aspects of repairs, not just procedures, but buildings and services, budgets, contracts, supervision etc.

10. EXAMPLES OF LOCAL REPAIRS ORGANISATIONS ILLUSTRATING DIFFERENT APPROACHES

Local repairs team from DLO or local contractors	Isle of Dogs in Tower Hamlets
Caretaker/handypersons employed by the Housing Dept.	Newton Court, Hull
Stand-alone microcomputers	Ocean Estate, Isle of Dogs in Tower Hamlets
Integrated central/local computer system	Broadwater Farm, Haringey
Local residents' employment initiatives involving environmental improvements	Broadwater Farm Memorial Gardens
Residents' involvement in maintenance of their estates	Islington Management Co-operatives
Stock condition surveys	Shadsworth Estate, Blackburn

11. CHECKLIST FOR REPAIRS

1. Does the local manager actually control the repairs operation?
2. Do the repairs workers like working on the estate?
3. Do the repairs workers and estate manager respect each other?
4. Are there agreed response times for different categories of repairs (e.g. emergency, urgent, day-to-day)?
5. What percentage of jobs are carried out **within** these timescales?
6. How often do repairs workers have to call back for the same job?
7. Do materials get to jobs at the right time?
8. Is there a planned maintenance programme?
9. How often are the outsides of houses re-painted?
10. Is the backlog of repairs increasing or reducing?
11. How would tenants respond to the question "has your repairs service improved?"
12. How would tenants respond if the Chair of Housing claimed at a public meeting on the estate that repairs were going well?

13. How often do tenants complain?

14. Does the estate get a fair share of the available capital to carry out major repairs?

15. How does the standard of service delivered on the estate compare with that delivered to the rest of the authority?

12. SOME USEFUL BOOKS ON REPAIRS AND MAINTENANCE

AUDIT COMMISSION (1986): Improving Council Housing Maintenance. HMSO, London.

HATCHETT, M. (1989): Building Studies Manual. London School of Economics.

HUDSON, A. (1970; supplement 1979): Buildings and Engineering Contracts. Sweet & Maxwell.

LOCAL GOVERNMENT TRAINING BOARD (undated): Repairs – Can I help you? Ref. No. HS0030.

LOCAL GOVERNMENT TRAINING BOARD (undated): Building Maintenance for Non-Technical Staff in Housing. Ref. No. HS0019.

POWER, A. (April 1987): The PEP Guide to Local Housing Management. DoE for the Priority Estates Project, London.

B Estate-based capital repairs and improvements

Contents

"We must learn the lessons of the past – a sudden expansion of the building programme to meet political objectives and deal with new housing crises has provided short-term solutions with devastating effects in the longer term."

Association of Metropolitan Authorities

1. SUMMARY

Building **structures**, their **components** and **surroundings** are built to last a long time, but not for ever; different parts of their structure need renewal at different times. Building **services** and **surface finishes** need frequent checking, maintenance, refurbishment and upgrading. Doing essential work at the **right time** to high standards for a reasonable price maintains the lettings value of the property and is central to housing management.

Like repairs, the most efficient capital programme will be:

● broken down into manageable units

● locally based

● locally controlled

● responsive to tenants

Diagram 2.5 highlights capital work issues.

Diagram 2.5
The interplay of actors and issues in capital works

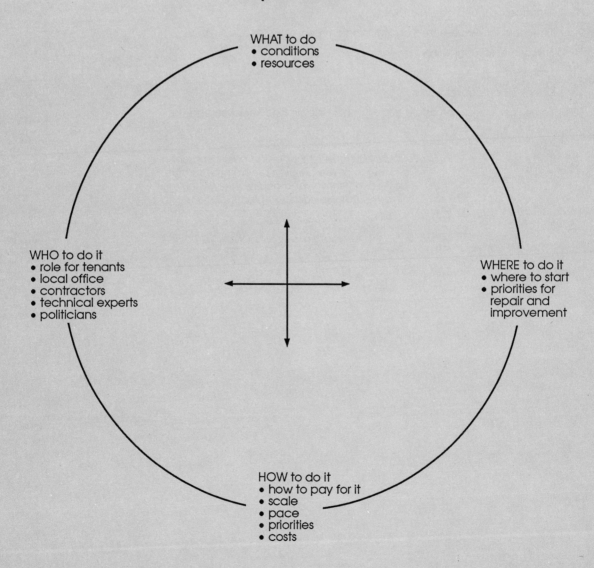

WHAT to do
● conditions
● resources

WHO to do it
● role for tenants
● local office
● contractors
● technical experts
● politicians

WHERE to do it
● where to start
● priorities for repair and improvement

HOW to do it
● how to pay for it
● scale
● pace
● priorities
● costs

2. KEYWORDS: RENOVATION; MAJOR REPAIR; FINANCE; ANNUAL CYCLE

Capital repairs and improvements should be treated as part of the overall **repairs** service. All priority estates require some **major** work to restore their condition. Some of them require an awful lot. Most capital works to council housing are **financed** by loans sanctioned by central government. It is the responsibility of the council to secure permissions and loans and to manage capital. It cannot be devolved onto the estate. Repayment of loans and interest charges are made from the Housing Revenue Account and have to be budgeted each year.

The **annual cycle** for capital spending has disadvantages for local authorities. It makes it hard to plan ahead. Sometimes permission to spend may come late in the financial year, making project management much more difficult.

Estate-based management staff and residents should work with the central housing and other departments in devising capital programmes of work to ensure that:

– there are agreed aims for the estate over a longer period than a single year.

– there are 'shelf' schemes for use at short notice should finance become available towards the end of the financial year.

– however limited the resources, the estate organisation gradually tackles the most basic and essential work, e.g. roof repair, replacement of faulty heating, strong, secure doors etc.

3. DEFINITIONS

Capital programme is an annually sanctioned plan for major physical works drawn up by housing organisations for their entire stock. This plan includes renovation and new-build schemes.

Housing investment programmes have been drawn up in order to help determine an annual allocation of resources for spending on capital investment in housing. A limit on the amount each local authority could borrow was set by the Department of the Environment through the Housing Investment Programme. Capital controls are now operated through the new Credit Approval system.

Credit approvals limit the amount local authorities can borrow or can spend on leasing arrangements. The size of credit approval for housing is set by the D.O.E., taking into account capital receipts.

Capital receipts are the income from sale of council property.

Condition survey is the assessment of the physical condition of buildings and external areas on an estate.

Structural survey is a special assessment of structural stability and safety of buildings.

Capitalised repairs are repairs which would normally be paid for out of the revenue budget but which are carried out and paid for out of the capital budget.

Decanting is involved where such extensive work is to be done that it becomes necessary to move tenants out of their homes temporarily – or permanently if the renewed dwelling will not be suitable. A majority of capital programmes are now geared to being done with existing tenants staying in occupation.

Capital works involve: **the structure** of the buildings, e.g. roof, windows, walls; the **inside fittings** of the dwelling, e.g. kitchen, heating, bathroom; the **common parts** of buildings, e.g. balconies, stairs, lifts, entrances; **common facilities,** e.g. refuse, parking, stores; the **immediate surroundings** and **access** areas, e.g. gardens, fencing, base of blocks; the **general environment,** e.g. open spaces, roads, paths. Depending on the age, type and layout of the estate, all these aspects will require capital spending over time.

4. TARGETS

– Organise regular **local** stock condition surveys with the help of local staff and residents.

– Involve residents and both office and manual staff in drawing up priorities, programmes and plans of work

– Get technical support staff locally based.

– Organise information, exhibitions, show houses and other **visual** ways of helping people understand building, repair and improvement problems and possibilities.

– Develop manageable-sized programmes.

– Find money for a tenant liaison worker.

– Draw up ways of improving the "look" of the estate as part of the general improvements.

– Deal with rubbish disposal methods – usually a dominant blight on rundown estates, often involving expensive bin-chambers etc. – as part of the physical improvement work.

– Work out ways of improving security.

– Work out the long-term links between major repairs, planned maintenance and capital improvements.

– Make sure that upgrading the environment of the estate is part of the capital programme.

5. LOCAL STEPS TOWARDS A CAPITAL PROGRAMME

Step 1: Analysis of possible sources of capital

There is more than one possible source of money, e.g. targeted Estate Action money[1], credit approvals, the repairs budget. Information is needed for each source of capital about amounts, time-scales, and constraints. The local management team, in trying to obtain funding, needs sound information, expert advice and strong political backing.

---

[1] Estate Action is a section of the DoE responsible for targeting resources for the improvement of run-down housing estates, linked to tenants' consultation, local housing management and local employment initiatives.

Step 2: Defining the problems

i)   Condition surveys

Where an estate is run-down, an initial full condition survey is necessary early on to establish the scale of the problems and reinvestment required. Regular stock condition surveys should then become part of the local estate management strategy.

The initial survey will show up the top priority structural and safety problems. The regular surveys give information for a repair and maintenance strategy for the estate including responsive repairs, planned maintenance and capital works. A localised survey is often more useful than a commissioned 'big bang' survey of housing stock conditions (see previous section on planned maintenance).

ii)   Structural survey

Major structural problems that show up in the condition survey may require special investigation through a structural survey. This should indicate how to treat structural and safety problems.

iii)   Management information

All workers on the estate have valuable knowledge. For example, recurring repairs may indicate a defect affecting a large number of dwellings. Locally based repairs workers and caretakers often know a lot about the state of the buildings which is not otherwise recorded. Discussions with them will reveal basic information about problems with roots, damp penetration, heating, drainage and refuse disposal systems. Local surveys involving local staff will make use of 'informal' information.

iv)   Tenant consultations

Tenants have a fund of knowledge about the condition of the estate, what works and what doesn't. Block or street consultations will show the tenants' priorities. Conflicts of interest between different groups of tenants need to be taken into consideration. **Technical decisions can only be taken with thorough technical advice**, e.g. choice of window frame or heating system. Tenants' information can be fed into local surveys but tenants must not be left to establish priorities without advice on structural, safety and other technical issues. This is as mistaken as not consulting tenants at all (Shenton, 1980). Sometimes tenants will be keen to participate in local condition surveys.

v)   Social surveys

It may be useful to undertake a survey of the tenants' needs as part of a capital programme. It is important to know how many disabled persons live on the estate, which families have young children, which dwellings are unoccupied during the working day, which dwellings have pets; these issues may be important if the project involves working in occupied dwellings (see Section on Monitoring).

16. *Major renovation. Bloomsbury Estate, Birmingham*

Step 3: Development of the Capital Programme

These programmes should be realistic in size, cost and time – a sequence of small-scale programmes is generally easier to manage. Remedial work should be done first:

i) to make dwellings wind and weatherproof;

ii) to make dwellings comfortable and warm;

iii) to make the environment clean, safe and attractive.

(See DoE Estate Action Handbook of Estate Improvements for detailed approach and proposals, 1989).

6. THE FIVE ELEMENTS OF THE PEP APPROACH TO CAPITAL SPENDING ARE:

– **Decisions** should be made at the estate level about the amount of work needed and the timing of work.

– **Tenants** should be fully involved in helping to make these decisions.

– Programmes should be devised within the **budget limits** so that residents' hopes are not raised then dashed.

– Competent **technical advice** and supervision should be available at the estate level.

– The works programme itself should be run from a **base on the estate** in close liaison with the local office.

7. HOW TO SET UP ESTATE-BASED MANAGEMENT OF CAPITAL PROGRAMMES

A technical officer should be found to work directly with the estate manager and the residents, drawing up plans and specifications, dealing with contractors, and liaising with the clerk of works.

There should be a **temporary office** base on the estate for the technical officer and clerk of works during the preparation and contract period. The contractor will also need a site base. Materials should be secured against theft. A night watchman may be necessary.

The following are essential elements of a successful programme:

(a) The staff should be skilled and experienced. Each should have defined responsibilities. The relationship of the estate-based housing staff to the architects, surveyors and contractors needs to be agreed and clearly stated. The estate manager should be in the client role, with the professionals acting as advisers. There should be regular progress meetings on the estate throughout the programme between management staff, technical staff, consultants (if employed) and contractors.

(b) There should be an agreed written procedure for operating the programme, setting out staff responsibil-

---

Diagram 2.6
Job Description of tenant liaison officer from Rhondda Borough Council

Penrhys PEP

Contract/Tenant Liaison Officer Grade: Scale 2

MAJOR TASKS

1. Responsible to the Principal Assistant (Architecture and Quantity Surveying) for encouraging and maintaining good liaison and co-operation between contractors, Council staff and tenants.

2. To maintain appropriate records and other information relative to the works.

DUTIES

1. Visit tenants and arrange for notification of the following:
   a) Works to be carried out.
   b) Commencing date of works.
   c) Expected duration of works.
   d) Specific requirements – moving furniture etc.
   e) Arrangements for entry of contractors.

2. Ensure that the Contractors and Council Technical Staff are made aware of any problems arising from the activities in (1).

3. Undertake regular visits to properties where work is being carried out and make detailed notes of the following:
   a) Rubbish left on site.
   b) Damage to property.
   c) Progress of works.
   d) Complaints from tenants.

4. Ensure that appropriate action is taken as a result of activities in (3) and provide tenants with appropriate information.

5. Assist tenants as required in completing documentation and/or claims for damages.

6. Inform tenants of times when you will be available in your office to receive complaints/queries.

7. Liaise with technical staff as required in order to deal with tenants' complaints/queries.

8. Report to Tenants' Association as required in order that they are kept fully informed about the works.

9. Set up and maintain appropriate records/system.

10. Attend meetings with Tenants' Association and other organisations as required.

ADDITIONAL POINTS

a) This post will be required for the duration of the contract work on Penrhys. The employment may not be continuous.

b) This post will be based on Penrhys and post-holder will be employed on a basic 37 hours/week (M–F) although there may be a requirement to work additional hours. Any overtime will be subject to the normal departmental authorisation procedures.

ities and the tenants' role at different stages of each project. Compensation and claims procedures should be agreed before actual problems arise. Care should be taken to ensure that all contractors are adequately covered by their insurance policies for working in occupied dwellings.

(c) There should be a formal agreement with the tenants' representatives about their role. Where there is a tenant management co-operative or an Estate Management Board, the local organisation is responsible for drawing up and sanctioning the programme in partnership with the council.

Where the local office forms part of the overall council structure, close liaison with tenants' representatives will be essential to making the programme work. With tenants helping, not only will the priorities be more accurate, but also the programme itself will be more likely to work. There are a great many detailed decisions and arrangements that can **only** be made with the tenants directly concerned.

(d) A training programme for all those involved, including tenants, is essential. In extended schemes this should continue through the programme. The training programme will explain the content of the work, its problems, the timescale and phasing, the roles of the estate office staff, contractors, professional advisers and residents, the equipment, the hoped-for results etc.

(e) Monitoring systems should be set up for individual properties and overall progress of the plan. Everyone should be clear about:

i)   what is to be done;

ii)   when it is to be done;

iii)   where it is to be done;

iv)   how and in what order it is to be done.

A progress chart marking the stages of the programme and the period over which the stages will be carried out is very useful (see below, p. 146)

(f) The council or local organisation should appoint a person responsible for day-to-day liaison with tenants affected by the programme, to work from the local office and to liaise between the tenants, the office, the contractor and the technical officer. The "capital works tenant liaison officer" should have a number of crucially important responsibilities. Rhondda Borough Council in South Wales has appointed a resident on the Penrhys estate to play this role. Diagram 2.6 shows a job description which applies to the tenant liaison officer.

(g) Support services may be necessary when tenants' daily lives are seriously disrupted, e.g. a day centre opened where tenants can go during noisy work; emergency cooking and heating facilities while power is turned off.

8. MANAGEMENT OF A CAPITAL PROJECT

The estate manager and technical staff should work together on each and every stage of the process. The management stages are shown in Diagram 2.7.

Stage 1: Establishing the brief

At this stage the aims of the project should be as clearly defined as possible. Through consultations, the local office and the tenants should produce detailed requirements for the design. This is set down as a brief to the design team (likely to consist of an architect and one or two surveyors, possibly from the council's technical service department).

Stage 2: Producing the design

Through a series of feasibility studies, sketch designs and outline proposals, the design team arrives at drawings, specifications, bills of quantity, and schedules which become a major part of the tender documents. The design team should consult continuously and widely as the design is refined. To do this properly they will have to prepare drawings and models which explain the design to tenants. It helps if the design team can be estate-based. Organisations such as Community Technical Aid Centres and community architects, whose method of work is geared towards maximum involvement of users, can be a great help to tenants at this stage.

It often happens that due to financial restrictions the design team have to modify the brief at the last moment, causing resentment amongst tenants who have been involved up to that stage. There should be contingency plans made i.e. an agreement about what is to be cut out if it is necessary − before the event − to avoid causing loss of confidence early in the programme of the capital works.

Tenants will be involved in decisions about:

− the degree of choice for individual tenants, e.g. about colour of decorations, type of fittings;

− whether to use employment training schemes for gates and fences, decorations etc;

− the phasing of building work;

− how to organise the work with tenants in occupation.

The estate staff, including repairs workers, caretakers and cleaners, are often able to see snags, to understand the buildings and to offer sensible 'inside' information. Therefore estate staff should be fully involved too.

Stage 3: The tendering stage

The tender documents should contain:

− a detailed description of the work

− starting and completion dates

− conditions of contract; with special attention to noise, working hours, access (including numbers of dwellings to be released at any one time and acceptable period for completion of work on any one property), security arrangements, particularly where sub-contracting is involved, services to be reinstated at night e.g. water, electricity, reinstatement of TV aerials, location of skips, removal of rubbish, use of dust sheets, removal of scaffolding, and emergency call-out for defects within Defect Liability Period. There should also be a clause spelling out compensation in case of any failures, damage or other problems.

Diagram 2.7

Stages in the management of a capital project with tenant involvement

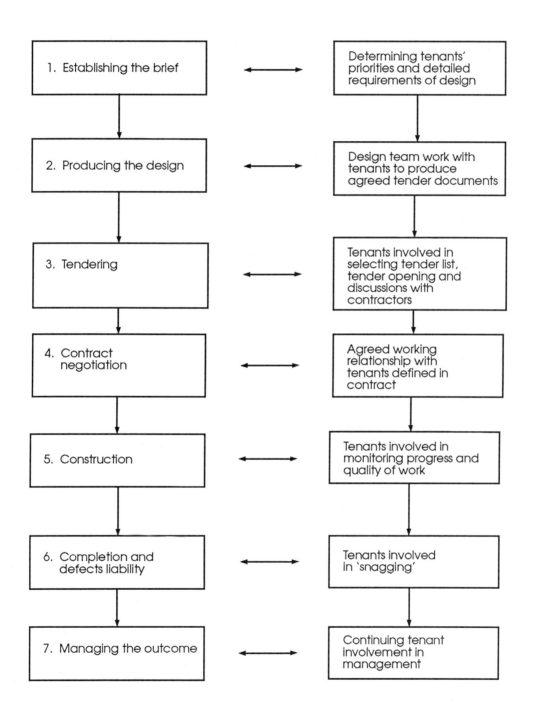

1. Establishing the brief ⟷ Determining tenants' priorities and detailed requirements of design

2. Producing the design ⟷ Design team work with tenants to produce agreed tender documents

3. Tendering ⟷ Tenants involved in selecting tender list, tender opening and discussions with contractors

4. Contract negotiation ⟷ Agreed working relationship with tenants defined in contract

5. Construction ⟷ Tenants involved in monitoring progress and quality of work

6. Completion and defects liability ⟷ Tenants involved in 'snagging'

7. Managing the outcome ⟷ Continuing tenant involvement in management

The tender documents should spell out tenant liaison arrangements during the contract period.

– who will be responsible for doing all the tenant liaison work

– requirements of the contractor to attend tenants' meetings

– attendance of tenants at site meetings

– arrangements for tenants to make choices regarding decorations etc.

– provision of refuge facilities for tenants likely to suffer from disturbance.

At this stage some small payment to all tenants for disturbance and use of electricity may be agreed.

Tenants' representatives should be involved with the estate manager in agreeing the details of the tender documents. On the basis of the tender documents, a contractor is selected and a price agreed. There should be an agreed list of contractors who are invited to tender for the work. Great care is required in the compilation of lists of approved contractors.

Stage 4: The contract negotiation stage

The outcome of this stage is a contract with a building firm to carry out the work, with start and completion dates, an agreed contract sum and agreed contract procedures.

Tenants' representatives should meet the contractor:

– to hear the contractor explain the programme of work;

– to satisfy themselves that the contractor will meet their requirements as laid out in the contract documents;

– to agree arrangements for tenant participation during the construction stage.

Stage 5: The construction stage

During the work, there **will** be problems which could not have been foreseen at the pre-tender stage. These will need to be ironed out by day-to-day liaison with individual tenants and at joint meetings of all those involved including tenants. If there is not someone directly responsible for tenant liaison at this stage, it is possible that the aggrieved tenants will refuse access, delay the contract, engage in direct argument with the contractor. This can be disruptive and costly to the contractor and the landlord. The outcome of this stage is the practical completion of the works.

Stage 6: Completion and defects liability stage

After the practical completion of the work, outstanding contractual obligations may need to be discharged before the final contract completion. During this stage, both individuals and groups of tenants should identify and report defects and damage to furniture and fittings. Where equipment has been installed such as central heating, tenants should receive information about how to use it.

Stage 7: Managing the outcome beyond the end of the contract

The estate manager manages the transition from contract work to maintenance of the work. Tenants are involved in:

– assessing the success of the project and feeding experience into the next project (or phase)

– agreeing suitable detailed programmes of maintenance

– spreading learning about the success and problems.

There may also be guarantees and warranties which mean that the contractor and suppliers of components and materials may retain some responsibilities for defects which arise beyond the defects liability period of the main contract. The local estate office should have details of all guarantees and warranties and the components covered should be identified in the property files.

Stage 8: Long-term maintenance

This is the ideal time to draw up longer term plans to maintain the improvements, ensuring that proper records are made of replacement materials, and plans are laid for ongoing renewal. All capital projects will require some ongoing maintenance or servicing. The capital investment must therefore be protected by an adequate long-term maintenance plan.

9. TIMETABLE FOR ESTATE-BASED CAPITAL PROGRAMMES

Throughout the works programme, the estate manager should manage three interlinked strands of work:

– the costings, budget and targets for the programme;

– the co-ordination of the contract work;

– the liaison with tenants.

In a big project, there may be a project co-ordinator who does this.

Early on, the technical officer should prepare a timetable for the programme to be used for:

– informing tenants and staff;

– co-ordinating the finance, the contract administration, and the tenant liaison;

– monitoring progress.

The timetable should take account of:

– the cycle of meetings of the committee responsible (e.g. the Housing Committee, Finance, Policy and Resources Committees, or the Estate Management Board)

– the constraints imposed by the funding

– time needed for individual and group consultations with tenants

– estimates of likely slippage in the timing (e.g. holidays and winter weather).

Often there is pressure for quick completion of a capital programme. It may be possible to shorten the timetable by:

– splitting a major project into several phases so that a pilot phase can be started very quickly, followed by short (e.g. one-year) phases covering the rest of the work.

– delegation of approvals to the chair or vice-chair of the committee or board responsible.

– speeding up the design stage by increasing the size of the design team

– going out to tender before finance is finally approved

– deciding if any of the phases can overlap.

The detailed plan, house by house, needs to be carefully drawn up. Meetings with tenants, and ongoing links with each household, will be vital. For each tenant, the part that matters most for them is **their** home, not the overall plan. But it is also important for them to understand where and how they fit in. A major programme must fit a particular house into phases of contracts. Liaison, timetabling and good relations between contractors, managers and tenants are vital as Diagram 2.8 shows.

Diagram 2.9 illustrates the timetable for a complex capital programme involving re-roofing, replacing windows, cladding the outer walls and enclosing the porches.

10. ENVIRONMENTAL UPGRADING

All estates need constant work to their common areas. Many rundown estates have poorly landscaped, inappropriately planted and badly maintained open spaces.

Tenants often register far more dissatisfaction about the environment and appearance of an estate than about their dwellings (Power, 1987).

Any capital programme needs to deal with this problem. Not only should grounds be made safe and attractive. They should also be made usable wherever possible and easy to maintain. Involving the young people of an estate is particularly important. The Estate Action Handbook of Estate Improvement (DoE, 1989) gives examples and techniques for improving the quality of the communal environment.

11. EXAMPLES

The priority estates shown in Diagram 2.10 (see p. 147) have had major capital works programmes, on which

Diagram 2.8

A model programme for the development of a capital programme	
Year	Activity
1985–6	Tenant survey to establish conditions and priorities
1986–87	Feasibility study and condition/structural survey
1987–88	Rehabilitation programme and funding agreed with Council
	Phasing of programme agreed – tenants are informed which Phase their house is in with estimated dates
	Detailed specifications drawn up for Phase 1
	Tenants consulted in detail in Phase 1 houses
	Small pilot scheme begins on 6 houses in Phase 1
1988–89	Phase 1 of works initiated on 330 houses – tenant liaison officer provides link between the local technical base, estate office, contractors and individual tenants
	Pilot scheme completed
1990–91	Phase 1 of works completed
	Tenants consulted in detail in Phase 2
	Phase 2 of works initiated on another 300 houses – tenant liaison officer provides link
	Environmental improvements to Phase 1 agreed including funding, work started
1991–92	Phase 2 completed
	Phase 3 initiated and completed – detailed consultation – tenant liaison officer provides link
	Phase 1 environmental works completed
	Phase 2 environmental works initiated
1992–93	Phase 2 environmental works completed
	Phase 3 environmental works initiated and completed

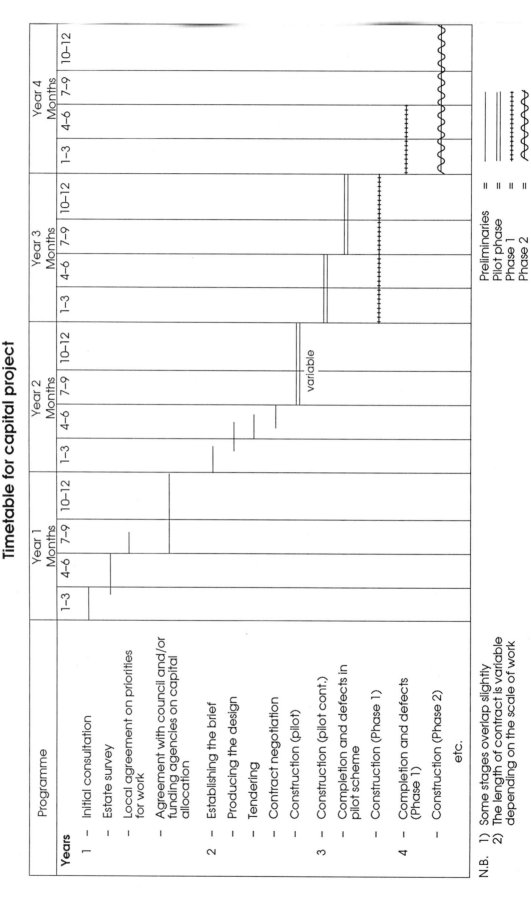

Diagram 2.9
Timetable for capital project

Diagram 2.10

Estates which are known to have established major capital works programmes

Broadwater Farm, Haringey

Ocean Estate, Tower Hamlets

Barnfield Estate, Greenwich

Orchard Park, Hull

Kirkholt Estate, Rochdale

Penrhys, Rhondda

Stoops and Hargher Clough, Burnley

Wenlock Barn, Hackney

---

this outline is based. Almost without exception the work includes environmental upgrading.

12. INITIAL CHECKLIST FOR CAPITAL WORKS AT OUTSET

1. What are the main physical problems?

2. How many dwellings are affected?

3. Have tenants been fully involved in identifying problems and drawing up the programme?

4. What about security? And the environment? And rubbish?

5. What is a **rough** estimate of the cost?

6. Is it feasible to do the work?

7. Where would the money come from?

8. How long would the work take per dwelling/across the estate?

9. Can the work be done around the occupants (i.e. without rehousing)? Are there any alternatives?

10. What is the most urgent priority?

11. How much can be built into a planned maintenance programme?

12. Will the improvements affect rent levels? If so, do tenants approve? Has the environment been discussed?

CHECKLIST FOR ASSESSING CAPITAL WORKS AFTER COMPLETION

1. Have the original problems identified at the outset been solved by the work?

2. Did the contract finish on time?

3. Did the contract cost the agreed amount?

4. Were any extra costs justified?

5. How much nuisance did the contract cause?

6. Were the tenants satisfied:

    a) with the work?
    b) with the liaison?

7. Did tenants receive sufficient warning of disruption?

8. Were problems resolved quickly and effectively?

9. Are estate staff pleased with the work?

10. Are repairs to areas affected by the contract easier/cheaper?

11. Are parts for maintenance obtainable for an agreed minimum period,

    e.g. in a lift renewal contract?
    e.g. window catches in modern prefabricated windows?

12. Does the estate look better?

13. Are the surveyors and technical staff satisfied?

14. Did the locally based contract system work?

15. Can the environment be maintained?

13. SOME USEFUL BOOKS ON ESTATE-BASED CAPITAL REPAIRS AND IMPROVEMENTS

ALDBOURNE ASSOCIATES (1986): Household Survey for PEP – Forms and Guidance. Ulmus Ogbourne, Marlborough

DEPARTMENT OF THE ENVIRONMENT: A Handbook of Estate Improvement. HMSO, London
Part 1: Appraising Options (1989)
Part 2: External Areas (forthcoming)
Part 3: Dwellings (forthcoming)
—— (1989): The Nature and Effectiveness of Housing Management in England. HMSO, London

DEPARTMENT OF EDUCATION & SCIENCE (1982): Playing Fields and Hard Surface Areas. DES Building Bulletin 28. London

HATCHETT M (1988): Building Studies Manual. London School of Economics, LSE Housing

HEALTH & SAFETY EXECUTIVE (1985): Deadly Maintenance – Roofs HMSO

HUDSON A (1970) Building and Engineering Contract. Sweet & Maxwell, London
—— (1979): First Supplement. Sweet & Maxwell, London

NATIONAL FEDERATION OF HOUSING ASSOCIATIONS (1987): Standards for Housing Management. London

RIBA & INSTITUTE OF HOUSING (1988): Tenant Participation in Housing Design – A Guide for Action. London

SAFE NEIGHBOURHOODS ADVISORY SERVICE & INSTITUTE OF ADVANCED ARCHITECTURAL STUDIES (1989): Safer Neighbourhoods – Redesigning Housing Developments to Reduce Crime and Enhance Community Safety. London

STANDFORTH J. MALCOLM J & MACLENNAN D (1986): The Delivery of Repairs Services in Public Sector Housing in Scotland. Scottish Office, Edinburgh

V. Caretaking, Cleaning and Environmental Maintenance

Contents

'The Priority Estates Project is a way of getting Government money for charismatic caretakers.'

Richard Rogers

1. SUMMARY

Caretaking means taking care of buildings and shared common areas. Housing estates have common areas and services that need supervision and maintenance. Caretaking works if:

- there is strong local support and supervision;

- there is good equipment and a local budget to buy necessary tools;

- caretakers are integrated into the estate team and feel a strong identity with the estate;

- there is agreement on high standards of cleanliness;

- there is enforcement of high standards on tenants, on the local workforce, and on other parties, e.g. contractors, other Departments.

Diagram 2.11 illustrates the importance of caretaking and cleaning.

Diagram 2.11
The importance of caretaking and cleaning

Estate problems –
rubbish/decay/vandalism

Estate sevices –
local office/local repairs/
resident caretaking and cleaning

Tenant involvement –
priorities/programmes/support/
neighbour nuisance/information/
enforcement & control

Action –
reporting/social and management pressure/
regular cleaning/status for caretaking

Standards of housing management –
team effort/better training/
better supervision/better equipment

Satisfaction –
high performance/recognition/
good feedback/easier enforcement/
motivation

Cleaner estates

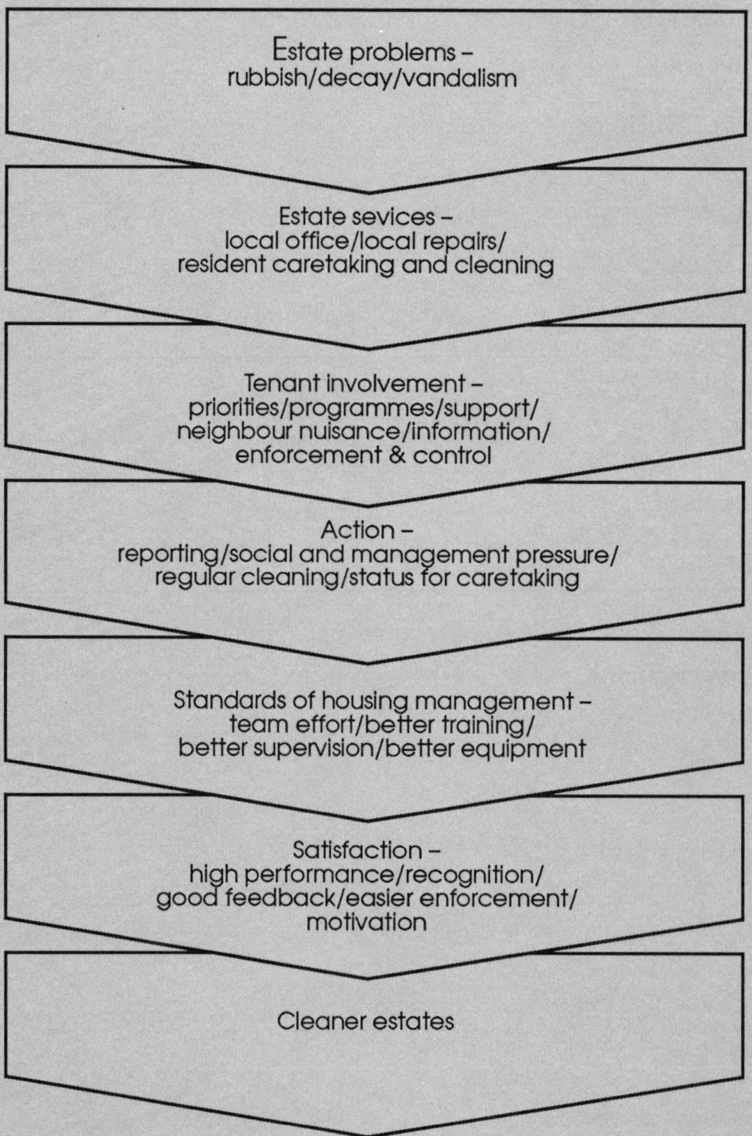

2. KEYWORDS: CUSTODIAL; COMMITTED; PERSONAL; EXPOSED

Estates almost without exception have been built with extensive communal areas. Even estates of houses need caretaking if they have verges, communal play areas and grassed areas, alleys, allotments, garaging areas, or some blocks of flats within an estate that is predominantly built of houses. Two-thirds of unpopular estates are built in the form of flats and need intensive caretaking. There are many **custodial** and maintenance problems that can only be dealt with through a caretaking or janitorial service.

The arguments for having resident caretakers are that they are:

– on the spot in emergencies;

– **committed** to the estate's condition because it is their own home;

– able to identify with residents and therefore get their support;

– familiar with the children and youth and therefore in a better position to control them.

However, where caretakers are non-resident, a similar set of needs apply.

The ideals of resident caretaking have often fallen far short in reality, partly because of changing social conditions, general reduction in authority at all levels, a changing population on many council estates, and a general removal of estate-based services and **personal** contact, leaving resident caretakers in a hopelessly **exposed** and impotent position. With an estate-based office, the role of caretakers can change radically for the better. Caretakers are being reintroduced on many estates to help restore and maintain the environment.

3. THE CARETAKING PROBLEM

a) The past

Traditionally, resident caretakers were the **front line** of housing management on flatted estates, carrying out a wide range of functions – showing flats to prospective tenants, cleaning, carrying out minor repairs, dealing with emergencies, enforcing tenancy conditions, con-

17. *The quality of caretaking makes or breaks estate conditions. Thorpes Estate, Hull*

Paul Herrmann/Profile

trolling car parking, keeping an eye on elderly tenants etc.

As local authority housing departments became increasingly centralised and impersonal, resident care-takers found themselves **stranded** on estates, lacking the back-up and resources necessary to carry out their jobs. The creation of specialist lettings sections robbed them of any role in the lettings process. Central housing offices were unable to back up caretakers' attempts to 'crack down on' **anti-social behaviour.** Tenants would look to caretakers as the **last vestiges** of personal housing management, just as caretakers were becoming incapable of fulfilling tenants' expectations. The result has been an **erosion of respect** and status for caretakers and widespread demoralisation. Caretakers have been widely blamed for failures of management.

The **custodial** aspect of caretakers' jobs has become particularly difficult to carry out. Gone are the days when a caretaker could give a troublesome teenager a clip round the ear or tell tenants to tidy up their landing or else! This is inevitable **progress** but it carried with it penalties for the caretaker's role and for the general condition of many estates.

b) The present

Resident caretakers have a crucial role to play in estate-based housing management. A **clean and tidy** estate is the most tangible sign of an efficient landlord service and is **a top priority amongst tenants.** The history of caretaking means, however, that many new projects will inherit a caretaking service with:

– unworkable job descriptions

– a demoralised workforce

– low status amongst tenants

– inadequate skills and resources

– lack of supervision or support.

It is hopeless trying simply to incorporate existing caretaking arrangements into a new estate-based management project. The estate manager must be given direct responsibility for caretaking. The housing organisation should:

– review the size of the workforce (in many cases it will need to be bigger);

– draw up new job descriptions – in most cases they will need to be simpler and more flexible. They will need to be carefully negotiated;

– introduce new training and resources for staff, includ-ing **much** better, tougher equipment;

– consult and inform tenants about caretakers' jobs;

– do everything possible to enhance the status of caretakers.

4. DEFINITIONS

The caretaking or cleaning service is the custodial, communal maintenance and cleaning service which

should be provided by landlords in order to maintain buildings and grounds in a fit and attractive state so that property is pleasant to live in and to let.

A **caretaker or warden** is a locally based housing worker with direct responsibility for seeing that the communal areas of estates and estate buildings are kept clean and in good working order. The caretaker or warden also has the most direct and continuous contact with residents of all ages.

Resident caretakers live on the estate and have as part of their job liaising with tenants and responding quickly to immediate needs arising from estate condi-tions.

5. TARGETS

– Carry out daily cleaning of all communal areas.

– Checking daily:

* all void properties
* all communal facilities, such as lifts and entry phones.

– Remove quickly:

* all dumped bulk refuse
* all graffiti – within 24 hours
* abandoned vehicles.

– Provide emergency contact for all tenants.

– Carry out daily inspection of patch – walk round every corner.

– Make use of training and meetings to become an integrated part of the team.

– Establish **good** relations with tenants' representatives.

– Think up ways of involving tenants, particularly young people and children in beautifying the estate.

6. LIAISON WITH TENANTS

In many local authorities, tenants living in flats have a shared responsibility for cleaning some communal areas such as access balconies, walkways, and land-ings. If this system works, it should of course be kept. It does work on many smaller, more popular estates. But in many cases the system has broken down. The reasons for the breakdown are complex, but among the most important are:

– the high turnover of residents

– the bureaucratic and impersonal style of much housing management

– the loss of status of caretakers and of council tenants, particularly on rundown estates.

It is virtually impossible for the landlord to enforce a tenants' cleaning rota and it causes endless conflicts and resentment amongst tenants, and between ten-ants, caretakers and estate officers. Where the system has broken down, it should be abolished and respon-sibility for cleaning **all** communal areas handed over to caretakers, with an appropriate increase in the size of the caretaking team in recognition of the additional responsibilities. If necessary, tenants should be charged for the service. It would cost about £1 per week per household to clean all balconies, landings and stairs on a flatted estate.

It is essential that tenants should know:

- who the caretakers are

- what their duties are

- what their system of working is

- what their hours are

- how often areas should be cleaned

- when/how tenants should contact caretakers directly.

This can be achieved by:

- new tenants being introduced to caretakers;

- caretakers wearing uniform where this is felt to be helpful;

- written information being delivered to all tenants, for example in a Tenants' Handbook;

- caretakers having their own patch which they become familiar with and feel responsible for.

Caretakers should always send a representative to report to formal management meetings with tenants. Because of the general decline in caretaking status, caretakers will need a lot of encouragement to participate.

Caretakers are normally resident on the estate they work on. Therefore they have a special relationship with other residents. Their effectiveness depends on their ability to relate well with the estate and with residents of all ages. Where caretakers are **not** resident, they should also be fully included in the local management organisation. They should also relate to tenants on a similar basis.

7. REQUIREMENTS

- Resident caretakers are needed on all flatted estates. There should be approximately one caretaker for every 110–120 flats.

- At least one caretaker/resident warden is needed on estates of houses with common areas. Such a warden may be able to handle up to about 500 dwellings depending on the design of the estate. The role of warden on an estate of houses is different from a caretaker on a small patch. It is more general, more dispersed, but just as vital and covering the same basic duties.

- Cleaners, usually part-time, are also needed on many estates. They can back up and share in the job of caretaker.

- The precise complement of caretaking and cleaning staff depends upon the amount of communal space on the estate and how difficult it is to look after. It also depends on other services such as rubbish removal.

8. RESPONSIBILITIES

The **core** caretaking responsibilities, which are essential on virtually all estates, should be:

- to keep communal areas clean and litter-free;

- to remove bulk rubbish;

- to remove graffiti;

- to check all lifts daily and to clean them out daily – to report any faults;

- to keep communal areas well-lit by replacing light bulbs and reporting faults;

- to inspect and report damage to communal areas or faults in communal services;

- to monitor repairs and replacements to communal areas or services;

- to check that empty dwellings remain secure;

- to call out emergency services as necessary.

There are other caretaking responsibilities, which strengthen the caretaking role. As many of them as possible should be included in the caretakers' responsibilities:

- to **patrol** the estate regularly in order to discourage vandalism and disturbance. Where there are serious problems of disturbance or threatened attacks on staff, caretakers should patrol in pairs;

- to report all incidents of vandalism or disturbance and all alleged breaches of tenancy conditions;

- to be an **emergency** contact for tenants out of office hours;

- to **carry out** some emergency work, such as boarding up newly vacated dwellings;

- to **clean out** empty dwellings;

- to **liaise** with and monitor other services, such as grass-cutting, domestic refuse collection, road-sweeping, garden maintenance etc.

- to liaise with **outside agencies,** such as the police, public utilities, when they are visiting the estate, or area of the estate the caretaker is responsible for;

- to **cut** the grass and maintain flowerbeds in communal areas, where this is required;

- to help **individual tenants** with gardening when in difficulty, e.g. clipping hedges for OAPs;

- to carry out specified **minor repairs;**

- to meet **prospective or new tenants** and to help with accompanied viewings;

- to help **deliver information** and publicity material to tenants on behalf of the estate office;

- to report **abandoned vehicles.**

Caretakers should be able to call on other services (e.g. Cleansing, Parks) and should be strongly backed by the local housing office. Caretakers are often unable to enforce a good service from repairs or refuse services and are expected to 'clean up behind' other workers or blamed for mess they did not make. The manager should be able to sort out co-ordination so that caretakers can do their job properly.

9. OTHER SERVICES AFFECTING CARETAKING AND CLEANING

Caretaking is dependent upon a number of crucial services. It is vital, if caretaking is to succeed, for there to be enough resources to get rid of ALL rubbish – from repairs and builders; from domestic rubbish; from dumping and from public litter accumulation.

a) Bulk refuse disposal

– The local authority should provide a prompt, well-publicised, **free service, collecting bulk refuse** direct from tenants' homes.

– Transport should be available to **pick up bulk rubbish** dumped on the estate or put out by tenants. Estate officers should have the discretion to call on this service immediately if necessary, for example, if dumped rubbish is causing a particular risk.

– **Skips** should be brought to the estate for short periods at **regular** intervals. The dates and times for skips should be well publicised amongst tenants. Permanent skips should be a last resort only – they are unsightly, smelly, a health risk, a fire hazard and a danger (particularly to children). They can actually lead to **more** refuse being blown or left loose on the estate.

– The local management organisation should take **legal action** against anyone caught dumping bulk refuse or causing a statutory nuisance through dumping rubbish.

b) Domestic refuse collection

– The local authority should provide a weekly refuse **collection service from tenants' homes.** On some flatted estates, collections may need to be twice or even three times weekly to keep rubbish chutes clear.

– Refuse collectors should take care not to leave a trail of refuse and should **clean up** after the collection. It is not fair to expect caretakers to clean up after collection, although there will probably always be some additional litter on refuse collection days.

– Each household should be provided with at least **one dustbin,** two where necessary. Tenants should never be expected to leave their refuse outside in black bags – these are **invariably** ripped open by dogs.

– In blocks of flats with refuse chutes, the **chutes** should be checked daily for blocking. **Paladins** should never be allowed to overflow. Where chutes are too small for modern use, they should be sealed up and tenants required to take their rubbish directly to a proper rubbish store, if necessary, at the base of the block. Tenants leaving bags of rubbish on landings and in public places should be traced and persuaded to dispose of their rubbish as requested. Rubbish normally contains evidence of identity such as discarded envelopes. Tenants, when identified and approached personally, usually co-operate. If tenants persistently refuse to co-operate and break the law by creating a health hazard or statutory nuisance, they

should be prosecuted. Enforcement is vital if caretakers are to keep their end up

c) Open spaces

– All open spaces should be put under the charge of **someone** – caretaker, tenants, parks or cleansing departments – and properly cared for.

– Areas on some estates which are in any way hidden from public view tend to invite dumping or simply accumulate litter over time. Such areas should either be given a proper public use or turned into private gardens.

d) Abandoned vehicles

The local authority, with help from the police should provide a prompt service for the **removal of abandoned vehicles.** There are, however, endless legal wrangles over this because of the private status of estate roads. All estate roads accessible to the public should be turned into public roads.

e) Central services and demarcations

The dividing line between the responsibilities of estate caretakers and of central departments providing services to the estate should be defined precisely, e.g. which roads and pavements should be swept by a community charge-funded Cleansing Department? Should the Parks Department remove litter before cutting grass and should it dispose of the cuttings? Such demarcations are the bane of caretakers' lives.

10. ORGANISATION OF WORK

– Each caretaker should have a clear written outline of the work he/she is expected to do each day, week and month. The way the job is carried out should be agreed with the estate manager.

– Each caretaker should be individually responsible for a defined **patch** of the estate.

– In addition, caretakers may need to spend a part of each day working in pairs or in **teams,** for example, to clean open communal areas beyond individuals' patches or to remove bulk rubbish.

– Communal areas should be cleaned **once a day.** So should checking on lights and secure doors, e.g. to electric cupboards, be done daily. But some jobs may be done weekly e.g. scrubbing out bin chambers; and some monthly, e.g. washing down tiled walls.

– The jobs given to each caretaker should make sure that the '**core**' caretaking duties are covered. There should be some time left **open** so that caretakers will have some time to carry out the less predictable work, such as coping with a sudden spate of rubbish-dumping or graffiti or giving extra attention to open spaces.

It is often the case that caretakers have to work particularly hard after the refuse has been collected. It is crucial that estate staff do stay on top of this and do not let careless, inefficient or even discriminatory refuse services mar the estate staff's efforts. Very often the general level of decay and sense of abandonment stems from demarcation disputes, the most common being between refuse collectors and caretakers. The manager should intervene to sort this one out.

– The question of **garden and grass maintenance** is a thorny one. Most estates, even in the least favourable inner city sites, have some planted areas. They are often poorly maintained, under-used and littered. When once there is an estate office and an estate management organisation, it makes every kind of sense to take on responsibility for all these spaces. Where this is done, it should be integrated with the caretaking service. There is nothing about mowing grass, weeding or even pruning roses that most caretakers do not already know or cannot learn. Maintaining the estate surroundings is one of the most visible signs of good housing management. Where open spaces or facilities on an estate do not belong to the housing organisation, agreement will be needed to ensure proper maintenance. Services provided from the Housing Revenue Account need to be properly co-ordinated with other services affecting the appearance of the estate. For example, a local management organisation could negotiate terms to take over the care of non-HRA land on an estate.

– It is important to build in **skills training** and development for caretakers. They are much more useful and get a lot more job satisfaction if they learn more and are able to do more as they go. Small repairs, securing broken windows or doors, gardening, lock replacement, are all examples. In addition, they can learn social, community and management skills. The philanthropic trusts, such as Sutton, Peabody, Guinness and Samuel Lewis, do this. So do the French equivalents of council housing. There the 'gardiens' (caretakers) are pivotal.

– **Private gardens** are the responsibility of individual tenants. But there are always some who cannot maintain them; and some who create nuisance and hazard by dumping rubbish in them, building and repairing in them, enclosing ground with makeshift and unsightly fences. Caretakers and wardens often have the job of contacting tenants over gardens, helping with maintenance where the tenant has particular problems and involving the manager where stronger action is needed.

11. SUPERVISION AND LIAISON

– Caretakers should be made to feel part of the **estate team,** using the estate office as their base. There should be meetings including all management and caretaking staff at least once a month to discuss progress and problems and to sort out ways forward.

– Each caretaker should liaise closely with the **estate officer** responsible for his/her patch. Estate officers should do weekly 'walkabouts' with the caretakers in their patch.

– Caretakers should be directly answerable to the estate manager in charge of the local office. The estate manager should have the power and authority to **discipline** caretakers who fail to perform.

– Caretakers should operate with the support of the local office in conjunction with the wider **cleansing** service. No estate can be kept clean and well-maintained without adequate bins, dumpers and frequent, efficient collection.

– There should be a special local caretaking **budget** within the estate budget to enable caretakers to replace equipment and introduce simple innovations without elaborate checking. Such simple items as

Diagram 2.12
Assessment of caretaking performance

Indicators	Ways of measuring	Assessment
Levels of cleanliness	– Checks by estate officers and manager – Inspection by resident representatives and caretaking supervisor	excellent good passable bad very bad
Regularity of cleaning	– Supervision by estate manager and caretaking superintendent	logbook
Feedback from tenants	– Sample surveys; meetings with tenants' representatives; local management organisation or forum discussions	office records minutes reports
Amount of graffiti and dumped rubbish	– Checks by estate officers and caretaking superintendent	a lot a little none
Incidence of vandalism or other repairs	– Written record by caretakers	logbook
Blocked chutes Lift problems	– Repairs requests; complaints by tenants; complaints by caretakers;	office records
Quality of equipment	– Caretakers' views; use of local budgets	logbook

new mop-heads or stepladders should not require bureaucratic sanction. It is easy to build in checks and safeguards for the small amounts involved.

Diagram 2.12 gives an idea of how caretaking needs and performance can be assessed.

12. EQUIPMENT AND FACILITIES

– Only the highest quality and most **durable equipment** is worth buying. Domestic quality equipment is a **waste of money.** Limited, carefully chosen, good quality equipment is more useful than plentiful shoddy equipment. Each caretaker should be responsible for his/her own equipment.

– The caretaking team should have a **store** for their equipment and materials, preferably in or attached to the estate office.

– As well as the standard handcart, shovels and brooms for external areas, there is now plenty of **cleaning technology** on the market which can be particularly effective for communal areas internal to blocks. Different cleansing agents (detergents, polishes, etc) are effective on different surfaces and should be selected with care. Cleaning equipment that is labour-saving, easy to use and maintain and reliable can make a caretaker's job far more satisfying. The more caretakers are encouraged to take responsibility for these things, the more likely they are to come up with ideas that will make their jobs easier and more rewarding.

– Good quality **uniforms, protective clothing** and wet weather gear should be provided. Caretakers should wear their uniforms when working, so that they are identifiable to tenants. Some caretakers are reluctant to be identified by their uniform because they feel that this makes them conspicuous and therefore potential targets of abuse and complaint. However, if the local management office is working properly and caretakers are properly integrated into the team, then the opposite should be the case. Certainly the caretaking staff on Broadwater Farm take a pride in being visible. This is natural since they do an excellent job and receive constant praise from visitors and residents alike.

– Many caretaking teams find **walkie-talkies** useful, enabling immediate contact for help, advice or information. It is particularly useful on large 'concrete jungle' or dispersed estates where people are hard to locate.

13. TRAINING FOR CARETAKERS

– All caretakers should receive an **induction training,** preparing them for their own jobs and introducing them to the principles and practice of estate-based management.

– Caretakers should be **integrated** into the training programme for estate-based staff and tenants. Topics of direct relevance to caretakers are cleaning technology, dealing with the public, health and safety at work, basic housing management, basic repairs and maintenance, communication skills, tenancy conditions and their enforcement, the role of tenants in management, and capital programmes.

– Many colleges now offer **courses** in cleaning technology leading to recognised qualifications, and caretakers should be given opportunities to attend these.

– **Rotas** should be organised so that training does not interfere with the completion of 'core' duties. Caretakers will resent training if it creates a backlog of essential work for the ones who are not selected for the courses or whose turn it is not.

Diagram 2.13 shows how the caretaking service can be organised.

14. CARETAKING MODELS

a) A caretaking model for flats

The following list outlines the **basic caretaking conditions** on a rundown flatted estate:

– 950 units, four tower blocks each with 90 dwellings. There are 12 other blocks

– Bin chambers and rubbish chutes

– Twice weekly refuse collection

– 10 areas of communal grass (each one about the size of a tennis court)

– Eight rose and shrub beds

– Private estate roads (not cleaned by the road service)

– Intake cupboards for electricity at the base of each block (16 in all)

– Store rooms in basements of all blocks and external store sheds

– 120 underground garages

– 80 free-standing garages.

The following list outlines the **problems** which the caretakers are constantly called on to deal with:

– Chutes block

– Paladins in bin chambers are too small

– Refuse service is regular but lots of spillage

– Tenants leave rubbish bags outside chutes and bin chambers because chutes or bin chambers are often blocked – where else should they put them?

– Stray dogs make messes on stairs and in lifts. They also tear rubbish bags

– Furniture is constantly dumped outside blocks as there are at least two new tenants a week

– Staircases look dingy and institutional

– Balconies and landings are unwelcoming though generally clean

– Lights often break; there is a total of 2,400 light bulbs on the estate to be checked

– Locks on wooden doors to bin chambers and electric intake cupboards are frequently broken

Diagram 2.13
Procedure for caretaking and cleaning

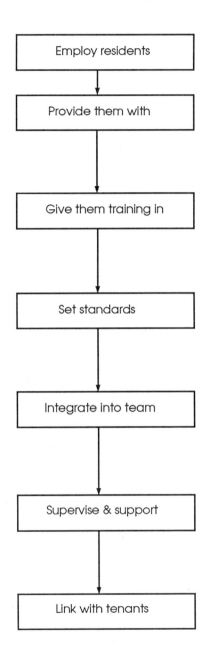

| Employ residents |
| Provide them with |
| Give them training in |
| Set standards |
| Integrate into team |
| Supervise & support |
| Link with tenants |

- offer good accommodation
- restrict hours of service
- provide office base on estate

- good equipment
- flexible job descriptions
- decent uniforms and protective clothing
- an equipment budget
- a local store

- cleaning technology
- dealing with the public
- communication
- basic repairs
- working as a team
- problem solving

- target
- inspect
- monitor
- recognise achievement
- write letters of recognition for outstanding service

- regular meetings
- share office or have adjacent office
- invite to contribute
- listen to caretakers' views
- do patch inspections

- direct answerability to local manager
- competent local superintendent
- good back-up from residents
- liaise with patch estate officer

- introduce new tenants
- get caretakers to help with viewing
- invite caretakers to meetings with tenants' representatives
- give caretakers their own patch
- improve status of caretakers
- make each caretaker responsible for knowing all tenants on patch

– Repairs workers do not always clear up after them

– There are contractors on the estate, creating a lot of mess around two blocks

– Underground garages are under-used

– Graffiti appears regularly on garage doors and intake cupboard doors, occasionally on stairwell walls

– Private gardens at base of blocks are not all well-maintained.

We list here the **staffing** requirements in order to tackle the problems effectively:

– One caretaking superintendent

– 9 caretakers: 4 for 4 tower blocks

– 1 cleaner responsible for the office, caretakers' room and voids cleaning

– 1 cleaner responsible for estate roads and underground garages

The caretaking superintendent is part of the estate team and works from the estate office. The nine caretakers work in two teams and cover for each other – the four tower block caretakers; and the rest (five).

The caretakers have weekly work meetings to sort out jobs and problems and to discuss any new hurdles and decide who can tackle them and how. The estate manager attends caretaking meetings when asked. Each caretaker keeps a logbook and fills in any incidents and any replacement or repair needed. There is a caretaking budget and equipment is a constant source of discussion.

All caretakers are resident. They are invited to the estate meetings with other staff and residents (four come). They have an official representative on the Estate Management Board.

The manager plays a vital role in the caretaking service. Without him/her the service would not work.

The caretakers face some problems daily: light bulb replacement; dumped rubbish; blocked chutes; split bags; litter on grass; and graffiti removal.

A small minority of **irresponsible tenants** cause quite amazing burdens on the caretaking service. The same names and families come up again and again. There are five well-known 'rubbish creators' on this estate. Only a combination of constant pressure – support from the manager, personal visiting to the households concerned, support by other residents and, in a very few extreme cases, court action – will make the caretakers' job possible. Prior to the local office, the whole estate was stigmatised with a general sense of unmanageable problems created by a tiny minority. These problems spilt over onto the whole estate. Now it is an uphill battle to keep on top, but it is working.

The following **method** shows what is required of a caretaker:

– Each caretaker cleans all of his/her communal areas for 3–4 hours daily (five days a week), including outside, grass, lifts, stairs, balconies, entrances etc.

– Each caretaker checks light bulbs, doors, garages in his/her patch daily and replaces bulbs, cleans graffiti, or reports repairs needed to the office.

– Each caretaker walks right round his/her patch daily to inspect. He/she does it **weekly** with the estate officer for that patch. It takes half an hour.

– The superintendent liaises daily with the estate manager, reports and chases repairs and other problems, and goes round the estate every day for 1/2 hour, concentrating on different areas and issues on different days. He/she has a caretaking meeting once a week. He/she also has individual meetings with caretakers whenever necessary. He/she attends estate meetings with staff and residents.

– Residents' representatives can be referred to the caretaking office about special problems.

– The caretakers normally wear donkey jackets and other protective clothing. The superintendent normally wears a uniform jacket. The caretakers say they like smart uniform and they like to be recognised. In practice, their jobs are so messy that they have no choice but to wear overalls, protective gloves and heavy-duty jackets.

– The caretaking office is just off the main office within the main office building.

Training. Three of the caretakers have been on short courses in estate-based management. The office is arranging on-the-job training in cleaning technology. The superintendent has been on a one-year course. This gave him many skills and a great boost in confidence.

The caretaking team has the aim of:

    a) a litter-free estate environment;
    b) no accumulated rubbish bags;
    c) clean, sweet-smelling lifts;
    d) clean stairs, landings and balconies;
    e) clearing **on the day** of all dumped rubbish;
    f) close relations with the office;
    g) close liaison with tenants' representatives;
    h) each caretaker knowing all the tenants on his/her patch.

b) A caretaking model for a cottage estate

Basic conditions

– 500 houses with front and back gardens and fencing

– 20 sheltered one-bedroom flats

– Back alleys behind all houses

– Four large, grassed common areas

– Sheds within each garden

– No garages.

Problems

– The back alleys are constantly dumped with rubbish.

– The grass verges are cut but littered.

– The four common areas have no trees, are mown, but are littered and have no obvious purpose. They are too small for football and groups of boys are constantly playing football in the street.

– About 20 tenants have very untidy rubbish-filled front and back gardens.

18. *Estate wardens help the elderly with their gardens. Kirkhold Estate, Rochdale*

Paul Herrmann/Profile

– Several tenants have built their own fences to replace broken and stolen wooden fencing. This looks 'untidy' too.

– About 30 gardens have uncut, overgrown hedges.

Staffing.   There is one full-time caretaker/warden.

Method.   His duties are:

– to keep all back alleys clean;

– to clean the four common areas;

– to pick up litter along verges and paths;

– to arrange for dumped rubbish and furniture to be removed;

– to talk to tenants who cause litter (e.g. leave rubbish bags out to be collected on wrong days);

– to help OAPs and one-parent families with very young children with hedge-clipping;

– to operate a garden tools loan system to tenants;

– to report serious nuisance in gardens to the manager.

The warden/caretaker covers all communal areas of the estate **daily** (five times a week). He calls into the estate office daily to report problems and to pick up any requests for help/jobs. He goes right round the estate once a week with the estate manager.

He liaises with individual tenants and encourages tidy

gardens by helping wherever possible. He talks to tenants who are causing a mess. He does small, emergency repairs to help keep things working e.g. latches or hinges on gates, missing planks from fences, leaking overflows, blocked external drains, etc. He attends estate meetings with staff and residents' representatives and staff meetings.

He has special protective uniform to protect his normal clothing. He has a handcart, broom, ladder, shovel, cleansing solvents, a store and a small budget to pay for additional equipment.

He can order repairs to common areas and, in some cases, on behalf of tenants (e.g. where tenant is in special need).

Management.   The warden/caretaker is directly answerable to the estate manager and is part of the estate team. He also liaises closely with the estate officer.

Training.   The warden/caretaker is invited to go on day conferences and special training sessions like the other staff. He has attended two so far.

Targets.   The local team has set these caretaking targets:

– The estate environment should look as **good** as a privately owned estate.

– The alleys should be clean.

– Tenants should start to keep their gardens tidy.

– No rubbish should be put out on the streets.

– The warden should like his job.

15. EXAMPLES OF RESIDENT CARETAKING SERVICES ON ESTATES

1. **South Bank, Langbaurgh – cottage estate**   846 dwellings: 33 flats/maisonettes, 813 houses.

There are **2 resident estate wardens** with primarily **custodial responsibilities,** and **3 resident cleaners** (p/t), who clean all communal areas on the estate once a day, seven days a week, on a rota basis. They also clear out voids. They report to the estate manager.

2. **Cubitt Town, Tower Hamlets, London – flatted estate**   643 dwellings – mainly flats/maisonettes.

There are 5 full-time, resident caretakers – 1 senior and 4 assistants. They work in a team to clean all communal areas on the estate every morning, and in the afternoons each caretaker returns to his/her own patch for other duties related to the upkeep of their areas. The senior reports to the team leader.

3. **Penrhys, Rhondda, S. Wales – mixed building types**   948 dwellings – 200 flats/maisonettes, 748 houses.

There is a **'clean-up gang'** with a **resident estate warden** in charge, **4 labourers and a driver** whose jobs are to clean communal areas of rubbish, cut grass, do some patrolling, and clean out empty property.

The team have a tip-lorry and small dumping machines, to clear bulk rubbish and clean up after building work. The warden reports to the co-ordinator.

In addition, there are **nine resident caretakers** for the maisonette blocks (part-time, hours ranging from 6 to 25 p.w.) responsible for cleaning communal areas in and around blocks. There is a supervising resident caretaker who reports to the co-ordinator.

16. CHECKLIST FOR CARETAKING

1. Do the caretakers clean all common areas?
2. Is the estate normally clean or dirty looking?
3. Do caretakers attend team meetings?
4. Do caretakers attend meetings with residents?
5. Do caretakers have a secure equipment store on the estate? Do they have adequate equipment?
6. Do caretakers have a patch each?
7. Who does patch inspections with caretakers?
8. Are caretakers answerable to the local manager or to a central or district supervisor?
9. Do caretakers do minor repairs?
10. Do caretakers meet new tenants?
11. Do caretakers help with viewings?
12. Do caretakers clean balconies and stairs?
13. Are caretakers being introduced on cottage estates?
14. What status do caretakers have on the estate? Are they normally blamed for the poor environment?
15. Can bulk rubbish be removed quickly?
16. Do tenants understand what caretakers' responsibilities are?
17. Are caretakers given instruction and ongoing training?
18. Who is in charge of garden maintenance?

17. SOME USEFUL BOOKS ON CARETAKING AND CLEANING

PARKER T (1983): The People of Providence. A housing estate and some of its inhabitants. Hutchinson, London

ROBERTS M (1988): 'Caretaking – Who Cares?' in Teymur N, Markus T A, Woolley T (eds), Rehumanizing Housing. Butterworths, London

Note: There is very little published material on this subject.

Part 3
Money

VI. Budgets and Accounts

Contents

'Take care of the pennies and the pounds will take
care of themselves'

(Anon)

1. SUMMARY

To make sensible spending decisions, you need to know how much you have to spend. You also need to know what your inescapable costs are.

Centralised budgets and administrative systems run up big overheads, are often inefficient and do not allow for local decision-making on spending and costs.

Local, autonomous budgets are:

- easier to understand
- easier to operate
- easier to target at local needs
- easier to control and account for.

They are the essence of local housing management, which should be businesslike as well as service-centred. Local budgets make for more economical management decisions and more savings.

Diagram 3.1 illustrates the advantages of a local budget.

Diagram 3.1
The advantages of a local budget

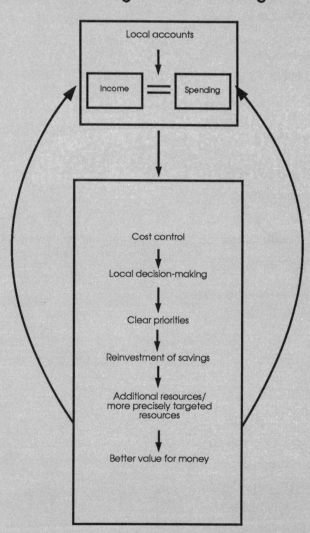

Local accounts

Income = Spending

Cost control

Local decision-making

Clear priorities

Reinvestment of savings

Additional resources/ more precisely targeted resources

Better value for money

2. KEYWORDS: COSTS; CONTROL; SAVINGS; IMPROVEMENTS

Budgeting and local authority accounts must be two of the most mystifying and dry topics in housing management. For this reason very few people have bothered about them. And for this reason, valuable resources have been wasted. Without budgets, no one knows where the **money's** coming from, going to, how much everything **costs,** who really makes the decisions or how things can improve. With budgets, it is possible to **control** spending, make **savings,** pay for **improvements** and make management work.

Estate budgets were 'discovered' by PEP in 1980 as the way to make councils put the money where it mattered – onto the estates. The original idea was to identify the money the Council already spent on management and maintenance so as to argue for full local services in the way that management co-operatives have successfully done. By breaking down total spending by area, it became possible to identify resources for local management.

Controlling a budget, making it work, helping staff and tenants to understand it and use it, and saving money so that you can **buy more for the estate** is the most exciting and rewarding management job. It is the main reason why co-operative tenants bother. But it is very difficult to achieve within a large, centrally run organisation.

3. DEFINITIONS

In any local authority, day to day spending on council housing comes from the **Housing Revenue Account.** This is a separate account into which rents are paid and from which the following housing activities are financed:

– general management of council housing,

– repairs and maintenance of council housing,

– interest charges (and repayment of loans), and

– most other housing services.

Some housing services, such as housing homeless people, are not charged to the Housing Revenue Account. Under the new financial arrangements, Housing Benefit will become an integral part of the Housing Revenue Account.

From April 1990 a new system of subsidies from central government to local authority Housing Revenue Accounts in England and Wales has been introduced (the existing subsidies in Scotland already worked much the same way). At the same time, Housing Revenue Accounts are being **'ring-fenced'** so that local authorities can no longer pay Rate Fund Contributions into them from their general funds – and only in rather rare situations pay money out of the Housing Revenue Account to the general fund (Hills, forthcoming).

The important parts of the new system will be the **rent guideline** and the **management and maintenance allowance.**

The rent guideline is what central government decides would be an appropriate rent for each local authority to charge.

The management and maintenance allowance is the amount that central government allows for each local authority to spend on management and maintenance. The rent guidelines and the management and maintenance allowance will be set by the government each year and will be different for each local authority. Basically, central government will pay enough subsidy so that if rents were set equal to the guideline and management and maintenance spending equalled the allowance, then the HRA would balance. If the authority wanted to spend more on management and maintenance; than the allowance, it would be free to do so, but this would have to be paid for from higher rents.

The Government Approach. Rent guidelines are going to be higher in parts of the country where house prices are higher. To start with, management and maintenance allowances only depend on how much an authority was spending on management and maintenance in the late 1980's (not including 'capitalised repairs'). However, the government has said that in future allowances will vary according to an assessment of the relative costs for different authorities of looking after each authority's stock, allowing for its age, type of building and so on.

A budget is an allocated sum of money, set aside each year to cover a discrete area of organisation or activity.

An estate budget is the annual sum set aside by the landlord to run the management and maintenance of an estate.

Accounts are the set of figures produced to show or account for spending under different agreed headings.

4. TARGETS

– Draw up a list of all the costs that should be covered locally.

– Check the income from rents and housing benefit.

– Check the loss of income through arrears.

– Check the loss of income through empty property.

– Work out how to make savings.

– Work out an allowance from the Housing Revenue Account for the management and maintenance of each dwelling.

– Estimate a budget for the estate.

– Set up a separate account for the estate.

– Make sure that caretaking, all day to day repairs, and cyclical maintenance are built in.

– Build in incentives to keep arrears and empty property down.

5. RING-FENCING AND LOCAL BUDGETS

None of the changes brought about by the 1989 Act should make any difference to whether an authority sets up local or estate-based budgets. Within the ring-fenced Housing Revenue Account, the local authority housing department can decentralise its management and maintenance budgets to local offices. In the long run, it may help local authorities to establish estate budgets if there are clear guidelines for the different costs of different kinds of estates and a clear allowance for management and maintenance spending. In working out the size of a budget, housing staff, councillors and tenants will be able to look at the authority's management and maintenance allowance and the influence that different types of stock will have on the allowance. Under the new system, an old or a complex-concrete estate should be eligible for more management and maintenance money.

The new system will bring local authorities closer to housing associations in three ways: a ring-fenced housing budget; a management and maintenance allowance; and rents to cover costs minus subsidy.

Diagram 3.2 illustrates a ring-fenced Housing Revenue Account.

6. ADVANTAGES OF A LOCAL BUDGET

– A budget for a local management office provides an agreed level of resources for the estate, an incentive for careful management, and local decision-making on priorities for spending. The budget should cover all day-to-day management and maintenance.

– Savings from careful management, especially on the maintenance budget, control of empty property and a reduction in arrears, can be spent on improvements to the estate.

– The local scale of an estate budget makes it easy to understand and manage. A local budget helps tenants to get involved in decisions. It greatly increases the control of the local manager and a tenant-led management body.

7. THE ALLOWANCE

An estate budget is made up from an allowance per dwelling from the Housing Revenue Account or an allowance deducted directly from the local rent income.

The amount allowed for each dwelling can either be based on the average unit cost of management and maintenance across the borough but allowing for any special management and maintenance demands of the estate; or it can be built up from costings for each part of the locally-based management organisation e.g. office rent, staff costs, equipment etc. The first year's budget should always be a trial budget. It is possible to arrive at a more realistic total after a year's operation.

In the first six months after a local office has been set up, there is likely to be a very heavy demand for repairs and the budget should reflect this. The upsurge in demand may be particularly marked on estates which have been badly neglected in past years. (See examples below.)

Diagram 3.2
1989 Local Government and Housing Act revenue system

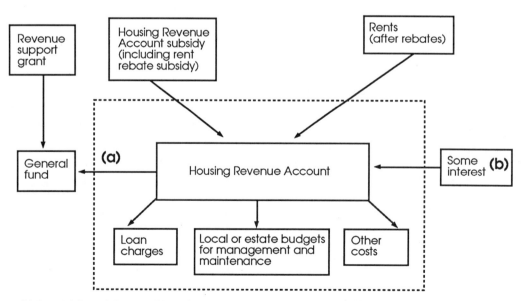

Notes: (a) Transfers out of Housing Revenue Account only allowed in rare circumstances;
(b) See J. Hills, 'Unravelling Housing Finance' (forthcoming) for explanation.

19. *Controlling budgets locally helps residents understand what is possible. Cloverhall Estate, Rochdale*
Paul Herrmann/Profile

8. THE ACCOUNT

An estate can have a separate account within a Housing Revenue Account. This normally happens with EMBs. Or the account can be held at estate level in a separate bank account. This happens with management co-operatives. However the account is organised, the local manager should have control but be accountable to the central organisation for how the money is spent. Where there is an Estate Management Board or estate sub-committee with a local budget, the local manager must present budget and spending reports and annual accounts locally, as well as centrally.

9. CALCULATING AN ESTATE BUDGET

There are two main ways of calculating an estate budget. In practice, budgets are usually constructed, using bits of both methods.

Method A

The following is a worked example of a budget for an estate of 600 flats.

1. From the Council's published annual Housing Revenue Account, identify the total cost of management and maintenance.

2. Divide the total by the number of council dwellings to identify the average cost per dwelling.

3. Special management and maintenance requirements, e.g. lifts, district heating, extensive communal areas, should have an additional allowance, based on estimated spending per flat for these services. This special allowance should be added. Identify any other additional management costs, e.g. a high level of void property; a large number of high rise flats; special maintenance problems requiring additional spending such as garages, flat roofs, infestations (cockroaches).

4. Multiply the unit cost by the number of dwellings.

   This estate budget includes all local staff costs including employer's overheads. About 20% of the budget should be deducted for these costs.

Diagram 3.3

Calculation of an estate budget by Method A

1)	Total Housing Revenue Account spending on management and maintenance	£8,622,000
2)	Total no. of council dwellings	15,000
	Therefore average cost per dwelling $= \dfrac{8,622,000}{15,000}$	$= £575$
3)	Special additional costs: central heating annual service of central boiler system at £25 per unit; annual lift servicing at £50 per unit; communal maintenance at £50 p.u.p.a.	
	– total special allowance – £125 p.u.p.a.	
	$\times\ 600 =$	£75,000
4)	Therefore budget for estate of 600 dwellings $= £575 \times 600 =$	£345,000
	$+ (£125 \times 600) =$	£75,000
		£420,000

Note: The figures would need to be revised according to actual accounts for the most recent year.

(The actual management and maintenance allowance for housing associations for 1989–90 ranges from £477 to £736 in the north of England; £552 to £829 in inner London, depending on the size of property and whether it is new-build or rehabilitated. These figures give some idea of how much the management and maintenance of rented property is likely to cost.)

Method A is the most simple and direct way of constructing a local budget.

Diagram 3.3 shows a worked example of calculating an estate budget by Method A.

Method B

The following method is more popular with central housing organisations.

1. Draw up a list of all the requirements of the local management organisation that need to be accounted for and paid for locally: staff, office, running costs, repairs, equipment, and contingencies.

2. Estimate the actual cost of each of these items broken down into all its parts, e.g. every member of staff required and the estimated cost including employer's overheads, grading, etc.

3. Total up all costs to produce an overall budget figure and unit cost.

Method B should produce roughly the same answer as Method A.

Method B, sometimes called 'zero-based budgeting', is a more exact and more commonly used method. Method A has the advantage of taking **only** what the Council currently spends as a base line. This is helpful in persuading councillors that estate-based management is affordable and even economical. It is also a quicker method.

10. ALLOCATING A BUDGET

Having calculated the budget in theory, it is important to work out an actual budget to cover estimated costs. When allocating a budget there are two main stages:

A. determining the total figure
B. allocating amounts between different items.

Diagram 3.4 illustrates the allocation.

11. CONTROLLING THE ESTATE BUDGET

Where an Estate Management Board or a tenant management co-operative is being established, the full allowances should be paid into a separate named account (either within the council's overall account or in a local bank account). The board or co-operative then allocates the budget and authorises the manager to spend under the various headings. The management agreement will spell out the areas that must be covered. Staff salaries are largely fixed costs, though even with salaries there is some leeway provided through the budget, e.g. when a post is vacant or when a more or less experienced person is appointed.

Local control of the repairs budget is absolutely central to the success of any local management project. In fact, the failure of central systems in this respect led to the development of the budget ingredient. The budget should be controlled in the following ways:

i) **Control** over spending of the estate budget should be vested in the estate manager, with the authorisation of the council, the Estate Management Board or the co-operative, depending on the local agreement.

ii) With the exception of staff salaries and central establishment charges which have been agreed, all charges against the local account should require the prior **authorisation** of the estate manager.

Diagram 3.4

Budget for an estate of 600 flats

STAGE A
Allowance per dwelling per week £11.50

Budget per year: £11.50 × 50 × 600 = £345,000
+ special allowances = £ 75,000
Total   £420,000

STAGE B

Budget item	Budget allocation
Office staff salaries:	£
1 co-ordinator/manager	15,000
2 estate officers	22,000
1 admin/book-keeper	9,000
Employer's overheads at 20%	9,200
Office costs	6,000
Equipment	2,000
Caretaking:	
5 resident caretakers	45,000
Overheads	9,000
Caretakers' accommodation	7,500
Maintenance: (£253,800 – 60% of budget)	
Cyclical maintenance	52,000
Day-to-day repairs including cost of depot (£5,000), 4 repairs workers (£44,000), materials (£22,000) + contract work	154,800
Special maintenance contracts	47,000
	£378,500
Allowance for emergencies, other costs[1]	41,500
Total	£420,000

1. There can be a contribution to central overheads in addition to employer's overheads. Training should be included.

iii) The estate manager can best keep track of expenditure through at least **monthly statements** which show **actual and committed** spend to date against **estimated** spend to date.

iv) The budget should have some **flexibility** to allow the estate manager to 'manage' the estate resources, for example:

– if there is underspending under one budget head, it should be possible for money to be transferred where necessary to another.

– buying in temporary help to keep control of voids and arrears may save money.

– improved performance on arrears or higher rent income through reduction in voids can lead to a small improvements programme, e.g. new fencing, better play equipment, new doors, etc.

Any savings which add income to the estate budget can be ploughed back into the estate.

v) The estate manager should be in charge of selecting suitable **contractors** in accordance with council policy.

12. SETTING UP BUDGET SYSTEMS

Within a local authority, there will be many different forms of payment made for services on the estate. For instance, leisure departments may charge for grass-cutting, the supplies department for stationery. When the local budget is negotiated, each of the systems set up for making payments should be changed to allow for the new local control and payment.

We have already stressed three essentials to local control:

– the budget should be held in a **separate account; or** the estate budget should form a separate cost centre within the local authority's accounting system.

– all charges against the budget should be **sanctioned locally** in the same way as if the budget holder held the only chequebook.

– the manager should be able to produce locally **up-to-date,** simple and intelligible **information** about committed and actual expenditure.

Diagram 3.5
Annual budgetary cycle

Before the start of the financial year: October to March

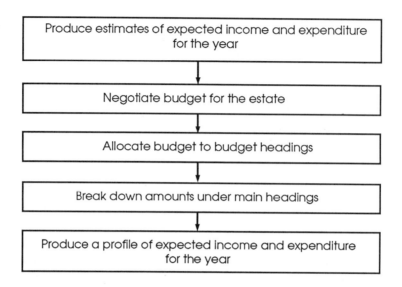

Produce estimates of expected income and expenditure
for the year

Negotiate budget for the estate

Allocate budget to budget headings

Break down amounts under main headings

Produce a profile of expected income and expenditure
for the year

During the financial year: April to March

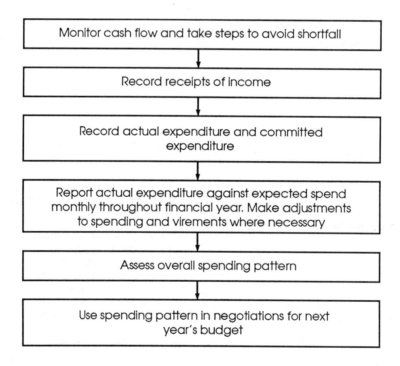

Monitor cash flow and take steps to avoid shortfall

Record receipts of income

Record actual expenditure and committed
expenditure

Report actual expenditure against expected spend
monthly throughout financial year. Make adjustments
to spending and virements where necessary

Assess overall spending pattern

Use spending pattern in negotiations for next
year's budget

After the end of the financial year: March

Close off the budget and prepare accounts
for auditing

In addition, the following mechanisms are necessary:

– the **system** for handling the budget should be manageable. If the account is held locally, this involves setting up a book-keeping system in the local office and hiring a book-keeper. Book-keeping may be done: in a ledger; or using a stand-alone microcomputer; or using part of the local authority's mainframe computer system. However, in order for this to work, the main computer should operate area-based or cost-centre based accounts rather than schedules of charges for particular categories of spending across the whole authority, such as stationery or office equipment. In most offices, except co-operatives, the accounts are held at the centre.

– if the account is held centrally, there should be **local recording** of all authorised expenditure and this should be checked **at least monthly** against central accounts.

– the estate manager should have powers to **vire** between budget headings within set limits.

– there should be built-in **safeguards,** e.g. two signatories for cheques or for authorisation of payments of over £500. There should be a blocking mechanism on the account if anything goes wrong.

– the systems should satisfy both **internal and external audit.**

In most cases management staff employed locally will remain on the local authority payroll. In this case it is important that there is local control of any variable staff items e.g. overtime, temporary workers, vacant posts, local cleaning arrangement, contract work for day to day repairs.

13. THE BUDGETARY CYCLE

When an allowance has been allocated and the system set up for a local budget, the management of the budget will have to fit into the local authority or other organisation's own budget cycle. There is an annual cycle (Diagram 3.5) starting each financial year in April. Other housing organisations follow a similar cycle.

14. EXAMPLES

In proposing Estate Management Boards, we are talking about a management and maintenance budget that is cut off from the local authority main accounts or is identified separately within the main accounts. Income would consist of an annual allowance which might vary to allow for local management conditions reflecting conditions on the estate, voids, lettings problems, rent collection and arrears. The income for management and maintenance may come directly from the rents collected locally. This happens in some tenant management co-operatives and in housing associations.

Example 1

The Cloverhall Estate, Rochdale, is a cottage estate of 236 units.

Diagram 3.6
Cloverhall Co-operative budget 1989/90

Management salaries	£30,750
Stationery and office equipment	£ 1,195
Telephone	£ 1,345
Bungalow lighting	£ 120
Office electricity	£ 415
Office heating	£ 645
Rent/rates	£ 4,440
Accounting	£ 1,200
Professional fees	£ 1,800
Insurance	£ 900
Caretaker	£ 5,790
Environmental maintenance	£ 420
Maintenance salaries	£23,355
Youth Training	£ 720
Void repairs	£ 7,200
Void decorating	£ 6,000
Day to day repairs	£24,200
Bin replacement	£ 200
Stock and maintenance: equipment	£12,000
Void cleaning	£ 480
Rent reconciliation	£ 9,000
Central heating service	£ 1,500
Essential improvement fund	£ 5,000
Emergencies and sundries	£ 2,640
Total	£141,315

The Cloverhall Tenant Management Co-operative budget (Rochdale) is negotiated each year. Each item is based on estimates from last year's expenditure, expected costs for next year and how much of the Housing Revenue Account should go to 1% of the council stock. Cloverhall's actual budget for 1989–90 is given in Diagram 3.6.

Points to note about the Cloverhall budget are:

– 25% of the budget is paid into a reserve fund for cyclical maintenance and contingencies. This also happens with the Islington co-operatives.

– savings through good performance on rent collection, voids and maintenance are kept and spent locally.

– the local management organisation can vire between headings, with the agreement of the council.

– the co-operative can retain any surplus.

– monitoring is by a formal quarterly review of performance plus both internal and external audits on a routine basis.

Example 2

The **Digmoor Priority Estates Project,** Skelmersdale, West Lancashire is a modern estate comprising 650 houses, 247 flats, 66 sheltered units and bungalows. It is in the process of setting up an Estate Management Board.

The budget (Diagram 3.7) reflects a detailed breakdown of actual costs. It is under the control of the Estate Management Board. The Manager is answerable to the Board for the estate budget. The account is held as a separate cost centre account, within the local authority's Finance Department. Monthly accounts are produced.

15. FLOW OF MONEY TO LOCAL BUDGET FROM LOCAL AUTHORITY

There are three main methods (Diagram 3.8) of allocating the local budget:

Integrated method

In method 1, the local authority collects all rents and arrears, pays an agreed allowance to the local management organisation (LMO) and receives a full account of spending. The LMO chases arrears but does **not** collect rent money.

Localised method

In method 2, the local authority allocates an allowance to an Estate Management Board (EMB) (or LMO), which collects rents and arrears and forwards all collected rents to the centre, out of which the allowance is paid.

Autonomous method

In method 3, the local authority agrees a management and maintenance allowance with a tenant management co-operative (TMC) or EMB, the TMC or EMB collects all rent and arrears, deducts the allowance **before** forwarding the balance to the local authority. The different types of local organisation (LMO, EMB, TMC) can use any of these methods, but normally the more autonomous the organisation, the more autonomous the method.

16. CONCLUSION

The discussion of estate budgets in this section is based on the PEP experience of working with local authorities on setting up estate budgets and accounts. It draws heavily on the experience of tenant management co-operatives.

It does **not** attempt to address the problems of central Finance Departments or borough-wide Housing Revenue Accounts, both of which are usually extremely complex. The central Finance Department is crucial to the establishment of local budgets.

Diagram 3.7

Digmoor Estate Management Board Budget 1990/91, including repairs and all management services

Notes: The Digmoor Estate Budget is agreed in two parts. The 'Budget Heads' are under the direct control of the EMB and cover direct, local and variable costs. The 'Account Heads' are controlled by the Council which reports to the EMB on spending. The 'Account Heads' cover salaries and employer's costs including national insurance.

Administration:	
Budget heads	£47,200
Account heads	91,571
Estate caretaking:	
Budget heads	21,296
Account heads	25,869
General community facilities[1]: Budget heads	15,500
Communal services[2]: Budget heads	2,000
Housing repairs[3]: Budget heads	384,783
Total	£588,219

[1] Redecoration and removal allowances.

[2] Tenants' meetings.

[3] Day-to-day contract repairs, specialist maintenance and general repairs.

Diagram 3.8

Flow of money to local budget from
local authority using: Method 1 – integrated;
Method 2 – localised; Method 3 – autonomous,
usually used in a tenant management co-operative

METHOD 1 — INTEGRATED

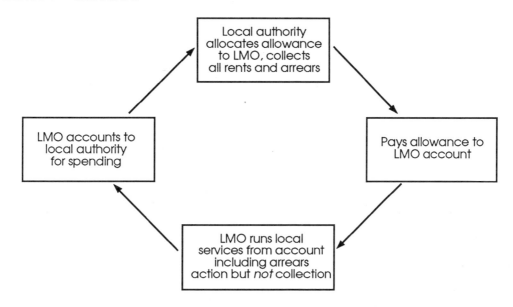

METHOD 2 — LOCALISED

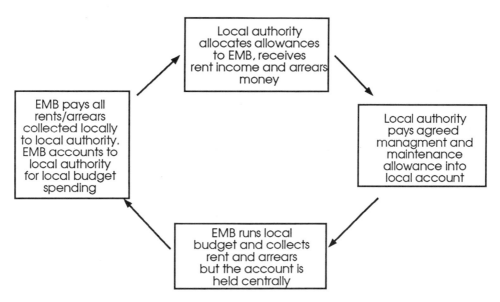

METHOD 3 — AUTONOMOUS

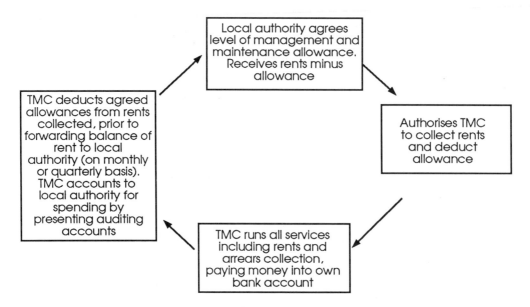

The approach outlined here aims to help local staff and tenants' representatives understand **and** learn how to operate highly simplified local budgets and accounts. The beauty of moving operations to estate level is that the money becomes manageable **at the local level.** In order to achieve this, the method has to be as simple as possible. Backup support and training from the centre will be necessary to make it work both locally **and** centrally.

17. CHECKLIST FOR BUDGETS AND ACCOUNTS

1. Is the budget adequate?

2. Will the budget cover:
   - day-to-day repairs?
   - cyclical repairs?
   - repairs to voids?
   - emergency work and contingencies?
   - funds for planned maintenance and replacement?

3. Will administration costs, including training and book-keeping, be covered?

4. Will the Estate Management Board be in control of the accounts for the estate?

5. Will the local manager or organisation have direct control over the budget for management spending?

6. Will the local manager or organisation be able to spend any savings resulting from good management performance on local improvements?

7. Will the local manager or organisation control all aspects of repairs contracts and payments?

8. Will the local manager or organisation be able to decide on staff to cover vacancies or absences, overtime cleaning, extra repairs, quality of materials, etc. etc.?

9. Will the local manager or organisation be able to spend any surplus on local improvements?

10. Will the local manager or organisation be able to organise ongoing planned maintenance?

11. Will tenants' representatives be able to influence how money is spent?

18. SOME USEFUL BOOKS ON BUDGETS

AUDIT COMMISSION (1985): Good Management in Local Government. HMSO, London

CAPITA (undated): Analysis of Cost Utility Methodologies and Development of the Evaluation Model. DoE/PEP Cost Effectiveness Project — Methodology Paper I. Priority Estates Project, London

CHARTERED INSTITUTE OF PUBLIC FINANCE & ACCOUNTANCY Manual of Housing Association Finance. London

HOUSING CORPORATION (undated): The Finance Guide. London

INSTITUTE OF HOUSING (1989): Housing Finance. London

NATIONAL FEDERATION OF HOUSING ASSOCIATIONS (1984): Housing Associations: Accounting and Audit Guide. London

— (1988): Understanding Accounts

— (1988): Private Finance Manual – update service

VII. Rents, Arrears and Housing Benefits

Contents

'A bird in the hand is worth two in the bush'

(Anon)

1. SUMMARY

The business side of rented housing depends on an efficient rent collection system and an intelligible and supportive housing benefit system.

People, whatever their income, will pay more readily:

- for a reasonable service
- to a known and friendly person
- through a simple and clear rent collection system.

Cases of personal hardship, tragedy or financial difficulty will often arise on low-income estates; there must be ways of helping to avoid as far as possible serious debt, unmanageable arrears and recourse to legal action.

Diagram 3.9 shows the operation of a businesslike rent accounts and benefits system.

Diagram 3.9
Rent accounts and benefits system

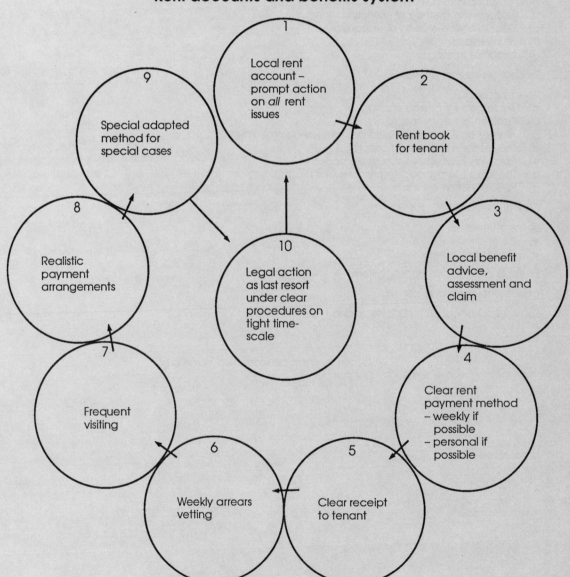

1 Local rent account – prompt action on *all* rent issues

2 Rent book for tenant

3 Local benefit advice, assessment and claim

4 Clear rent payment method – weekly if possible – personal if possible

5 Clear receipt to tenant

6 Weekly arrears vetting

7 Frequent visiting

8 Realistic payment arrangements

9 Special adapted method for special cases

10 Legal action as last resort under clear procedures on tight time-scale

2. KEYWORDS: PRIVACY; SELF-RESPECT; PREVENTION; MISINTERPRETATION

Rent and other financial matters are the private business of each household. At all costs, each tenant's **privacy** and **self-respect** must be preserved. At the same time, each landlord must collect rent if the property is to be maintained. The relationship between landlord and tenant is most delicate and most open to misinterpretation and breakdown over rents.

Distant, impersonal and paper methods reduce contact and sensitivity. They also make collection in the case of irregular or poor payers much more difficult.

In principle, rent collection forms part of the estate-based management service. In some areas door-to-door rent collection is a valued estate-based service; in most cities tenants may pay to an office or by Giro, cheque or standing order. In all cases the local office should take responsibility for chasing arrears. The way a local office deals with tenants will greatly influence progress in rent collection and arrears. Relations between tenants and local staff will make or break effective rent collection and arrears control.

In practice, local rent accounts and arrears are usually part of a large central system. Therefore the degree of local control and discretion over collection and arrears methods is strictly limited, except in the case of co-operatives. Where rents and arrears are fully integrated into the local system with fully generic estate officers, staff can get enormous satisfaction from helping tenants, dealing with them personally and containing arrears.

3. DEFINITIONS

Rent Accounts are the weekly figures showing payments due, payments received and debts outstanding for each household/tenancy **within** the office area. It is unusual for there to be an estate-based rent account, although increasingly this will happen with Estate Management Boards.

Rent Arrears are the debts attaching to any households that are behind with rent payments. Added together for an estate, they show how much of the rent income due to be paid to the local office is outstanding.

Housing Benefit is a personal allowance to meet the housing costs of a household on a low income (assessed according to laid-down Government standards) or of any household dependent on state support. It can meet 100 per cent of rent or only part depending on a scale of need. Local authorities are statutorily responsible for assessing and approving Housing Benefit.

4. TARGETS

– Establish benefits advice.

– Establish local weekly rent accounts.

– Visit all tenants in arrears within a week.

– Hold weekly case meetings for tenants in serious difficulties.

– Plan small weekly steps to help tenants in arrears and to help staff, e.g. restore regular **current** rent payments **before** tackling arrears.

– See if there is any way of arranging to collect **cash** from tenants with serious problems.

– Make staff and tenants' representatives understand that reducing arrears will help to pay for improvements.

– Set targets for arrears control with staff, e.g. reduce total arrears for the estate each week by a small amount such as £50.

5. RENTS AND ESTATE BUDGETS

Tenants need to see that the money they pay in rents goes into providing a good estate management service. Where rents are paid into a central account, a management and maintenance allowance may be paid to the estate budget from central accounts. Where there is an estate budget, the connection between management services and rent payment can be clearly seen. Residents and staff then have a direct incentive to reduce arrears (see previous Chapter).

It is vital for the operation of an estate budget that: benefits are paid, arrears are kept down, and any improvement in arrears performance on the estate benefits the estate directly by savings going back into the local budget. Otherwise there will be little incentive for local staff to give priority to arrears.

Serious arrears will become a much higher profile issue under the new ring-fenced system because of their direct impact on budgets. Estates with particularly bad arrears will be more noticeable.

6. HOW TO SET UP A RENT SYSTEM

The following steps show a way towards estate-based control of rent collection:

a) Establish the method of collection

There are three main methods of rent collection:

– door to door collection ⎫
– office collection   ⎬   personal

– bank or giro collection —   impersonal

Bank, Giro or office collection may suit many tenants but are not ideal for housebound people, for people with budgeting difficulties or for households in arrears. Probably a combination of methods of rent collection will suit most tenants. Personalised methods of estate-based collection are generally more effective in preventing arrears. It is important to look at the costs of the different systems and the likely effect on the estate budget.

Where a local authority has a serious arrears problem, it is important to establish a separate system for the estate, so that there is a chance to sort out the area locally without being affected by wider arrears problems. This is likely to apply in some large city authorities with multiple management difficulties.

The cost of collection should be weighed against the cost of arrears. Efficient collection through personal service is better than expensive arrears recovery through courts. Prevention of arrears is all-important.

It is important to consider what is possible. For instance in some areas door-to-door collection may be felt to present too great a security risk. There are also security risks with office collection. We have to accept that fewer and fewer financial transactions involve cash. But it should be remembered that households on low incomes may have many difficulties with banks or giro.

Budgeting is vastly more difficult for people with a low income. Therefore the method should aim to suit the people and their income levels. There should be some flexibility so that individual tenants can be called on where necessary in a remote system or can pay by cheque or giro where appropriate in a door-to-door system. Estate officers and the local office should work out how to accept and record impromptu payments safely so that arrears can be contained. It is bad management practice to refuse arrears payments offered in cash because there is no safe method of recording and paying in the money.

b) Decide on the division of responsibility

Responsibilities should be clearly divided between the estate team and central departments so as to suit the tenants, produce an efficient estate-based service, keep down the cost, contain arrears and avoid delays or mistakes in the system.

Services which should be **local** are:

− informing tenants about their rent account

− housing benefit advice and an estimate of housing benefits entitlement

− initial debt counselling

− the first stages of arrears chasing, especially visits.

Services which should be **local if at all possible** are:

− rent collection

− processing benefit claims

− enforcement of arrears payment up to court action.

Services which are **normally central** are:

− benefit authorisation

− rent and budget monitoring

− legal action after arrears have gone beyond a certain point.

c) Help tenants

The estate office should have a full local record of each tenant's rent and housing benefit position. This should be updated weekly. It should be possible for estate staff to check any computer printout from the centre against their records so that errors can be picked up. The tenant too should have an accurate up to date written record. It should be possible to produce regular summaries of the information for monitoring.

Publicity information describing procedures from a tenant's viewpoint should also be prepared. Benefit information should be widely displayed and available. Links should be made with the DSS, Social Fund, Citizens Advice Bureau, local voluntary bodies, etc.

Families with particular difficulties affecting their arrears of **whatever** nature should be given special support. Some people cope much better than others with financial difficulties. Some households, once in debt, find it very difficult to get out again. Therefore debt **prevention** should be paramount.

d) Organise training

Estate-based staff should be trained in:

− the rents, benefits and arrears procedures

− giving advice, interviewing, negotiating and counselling

− benefit assessment

− the legal aspects of enforcement of rent payments.

Training may also be needed in processing benefit claims if this service is local.

Tenants' representatives will greatly benefit from training in rents and arrears.

Tenants understand readily the issue of rent arrears debts, the budget implications and the special problems for certain tenants, but they need training in rents and benefits systems, in arrears and debt handling, and in the basic legal requirements of rent payment, accounts and arrears action.

7. PROCEDURES FOR RENT COLLECTION

The procedures need to be clear and simple and preferably drawn up in consultation with the local staff involved. In particular the timescale for each stage of chasing arrears needs to be defined. The timescale should be as short as possible as prompt action is the best arrears weapon.

The possibility of including incentives for rent payment such as rent-free weeks or discounts should be considered, especially where there is a long history of inefficient rent collection and arrears control.

Stage 1: The tenant pays in the rent

The tenancy agreement should make clear:

− the amount of rent,

− when it is due; any changes to this must be notified well in advance in writing, and

− the method of payment.

These things should be explained to new tenants when they sign the tenancy agreement.

20. *Direct contact with tenants is the best rent system. Norley Hall Estate, Wigan*

Paul Herrmann/Profile

Where staff collect rent direct from tenants, it is possible to discuss the ongoing position on rent payments and to give welfare advice where necessary. When tenants offer cash to staff in payment of arrears, it is good management practice to accept it! – subject of course to proper recording.

Stage 2: The payment is recorded

A payment record is required both for the local authority and for the tenant:

– the tenant needs an immediate receipt and regular statements

– the estate office needs up-to-date accurate information on individual tenants.

Stage 3: Arrears action

Arrears advice, visits and other procedures are put in train immediately the tenant fails to pay.

8. ARREARS CONTROL

The guiding principle of arrears control is to take **early action**. Information on arrears should be checked and should be acted on by immediate contact with the tenant.

The two aims of arrears control are to maximise rental **income** and to **support** tenants in difficulties. These aims are sometimes hard to reconcile. It is important always to remember that accumulating debts push families into a downward spiral. Containing arrears, however hard, reduces the burden on low-income families. Firm action is the most helpful (Duncan & Kirby, 1984).

Arrears procedure should have the following steps:

a) **Set targets for arrears chasing**. Targets should be set for **when** action needs to be taken, and **what** action should be. It will help to make these targets realistic if this is done by all staff at a meeting. Tenants' representatives should also discuss targets and give ideas.

b) **Establish a weekly record** at the local office. Check it for new arrears cases and for any breakdown of existing agreements to repay debts. The local records must be accurate and up-to-date, if necessary by replacing a central system with a specially instituted local one. Even where rent is collected fortnightly, some tenants will pay in between, and the weekly review makes chasing and payments more manageable.

c) **All new arrears cases should be contacted immediately** by estate staff. If possible the tenant should be given help with all aspects of the arrears including debt counselling and welfare benefit advice. It is important to meet the tenant at this stage to agree when payments will be made. This agreement should be realistic and should be in writing and signed by the tenant. It is better to agree small frequent repayments that can be adhered to on a limited budget, than commitments to swift settlement that quickly break down. If arrears are contained and acted on swiftly, they can be cleared within a few months. If a tenant cannot be contacted personally, then the estate officer should write a letter to inform the tenant and urge payment. Estate officers need to handle arrears with tact and sensitivity on a **personal** basis. They need to know of special circumstances and respond accordingly.

d) **The estate staff should monitor** payments made by tenants in arrears.

e) Where one month's arrears have accumulated and it has not been possible to reach agreement to pay off arrears or agreements have been broken, **recovery procedures should be started** This will initially involve a formal warning letter, followed by application for court action. At this point a lawyer or the Council's legal department should be involved.

f) **The local team should regularly review progress** in arrears control against the targets set, looking at the particular problems presented by tenants on the estate, at possible solutions and at overall progress. There should be an arrears chart on display in the local office. It is important to show whether total arrears are going up or down, the number of tenants in arrears of two weeks or more, and the average amount of arrears for all households in arrears. Any big changes in arrears should be looked at carefully, e.g. changes in Housing Benefit payments, to try and explain what is happening. This helps the team choose the right action.

Diagram 3.10   Total arrears on an estate of 600 flats, month by month

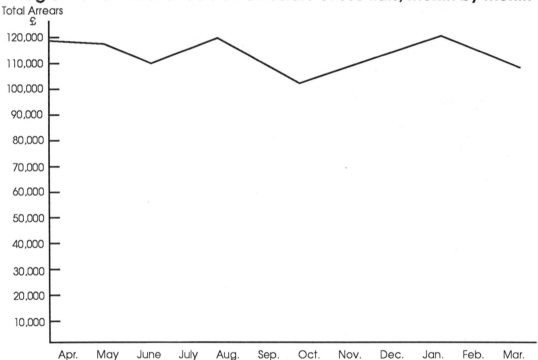

Diagram 3.11   Total number of tenants in arrears of 2 weeks or more

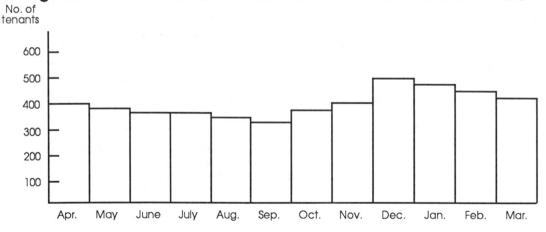

Diagram 3.12   Average amount of arrears per household in arrears

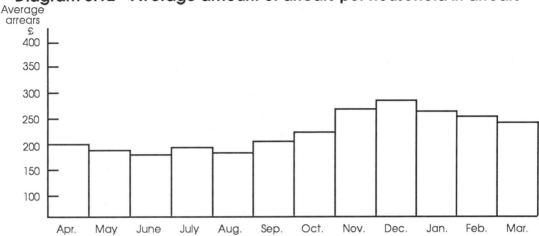

Diagrams 3.10 to 3.12 illustrate arrears monitoring.

g) **Special action** should be agreed for any household having special difficulties. These special cases should be reviewed **weekly** by the manager. For example, personal collection should be arranged where this will overcome the problem.

9. RENT PROCEDURE

Diagram 3.13 illustrates the rent collection and arrears procedure.

10. HOUSING BENEFITS

On the majority of estates most tenants receive some housing benefit. From the tenants' point of view, it is essential that the local office has an up-to-date record of individuals' rent accounts showing arrears owing and benefits due. Housing Benefit for local authority tenants is deducted directly from the amount of rent a tenant is expected to pay. Therefore **rent due** is net of Housing Benefit. Rent accounts and Housing Benefit accounts must therefore be closely linked. Estate-based staff should be able to offer general welfare advice and initial debt counselling. On all estates it should be possible to estimate quickly benefit entitlement. It is helpful if benefits are assessed and processed locally. It should be possible to process benefit claims, as long as sufficient trained staff are locally based and there is a direct link to the central housing benefit system. This requires an advanced computer system.

There are two parts of the Housing Benefit service – information and claims processing:

Information

Information on Housing Benefit **should** be locally available. The aim should be to:

– give all new tenants general information and individual welfare benefits advice,

– give out publicity about benefits in the local office,

– build links with other agencies such as the Citizens Advice Bureau, DSS, and Social Services, and involve them in helping tenants, and to

– ask all new tenants to fill in a Housing Benefit form, when signing up in case they are entitled to assistance. Do not prejudge any cases on the basis of what you think about their circumstances.

Changes in tenants' circumstances affect eligibility. Delay in notifying the Housing Benefits section of such changes is a major cause of arrears. It is therefore important to stress to tenants the need to report changes as soon as possible.

Claims processing

More and more local offices are taking on responsibility for housing benefits. Here are some of the tasks:

i) Watch out for any sign that a tenant is in financial difficulties and offer help with welfare benefits advice and debt counselling **if the tenant wants help**.

ii) Calculate the benefit entitlement of tenants who are not currently claiming but who are likely to be able to claim. This estimate will help, for instance, in producing an agreement about arrears repayment. This calculation can be done with the help of special tables and housing benefit calculators or local micro- or minicomputers. Some local offices are linked to the main council benefit system via computers. This enables a full local benefit service to be offered.

iii) Help the tenant to apply for benefit.

iv) Process the claim.

v) Make sure the tenant is kept informed about progress on the claim.

It is important for staff to know:

– rent levels and increases

– service charges and other costs to the tenant

– changes in benefit entitlement

– income levels and changes in income and employment

Diagram 3.13

Rent collection and arrears procedure

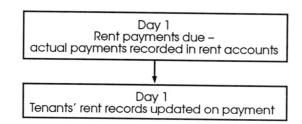

Day 1
Rent payments due –
actual payments recorded in rent accounts

Day 1
Tenants' rent records updated on payment

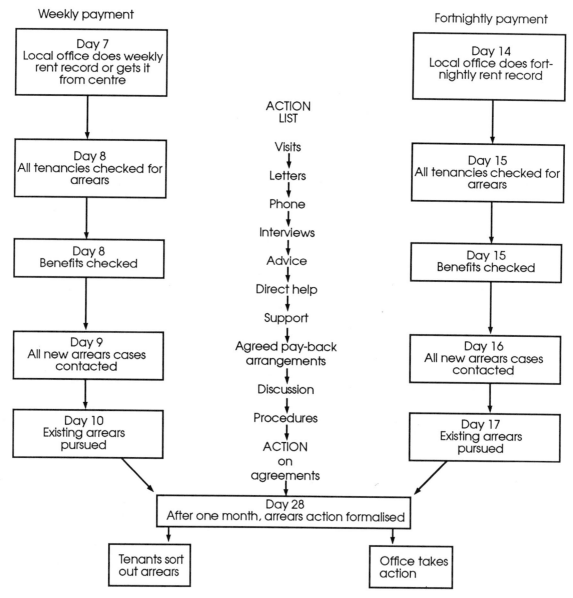

Weekly payment

Day 7
Local office does weekly
rent record or gets it
from centre

Day 8
All tenancies checked for
arrears

Day 8
Benefits checked

Day 9
All new arrears cases
contacted

Day 10
Existing arrears
pursued

ACTION LIST

Visits

Letters

Phone

Interviews

Advice

Direct help

Support

Agreed pay-back
arrangements

Discussion

Procedures

ACTION
on
agreements

Fortnightly payment

Day 14
Local office does fort-
nightly rent record

Day 15
All tenancies checked for
arrears

Day 15
Benefits checked

Day 16
All new arrears cases
contacted

Day 17
Existing arrears
pursued

Day 28
After one month, arrears action formalised

Tenants sort
out arrears

Office takes
action

Note: Where rent is paid fortnightly, swift action is even more
important and should follow the same procedure. This
procedure should be repeated weekly for both weekly and
fortnightly rent payment systems.

– personal circumstances and changes in household size and composition

– particular financial pressures and debt problems, e.g. a child in hospital, responsibility for a family member in need of care

– particular problems affecting the family's ability to budget and to cope.

It is also important to understand the basic operation of Community Charge and how assistance for that works. All local offices should have available basic guides to benefits (e.g. the Welfare Rights Handbook and the Guide to Housing Benefit and Community Charge, Child Poverty Action Group, 1990).

11. EXAMPLE OF RENTS AND BENEFIT SYSTEM

On the PEP estate of Barnfield (575 dwellings), in the London Borough of Greenwich, rents are paid into any area office in the borough, or by Giro. Rents are not collected in cash at the estate office for the following reasons: local collection was abolished some years ago because of security risks; and it suits many tenants to pay by Giro or at an area office.

There are two estate officers on Barnfield, based in the local office, each managing half the estate. As part of their jobs, these officers undertake arrears control. They are supplied weekly with a printout showing a statement of each tenant's rent account. These officers do debt counselling and all stages of arrears control, but action for recovery is taken in concert with the legal department.

Estate officers deal with queries regarding housing benefit. A local system is being devised that will enable officers to assess eligibility of tenants for benefit. Processing applications for benefit is currently a function of the area offices: this cannot be devolved at the moment because of all the other pressures on local staff. However, the aim is to employ more local staff so that benefits can be done locally too.

On Penrhys Estate, Rhondda (948 houses and maisonettes) rents are collected door to door by locally based estate officers. In addition, tenants can pay rent into the local office. All arrears are controlled locally. Housing benefits are also run from the estate office.

12. CHECKLIST FOR RENTS AND BENEFITS

1. How much is owing in arrears: What is the total arrears as a percentage of the rent due? What is the average arrears per tenant in arrears? How big are the biggest arrears cases? How many tenants are in arrears, according to amounts? e.g. up to £100, £101–200, etc. How many cases are increasing arrears? How many cases are reducing arrears? Are arrears improving/deteriorating?

2. Do the estate officers know which tenants are in arrears? How many arrears cases are visited and how often?

3. What other arrears action is being taken? How many legal recovery actions are under way, with dates? How many cases reach court action with unclaimed benefit entitlement? Does the Legal Department follow up swiftly?

4. What is the progress on repayments through agreement?

5. Are the rent printouts accurate? Are the tenants' rent records accurate?

6. What techniques work best for reducing arrears on your estate? What has been tried and fails? Are any tenants allowed to pay cash/pay at the door?

7. What proportion of estate officers' time is taken chasing arrears? Should more or less time be given to collecting arrears? Is the time given well used?

8. What are the security problems connected with the collection of arrears? How can these problems be overcome?

9. What proportion of residents are entitled to housing benefit? Can local staff estimate housing benefit? Do local staff have training in financial advice?

13. SOME USEFUL BOOKS ON RENTS, ARREARS AND HOUSING BENEFITS

AUDIT COMMISSION (1984): Bringing Council Arrears under Control. HMSO, London.

—— (1989): Survey of Local Authority Rent Arrears. Information Paper No. 1.

CHILD POVERTY ACTION GROUP (1990): National Welfare Rights Handbook 1990/91. London.

—— (1990): Guide to Community Charge.

DEPARTMENT OF THE ENVIRONMENT (1989): The Nature & Effectiveness of Housing Management in England. HMSO, London.

DUNCAN S & KIRBY K (1984): Preventing Rent Arrears. HMSO, London.

INSTITUTE OF HOUSING (1989): Guide to Housing Benefit and Community Charge. London.

—— (1989): Guide to the Community Charge.

LOCAL GOVERNMENT TRAINING BOARD (1986): Can you come back next week?. Ref. No. HS 0028. Luton.

NATIONAL FEDERATION OF HOUSING ASSOCIATIONS (1987): Standards for Housing Management. London.

Part 4
The Outside World

VIII. Monitoring and Support

Contents

'People use statistics like a drunk man uses a lamp-post, for support rather than illumination.'

1. SUMMARY

No man is an island and estates do not thrive in a vacuum. The outside world, as well as local residents and staff, need to know about progress and problems.

Local management performance can be measured in different ways. Charts can show rises and falls in:

- progress on modernisation

- arrears

- repairs completions

- callers to the office

- staff attendance

- costs

- empty dwellings

- re-letting times

- demand.

Monitoring helps with decisions and can make councils and Government sustain or increase their support.

Diagram 4.1 shows the process.

Diagram 4.1
Monitoring process of estate-based management

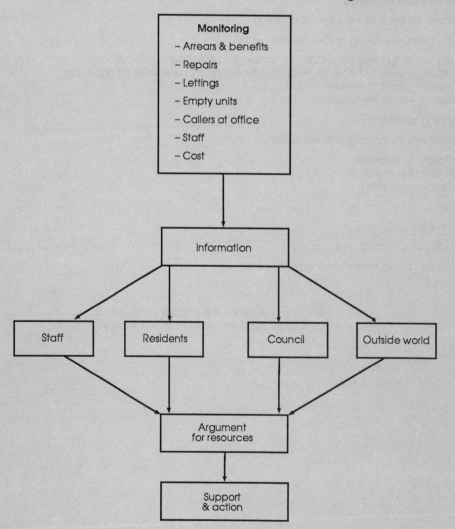

Monitoring
- Arrears & benefits
- Repairs
- Lettings
- Empty units
- Callers at office
- Staff
- Cost

Information

Staff   Residents   Council   Outside world

Argument
for resources

Support
& action

2. KEYWORDS: MOTIVATE; TARGET; SAVINGS; ACTION

Monitoring is important because it tells you whether you are succeeding; it helps answer the question 'Is estate-based management successful here?'

Monitoring should help the estate manager to manage the estate and **motivate** the staff.

Monitoring can:

– show **progress,** partly as a reward for the team;

– **target** areas for action, e.g. if arrears are climbing;

– provide information on performance to senior officers, members and tenants, e.g. **savings** on reduction in voids or quicker reletting.

It is crucial to remember that monitoring on its own is **absolutely pointless**. It is only of use if it is **aimed** at a problem and at **action**.

Support is needed to ensure that local management works efficiently, survives crises, receives all the inputs it needs in terms of budget, training, good staff, advice, workable agreements, good links to the centre, etc.

Support should make the local team and estate residents feel part of something greater than their area, as well as helping them control affairs locally. The raison d'être of the central housing organisation is the support of those **delivering** the service, so that they can do their jobs properly.

3. DEFINITIONS: MONITORING; EVALUATION

Monitoring literally means '**keeping watch over**' and in local offices it means keeping watch over repairs, rents, lettings, costs, callers, staffing problems and other issues affecting performance. If 'monitoring' consists of a pile of **figures** or computer sheets that no one **does** anything about, it is useless.

Monitoring **must** lead to evaluation.

Evaluation means **working out the VALUE** of an activity. Evaluation implies judgement. For monitoring to be useful, aims have to be clear, monitoring information available and decisions on how to react made. Any good local organisation will change the way it acts as a result of monitoring and evaluation.

4. TARGETS

– Ensure that monitoring relates directly to the aim of the local management organisation.

– Produce simple monitoring systems so that **all** staff can do it, e.g. repairs logbook, voids chart.

– Produce single-sheet progress reports monthly.

– Have three core aims displayed, e.g. lower voids, quicker re-lets, and quicker repairs.

– Prepare quarterly monitoring report to residents' representatives and councillors.

– Identify at least one problem a month as a target area.

5. THE FOUR STAGES OF MONITORING

Monitoring the use of the office illustrates the four stages in monitoring:

STAGE 1: AIM of monitoring the use of the office: To encourage tenants to use the office.

STAGE 2: MONITOR what happens: Record the number of callers and why they called; look at the figures.

STAGE 3: DECISION on how to change office organisation to make it more accessible: Decide on the best opening hours; ways of making the office attractive; arranging for the right staff to be available.

STAGE 4: ACTION as a follow-through to monitoring: Put up new posters; deliver leaflets to all tenants; do staff training in dealing with the public.

6. VALUE OF MONITORING

Where estate-based management has been set up, the local authority is generally keen to find out how successful it is in relation to the objectives set for it. Where an Estate Management Board is set up, local staff and the council want to know how it is doing. As soon as residents become involved in decisions, they want to know what is happening and why. They need to make informed choices.

All these needs make monitoring very useful. Monitoring can do a number of things:

– ensure that the local team is meeting its aims for the estate;

– show the efficiency of local ways of working;

– help the local team continuously to revise its own aims and methods of work;

– inform the tenants, local authority and others about the work of the team;

– provide backing for bids for more resources, e.g. capital or increased staffing;

– provide protection for the team and its work;

– highlight problems and weak areas;

– show where things are getting better or worse.

In order to see the local office in context, local performance can be compared with local authority-wide performance, or even national figures.

This sort of comparison can also highlight where a local team has not escaped the effects of national housing policies. It helps stop it becoming too parochial. It is also useful for tenants to see what is happening in their area in a wider context, as they can then understand the pressures their local team is under in dealing with problems such as rent arrears.

The local management organisation needs to **set**

targets for each area of management. Some possible targets are shown below:

Lettings

- encourage a cross-section of applicants
- rehouse a cross-section of applicants
- stabilise turnover
- encourage homeless family nominations
- build up the local waiting list

Empty dwellings

- have no more than 2% empty at one time
- make sure there are no squatters

Re-let times

- re-let within 4 weeks maximum, aim for 2 weeks

Turnover of tenants

- try to keep turnover below 10% a year
- encourage internal transfers to reduce turnover
- try to help overcrowded or sharing households

Rent arrears

- keep arrears below 4%
- gradually reduce total arrears
- reduce number of arrears cases

Repairs

- get all normal repairs done within three weeks
- get all emergencies done within 2 days

Callers

- see any caller within 15 minutes
- take action on all problems within a day

Budget

- make savings to invest in improvements

Targets will vary according to the needs of the area.

7. MEASURING PERFORMANCE IN HOUSING MANAGEMENT

In order to draw up monitoring targets, the following steps will be needed:

- determine what the local management organisation wants to know;
- think through the causes and effects in the area concerned;
- pin-point key measures;
- look at how often the key indicators and supporting information should be supplied;
- design an appropriate way of monitoring.

The important question is, will people go on using a system of targets and monitoring once its novelty value has worn off? Three features help greatly:

- the system of monitoring should be **unburdensome** to staff;

- it should be **owned** by the users;
- it should be **fed back** to customers, e.g. tenants, council, etc.

In the case of one of PEP's EMBs, the tenants and staff will both have helped establish the organisation and jointly determined the way their performance is to be measured. They should be committed to maintaining and adjusting the system. Although the landlord authority will also want the performance measurements for its own purposes, they should be wanted **locally** too.

There is then a tension between the need for national or local authority-wide performance data, and the need to **own** it at the level where performance is generated.

New government interest in monitoring

Monitoring helps the local offices to keep up their performance as well as helping to get national standards for housing management. It is one of the important recommendations of the recent report from the University of Glasgow on the effectiveness of housing management (DoE, 1989). If the Government and the public can measure performance and see results, then housing provision will get more support.

In 1989, the Government produced initial requirements for monitoring performance in housing management. All social landlords should produce clear information on performance. As a result, all local authorities and housing associations will need to pay a lot more attention to monitoring. New monitoring methods are being developed very fast at the moment. A key problem is that all systems multiply quickly once instituted and often become over-complex and therefore an impediment to action.

It is most important to keep monitoring simple and easy to do and use so that all levels of staff can see its purpose. Otherwise, monitoring figures will be either invented or discarded! (PEP, 1990).

8. AN EXAMPLE OF LOCAL MONITORING

The PEP monthly monitoring form (Diagram 4.2) shows the key management areas that should be monitored. The example can be adapted to local circumstances, and changed as a result of new monitoring requirements.

In addition, each estate manager should do a simple progress report (two sides of one sheet maximum). The monthly progress report is indispensable for an Estate Management Board or local forum and very useful for the local authority. The fictitious example shown in Diagram 4.3, based on a real PEP Progress Report, illustrates how a progress report can give estate staff a chance to catch up on and review progress. It also forces the person responsible for the project to take stock and to work out what problems should be tackled next and how. Most importantly, it sets targets and a timetable for the coming month. The exact form will obviously vary according to the type of local organisation.

Diagram 4.2
An example of a monitoring form

PEP MONITORING: MONTHLY STATISTICS

Name of Project
Gross weekly rent
No. of dwellings
Month
Total No. of Working Days

1   Tenant enquiries
i)   Total number of callers at PEP office during month

2   Repairs
i)   Number of jobs ordered during month
ii)   Number of jobs completed during month
iii)   Number of jobs cancelled during month
iv)   Average turnaround time of jobs completed
v)   Number of repair jobs outstanding at end of month

3   Rent arrears
i)   Value of rent arrears at end of month (incl DSS)
ii)   Number of tenants in arrears at end of month

4   Vacant properties
i)   Total number of voids at end of month
ii)   Number of voids due to major physical work
iii)   Number of dwellings squatted
iv)   Total rent loss on voids during month
v)   Average re-let time (working days)

5   Allocations
i)   Number of applicants on local waiting list
ii)   Number of new tenancies during month
iii)   Number of transfers off during month

6   Housing benefit
Number of tenants on Housing Benefit at end of month
i)   Certified cases
ii)   Standard cases

7   Sales
i)   Number of dwellings sold during month

PEP MONTHLY MONITORING RETURNS

Definition of Terms

GENERAL
Statistics should relate to the calendar month.
If statistics are collected on a weekly basis,
then it should be stated clearly the period of
time covered, e.g. 4 May–2 June.

GROSS WEEKLY RENT
The total value of weekly rent for the whole
of the estate including rates and any
additional service charges, e.g. heating
charges. Exclude water rates and garage
rents.

VALUE OF RENT ARREARS
The total rent due (as defined above) but
not paid at the end of the month, including
DSS payments.

VOIDS DUE TO MAJOR PHYSICAL
WORKS
Dwellings empty because of major
modernisation or other physical work,
or extensive fire damage.

---

9. OFFICE INFORMATION SYSTEMS

Information for monitoring should first and foremost be useful for staff and should help them do their jobs properly.

The information for monitoring and progress reports should be directly obtainable from the office records. Therefore, clear, simple systems need to be set up. Monitoring becomes a complete chore if staff have to spend time **in addition** to ordinary record-keeping in order to produce monitoring information.

Monitoring information needs to be shown in a simple way. Graphs and bar charts show at a glance, how the team is performing in key areas.

These should be mounted around the office and kept up-to-date by the estate manager.

They can also be used in team meetings to review performance and discuss strategy.

Diagrams 4.4 to 4.7 are simple illustrations of what monitoring charts can show.

10. EVALUATION AS THE FOLLOW-ON FROM MONITORING

Evaluation is intrinsically linked to **useful** monitoring. The estate manager is constantly **questioning** the worth of different activities, the use of certain systems or equipment, the performance of staff, the roles of different team members. There should be some ways of **making sense** of all the messages. In the same way, each worker is wondering how well he or she is doing,

---

Diagram 4.3

An example of a monthly progress report, filled in by PEP

Note: All names have been changed to disguise identity.

Name of Local Authority:	West London	Date: Jan. 89
Name of project:	Thames Estate	No. of dwellings: 2000

Local Co-ordinator/Manager:	Sheila Perry

Input from PEP Team:	PEP Associate –	1 day per week
	Tenant Support worker –	3 days per week

Local Management Proposals/Agreed Arrangements:

Local office	:	2 converted flats. Open 5 days per week 9.30–12.30, 1.30–4.30. Closed Wednesday 3.30 for training/team meeting.
Staffing	:	1 Co-ordinator; 1 Estate Manager, 1 Deputy Estate manager, 6 Estate Officers, 2 Admin. Assistants, 2 Technical Officers.
Caretaking	:	12 Caretakers (resident)
Lettings	:	At District
Rent arrears	:	At District
Repairs:		DLO Local Team – 12 operatives. 40 % of work done by Private Contractors.
Budget	:	Repairs and Maintenance Budget at local level.
Tenant Consultations	:	Liaison Committee meets monthly.
Capital works	:	£1m programme 88/89 – Frensham/Highland Block – on target

Outstanding issues/problems

1. *Planned maintenance programme*: new staff/computers needed to implement programme; proposals are presently 'frozen' because of budget overspend.
2. *Dilapidated blocks* – no clear way ahead.

Progress made this month

1. *Estate committee*: new constitution agreed by Tenants' Association – now to go to local office and Neighbourhood office for approval.
2. *Estate action* visit arranged for early February.
3. *New PEP Associate* to take over – initial handover begun – introduced to local and chief officer.
4. *EMB proposal* being discussed by officer and tenants.

The way forward

Continue to promote/encourage EMB idea.

Future timetable

Planned Maintenance Programme implementation – March deadline
Review situation re PEP's future input – September.

---

whether to stay or move on, how to handle a particular problem.

We are all constantly evaluating what we do and what others do, what is worth what. How can you measure at all accurately what is happening? **Cash** is one way – crude and finite. **Satisfaction** is another way, elusive and imprecise, but often easily recognisable nonetheless.

Evaluation is one of the main functions of **team meetings**, particularly for setting local aims and turning the results of monitoring into action. Monitoring and evaluation are part and parcel of the same process of setting goals and working out how to achieve them, measuring success and failure, then seeing what new goals can be set.

Monitoring and evaluation do not always have to be

Diagram 4.4

Graph showing monthly progress on letting and empty dwellings

Each month the graph would be extended to show progress on problems

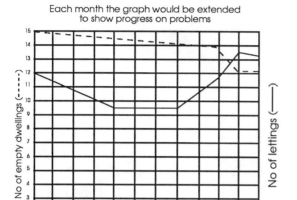

Diagram 4.5

Bar chart showing the numbers of tenants in arrears (over £50 owing)

This bar chart illustrates one form of arrears monitoring

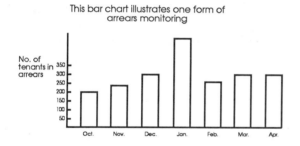

Diagram 4.6

Repairs requests by trade

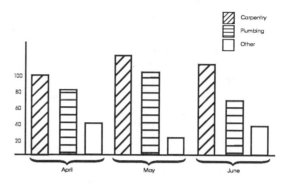

Diagram 4.7

Internal transfer requests and completions

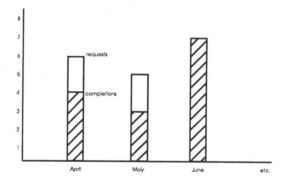

ongoing. Something may need monitoring for a finite period to discover a particular problem/blockage in the system that has been identified.

11. HOW TO MAKE MONITORING AND EVALUATION WORK

The local team cannot monitor and evaluate everything they do at once. It is necessary, in a team meeting, to choose the most important areas to evaluate first, e.g. the cost of the local repairs work; the speed of repairs in relation to tenants' complaints; the number of empty dwellings and lettings problems.

After agreeing an area of activity that needs evaluating, the staff have to go through four stages: **aim**; **monitor** – quantitative and qualitative surveys; **decision**; **action**.

Stage 1. AIM – Setting clear aims that are agreed by all staff/tenants/councillors

The aim should be clearly spelt out. For instance, the

aim of the local repairs service is to deliver repairs quickly and well. The whole team should agree on this since they all have to aim for the same or similar targets. It is also necessary to be as precise as possible about the target. In this case, what does 'well' mean? – 80% of all job requests completed within a week of ordering them.

Stage 2. MONITOR – work out how to measure success, how to see what is happening

For each part of the aim and result, it is necessary to work out a measure which will help lead to action, and an actual target for action. The example of repairs illustrates this. The team will want to measure speed.

– How many days does it take to complete a repair?

– What is the target time for doing repairs, e.g. 'urgent', 'non-urgent', etc.

– If completing 80% of jobs within a week is a good performance, then all outstanding jobs should be checked to see if they are being done within a week.

21. *Staff need to understand why they are collecting information. Monitoring at the Bacup Estate, Rossendale*

Paul Herrmann/Profile

– If urgent repairs should be done in 24 hours, then all urgent jobs should be checked: to see if they are urgent, i.e. a threat to the well-being of the family; and to see if they are done on time.

– All non-urgent jobs should become **urgent** after a certain time, e.g. 6 weeks, to ensure that they get done.

How to measure

There are two ways in which measurements are usually made – statistical records and satisfaction surveys.

i) **Statistics monitoring in the local office** or elsewhere in the local authority produces statistical information in the form of figures. A problem here is that a recently set up estate office usually inherits centralised, often computerised, information systems which often do not produce the information needed or do not break it down in the right way. For instance, repairs information may be collected on an area basis; police statistics of crime relate to beat areas which may be different from estate areas.

The biggest fault with statistics and monitoring is that pages of figures which are indigestible and hard to

follow are produced on computer print-outs which no one makes use of. The local office **must** collect its own information in a totally simple form so that all staff can help produce it, use it, and get satisfaction from it.

Local managers need to change the existing systems to meet their needs. Local, ad hoc, often manual, systems of recording information can work just as well as or better than sophisticated computer systems. For instance, the number of callers may be recorded in a visitors' book, the voids may be monitored on a wall chart, repairs orders may be logged in a daybook or logbook. If the local office has its own micro and local staff enjoy using it, then it becomes possible to produce exciting information and graphs **very** quickly and easily that way. This will make it easier to feed information back to the centre.

ii) **Measuring tenant satisfaction** is more difficult. It involves learning about social survey methods. These can be **very** simple and basic, involving only a few questions. The main characteristic of social surveys is that you **ask** people for their views, which either you, an interviewer or the person being asked records on a form.

It is very important to **keep control** of surveys. They can run away with themselves and end up taking a long time and being more useful to researchers than to the estate.

Stage 3. DECIDE how to present

Decide what to do with the information from statistical monitoring, from surveys, research and from other sources, e.g. log books.

It is important to learn how to analyse findings. The results can be **very** useful. The way results are presented has a major impact on their use. Graphs are easy to follow and can be enthusiastically produced and followed by staff. **Short** reports are helpful. Long reports 'kill off' most interest. If detail is important – and sometimes it is – short summaries must be put at the beginning.

Stage 4. ACTION – using the results

To be of any use, the results of monitoring and evaluation must be fed back into policy and lead to action. At the local level, one way of doing this is to look at the results in a team meeting. The results are likely to provoke a discussion about the work of the team which might lead to:

– changing and adapting aims

– re-allocating resources

– re-defining roles

– changing work practices

– bidding for further resources

– renewing enthusiasm (e.g. if tenants report great satisfaction with repairs).

Findings should be presented to residents, to senior staff, to councillors and to other organisations. They will help develop ideas on follow-up.

Sometimes the results of a survey look good but some things are still not working as efficiently as they could. For instance, repairs may be done 'quickly and well' but the local plumber may be wasting time waiting for materials. In this case, a new aim could be for the repair team to operate without waiting time; the measurement would be how much time is wasted and how much could it be cut by?

Or the results may need to be broken down so that small areas of work or of the estate can be tackled separately for special problems.

Surveys and monitoring are not enough on their own. They **must** help the quality of service.

12. ORGANISING SURVEYS

We give only in outline the main approaches to surveys. Colleges and survey firms will help develop estate surveys.

Organising social surveys

– **doorstep interviews** involve knocking on each interviewee's door to fill in the questionnaire. They are time-consuming but do reach a wide cross-section of tenants including, for instance, housebound elderly people.

– **customer interviews** with tenants visiting the local office. Each tenant who calls is asked to fill in a form or is interviewed. These are relatively easy to achieve but exclude those tenants who do not call.

– **postal surveys** are easy to organise but limited in scope. A questionnaire is sent to every tenant and tenants are asked to return the questionnaire to the office or by post. Often less than half of all households return completed surveys. However, they can give an indication of how things are going.

– **self-completion surveys** can be sent to all households with clear instructions on how to complete and are then collected door to door. When they are collected, the collectors can offer help to those having difficulty in filling out their form.

Whichever method is used, it is important for the form to be simple and easy to read and fill in; for the questions to be unbiased, offering a full range of possible answers; and for the questionnaire to take as little time as possible to fill in. A biased question would be: 'Do you think the repairs service has got better?' (Yes/No). It invites the answer 'yes'. An unbiased question would be: 'What do you think of the repairs service since the office opened?' (Same as before/getting better/worse).

It is also important to aim to get back 80 per cent of all forms. Therefore personal collection of postal and self-completion forms is important. In practice it may be difficult to achieve this much.

In-depth interviews or group discussions

These produce more qualitative information from fewer people. They depend on skilled people carrying out interviews or running group discussions. They rely on different methods. Recording and analysing the findings are much more difficult since the information is not collected in fixed and uniform questions. There are a number of reasons for doing 'in depth' interviews. Many people believe they are far more valuable than quantitative surveys, even though they cover fewer people. Tenants from different cultures may not understand quantitative questionnaires, but can be reached by qualitative surveys. Sensitive and difficult areas, such as elderly people's problems with heating, can be reached by in depth interviews or discussions. People's views on disputes and tensions can be learnt more easily. Young people will often give their views informally but do not like set questionnaires. There are two main approaches:

– group discussions with invited participants discussing an issue in depth, e.g. youth discussing relations with police or vandalism;

– individual interviews, which are lengthy one-to-one discussions of an issue, e.g. social questions affecting the estate and the tenants.

Some skill, training and experience is needed to organise and run a qualitative survey. Expert help may be needed. It is important to inform people of what you are intending to do and get the support of tenants for gathering the information. It is important to agree in advance with whoever is doing the survey that they will:

a) record clearly their findings;
b) hand over their records on completion, while respecting any promised confidentiality;
c) produce a report of the findings that is simple and reflects accurately the interviews or group discussions;
d) separate out all speculative or evaluative comment.

Often qualitative and quantitative methods are used together, since they produce different kinds of information and can complement each other.

Example

A quantitative survey about the physical problems on an estate may show the proportion of households suffering from damp and condensation. It may also show which areas or blocks or floor levels are worst affected.

Qualitative research among those affected may show the full extent and impact of damp, e.g. on children's health, on furnishings, on the tenants' satisfaction and the effectiveness of remedial measures.

A quantitative survey may show the number of children, of one-parent families, of elderly. It may also show priorities for improvement.

Qualitative research may reveal what it is like bringing up a family and what special needs different individuals share.

13. PROBLEMS WITH MONITORING AND EVALUATION

There are three main problems in practice:

Starting to evaluate

Doing an evaluation means mentally stepping outside the normal run of activity. In local offices pressured by new activity often with new staff, this is extremely difficult to do. This is one reason why new local teams should have an induction course before the office opens. During the induction, the team can discuss its aims and start thinking about how it will measure success.

After this, evaluation will only be possible if it is given a high enough priority by the team in team meetings. It can of course be linked clearly with training.

Finding the resources

Monitoring and evaluation do require resources, staff time and possibly new systems. The more efficient the systems for collecting information, the less staff-time will be needed. Therefore someone who **likes** monitoring and who is good at thinking up systems – preferably the manager – should be made watchdog. Sometimes reception and administrative staff **like** monitoring as long as they know what they are doing it for.

Resources for social surveys may be harder to find. Sometimes students from local colleges may be willing to help, especially if this work can form a part of their course (for instance, the survey may contribute

to a thesis). Sometimes tenants will be willing to help especially if they are involved in the management of the estate. If small amounts of money are available for survey work, it becomes possible to recruit local volunteers to do the door-knocking and collecting of information. But it is not always appropriate to use local people where sensitive areas are being disclosed. Training for survey helpers is very important. As long as the questionnaires are simple, working out results should not be too difficult. They can be done on simple tables if a computer is not available, but it is much easier if questions can be pre-coded and analysed by computer. It is important always to get expert advice before starting work on a survey.

Obtaining training

The whole management team will need training, so that all staff can help with monitoring and evaluation. In addition, training will be needed so that new local information systems can be set up and operated smoothly.

14. SUPPORT

Effective monitoring of good performance and of real problems encourages support. This is one of the most important reasons for monitoring and evaluating progress. The local authority, politicians, estate committee, liaison groups of other services, will help more if they can see what is happening and if they are convinced by the **facts** that their help will not be wasted.

If it is true that locally based teams work better and estates generally require their own management structure, it is also true that they cannot work in a vacuum. They need to feed their monitoring, their reports and their performance into the wider organisation or into the sponsoring body, whether voluntary committee, shareholders or government agency, so that they see the **point** of struggling with problems and of aiming for better performance. Even if there are cash incentives, which is uncommon, these are rarely enough as they are short-term and they are rarely shared with the less skilled staff on whom local management depends. The local authority, the press, professional bodies need to recognise progress.

Most importantly, proper monitoring should lead to support from the tenants in the shape of ideas and satisfaction. If monitoring is fed regularly to tenants' representatives, they will come to understand management issues and choices much better. Understanding will help them back the staff. This in turn will more than anything else inspire better performance. Support from the wider housing body is harder to define, but it must be active, constructive and innovative. It must create a climate of change, of service and of front-line decision-making.

15. GOLDEN RULES

Monitoring housing management in new ways that make good performance rewarding is not at all easy.

Endless paper transfers and bureaucratic checks on initiative have made staff in local offices want to break with the idea of more records, more figures, more reports, more piles of unused and deadening information.

Our emphasis is therefore on a few keys. Here are the golden rules of monitoring:

– monitor a limited number of revealing aspects of management such as number of empty units.

– set up a simple system for recording basic management tasks **as they happen**, e.g. log-books, charts.

– produce **pictures**, e.g. bar charts, of what is happening **such as** empty units going down, number of repairs completed rising, so that staff can enjoy the sense of success.

– do **not** go on collecting useless statistics for a central system that cannot use them. Only produce statistics that **mean** something to your team. **But** do send on your reports (clear, readable, short and pithy) to the centre and to outside supporters.

– teach all staff, manual and non-manual to use log-books – so that **as they walk around**, they record what happens. This is the **best** form of monitoring.

– discuss progress and problems in **weekly** team meetings so that everyone gets used to the sequence of **see**, (monitor), **discuss** (decide), **act** (results).

– produce brief notes of each meeting, pin-pointing **WHO** is responsible for acting on what is discussed. Keep checking.

– At all cost **don't** monitor for the sake of it. It then becomes a time-consuming and pointless chore.

– Remember that a few convincing **figures** can win arguments much more quickly than years of campaigning e.g. 10 less empty properties on an estate pay for an extra staff person full-time.

– Make sure the **central** housing organisation is kept informed.

– Work out ways of providing **support** to staff, both locally through tenants, ward councillors, etc. and from the centre, through seminars, training, reports, newsletters, exhibitions, and other special events.

16. CHECKLIST OF MONITORING AND SUPPORT

– Are there regular team meetings – at least fortnightly?

– Does the local office monitor basic management performance?

– Is the monitoring relevant to the local office? To the local authority? To tenants?

– Does the local manager produce regular short progress reports?

– Does the local team know performance on arrears, lettings, repairs etc.?

– Is the information used to change tactics?

– Is success proudly displayed, e.g. graphs?

– Are problems discussed and ways out developed in team meetings? Are problems and poor performance shown in graphs?

– Is information presented to other interested groups e.g. tenants, councillors?

– Are aims changed/adopted/reviewed?

– Is the local office working out according to objectives set at the beginning?

– How does the central organisation use the monitoring information?

– What support to local staff does the central housing organisation provide?

– Is advice, training, access to information available to help the local office perform well?

17. SOME USEFUL BOOKS ON MONITORING AND SUPPORT

ALDBOURNE ASSOCIATES (1986): Household Survey for PEP – Forms and Guidance. Ulmus Ogbourne, Marlborough.

AUDIT COMMISSION (1986): Managing the Crisis in Council Housing. HMSO, London.

DEPARTMENT OF THE ENVIRONMENT (1983): Housing Appraisal Kit 2 – HAK for Improvement Work (survey methods on tenant satisfaction). Publication Unit, South Ruislip.

FOWLER F J (1984): Survey Research Methods. Applied Social Research Methods Series, Vol 1. Sage Publications, London.

GARDNER G (1978): Social Surveys for Social Planners. The Open University.

HOUSING CORPORATION (1989): Performance Expectations. Housing Association Guide to Self-Monitoring. London.

LYONS MORRIS L & TAYLOR FITZ-GIBBON (1983):
  No. 1 – Evaluation Handbook
  No. 2 – How to deal with goals and objectives
  No. 3 – How to design a programme evaluation
  No. 4 – How to measure programme implementation
  No. 6 – How to measure achievement
  Sage Publications, London

NATIONAL FEDERATION OF HOUSING ASSOCIATIONS (1987): Standards for Housing Management. London.

PHILLIPS D (1981): Do-It-Yourself Social Surveys – A Handbook for Beginners. Research Report No 4. Polytechnic of North London, Survey Research Unit, School of Applied Social Studies and Sociology.

IX. Training

Contents

*"I can easier teach twenty what
were good to be done
Than be one of the twenty to
follow mine own teaching."*

*W. Shakespeare
(The Merchant of Venice)*

1. SUMMARY

Housing staff and tenants need training to help them tackle with confidence the new style of housing management.

Training needs to be:

- part on the job
- part away from it all.

Training prepares staff for new tasks, equips them to find solutions to problems and develop new systems, gives them confidence to take responsibility, inspires them to do a good job.

Training costs money and requires outside support, so the budget should allow for training. Investment in training is investment in good performance.

Diagram 4.8 illustrates training needs.

Diagram 4.8
Training needs

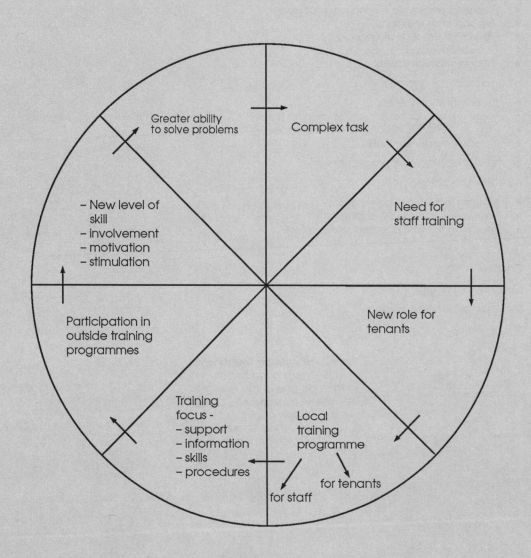

2. KEYWORDS: EUROPE; PEOPLE; CRISES

At most levels, people in Britain are poorly trained. Employers and Government devote less time and money to training than other countries. Far fewer young **people** get higher education or attain basic school-leaving certificates than they do in France or Germany. As a result, Britain's performance compares badly with other **European** Community countries (*Economist*, January and March 17–23, 1990).

Running an estate in an integrated and localised way, taking full responsibility for local decisions and attempting to get a good response from other services, are not easy organisational tasks. **Human problems** are never easy to solve and, above all, managing housing is a job involving the combination of "people" skills with business skills. Housing management without doubt requires good training. Not everyone is naturally good at it.

We have already shown how the basic tasks of rents and budgets, lettings and empty property, repairs and major improvement, communal maintenance and caretaking, welfare and resident involvement, do **NOT** work well with a fixed set of rules and procedures or rigid job descriptions. Training is needed not only to impart basic skills and knowledge but also to develop **flexible approaches** to estate management and **innovative responses** to infinitely variable human **crises** and needs.

Where residents are going to play an active role in decision-making, they too have training needs in understanding the role and the constraints of the council – learning about housing management, organisational development and problem solving from the residents' point of view. They are being asked to take on major responsibilities. To do this, they need training.

3. DEFINITIONS

Training means:

– the structured exchange of information;

– giving participants understanding of the information;

– developing practical skills;

– learning by experience with the support of a more experienced person;

– learning by exchanging ideas, by seeing what others do, by participating in new experiences;

– linking learning with work;

– helping people to expand their abilities so that they can take on more responsibility;

– making information more readily available and more understandable;

– building up a person's confidence;

– developing new ideas.

4. TARGETS

For staff training

– Hold regular team meetings from the beginning.

– Organise a follow-up review within 6 months of opening the office.

– Set up training sessions that appeal to staff.

– Find ways to involve local staff in training.

– Close the office for two hours a week specifically for training.

For tenant training

– Organise an inspiring induction course for local residents.

– Help develop ongoing training sessions that appeal to residents' representatives.

– Get regular outside speakers.

– Arrange visits.

– Get a training budget, no matter how small.

– Make sure tenants can attend seminars, conferences and outside training courses.

5. TRAINING NEEDS

The training needs of estate-based staff and residents' representatives are somewhat different and can be summarised in the following way:

For staff

Even those with a lot of experience in council housing need to acquire new skills and knowledge, and a different approach to management when moving to the estate level. Training should help staff to:

– acquire the necessary **professional and technical** knowledge;

– learn to work as **generic housing managers**;

– appreciate the potential **role of tenants** in housing management;

– work effectively as a **team**;

– develop **procedures** appropriate to estate-based management;

– understand the **needs of the community** on their estate;

– cope with and contain aggressive and potentially violent **behaviour**;

– understand **wider issues** affecting housing management and estate life;

– understand council **systems** and how to use them;

– understand other **resources** (e.g. private firms) and draw them in.

Staff training aims to develop four basic skills: management skills; social skills; problem-solving skills; and building skills.

Diagram 4.9

The training needed to tackle management problems

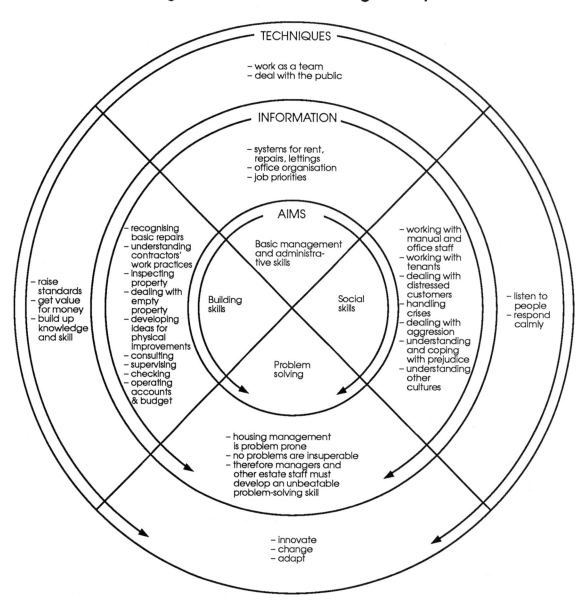

TECHNIQUES
– work as a team
– deal with the public

INFORMATION
– systems for rent, repairs, lettings
– office organisation
– job priorities

AIMS

Basic management and administrative skills

Building skills

Social skills

Problem solving

– recognising basic repairs
– understanding contractors' work practices
– inspecting property
– dealing with empty property
– developing ideas for physical improvements
– consulting
– supervising
– checking
– operating accounts & budget

– raise standards
– get value for money
– build up knowledge and skill

– working with manual and office staff
– working with tenants
– dealing with distressed customers
– handling crises
– dealing with aggression
– understanding and coping with prejudice
– understanding other cultures

– listen to people
– respond calmly

– housing management is problem prone
– no problems are insuperable
– therefore managers and other estate staff must develop an unbeatable problem-solving skill

– innovate
– change
– adapt

Diagram 4.9 shows the link between the aims, the precise skills, and the techniques for putting the aims into operation. Without training, it is very hard to develop the right techniques or to know enough to stay ahead of problems.

For tenants

Tenants who become representatives on Estate Management Boards, Estate Forums, or other forms of local management organisation, or who want to get involved in forming co-operatives, need training in order to:

– learn about **housing management**;

– understand budgets and basic **accounts**;

– learn about **organisations**, constitutions, council structures;

– understand **tenants' rights and responsibilities**, for example under a local management agreement;

– acquire the **skills and confidence** to play an effective role in housing management;

– win the support of and keep in touch with the wider body of tenants and **build up participation**;

– understand staffing matters, **employment issues** and the problems of organisations;

– develop skills in working as a **team**;

– learn how to run **meetings**;

– develop **procedures** for Estate Management Boards, co-operatives, forums, estate committees, etc.;

– in particular, learn to cope with **conflicting interests** and to contain actual conflicts.

6. GROUND RULES FOR TRAINING

● Training should be given a **high profile**:

– job descriptions/contracts of employment should specify that staff will be expected to participate in training programmes;

– there should be strong commitment to training from the beginning of an estate-based management project.

● There should be a definite **training budget**, however limited, for the estate staff and tenants.

● Training needs, courses and programmes, should be discussed as far as possible by the **participants** so that they approach the training with positive attitudes. Practical arrangements, such as staffing cover and overtime, should be taken into account.

● Programmes should take account of the **turnover** of both staff and tenant representatives (e.g. induction courses will be needed for new members of staff and for new tenant representatives after annual elections).

● Training for **tenants** should be at a time and place convenient to a majority. The meeting place should be attractive and easy to find. Training for tenants should set high standards and require an input from them.

● Training cannot assume **fluency in reading** and writing, nor a faith in education. It needs to be designed in a friendly and attractive way.

● All training should involve **practical exercises** and direct involvement in problem-solving.

● Training for **tenants** should take account of the need for translations and interpreters in some situations. Some training sessions may have to be offered in non-English languages on estates with groups of ethnic minority tenants, e.g. to inform tenants about changes in management and develop their input. This most often applies to house-bound mothers of young children who may be recent immigrants.

● Arrangements for **child care** should be discussed and ways found of allowing mothers with young children to participate.

7. TRAINING PROGRAMMES

Induction course for staff

An induction course for staff is needed when the local office is set up on an estate, to prepare the estate team for their new role. The initial training should be carried out shortly **before** the local office is to open, and after all staff are in post. All members of the estate team, manual and non-manual, should be involved in the induction course. Management staff should attend the whole of the course, while other estate-based staff, such as caretakers, technical staff

22. *Holding training events with tenants and housing staff helps. PEP National Conference, Liverpool 1988*
Paul Herrmann/Profile

23. *Induction course for tenants' representatives. St Paul's Gardens, Bristol*

Priority Estates Project

and the repairs workers should attend those sessions which are relevant to them. Manual staff may find detailed sessions about office systems very frustrating. But they do need to understand their role and how they fit into the team.

The induction course would normally last three days and would cover the following:

– Background to the estate-based management project and future plans for the estate.

– An examination of staff experience and queries, fears and doubts about the project.

– The role of tenants in management.

– Key aspects of estate-based management, e.g. repairs, lettings, the budget, caretaking, monitoring.

– Dealing with the public: standards of service.

– A study visit to an existing estate-based management project.

– Working as a team; agreeing priorities; time management.

– The estate team's aims and objectives; tasks for the next six months; standards and targets; action plan.

Induction course for tenants

An induction course for tenants is also needed. (See Chapter I on a role for tenants in running estates).

The course should include the following:

– Housing finance: where the rents/housing benefits go; capital and revenue funding; estates budgets.

– Basic housing management; what is involved in running an estate.

– The tenants' role in management.

– Developing and running a representative organisation.

– The links between the team, tenant representatives and the rest of the tenants; how to consult/inform.

– Review session; planning ahead.

– Establishing a code of conduct and good practice for dealings with the housing office, other organisations, and fellow residents.

Follow-up sessions to the induction training

There should be follow-up courses for both staff and residents after approximately six months, to review decisions taken at the induction course and to assess progress. New targets can be set, problems aired, new approaches agreed. It is possible also at this point to review the initial procedures and see if they are working or how they need to be modified.

Regular team meetings

Regular team meetings are vital to the development of the team. Learning how to run team meetings in order to help staff 'learn on the job' and perform to the best of their ability is one of the most important skills of a manager. Team-building begins with the induction but should be carried on **at least** fortnightly with all staff, under the leadership and inspiration of the manager. The 'ethos' of a team is a very elusive and indefinable thing, but continual on-the-job training through team meetings and support will help develop and clarify it. Such qualities as working flexibly and covering for each other, setting high standards of service on a poor estate, treating all tenants equally, creating a warm and welcoming atmosphere, depend on a **strong** ethos. Good initial training, followed by ongoing in-house training, will help.

Programme of regular ongoing training

A programme of regular ongoing training should be drawn up by the staff on each estate. A regular time each week or fortnight, during working hours, should be set aside for staff training. It is often best to hold training sessions **out of the office** to avoid constant distractions. The content of training programmes will vary according to each team's particular needs.

Training can often be built in to team meetings with local staff preparing ideas and contributing experience. However, it is important to set aside training times exclusively for training. Sometimes a specialist is needed, either from the council or outside. Caretakers and repairs staff should be included in team meetings and training sessions.

Outside courses

Many organisations provide regular seminars, training sessions and conferences for housing staff, including specialist subjects like homelessness, housing benefits, housing finance, co-operatives etc. There should be a local training budget so that staff can make rational decisions on the best use for the money. A conference fee for one member of staff (£150) may pay for more than one speaker to come and talk to all estate staff in a local training session. On the other hand, one member of staff attending an outside two-day housing benefits course may enable the local office to take over housing benefit. When someone from the team goes on a special course, they should come back and share what they have learnt.

Tenants' representatives

Tenants' representatives need regular, ongoing training, new induction courses for new members; exchanges with other organisations and projects etc. (see Section IA, A Role for Residents).

8. WHO SHOULD TRAINING BE DONE BY?

There are several ways of **delivering** the training.

Local team 'on the job'

Individuals in the estate team will each have experience or knowledge of particular areas, which should as far as possible be tapped when setting up the training. Training sessions which rely on each team member contributing their experiences in relation to a particular issue, e.g. caretaking, can sometimes 'crack' a problem by making solutions more accessible.

Local Authority or Housing Association 'in house'

Many local authorities have their own training units whose members can be used to run training sessions on the estate, or to act as 'consultants' – helping develop training programmes, giving local staff the skills and confidence necessary to run their own training. It is also possible to invite specialist staff to come and talk at training sessions about their work.

Outside trainers and national support bodies

Experts in particular fields, teachers in higher education and staff in other organisations are often willing to speak at training sessions. Outside trainers can be valuable catalysts, helping teams to look critically at existing attitudes and practices. It is important to draw in outside speakers, as they are often more stimulating than a familiar 'prophet in his own country'. People are often prepared to give up time **free of charge** to talk about their work to others.

All sorts of people have skills and an interest in developing and communicating them. Computer experts, technical staff, social workers, health workers, legal staff, accounting staff, are a few examples. Just to hear about other approaches and other professions and their views on an estate's problems can provide a stimulating challenge to new ideas.

Outside courses/seminars

These can be particularly useful for issues that apply to housing generally, e.g. benefits; law; finance; budgeting. Staff should be sent on specialist courses where this is necessary for the local office to work properly. Day-release professional housing management courses are very helpful in supporting and stimulating staff. (See Appendix 4(f) for training bodies).

Diagram 4.10 shows how many different training needs different groups have.

9. EXAMPLE OF LOCAL TRAINING PROGRAMME

The following training has been carried out with staff and tenants at the **Ocean Priority Estate in Tower Hamlets**:

- **A 3½-day staff induction course** before the estate office opened, covering:

  – key ingredients of estate-based management;

Diagram 4.10
Some training needs of different groups in local housing

Topics/issues	Who for?				
	Tenant reps.	Management staff	Caretakers	Repairs staff	Admin. staff*
Procedures for estate-based management (lettings, repairs, rents)	*	*	*	(some)	*
Housing finance	*	*	*	*	*
Controlling the budget	*	*			*
Employing/secondment of staff	*				*
Meetings skills	*	*	As appropriate		*
Negotiation skills	*	*			
Involving/informing residents	*	*	*	*	
Study visits to other EMBs	*	*	*	*	
Basic housing management	*	*	*	*	*
Writing minutes and reports	*	*			*
How the council works	*	*	*	*	*
Other agencies/resources for the estate	*	*	*	*	*
Team-building		*	*	*	*
Supervision/motivation		*			
Standards, monitoring & review	*	*	*	*	*
Time management	*	*	*	*	*
Developing and managing capital programme	*	*	*	*	
Working with residents		*	*		*
Responding to the public		*	*	*	*
Cleaning technology		*	*		
Legal aspects of housing management	*	*	*		*
New developments/changes in the law	*	*	As appropriate		*
Computers and computing		*		*	*
Word processing		*			*

*Book-keeper, clerical, reception, computing.

— tenant participation and consultation;

— capital and revenue spending plans;

— estate budgets;

— monitoring and information systems;

— study visit to another estate-based management project;

— dealing with the public;

— team-building.

● **A 1-day follow-up session for staff** six months after the induction course, in order to:

— assess progress on aims and objectives

— review team-working.

● **A programme for tenants' representatives** of six 1½ hour sessions covering:

— housing finance;

— housing management;

— tenant involvement in management;

— running meetings;

— representing the community;

— review session/the "way forward".

● **A 3-day course for staff** at Tottenham College:

Technical training for non-technical staff

● **One-off sessions** for staff (the office is closed half a day a week for training and team meetings) on:

24. *Local training programme at Shadsworth Estate, Blackburn*

Paul Herrmann/Profile

– repairs ordering/specifying and pre-/post-inspections†

– the schedule of rates

– planning and prioritising work†

– time management†

– housing benefits and welfare rights

– use of office micro-computer†

– planned maintenance (3 sessions)†

– right to buy

– tenant/landlord law†

The superscript cross (†) indicates that the course was run by outside trainers.

● In addition, there have been **special sessions** for staff on internal procedures, including:

– compensation claims

– repairs invoicing

– lettings/voids

– rent arrears control

See Appendix 4(f) for fuller Tenant Training programme.

● Attendance at **PEP conferences and seminars** by staff, caretakers and tenants, including:

– National Tenants Conference

– National PEP Conference

– "Dealing with the Public" Seminar

– Caretaking Conference.

● Attendance at **other outside training**:

– Two estate staff are doing the Diploma in Housing at the London School of Economics.

Diagram 4.11 illustrates the kind of training programme that staff need to develop in local management organisations.

Residential training courses lasting 2, 3 or 4 days are invaluable to groups of local staff and also to groups of residents' representatives. They:

a) accelerate the pace of learning;

b) transform people's belief in change;

c) generate enthusiasm of new ideas;

d) create learning exchanges, support networks, links between projects.

Diagram 4.11

Training Programme for 8 Estate-Based Offices
–Isle of Dogs Neighbourhood London Borough of Tower Hamlets

Names of local offices / Dates	St Johns	Samuda	RHG	Barkentine	Millwall	Cubitt Town	Poplar	Birchfield / St Vincent
8/10	Procedure manual training		(R.S. S.G.)				In-house law training	
4/11		In-house law training		Procedures manual training		(R.S. S.G.)	Time management training	(S. P.)
11/11	In-house law training				In-house law training		Procedure file training	(R.S. S.G.)
18/11	Half of all management staff including all team leaders	Law training ALL DAY (M.McE.)						
25/11	Team leaders	Managing capital budgets	(T.P.)	Half of all management staff Law training ALL DAY		(M.McE.)	Half of all caretaking staff TUESDAY 24/11 ALL DAY Health + Safety	
2/12	Team leaders	Planning and Programming Projects (S.G.)		Half of all Estate officers	Patch management (A.P.)	Admin. Assistants Book keeping	Half of all caretaking staff TUESDAY 1/12 ALL DAY Health + Safety	
9/12	Team leaders + chargehands	Planned maintenance follow-up (R.McN.)		Half of all Estate officers	Patch management (A.P.)	Admin. Assistants Monitoring		

Note: Initials in brackets represent outside trainers/speakers

PEP uses short residential training sessions to help tenants get ready for taking on estate management responsibilities. They represent the quickest learning route, particularly for people not used to training. Sweden, Denmark and Germany all have residential national training centres for housing staff, caretakers and residents' representatives. (See Appendix for a residential training programme).

10. ASSESSMENT OF TRAINING

Training is expensive and time-consuming. It often appears less important than 'getting on with the job'. Therefore it is important to be able to show how useful it is. Training can be measured for its effectiveness in three key areas: –

Diagram 4.12   How to develop staff training

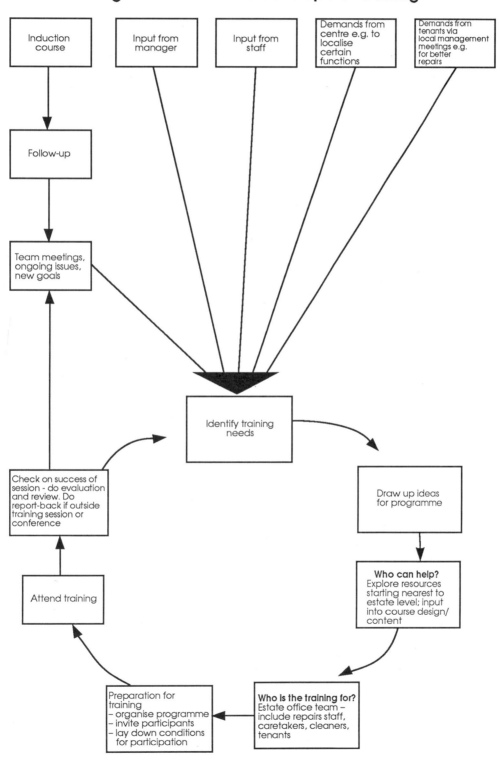

Meeting individuals' expectations

After each session or course, individuals can do a very simple feedback to the estate manager answering these questions:

– Did you enjoy the course?   Yes/No

– What were the most useful parts?

– What were the least useful parts?

– What would you like to tackle in your next training session?

Diagram 4.13   How to develop tenants' training

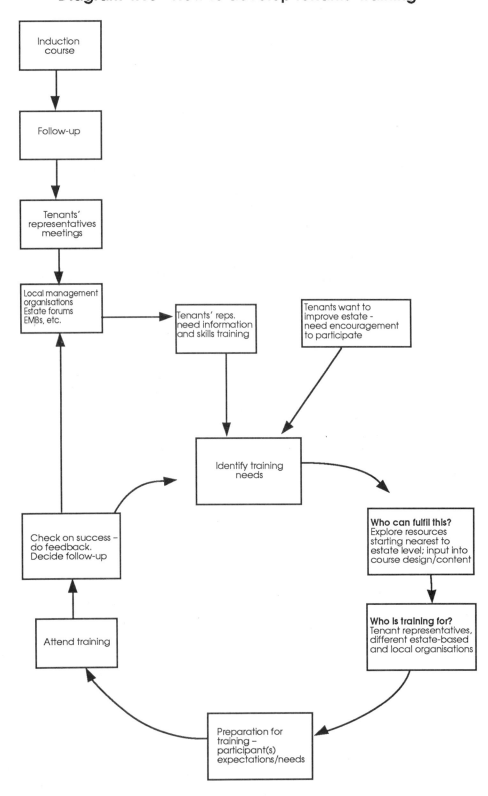

Developing individuals' abilities

The estate manager should review training regularly – approximately every six months – to assess the extent to which the training is enabling staff to do better jobs, and tenants to play a more effective role in management.

The main judges of this should be the participants for a main purpose of training is confidence building.

Improving the management of the estate

The training should be assessed not only by its effectiveness for individuals, but by the extent to which it is translated into practical improvements for the estate. The periodic review should also assess, therefore, the effects of the training programme on management performance, e.g. has the session on meeting skills resulted in better meetings; has the session on repairs or caretaking improved performance?

11. Procedure

Diagram 4.12 illustrates how to develop staff training, and Diagram 4.13 illustrates how to develop tenant training.

12. Conclusion

Training should not be boring, an élite privilege, or marginal. It should be exciting, frequent, and relevant. It should include outside speakers but it should draw on the skills of local staff. It should draw staff into wider areas, national and regional training events, as well as galvanising their local team. It should stretch people's ability and imagination so that they achieve more through knowing more and through learning that they have greater abilities.

Training should involve all staff and tenants' representatives. It should take place across a full range of skills and help senior managers as well as local staff.

Paying for training is very difficult. It will always get squeezed in tight budgets. Its value must be recognised. It is then **always** worth paying for.

The new funds available for tenant training as a result of the DoE's Co-operative Review (DoE, 1989) should help all estate-based tenant participation and control initiatives.

13. Checklist for training

– Do staff enjoy training?

– Do tenants enjoy training?

– Do repairs workers, caretakers and cleaners attend training?

– Does training help team work?

– Is the training relevant?

– Does training help management standards?

– Do staff want to get qualifications?

– Do you hold regular team meetings? Do they include training on the agenda?

– Do you organise office routines, reception rota, etc. to accommodate training?

14. Some useful books on training

Commission for Racial Equality (undated): Racial Equality Training in Housing: A Guide. London

Department of the Environment (1988): Training for Employment HMSO

Fuchs S (undated): Tackling Training – Practical Training Guidelines for Voluntary Organisations. LVSC, London

Local Government Training Board (1983): Housing Training and Small Authorities. Ref. No. HS 0017. Luton

—— (undated): Housing Caretakers; Training Recommendation 10

National Federation of Housing Associations (1989): Race & Housing: Employment and Training Guide. London

—— (1985): Women in Housing: Employment

Tenant Participation Advisory Service (1988): Tenant Participation in Cambridge: An Analysis of the Possibilities for Developing Tenant Participation within the Housing Service. Salford.

X. Co-ordination and the development of other services

Contents

> 'But Mousie, thou art no thy lane,
> In proving foresight may be vain:
> The best-laid schemes o'mice an' men
> Gang aft agley,
> An' lea'e us nought but grief an' pain,
> For promis'd joy!'
>
> R. Burns
> (To a mouse)
>
> (aft = often; agley = awry; thy lane = alone)

1. Summary

It is easy to blame housing for other problems. It is a mistake to expect reasonable housing conditions to solve **all** other problems. Estates and people living in them need many different things.

A good local office will become a conduit for other ideas, functions, initiatives and services.

Co-ordination will:

- attract resources
- prevent overloading
- support varied inputs
- encourage independent but co-operative initiatives

- link the estate to the outside world.

The four main elements of estate life that build links with the outside world are:

- the landlord service and the way the estate is managed;
- other services to the estate that affect estate life;
- employment, training and economic activity, or lack of it;
- the estate as part of a neighbourhood, a town, a region.

Diagram 4.14 illustrates these interlocking elements.

Diagram 4.14
Co-ordination

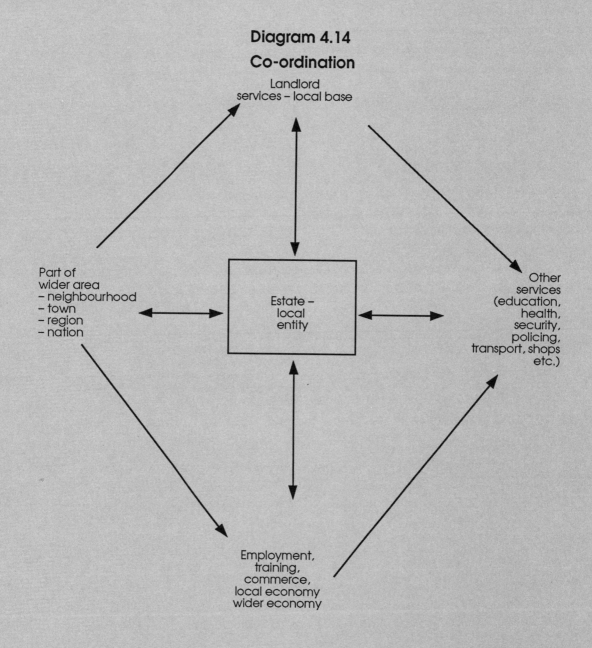

2. KEYWORDS: POOR; HAPHAZARD; CHASING; OVERLAP

An estate that is **poor**, rundown and stigmatised, will tend to have services that match the image. They too will often be rundown, poor-quality, **haphazard**. A local management organisation running housing can only succeed with **co-operation**, help and back-up from many other bodies. It will be important to talk to everyone doing jobs of whatever kind on the estate to make sure that they are willing to help and to fit in with the project.

Why should the housing office build links?

– because the tenants do not see their problems and their needs as belonging to housing **or** social services **or** the DSS; they are often sent "from pillar to post" **chasing** solutions to their problems;

– because services often **overlap**; and often deal with the same households from different points of view;

– because services other than housing are essential to help tenants;

– because other services and agencies can greatly help tenants in aspects of their lives that are not directly affected by housing management;

– because housing staff cannot do everything and it is important to 'stick to the knitting' and to do the basic housing management jobs well.

3. DEFINITION: THE MEANING OF CO-ORDINATION

The central function of co-ordination is to get as many services locally based as possible; to get **all** services affecting the estate to take account of residents and local conditions; and to ensure that each additional effort adds to the total so that the culminative impact is greater than any individual effort. A further aim is to create sufficient momentum for change to help other services, public and private, get caught up in the local effort and co-operate fully with it.

Proper co-ordination means:

– better services

– greater understanding of problems

– help for other bodies in linking their work more closely with residents

– a vehicle for residents to 'get a handle on' conditions

– a reduction in duplication, power struggles and jealousy

– additional resources for the estate

– better use of existing resources

– a multiplication of effort

– initiatives on the estate

– a better image for the estate

– drawing in agencies that were not previously involved.

4. TARGETS FOR LIAISON WITH OTHER ORGANISATIONS

– Establish a local liaison forum for all bodies involved in or serving the estate directly.

– Co-ordinate services, e.g. caretaking with refuse collection; landscape and garden maintenance with open space cleaning.

– Aim to get a locally based Social Services team.

– Get beat policing established in collaboration with residents.

– Get at least one playgroup or nursery with local staff, a youth club or youth facility, a summer playscheme or camp.

– Get at least one shop open, re-opened, smartened up.

– Support some local employment initiatives.

– Contact major local firms to sound them out about helping the estate, e.g. offering a trainee position for a young resident within the firm.

– Contact the local school(s) or college suggesting a joint school project linked to the estate and to future work.

– Involve young people in estate improvements.

– Encourage initiatives for the elderly.

– Establish, with the support of the landlord a local initiative fund or a project fund. With £5 per dwelling per year, the estate committees or liaison forum or Estate Management Board can encourage activities through small pump-priming grants. It can also pay for residents to go and learn about initiatives elsewhere. (See Chapter I on "A Role for Residents").

5. THE LOCAL HOUSING OFFICE'S ROLE IN DEVELOPING CO-ORDINATION

Co-ordination needs to be given high priority by the co-ordinator or estate manager. As it involves other council departments, it needs the backing of the Chief Executive of the Council. Tenants will want to get as many services localised as possible.

Very often other services will have gradually declined, or even withdrawn completely, over the life of rented housing estates. In many cases, essential services, such as shops, were never set up adequately from the outset.

Co-ordination is likely to work much more quickly and effectively if residents' representatives press for help over other things affecting the estate. They will invariably use the housing office to do this. Liaison with other services will then prove to be essential in order to maintain momentum behind improvements. Tenants' representatives will leap at the opportunity to participate in liaison meetings; they will want to co-operate actively with other services in the way that they have experienced with local housing offices. As a result many of the service leaders, whether police, shopkeepers, publicans or youth leaders, will show much greater willingness to help. As with the housing service itself, residents have a pivotal role to play in developing ways out of the economic and social problems that often compound their housing situation.

The most important immediate effect of liaison and co-ordination is to convince other services that conditions can improve and that there are responsible residents willing to co-operate.

6. KEY COUNCIL SERVICES AND OTHER STATUTORY SERVICES

Up to 12 different council departments may be involved in delivering services to estates (Power, April 1987). The most important ones would be:

− **Cleansing Services** for domestic refuse, bulk household refuse and street sweeping services;

− **Environmental Health** for rubbish accumulations, dog warden services, noise problems, other statutory nuisance, health and infestation problems.

− **Parks/Leisure Services** for open space maintenance, new landscaping projects, children's play facilities and equipment.

− **Economic Development Units** for training for jobs, links with local employers, enterprise.

− **Education** for schools, youth service, adult education.

− **Library services** − sometimes actively involved in helping with visiting mobile libraries, children's hours, holiday activities and homework sessions.

− **Social services** for statutory duties towards vulnerable, elderly, disabled and children at risk.

− **Architects** for improvements to dwellings and environment.

− **Surveyors** for technical advice and supervision of complex building and contract matters.

These last two are most directly connected with the housing service.

Other statutory agencies which are likely to have contact with estate residents and/or the estate office are:

− **The Police** in response to emergency calls and residents' desires for more preventive policing. Where the police have good contact with the residents and with the local office, they can help reduce fear and increase people's confidence in overcoming crime.

− **The Probation Service**, to deal with a range of individual problems linked to the courts such as child care, young offenders.

− **County Councils** for roads and other services where the estate is in a non-metropolitan borough or under a District Council.

− **The DSS**, for benefits and support claims and problems.

25. *Liaising with key services makes estate living work. Pensioners' lunch club, Broadwater Farm Estate, Haringey*

Priority Estates Project

– **Job Centres**, for residents registered as unemployed.

– **The Training Agency** where people are seeking work and claiming benefit. Also the local Training and Enterprise Council for Employment Training and Youth Training Schemes.

Gas and Electricity Boards (and their private successors) are important because of problems of poverty, non-payment of bills, threatened and actual cut-offs. These can arise from difficult and sometimes tragic circumstances. Intervention by the housing office may be necessary to help desperate households.

Local health services, GPs, children's clinics, dentists, health visitors play a most important role in helping life on an estate. Their services are often delivered in a fragmented and unco-ordinated way. Usually, but not always, there is a health clinic and a doctor within reach of an estate. Often there is scope for preventive action, for education, for help with small children and needy mothers, particularly young mothers on their own. Women from some minority groups are often very cut-off and isolated. Health visitors can help them in a real way if support services are set up in a way that makes them accessible to these groups. (See Monika Zulauf on Women and Children on Priority Estates, 1990.)

Voluntary bodies, such as the Family Service Unit, Safe Neighbourhoods Unit, the National Association for the Care and Resettlement of Offenders, local churches, community organisations, often work on or have contact with estates such as PEP is working on. These bodies help by bringing experience, added resources and goodwill. They should be encouraged. But liaison helps to avoid 'swamping' the estate.

Too many cooks. There was one situation where 3 different churches set up special initiatives on an estate, all with an underlying aim of both helping residents and of proselytising. Some residents were amused; some annoyed; the churches fell out. Only one project, involving several major churches together, survived. It must be said that better co-ordination might not have dissuaded the other two from trying! But it might! Often the estate manager or co-ordinator can head off duplication or conflict which can result from too many agencies 'dabbling' in the affairs of a community.

7. MULTI-SERVICE PROJECTS

Several Priority Estates Projects have from the outset included other services, particularly social services. Environmental health and technical services are two others sometimes included. This leads to much more collaborative working relationships and usually expands the input on the ground. However, rarely are all services from the local authority both locally based and integrated under one co-ordinator. In practice it is difficult for different services with a different set of statutory duties and professional skills to do more than collaborate and work towards agreed aims for the estate. But the approach **can** be shared – small-scale, flexible, resident-oriented, forward-thinking, locally-based. Collaboration, exchange of information and mutual support can bring much swifter success than 'paddling your own canoe'. While this applies directly to council services, e.g. the role of housing and social services in the case of a family with children, facing court proceedings for serious arrears, it can also apply to links between the housing office and shops over removal of rubbish, van deliveries, security and insurance problems. Or the housing office may be indirectly responsible for leisure facilities, such as a community centre or play equipment if these need maintaining, break down or cause conflict.

The housing office may be the only place residents can go to get an answer or get a problem solved, that affects the estate but is not specifically a housing problem. At the very least the housing office may be able to chase other departments responsible. The closer the working relations and the greater the stake of the other organisations in the estate, the more likely it is that problems will get sorted out and progress made.

The housing office may need to take an active role in getting local facilities properly managed by the responsible department or body. This is particularly likely to apply to community centres, youth clubs, and other social centres. (See Chapter I, 'A Role for Residents' for fuller discussion of the provision of local facilities with resident involvement).

There may be a case for the local housing organisation taking on a direct co-ordinating and management role for some local facilities and services on an agency basis. But such a role must be carefully negotiated, clearly defined and properly resourced.

The role of housing services

We have found that on estates of primarily rented housing, housing services often take the **lead** because housing influences the lives of all residents and forms the organising base around which other services can perform better. Basic repairs, keeping property filled, keeping communal areas maintained and liaising with residents make it possible for other services to begin to help. Without the basic housing service, it is much more difficult. The housing office therefore plays a crucial role in co-ordination and liaison with other services. For this reason all housing staff need to understand the wider social and organisational context. They need to see the link between the welfare of residents on a broad front and specific housing responsibilities.

The role of social services

Whether or not housing and social services are combined within a single estate based project – in general they are not – the role of social services on an estate with many low-income and vulnerable households is closely linked to housing. In some circumstances the two roles are in conflict, for example a social worker may support and defend a family that is causing difficulties on the estate on the grounds that the family cannot cope or has other major problems leading to the dislocation. But the housing office may need to enforce tenancy conditions and attempt to contain the problem because of the disruption to other tenants. Noise, rubbish, crime, children in custody, domestic fights, alcohol or drug abuse, may all be examples of social problems that may involve the two services from different angles. In practice, close collaboration

26. *Estates need a wide variety of inputs. Bloomsbury Estate, Birmingham*

Priority Estates Project

can lead to both services accepting the need for the other perspective, and hopefully supportive action, which may sometimes involve constraining the family.

Housing officers must know **how** to work with social services and must involve them, at least by informing them, in the management changes under way through the local office. There is huge scope for expanding collaboration between housing staff and social work staff (Finkel, 1989).

At the same time, many staff find that collaboration works best if the two services maintain their separate identities. This can help households needing social services support by creating a certain distance from the estate as a whole. Scape-goating and stigmatisation can more easily be avoided.

8. POLICING

We have already mentioned the importance of policing. But it is not always easy to bridge the long-standing gap between the enforcers of the law and the communities that suffer disproportionately from crime. While residents' representatives invariably want more sensitive, more local and more active policing, they often find themselves caught 'in between' when the police struggle to catch offenders and end up in conflict with many local youth (see Downes, 1989, concluding chapter for detailed discussion).

Thus liaison with the police, while maybe the most necessary link, can be the most fraught. Here are some reasons:

– politicians are not always supportive;

– it is difficult to obtain sufficient beat policing to combat fear and actual crime effectively;

– the police often regard estates as private council property and do not have a tradition of patrolling them frequently;

– sometimes the police have other priorities such as responding to emergency calls, or helping with major events;

– sometimes the police argue that their powers are limited, and find it particularly difficult to deal with young people;

– community policing is sometimes considered a second-rate approach, including by the police themselves;

– policing of drug abuse is fraught and where it exists on estates, can lead to raids that cause disruption and press-reporting without necessarily solving the problem;

– issues of race are critical, and in many inner city areas relations between the police and minority groups are very poor (Scarman, 1982; 1986);

– there are sometimes tensions between young people and police which can explode, leading to serious violence. The 1980s have seen several such eruptions;

– tenants may have negative views about policing based on the failure of police to respond quickly to 999 calls;

– some residents may not wish to be seen as liaising closely with the police for fear of intimidation or because of lack of confidence.

Police in many areas alter their policing methods radically in response to a local office and resident involvement. This has produced results in many areas where previously relations were very bad (see Downes, 1989). The crucial changes are:

– institution of regular beat policing;

– a small group of policemen responsible **regularly** for the estate;

– frequent links with the estate office;

– meetings between residents' representatives and the police;

– positive involvement of young people (see below on involving youth).

9. SHOPS

Improved security and better housing will lead to the re-opening of previously boarded up shops or the establishment of new small businesses (see PEP Working Paper on Small-Scale Employment Initiatives, March 1988, or Appendix 4(f)). This will almost certainly generate jobs, often part-time, for local residents. If a group of shops develops, or an existing row of shops is revitalised, one shop actually helps the other, even if they are in competition to some extent, because a certain level of exchange, street life and service is necessary for any one shop to succeed. There is therefore a strong argument for the Council to help develop, re-open, facilitate groups of shops on estates; for shops were often closed down forcibly through redevelopment, leaving new low-income communities deprived of easy access to basic services.

Shops not only service residents and create a few jobs; they also help attract staff to local offices by making the estate a more attractive place to work. There is nothing worse than not being able to buy anything for lunch locally or pick up a paper on the way home if you are working hard in a small and pressurised estate office.

Shops often create a momentum of their own, offering evening opening, a gathering point after school, an exchange service through cards in windows, and a rise in morale on the estate as shops signal economic life. Shopkeepers will often want to live nearby or above

the shop, creating more stability in the community. It has often taken a whole generation to get shops and pubs back into estates.

10. ESTATE-BASED LIAISON COMMITTEES

The Estate Manager needs to work out a formula for liaising with the other services on the estate. Representatives of these services should be invited to an estate-based liaison committee. Sometimes a special forum needs to be set up where all bodies are represented in order to discuss and sort out issues affecting the estate as a whole. Residents' representatives should be included. The Estate Manager in a local management organisation needs to 'broker', monitor and liaise with other services as far as possible, since housing is invariably the lead department. This does **not** mean that the local office **organises** other services.

A good example of estate-based co-ordination is the Workers' Forum on Barnfield estate. This is a small regular meeting of all those who work on the estate (not just council staff). The discussions focus on common approaches to specific problems, e.g. the difficulties experienced by single-parent families, the residents' ambition to develop better child-care; the possible new uses for an old building.

Another example of co-ordination is the Round Table Meeting in the Rhondda, where all services involved in the Penrhys Priority Estates Project, including **all** those listed in this section, have met quarterly with the Chief Executive to report on their input to the estate and progress made. This included the DSS, the Police, British Gas, and the Youth Service. Even Spar Supermarket and the local brewery have been invited. Residents' representatives attend. The Round Table has been supported by a local liaison forum on the estate that meets more often.

Now the Rhondda Borough Council has decentralised across its entire stock, each area has its own liaison arrangements and other services are expected to link with the local housing office.

11. RESIDENT EMPLOYMENT

'– thousands at his bidding speed
And post o'er land and ocean without rest; –
They also serve who only stand and wait.'
J. Milton (on his blindness)

One particular area of activity that more and more tenants and local offices are getting drawn into is employment. Many estates are islands of low opportunity with a shortage of jobs and of officially recognised skills. The lack of employment opportunities and the increase in activity on the estate that stems from the local office will almost certainly lead to the demand for local jobs and the realisation that there is potential for creating them. This is a large issue and we only touch on some of the key ideas here, without going into the detail of **how** to do it.

27. *Employing residents to carry out environmental work. Digmoor Estate, Skelmersdale, Lancashire*
Paul Herrmann/Profile

It is important to stress at the outset that while we mainly discuss estate-based jobs, it is most important to link people into the wider job market and to open up opportunities, particularly among young people, for training **outside** the estate.

In a successful local management initiative, maybe 100 jobs can be created for residents in and around the estate over five years. These will not all be permanent but they do significantly change the estate and residents' view of its potential and opportunities (Bootstrap Enterprises and MacFarlane, October 1989; PEP, March 1988; also see Appendix 4(g) on Broadwater Farm).

The employment of residents in local posts is one way of creating more jobs on the estate. This not only **improves** the standards of management because of the commitment residents are likely to feel; it also creates economic opportunities for households who previously found their energies and talents underused. It generates income **within** the local area. Because locally-based management **reduces** the number of centrally based administrative jobs, and increases the number of local **manual** jobs, in line with the emphasis on repairs and caretaking, residents can often take up this opportunity if they are given the chance. A major benefit of employing residents, even if it is only for a few jobs, is that it creates a climate of confidence and it links people on estates, who have often been marooned because of lack of opportunity, with wider developments in the area. For example,

a locally recruited worker becomes familiar with housing management, with local authority structures and practices and with the place of the estate in the wider community and economy. S/he also starts to meet staff from other areas.

Locally-based jobs are often a first step to greater contact and help build confidence. Jobs off the estate for residents can do as much as entirely local jobs – or even more. Jobs **off** the estate bring an **income** into the estate. The spin-off in shops, transport and general ambitions among residents can be very important.

Steps in encouraging employment initiatives

The following list shows the steps that can be taken to help respond to residents' need for employment.

1. Open up any possible jobs in the local office to residents, from the most humble and unskilled to more skilled ones, e.g. cleaning, caretaking, repairs, labouring, landscaping, garden maintenance, administration, reception, book-keeping, and estate management.

2. Provide the necessary training and support.

3. Encourage local shops and other businesses (e.g. pub) to open/re-open/provide more services – smarten up their goods, presentation, tills. They will almost certainly recruit some local staff.

4. Invite the Training Agency or local Training and Enterprise Council to come and build links on the estate.

5. Contact schools, careers advice, job shops, colleges of further education, for materials, ideas, prospectuses, about training and work – also see if they can provide opportunities. Generate a climate among residents and particularly young people of looking further afield for opportunities.

6. Contact the youth service, voluntary organisations, churches, play associations to see if they can help involve local people; and set up more locally-based facilities.

7. Contact employment creation organisations (e.g. local authority Economic Development Unit, Bootstrap Enterprises) to see if they can give advice, develop initiatives.

8. Contact local and national firms with an interest in the area about whether they might help fund business ideas – they are sometimes keen to get involved – or whether they are prepared to recruit actively on the estate and in the local schools? e.g. Marks & Spencer; Barclays; Wates; Sainsburys.

9. Persuade the local authority to do more to boost the confidence of residents. Broadwater Farm has greatly benefited from the local council being willing to recruit locally, to allow estate-based organisations to bid for work, to provide training and support to residents, to allow tenants' representatives to be represented on interview panels for local staff recruitment. This exposes tenants to employment procedures and puts them in touch with new ideas.

The following sections explore a number of issues linked to employment initiatives that are important to consider.

Cleaning

One of the reasons why rundown estates are often extremely dirty is because they receive **less than their share** of cleaning services. 'What goes in Bermondsey does not go in Belgravia' is an apposite legal dictum. It is common for outsiders to shrug off the suggestion that cleaning is important in the eyes of residents on rundown estates or that cleaning jobs represent economic gain for those who do them. But it is an important step forward for someone out of work and with little prospect of work or in need of a part-time local job to become employed. It is also important to keep the environment of an estate clean. This is invariably a high priority for residents.

In practice many cleaning jobs either exist or need to be created on and around estates. Shops, pubs, schools, the office, community centre all require cleaning staff, usually part-time. On the Penrhys estate in Rhondda, four young people were recruited as full-time 'clean-up boys'. Twelve tenants were recruited as part-time caretaker/cleaners in the small blocks of flats.

On Broadwater Farm resident-cleaners have been sent on training programmes and do an excellent job of keeping the long walkways, lifts and open areas clean, graffiti-free and attractive to users.

An interesting side-effect of residents taking on cleaning jobs is that these jobs can lead to involvement in training, in team development, in resident forums. It **can** actually lead to other jobs too.

The most important aspect of **cleaning** and its link to resident employment is that, if done properly and given proper recognition, it transforms the appearance of an estate and can indirectly influence lettings, the performance of other staff, e.g. repairs workers, and the whole atmosphere of the area. There is thus a double benefit from persuading local organisations to **pay for** cleaning. It involves relatively small amounts of money and has a ripple effect.

Some cleaning jobs arise directly through the housing office; some through other organisations. The important role of the Housing Office is:

a) encouraging the employment of residents;

b) supporting tenants in their near-universal ambition for a cleaner, more attractive environment;

c) shifting the emphasis of management to less bureaucratic, more direct service. This creates, early in the life of a local office, the opportunity to employ residents with previously poor training and limited experience. This can then be built on.

Community activities

Community activities, such as youth clubs, under-fives provision, after-school clubs, also require some staff. The housing office may actively encourage these activities because of the damage and bad relations that can be caused by a lack of purpose and lack of facilities among unskilled, unemployed, under-achieving young people. Often local residents can become play-leaders, supervisors, attendants, receptionists. In fact, young people themselves need to find a direct role and outlet through helping provide facilities and also through working on the environment.

Using local residents to help run local activities makes the activities themselves more useful.

However it is important **not** to assume that groups of residents can automatically run a youth club, simply by virtue of wanting one. Skilled, experienced and trained staff and solid outside support are needed in the provision of facilities. Too many estate facilities have closed down after initial resident enthusiasm, because of management difficulties, conflict, inexperience or loss of support. Therefore helping residents set up, and get jobs in, community facilities requires an investment in training; they also need to be closely supported by an established body. (See Monika Zulauf, PEP Working Paper, Women and Children on PEP Estates, 1989).

Training

Training is a vital part of the process of local recruitment and employment. Outside bodies should be used to help establish training on the estate and also to advise on the development of employment opportunities both within and off the estate. It is important to create a 'training climate' among young people, so that they will also go out to training courses, college, day release, etc.

Employment Training, the Government Training Agency or local Training and Enterprise Councils can do a lot in placing unemployed young people in training programmes.

But until training for young people in Britain is on a par with our counterparts in Europe, we will have both a serious skills shortage and continued high unemployment among young people in some areas (*Economist*, February 19 1990).

Schools

It is important also for local offices to liaise with schools and colleges, not only because of their role in training young people and offering valuable (and sometimes poorly used) resources to the community; they can also help generate ideas for activities and create a 'work' ethos that encourages young people to try. The success of COMPACT in Sheffield and parts of Inner London in linking older school children with prospective employers has shown the value of enlisting the collaboration of schools around employment issues. Because on many estates there are two (or even more) generations of households who have rarely or never known work, it is crucial to find ways of breaking out of that cycle. Schools can help play a role.

Concluding point about employment

Employment initiatives are unlikely to flourish in a vacuum, though they are wanted everywhere where unemployment is severe. They do however develop, if only on a small scale, in the wake of a successful local management project, if the local office develops its role as co-ordinator and liaison point for other services and initiatives.

12. THE ROLE OF YOUTH

'Crabbed age and youth
Cannot live together.
Youth is full of pleasance,
Age is full of care...
Youth is full of sport,
Age's breath is short...
Youth is wild, and Age is tame...etc.'
W. Shakespeare (A Madrigal)

Issues of unemployment hit youth particularly hard. On many unpopular estates, the majority of young people aged 16–21 may be unemployed. The role of young people on an estate has a lot to do with the viability of local management. The impact of young people on estate conditions cannot be over-estimated. Their energies, their needs, their frustrations and difficulties should be understood and tackled in ways that make the job of running the estate possible.

The impact of young people on their surroundings makes liaison with other services and wider developments on the estate essential.

On an estate of 1,000 dwellings, there may be 300 young people between the ages of 16 and 21, many of whom will neither be in school nor in regular work. If there are initiatives to involve, train and employ them, the estate can see vandalism, graffiti and crime go down, and management standards and tenant satisfaction go up. The young people must feel **part** of the initiatives. It will be **most** important, initially, at least, for developments involving youth to be estate-based.

From this base it will then be possible to attract some into courses, and jobs further afield. Young people learn quickly, have energy and enthusiasm, and can change and adapt. However, some young people also leave school with poor literacy and numeracy and with little readiness for work. A few months doing nothing can set in train a pattern of late sleeping, low activity, and low morale that is hard to break. Much more ambitious programmes are needed to tackle this problem. It is one very specific area where Britain is far behind and should look to Europe. The French government initiative to help restore rundown areas of social housing lays a very heavy emphasis on integrating training and employing estate youths (*Ensembles*, March 1990). We should do the same.

There are two scenarios (Diagram 4.15) at work on estates, stemming from the often large concentration of young people. The first sequence illustrates their difficulty in finding a constructive role; the second shows the way youth initiatives can interact with other services and the co-ordinating role of the local housing office, resulting in young people playing a more positive role.

One of the greatest assets of estates is that they rehouse disproportionate numbers of young people. It is also a great problem. They are needed for the future. Unskilled, unemployed, marginal and unwanted, they can be menacing. With training, involvement and a role to play, they may be very differently regarded by society. In that sense the estates we are referring to here can either be seen as a tinder-box, or as a unique opportunity. Making sure that something is done to help young people is a **must**.

There are thus several areas of co-ordination – youth work and employment are salient examples – that are strongly interrelated, highly complex and linked to some of our most intractable social problems. Here we have only touched on their relevance and importance. Library shelves are stacked with studies of their many dimensions.

Local housing offices will inevitably face these issues and must find ways of **drawing in** other resources, other skills and other activities. Thus co-ordination is probably one of the most important functions of a local office.

13. PROBLEMS WITH CO-ORDINATION

It can be seen by now that making an estate work is complex indeed. Each organisation providing services to an estate has its own internal structure, policies, style, method. There are inevitably endless, detailed operational difficulties, stemming from these differences. Here are a few of the main problems:

- conflicting priorities;

- different ethos within different organisations;

- jealousy, rivalry, professionalism and defensiveness;

Diagram 4.15
Youth difficulties and the positive role of youth

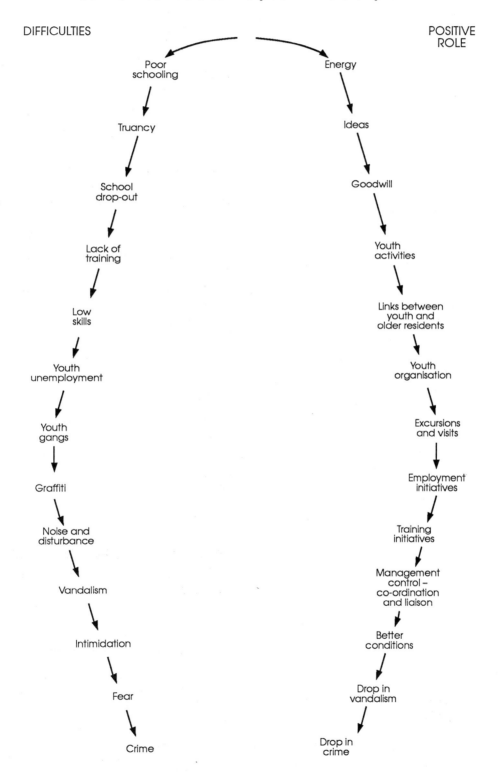

DIFFICULTIES

POSITIVE ROLE

Poor schooling

Energy

Truancy

Ideas

School drop-out

Goodwill

Lack of training

Youth activities

Low skills

Links between youth and older residents

Youth unemployment

Youth organisation

Youth gangs

Excursions and visits

Graffiti

Employment initiatives

Noise and disturbance

Training initiatives

Vandalism

Management control – co-ordination and liaison

Intimidation

Better conditions

Fear

Drop in vandalism

Crime

Drop in crime

– attitudes of some politicians, not wanting housing to take a lead, e.g. over technical services or employment;

– staff turnover;

– the range of services, particularly on a big and rundown estate.

Sometimes a multitude of organisations all try to help. This can also cause friction, resentment and inter-agency competition. It is important for the estate manager to make use of the additional resources but try to prevent "overkill". It has been known for very stigmatised estates to be "crowded out" with agency initiatives. Naked competition for the job of helping a disadvantaged community has a certain ugly irony to it. Most organisations in practice observe a kind of unwritten code of not moving into areas where other similar organisations are already active.

If there is no one to broker inputs, there is likely to be breakdown in communication. If the local office plays this role, in however informal a way, the estate will certainly benefit.

14. CONCLUSION

Social rented housing, especially where it is built on large estates, houses disproportionate numbers of low-income households. There is a lower than average level of skill and higher level of unemployment in these areas. There is also often a higher level of crime and insecurity (Hope & Shaw, 1988) and a higher demand for services (Reynolds, 1986). But poor services, few opportunities, isolation, reinforce the decline of many estates into islands of deprivation and depression.

Some positive steps can bring about the beginnings of a turn-around:

– a local housing office;

– local services;

– employment and youth initiatives;

– resident participation;

– beat policing;

– local co-ordination.

The upward climb depends on wider factors than the estate itself. But having a well-organized local base with people already pushing out the boundaries of change is a first step.

15. CHECKLIST FOR CO-ORDINATION OF SERVICES AND LINKS WITH OTHER ORGANISATIONS

– Does the estate manager have regular contact with Social Services and police? – a **very** good litmus paper.

– Does the estate have a liaison forum for all the local agencies?

– Are there any new developments from other services, e.g. better shops, better transport, more play facilities; a renovated pub?

– Do residents play a role in relation to other agencies and services?

– Are they consulted? Do they use other services? Are there local training opportunities?

– Are young people going on to college or further training from the estate?

– What role do the young people play? Are they part of the estate activities? Do local staff know them? Do residents' representatives try to involve them?

– Are there youth initiatives?

– What is the unemployment level?

– Who is most affected?

– Are crime and vandalism a problem?

– Do young people congregate in gangs? Does this cause problems? What positive measures can be taken to engage young people further?

– Are residents invited to apply for local estate jobs?

– Are residents' representatives involved in interviews for staff?

– Is there demand/need for more local businesses/services?

– Do any local businesses/services need/use local labour?

– Is the office in touch with an organisation that could advise, take the initiative on local employment opportunities?

– Are there links with schools?

– Is there a local Economic Development Unit? Is it involved?

– Is there any targetted recruitment on the estate?

– Are there any compact arrangements with local schools?

16. SOME USEFUL BOOKS ON CO-ORDINATION – LINKS WITH OTHER SERVICES

AUDIT COMMISSION (1987): The Management of London's Authorities: Preventing the Breakdown of Services, Occasional Papers, No. 2, January. HMSO.

—— (1989): Urban Regeneration and Economic Development. The Local Government Dimension. HMSO

ASTON UNIVERSITY (1980): Local Authority Employment Initiatives. HMSO

BOOTSTRAP ENTERPRISES, HACKNEY & MACFARLANE R (1989): Economic Development on Housing Estates. Priority Estates Project, London

CHANDLER J A & LAWLESS P (1985): Local Authorities and the Creation of Jobs. Gower, Aldershot

COMMISSION FOR RACIAL EQUALITY (undated): Learning in Terror. A Survey of Racial Harassment in Schools and Colleges. London

DEPARTMENT OF THE ENVIRONMENT (1990): Getting People into Jobs. Good Practice in Urban Regeneration. HMSO

DEPARTMENT OF HEALTH & SOCIAL SECURITY (1988): Strategies for Accident Prevention. HMSO

GIFFORD, LORD (1986): The Broadwater Farm Inquiry Report. Kana Press, London

GOSSOP M & GRANT M (eds) (1990): Preventing and Controlling Drug Abuse. World Health Organisation, Geneva. HMSO

GRIFFITHS SIR R (1988): Community Care. Agenda for Action HMSO

HAMBLETON R & HOGGETT P (undated): The Politics of Decentralisation: Theory and Practice of a Radical Local Government Initiative. Working Paper 46, University of Bristol, School for Advanced Urban Studies

HAUGHTON G (1990): Targeting Jobs to Local People. The British Urban Policy Experience. Urban Studies, vol 2 No 2

HOUGH M & MAYHEW P (eds) (1982): Crime & Public Housing. Home Office, Research & Planning Unit, Paper 6

LONDON BOROUGH OF ISLINGTON (1987): Putting Islington back to work. Press, Campaign and Publicity Unit.

LOCAL GOVERNMENT TRAINING BOARD (1987): Getting closer to the public. Parts 1 to 3. Luton

LONDON VOLUNTARY SERVICE COUNCIL (1988): Education in Inner London: ensuring a service to the whole community. London

MUNRO M & SMITH S J (1989): Gender & Housing – Broadening the Debate. Housing Studies, January

MCARTHUR A A (ed) (1989): Community Economic Initiatives in Public Sector Housing Estates. Glasgow University Training and Employment Research Unit

MCENERY M (1989): Bootstrap Enterprises: 10 Years of Employment Initiatives. Calouste Gulbenkian Foundation

NACRO (1989): Growing Up on Housing Estates. London

—— (1989): Crime Prevention & Community Safety. A Practical Guide for Local Authorities

POWER A (1988): Working Paper on Small-Scale Employment Creation on Unpopular Estates. Priority Estates Project, London

SAFE NEIGHBOURHOODS ADVISORY SERVICE (1989): Safe Communities 1989 – Local Government Action on Crime Prevention and Community Safety

SCARMAN, LORD (1986): The Scarman Report – the Brixton Disorders. Pelican Books, Harmondsworth

SCOTTISH OFFICE (1989): Strategy for the Regeneration of Ferguslie Park

SHELTER (1984): Some Public Health Aspects of the Effects of Defects in Houses. London

TINKER A (1984): Staying at Home. Helping Elderly People. DoE

TODD G (1986): Job Creation in the UK: A National Survey of Local Models. The Economist Publication, Special Report 1075

TUROK I & WANNOP U (1990): Targeting Urban Employment Initiatives. Department of the Environment. HMSO

WORLD HEALTH ORGANISATION (1989): Health Principles of Housing. HMSO

ZULAUF M (1989): Women and Children. A Survey of Existing Service Provision and Unmet Needs on PEP Estates. Working Paper Priority Estates Project, London

Part 5
The Law

XI. Legal Aspects of Estate Management

Caroline Hunter

Contents

"You have two ears and one mouth –
Use them in that proportion"

1. INTRODUCTION

The legal control of housing management comes from two sources. First, there is much statutory control over local housing authorities. The meaning of some of these statutes and the secondary legislation, such as statutory instruments and directives derived from them, has been further interpreted by the courts and can be found in various cases. Secondly, the courts have developed the law independently through cases. This latter is generally known as the common law. In this chapter we present a brief introduction to law as it affects housing management. According to legal custom, we illustrate specific points by reference to particular cases. Each section of the book is discussed briefly in relation to the law, with relevant sections of Acts of Parliaments and secondary legislation spelt out. The law stated is up-to-date to August 1990.

The statutory control of authorities covers many aspects of housing management: from the imposition of statutory repairing covenants, to obligations to consult with tenants, to control over capital funding and tendering procedures for works programmes. While it is not necessary for estate staff to have detailed knowledge of all the law, they should be aware that there is nearly always a legal aspect to their work and decision making, and they may often need good legal support from central legal services where necessary.

A local authority cannot act unless it has specific power to do so. Most of the powers exercised by an authority in relation to its housing stock are to be found in Part II of the Housing Act 1985 which contains, e.g. in section 9, the power to provide accommodation and to improve and repair that accommodation, and in section 21 the general powers to manage that accommodation. Section 111 of the Local Government Act 1972 empowers authorities to do anything "which is calculated to facilitate, or is conducive or incidental to the discharge of any of their functions".

The Housing Act 1985 also controls the relationship between the authority and its tenants. Part IV of the Act creates the secure tenant, giving such tenants certain rights, e.g. to sublet with consent, to take in lodgers, to carry out repairs and improvements and to be consulted. It also limits the right of the authority to gain possession, except on the grounds prescribed in Schedule 2 of the Act and subject to service of a notice of seeking possession.

Much of the law relating to housing management gives local authorities **power** to carry out certain functions, without regulating closely **how** they should carry them out. The courts are therefore reluctant to interfere with the exercise of their powers by authorities. It should be remembered, however, that in all decision making by an authority, whether at councillor level or through a local housing management office, the authority must not act "unreasonably" (Associated Provincial Picture Houses v. Wednesbury Corporation, 1948). This does not provide too narrow a constraint, however, since it is only unreasonableness which "verges on an absurdity" that is outside the ambit of local authority power (R. Secretary of State for the Environment, ex p. Nottinghamshire County Council, 1986).

Although not strictly speaking a "legal" remedy, where tenants or others coming into contact with a local authority are unhappy with the conduct of the authority, they may complain to the Local Commissioner (ombudsman) appointed under the Local Government Act 1974. The ombudsman may investigate injustice in consequence of maladministration. While authorities must consider any report of the ombudsman, and the authority may make a payment or provide some other benefit where a person is found to have suffered injustice as a consequence, there is no statutory remedy if an authority chose not to take any action. The authority may be required to publish their reasons for inaction (Local Government Act 1974, s.31, as amended by the Local Government and Housing Act 1989, s.26).

2. THE LOCAL OFFICE AND STAFF

Office safety

There is a common law duty on an employer to provide a safe system of work and safe plant and equipment. Under the Health and Safety at Work etc. Act 1974, S.2 there is a general duty upon all employers to ensure so far as is reasonably practicable, the health, safety and welfare at work of all employees. Specific statutory duties are to be found in the Offices, Shops and Railway Premises Act 1963. These include by section 16 the provision of safe floors, passages and stairs and by section 9 the provision of suitable and sufficient sanitary conveniences.

It is not only staff whose safety must be considered. Where the public are to be admitted to the office the authority is under a duty to take such care as in all the circumstances of the case is reasonable to see that the visitor will be reasonably safe in using the premises for the purpose for which s/he is invited or permitted by the occupier to be there: Occupiers Liability Act 1957. Special care must be taken with children since the law does not expect them to be as careful as adults.

Staff

Local authorities are empowered to employ staff by the Local Government Act 1972, s.112. There is an enormous amount of legislation controlling the employment of staff. It is not possible to consider it here. But staffing and employment issues should be carefully handled with proper advice relating to: terms and conditions; sickness and other leave; discipline;

performance; union membership; and termination of contract etc.

Violence against staff

If any act of violence is committed against any member of staff, the perpetrator will almost undoubtedly be committing a criminal offence e.g. of assault. If the police refuse to commence a prosecution in these circumstances, the member of staff involved could take out a private prosecution. If the authority wish to assist the member of staff, e.g. by providing financial or legal assistance, they could do so under the Local Government Act 1972, s.111, if they conclude it would facilitate the discharge of their functions. The perpetrator may well also commit a civil tort as well as a crime. Again the authority may seek to assist a member of staff to obtain damages against a perpetrator, or an injunction banning them from the office. They might also consider obtaining an injunction in their own right under section 222 of the Local Government Act 1972, if they consider it expedient for the promotion or protection of the interests of the inhabitants of their area.

3. CONSULTATION WITH TENANTS

The Housing Act 1985, section 105

The main consultation provision is contained in this section. It obliges authorities to maintain appropriate arrangements to inform tenants of matters of housing management which substantially affect them and for the tenants to make their views on those matters known to the authority. Before making any decision on the matter, the authority must consider any representations made to it in accordance with those arrangements. It is up to the authority to decide what arrangements are appropriate, and there is no reason why different forms of consultation should not be adopted dependent on the type of matter and the number of tenants to be consulted.

A matter of housing management is defined as one which in the opinion of the authority relates to "(a) the management, maintenance, improvement or demolition of dwelling-houses let by the authority under secure tenancies or (b) the provision of services or amenities in connection with such dwelling-houses" (section 105(2)). It does not apply to rents or charges for services or facilities.

The section only applies to matters of housing management which in the opinion of the authority represent: "(a) a new programme of maintenance, improvement or demolition or (b) a change in the practice or policy of the authority, and are likely substantially to affect either its secure tenants as a whole or a group of them which form a distinct social group or occupy dwelling-houses which constitute a distinct class (whether by reference to the kind of dwelling-house, or the housing estate or other large area in which they are situated" (section 105(3)).

It has been held that this means that an authority does **not** have to consult where they decide not to go ahead with a particular scheme under consideration, nor do they have to consult when taking "in

principle" decisions, only where there is a real question of implementation (Short v. London Borough of Tower Hamlets, 1985).

Details of the arrangements for consultation must be published by the authority (section 105(5)).

Housing Act 1985, sections 27 and 27A

Where an authority and the residents want to go much further than mere consultation, the whole management of the estate can be delegated to a tenant management co-operative or an Estate Management Board. This can be done under the Housing Act 1985, s.27, which permits the authority's management functions to be exercised by an agent. The agent does not have to be a management co-operative or Estate Management Board, and could be a private management company. This can only be done subject to the approval of the Secretary of State, and to consultation with the tenants.

The consultation provisions in section 105 do not apply when the proposal is to set up a management co-operative or an Estate Management Board. In those circumstances consultation must comply with section 27A of the 1985 Act. The authority must write to every tenant affected by the proposal, informing them of: (a) such details as the authority considers appropriate, including the identity of the new manager; (b) the likely consequences of the agreement for the tenant; and (c) the effect of the provisions of section 27A.

Further the tenant must be informed of the right within a reasonable period, specified in the notice, to make any representations to the authority. The authority must consider any representations made to them within that period. They must then serve a further notice informing the tenant of any significant changes to the proposal and that s/he may within a reasonable period (which must be at least 28 days) communicate his/her objection to the proposal. The Secretary of State may not give his approval "if it appears to him that a majority of the tenants of the houses to which the agreement relates do not wish the proposal to proceed" (section 27A(5)).

Once the delegation has taken place, further consultation in relation to individual lettings is not required.

4. AN ESTATE BUDGET

Local Government and Housing Act 1989

Section 75 requires a local housing authority to keep a Housing Revenue Account. Schedule 4 of that Act details how the account must be kept, and what items are to be debited and credited to the account. The Act, which came into force on April 1, 1990, places much stricter controls than its predecessor, the Housing Act 1985, on the keeping of the Housing Revenue Account. In January and February each year the authority will have to produce a budget for the Housing Revenue Account for the year beginning on the following April 1. The budget must secure that the account does not show a debit: Local Government and Housing Act 1989, s.76. This budget will have to include proposals as to the level of rents and the expenditure for the year in respect of repair, maintenance, supervision and management of the authority's housing. The authority is obliged to implement these proposals, and keep the budget under review, and revise the proposals as far as practicable if a deficit looks likely to occur. An authority is not allowed to make up deficits from other council funds (Local Government and Housing Act 1989, Schedule 4).

Within this system of control there is no statutory control over the operation of a local budget, although it must of course fit into this overall legal framework. The local budget will have to be allocated from the Housing Revenue Account.

5. LETTINGS/TRANSFERS

The Housing Act 1985

By section 22, a local housing authority must "secure that in the selection of their tenants a reasonable preference is given to:

(a) persons occupying insanitary or overcrowded houses;

(b) persons having large families;

(c) persons living under unsatisfactory housing conditions; and

(d) persons towards whom the authority are subject to a duty under section 65 or 68 (persons found to be homeless)".

This duty is only to give a "reasonable preference" to such people and does not lay down **how much** preference should be given. However, any selection scheme must in some way reflect these priorities. If a waiting list is operated, it must not be operated so rigidly as to fetter an authority's discretion in a particular case. There must always be room within the system to consider the needs of a particular case (R. v. Canterbury City Council, ex p. Gillespie, 1986). On the other hand if there is a waiting list in operation it must not be departed from for irrelevant reasons (R. v. Port Talbot D.C., ex p. Jones, 1987, where the needs of the applicant as a councillor erroneously led to an allocation to which the applicant would not otherwise have been entitled).

Section 106 requires an authority:

(a) to maintain a set or rules for determining priority between applicants in the allocation of its housing accommodation, and to publish a summary of those rules;

(b) to maintain a set of rules governing cases where tenants wish to move (whether or not by way of exchange) to other dwelling-houses let by the authority or another body (e.g. another authority or a housing association) and to publish a summary of those rules;

(c) to maintain a set of rules governing the procedure to be followed in allocating its housing accommodation;

(d) to make available for inspection, without charge, a copy of all these rules at the authority's principal office;

(e) to provide to the public copies of the summaries without charge and copies of the full rules on payment of a reasonable fee;

(f) to allow applicants for housing to have access, without charge, to those details which they have provided to the authority, which the authority has recorded as being relevant to the application.

Access to Information Act 1987

Under this Act applicants for tenancies and tenants have a right to access to personal information held about them or their families. Applications have to be made in writing and a fee not exceeding £10 can be demanded. The authority must tell the applicant whether it holds any such information and give him/her access to it, and in certain circumstances supply copies. Provision is made for inaccurate information, or expressions of opinion based or apparently based on inaccurate information, to be corrected or erased.

Data Protection Act 1984

If records are computerised local authorities must register under this Act, and applicants and tenants have the right to access to information held about them on computer.

The Sex Discrimination Act 1975

By section 30 it is unlawful for a person (including a local authority) to discriminate against a woman in relation to:

(a) the terms on which premises are offered;

(b) refusing an application for premises; and

(c) the treatment of her in relation to any waiting list for premises.

Discrimination may be direct or indirect (section 1). Indirect discrimination occurs where a person applies a requirement or condition to a woman which is equally applied to men, but which is discriminatory in its effect because a smaller proportion of women can comply with it than men, and which that person cannot show to be a requirement or condition justifiable irrespective of sex and which in fact causes detriment because women cannot comply with it. Such discrimination could occur e.g. where authorities apply punitive policies against unmarried mothers.

Race Relations Act 1976

By section 21 it is unlawful for a person (including a local authority) to discriminate on racial grounds against another in relation to:

(a) the terms on which premises are offered;

(b) refusing an application for premises; and,

(c) the treatment of her in relation to any waiting list for premises.

Discrimination may be direct or indirect (section 1). Indirect discrimination occurs where a person applies a requirement or condition to persons of a racial group which is equally applied to other persons, but which is discriminatory in its effect because a smaller proportion of the racial group can comply with it than others, and which that person cannot show to be a requirement or condition justifiable irrespective of race and which in fact causes detriment because people of the racial group cannot comply with it. Direct discrimination may occur in trying to achieve an ethnic balance on an estate. (However, local authorities may expand housing opportunities for racial groups that may have suffered discrimination, thereby creating a greater "ethnic balance" on estates, see section on lettings above). Indirect discrimination may occur in operating a waiting list policy which favours local residents or requiring an applicant e.g. to have his/her family resident in this country before registering them on a waiting list.

Further guidance on eliminating discrimination in rented housing and promoting equality of opportunity may be obtained from the code of practice issued by the Commission for Racial Equality under section 47. The code is admissable as evidence in any court proceedings for breach of section 21.

The homeless

Local authorities' duties towards the homeless are contained in the Housing Act 1985, Part III. Where an applicant is found to be homeless, in priority need, and not intentionally homeless the duty of the authority is "to secure that accommodation is made available" for him/her, section 65. That accommodation must be "suitable", section 69. There are four groups in priority need: households with dependent children; pregnant women; the vulnerable, including the old and sick; and those made homeless by a disaster such as fire or flood, section 59.

Squatters

Squatters can nearly always be evicted quickly and easily through the county court using the summary procedure in Order 24 of the County Court Rules 1981. This requires an efficient system, for filing proceedings, affidavits, etc. usually organised through the authority's legal department. Under the Criminal Law Act 1977 squatting may also be a criminal offence, where there is a protected intending occupier of the premises who is excluded from the premises by the squatter.

6. RACE AND HOUSING

There is a general duty imposed on local authorities to "make appropriate arrangements with a view to securing that their various functions are carried out with due regard to the need: (a) to eliminate unlawful racial discrimination; and (b) to promote equality of opportunity and good relations between persons of different racial groups": Race Relations Act 1976, s.71. This therefore should be a factor considered by all authorities when drawing up their housing policy and practice.

As well as outlawing direct and indirect racial discrimination in lettings (see above) the Race Relations Act 1976 also outlaws racial discrimination in employment. By section 4 it is unlawful for an authority to discriminate in the recruitment, promotion, transfer or training of staff, in the way staff are offered access to benefits, facilities or services, and by dismissing staff or subjecting them to any other detriment. There is a large body of case law which has developed on the subject of discrimination in employment which it is not possible to detail here. Some positive action may be adopted in recruitment without unlawfully discriminating, where the job provides personal services to persons of a racial group and those services can most effectively be provided by a person of that racial group. This provision may for example be used to recruit housing workers with foreign language abilities to provide advice for tenants who cannot communicate effectively in English (see also section on training, below). Positive action may also be taken where minority groups are under-represented in particular areas or in levels of the workforce by, for example, providing specific training for particular groups or encouraging particular groups to apply for jobs. Funding for staff for minority racial and ethnic communities employed by local authorities to work on issues relating to their particular communities may be available from the Home Office under the Local Government Act 1966, s.11.

Authorities may wish to promote local organisations and community groups which represent particular ethnic minorities in their area, e.g. by grants under the Local Government Act 1972, s.137 or the provision of premises and may do this on a discretionary basis. In addition under the Local Government (Goods and Services) Act 1970 authorities may enter into agreements with Community Relations Council and "community associations" for the supply of goods and materials, the provision of administrative, professional or technical services, the carrying out of maintenance in connection with land and buildings, and providing a driver where a vehicle is also provided to the organisation by the authority.

Racial harassment

Many authorities now include a clause in their tenancy agreements requiring the tenant and those residing in the dwelling-house not to commit any act of racial harassment or abuse. If this clause is then broken there is a discretionary ground for possession under Ground 1 of Schedule 2 of the Housing Act 1985. Even if there is no such clause some behaviour, such as making noise, spraying graffiti may be such as to be a ground for possession under Ground 2, i.e. conduct which is a nuisance or annoyance to neighbours.

Where no racial harassment clause is contained in current tenancy agreements these can be amended to include them by service of a notice of variation on the tenant in accordance with section 103 of the Housing Act 1985. First a preliminary notice of variation must be served, detailing the variation and inviting comments from the tenant. Once these comments are considered, the authority must then serve a notice of variation of at least four weeks duration.

Local authorities may also prosecute perpetrators of racial harassment for criminal conduct such as graffiti, damaged doors and windows, under the Local Government Act 1972, s.222, where the authority considers it expedient for the promotion or protection of the interests of the inhabitants of their area.

7. NEIGHBOUR DISPUTES

Where one tenant is causing disruption to those around through his/her anti-social behaviour the authority have a ground for possession under Ground 2, Schedule 2, of the Housing Act 1985, if the behaviour is a nuisance or annoyance to neighbours. It is also often a term of the tenancy agreement that the tenant does not commit such acts. The authority may seek to enforce this term by an injunction from the court, rather than a possession order.

In many neighbour disputes however, it is not one tenant disturbing those around him/her, but rather a dispute between two particular tenants, who have fallen out. In these circumstances it may be very difficult to attach "blame", and it may be inappropriate for the authority to step in and take action against one of the tenants, thus seemingly taking "sides" in the dispute. In these circumstances the tenants can take their own individual action at civil law, preventing e.g. nuisance, or assault by the other. The most appropriate action by the authority may not be legal, but management action e.g. to rehouse the tenants apart from one another.

8. RENT, ARREARS AND HOUSING BENEFITS

Rent levels

Housing Act 1985 By section 24 local authorities "may make such reasonable charges as they may determine for the tenancy or occupation of their houses". They must also from time to time review their rents. This discretion has been very widely interpreted by the courts which have been very reluctant to interfere with local authority rent levels (see e.g. Belcher v. Reading Corporation, 1950 and Luby v. Newcastle-under-Lyme Corporation, 1964).

Local Government and Housing Act 1989 This amends section 24 of the Housing Act 1985, so that in setting their rent levels authorities are now required to have regard to the principle that the rent of one particular class or description of houses should bear broadly the same proportion to private sector rents as any other class or description of houses. Thus if semi-detached houses are more expensive on the private rented market than flats, their rents should be proportionately more within the local authority structure. Similarly different size properties will require different levels of rent. Rent levels will also be affected by the new budgeting exercise for the Housing Revenue Account, since rents are likely to have to rise in order that the Housing Revenue Account does not incur any deficit.

Increasing rents

Housing Act 1985 Unless an increase in rent is agreed between the landlord and tenant, rent can only be increased by the service of a notice on the tenant: s.102. The notice must be of at least four weeks' length: s.103. As the level of rent is at the discretion of the authority, the tenants cannot "force" a rent increase in order to provide for better services.

Rent collection and arrears

Rent is owed by the tenant to the authority under the terms of the tenancy. A tenancy agreement is a contract and on any failure to pay the rent the authority can sue for the arrears. The method of rent collection is a matter for the local authority, although unless it is a term of the tenancy agreement that rent is to be paid in a certain way, the local authority cannot insist on a particular form of payment.

Housing Act 1985 Rent arrears are a discretionary ground for possession under section 84 and Schedule 2, Part I, Ground 1. A court will often make a suspended order for possession of the dwelling on the condition that the tenant pays off the arrears at a certain rate. If the condition is broken the authority is entitled to immediate possession (Thompson v. Elmbridge Borough Council, 1987).

Alternatively if the authority does not wish to issue possession proceedings they may issue a rent action under the County Court Rules 1981, Order 24, Part II, p.8. This is a fairly simple legal action and quicker than a full possession hearing. Where the tenant is working, enforcement of the debt can be achieved by an attachment of earnings under the Attachment of Earnings Act 1971.

Finally, outstanding rent can be recovered by the use of distress, i.e. the seizure of goods and chattels found upon premises in respect of which the rent is due. Certain amounts of bedding and clothing may not be taken. This has been described as an archaic remedy and should not be necessary where rent collection and arrears are properly managed. However, certain housing organisations use it as an effective threat, thereby preventing resort to eviction in most cases.

Housing benefits

The Housing Benefit Regulations are made under the powers in the Social Security Act 1986. The current regulations are to be found in Statutory Instrument 1987 No. 1971, as amended. Housing benefit is paid towards rent. Rebates for Community Charge are dealt with under separate regulations. Eligibility is dependent on the income of the applicant and his/her spouse. Those on income support receive all of their rent. Those not on income support have eligibility determined by assessing their income against their needs requirements. The formulae for such calculations are very complicated. By regulation 76(3) an authority must determine a claim for housing benefit within 14 days of receiving all the necessary information, or as soon as reasonably practicable thereafter.

9. THE REPAIRS SERVICE

Repairing obligations

An authority's obligation to repair a property is a matter of contract between the authority and the tenant. The obligations can be set out specifically in the tenancy agreement, and can be as extensive as the authority wishes. Statute imposes a minimum obligation, which cannot be contracted out of, but there is no reason why a greater obligation should not be taken on by the authority, for example setting specific times for carrying out certain types of repairs, which if not met entitle the tenant to compensation. The Housing Act 1985, section 104 obliges authorities to publish and provide all secure tenants with information about the provisions of sections 11 to 16 of the Landlord and Tenant Act 1985.

Landlord and Tenant Act 1985 Section 11 of the Act contains the major repairing covenant imposed upon landlords of tenants with leases of less than seven years, which includes weekly and monthly tenants. The obligation is:

(1) to keep in repair the structure and exterior of the dwelling, including drains, gutters and external pipes;

(2) to keep in repair and proper working order the installation in the dwelling for the supply of water, gas and electricity and for sanitation, including basins, sinks, baths, and sanitary conveniences, but not other fixtures, fittings and appliances for making use of the supply of water, gas or electricity;

(3) to keep in repair and proper working order the installations in the dwelling-house for space heating and heating water.

There has been a considerable amount of litigation concerning the extent of the covenant and in particular the meaning of the word "repair". The covenant can oblige an authority to carry out works to correct inherent design defects in a dwelling, but only where these are causing disrepair to the structure and exterior of the dwelling (Quick v. Taff, Ely Borough Council, 1986). In the Quick case design defects were causing extensive condensation in the dwelling, however there was no actual damage to the structure or exterior, simply extensive mould growth. It was held that the state of the property did not mean that the authority were in breach of the covenant to keep the structure and exterior in repair.

Another limitation on section 11 has been that it did not apply to the common parts which the tenant used in getting to and from flats. This has now been dealt with by an amendment to section 11, which applies the repairing covenants to other parts of the building, if the defect is such as to affect the tenant's enjoyment of his/her dwelling or is of common parts which s/he is entitled to use. The new obligation only applies to tenancies granted on or after January 15, 1989, the date on which the amendments came into force. If it does not apply there may still be a term implied at common law to maintain the common parts in reasonable conditions, where these are required for access (Irwin v. Liverpool City Council, 1977).

No obligation arises under section 11 until the authority has notice of the disrepair (O'Brien v. Robinson, 1973), but the notice does not have to come directly from the tenant (McGreal v. Wake, 1984). The obligation in section 11 cannot be contracted out of, except under the county court order or under the "right to repair" provisions of the Housing Act 1985: section 12.

Defective Premises Act 1972 Section 4 of this Act adds a further liability upon landlords who are under an obligation to maintain or repair the premises. Where such an obligation exists "the landlord owes to all persons who might reasonably be expected to be affected by defects in the state of the premises a duty to take such care as is reasonable in all the circumstances to see that they are reasonably safe from personal injury or from damage to their property caused by a defect arising from the landlord's failure to repair". Thus if due to the landlord's failure to repair, a ceiling collapses the landlord would be liable under this section for any injury or damage to property of the tenant and his/her family, and their visitors.

Housing Act 1985, section 96 The obligation of a landlord under section 11 of the Landlord and Tenant Act 1985 is suspended if a tenant undertakes repairs under the "right to repair" scheme set up in accordance with this section. Secure tenants are given the right to carry out repairs and recover the cost from the authority. Repairs to the structure and exterior of flats are excluded, and the landlord may refuse to consent to works of a value over £200. The procedure for applying to use the right to repair is a complicated one set out in SI 1985 No. 1493, involving notices to be served by the tenant and the authority. It has only rarely been used since it was introduced.

Public Health Act 1936, Part III Although this part of the Act is generally concerned with the powers of local authorities to take action against others who may be causing a statutory nuisance, authorities may themselves be prosecuted for causing a statutory nuisance, by a person aggrieved by the nuisance: section 99. This has often proved an important avenue for tenants to force authorities to carry out works which they may not be required to do under the repairing covenant for the dwelling. Thus while a property suffering from condensation because of poor design, may not be in disrepair, it may well be a statutory nuisance and action can be taken under this section to improve the thermal insulation and/or heating to the dwelling. A statutory nuisance arises if premises are "prejudicial to health or a nuisance": section 92(1).

The carrying out of repairs, maintenance and capital works

Access Section 11(6) of the Landlord and Tenant Act 1985 gives the landlord or his agent the right to enter the dwelling for the purpose of viewing its condition and state of repair at all reasonable times, providing that 24 hours' written notice has been given. Works must be carried out in such a way as to not disturb the tenant's quiet enjoyment of the property. If works cannot be carried out with the tenant in the property, and the tenant refuses to move voluntarily it is a ground for possession under Schedule 2, Ground 10 of the Housing Act 1985, that the landlord intends, within a reasonable time, to demolish or reconstruct the building or carry out work to it and cannot reasonably do so without obtaining possession. The authority must provide suitable alternative accommodation for the tenant.

The standard of work Section 1 of the Defective Premises Act 1972 obliges authorities to ensure that any work carried out in connection with the erection, conversion or enlargement of a dwelling is done in a professional manner, with proper materials and so that the dwelling will be fit for habitation when completed. This obligation is owed to those with a legal or equitable interest in the dwelling, such as tenants, but not to others such as children or visitors.

Direct labour organisations The use of direct labour organisations is controlled by the Local Government Planning and Land Act 1980, Part III. All works of new construction of a value over £50,000 and works of maintenance of a value over £10,000 must be competed for by the DLO by tender with other private contractors: section 9, 1980 Act, and see SI 1983 No. 685 as amended. The Secretary of State also has powers in certain circumstances to stop DLOs carrying out certain types of work e.g. if the DLO fails to make a sufficient rate of return on their capital. The rules relating to the calculation of the £10,000 works of maintenance limit, prevent contracts being broken up into smaller ones to come in below the limit where the works can be carried out "most efficiently and economically under once arrangement", see SI 1983, No. 685, reg. 2, and also reg. 9. The statutes regulating DLOs are extremely complex (see useful books at end of chapter). Strictly speaking, the relationship between the DLO and the client department is not a contractual relationship, in the sense that the housing department could sue the DLO. At the end of the day they are the same legal entity. But it is good practice for the department to treat the relationship in the same manner, and the accounts of each to be drawn up accordingly, so that e.g. losses due to housing's failure to give possession of buildings are put down to the housing department, whereas delays and inadequate workmanship etc. are put down to the DLO accounts.

The use of outside contractors Part II of the Local Government Act 1988 prevents authorities from introducing matters into the contractual process with outside contractors who are to carry out works for the authority, which are non-commercial, e.g. requirements as to conditions of employment of staff, or of non-involvement in countries such as South Africa. This prevents an authority from requiring the contractor to employ local labour. This prohibition runs from the stage of drawing up lists of approved contractors to the granting of contracts, see section 17 of the 1988 Act.

There is an exception, however, where the authority is seeking compliance with the Race Relations Act 1976, section 71. This section requires authorities to have regard to the need to eliminate unlawful racial discrimination and to promote equality of opportunity and good relations between different racial groups. The 1988 Act specifically provides that section 17 does not preclude an authority from asking approved questions seeking information or undertakings relating to workforce matters and considering the responses to them, or including in a draft contract or draft tender for a contract, terms or provisions relating to workforce matters and considering the responses to them, if such is reasonably necessary to secure compliance with section 71 of the 1976 Act.

Capital financing

The financing of capital works cannot be separated from the very complicated legal structures of general local government finance. These place strict controls on both capital and revenue expenditure of authorities. It is not possible here to give anything more than the briefest outline of the system.

Capital expenditure and its financing are now controlled by the Local Government and Housing Act 1989, Part IV. Unless within an authority's credit approval (i.e. the amount approved by the Secretary of State for borrowing purposes) any expenditure, including capital expenditure must be charged to a revenue account.

Borrowing itself must be by one of the methods approved by the Act. Thus unless the capital expenditure is funded other than by borrowing, e.g. from capital receipts or from revenue, it must fall within these controls, i.e. be taken from the credit approval and by an approved method of borrowing.

Where related to dwelling within the Housing Revenue Account, expenditure on capital works (in the main represented by the cost of borrowing), and on maintenance and repairs must be charged to the Housing Revenue Account, maintained in accordance with the Local Government and Housing Act 1989 Part VI, section 75 and Schedule 4. Thus the cost of financing works will have to be met by those amounts credited to the account. The main elements of this are the rents paid by the tenants and Housing Revenue Account subsidy, received from the government.

Housing Revenue Account subsidy is payable by the Secretary of State under the Local Government and Housing Act 1989, section 80. This lays down no rules as to how it is to be calculated, but the Department of the Environment have indicated that it will be calculated "to make good the deficit which would arise in the HRA, if the housing were managed with reasonable efficiency" (DoE Consultation Paper, New Financial Regime for Local Authority Housing in England and Wales, p.8.) It has also been indicated that this will take into account actual changes in loan charges.

10. CARETAKING

There is no legal requirement to provide a caretaker as such. However, where the tenancy agreement provides that the authority will keep common parts clean and tidy the tenant may enforce the agreement through the courts and receive damages for any failure to do so. Furthermore even if there is no specific term in the tenancy agreement, the courts have implied a term that means of access to dwellings and waste disposal must be kept in a reasonable condition (Irwin v. Liverpool City Council, 1977).

Under the Control of Pollution Act 1974 a local authority is under a duty "to arrange the collection of all household waste in their area", except in certain isolated and inaccessible places. Under section 13 of the 1974 Act the authority may require the waste to be placed in a specified type of receptacle. It is a criminal offence not to comply with such a requirement.

If tenants fail to dispose of their rubbish properly or if they or residents in their house e.g. their children, vandalise, spray graffiti on common parts or the like, then they may be guilty of conduct which is a nuisance or annoyance to neighbours. In such a case the authority has a discretionary ground for possession under Ground 2, Schedule 2, of the Housing Act 1985.

Dropping litter in an open place is an offence under the Litter Act 1983 for which a local authority may prosecute. It is also an offence under the Control of

Pollution Act 1974, s.3 to dump household waste on any land.

Tendering for cleaning work

Under the Local Government Act 1988, Part I, some cleaning and caretaking work by local authorities must be put out to tender. This includes the cleaning of the interior of buildings, of windows (unless they are windows of a dwelling), the removal of litter from any land and the emptying of litter bins, Local Government Act 1988, section 2 and Schedule 1. The authority may itself tender for the work, but cannot award it to itself unless the tendering procedure has been complied with.

Where cleaning tasks are carried out by caretakers, even such work will have to be put out to tender unless the caretaker spends a greater part of his/her work doing other activities, e.g. security work or maintenance of boilers, which do not fall within the specified categories, Local Government Act 1988, s.2(6).

11. TRAINING

In order to provide staff with a safe system of work (see office safety, above) it may be necessary for the authority to provide training, particularly with regard to use of computers and other equipment.

Race Relations Act 1976, s.35 This permits the provision of facilities or services to meet the special need of a particular racial group in regard to their education, training or welfare, or any ancillary benefits.

12. MONITORING AND EVALUATION

There is now a specific legal requirement to measure performance (Local Government and Housing Act 1989, s.16), which requires a report to be made to the authority's tenants and the Secretary of State. In any event a local authority can only be confident that they are fulfilling their statutory obligations if they know **what** their performance is, if they establish targets and criteria against which to measure performance and if they have information with which to respond to tenants' inquiries. Legal enforcement in relation to housing management is difficult because information on standards and performance is incomplete and imprecise.

13. CO-ORDINATION AND LIAISON

There are no specific legal aspects to this.

14. SOME USEFUL BOOKS ON THE LEGAL ASPECTS OF ESTATE MANAGEMENT

ENCYCLOPEDIA OF HOUSING LAW AND PRACTICE, The Local Government Library, Sweet and Maxwell, contains most of the relevant legislation with annotations.

HOUSING LAW, A. Arden and M. Partington, Sweet and Maxwell (with 2nd Supplement, 1986). this is the most comprehensive book on housing law, but is now rather out of date. A second edition is due out in 1991.

PUBLIC HOUSING LAW, (1989) D. Hoath, Sweet and Maxwell, and **Manual of Housing Law** (4th Edition, 1989) A. Arden, Sweet and Maxwell, both provide useful short guides, which are easily read by non-lawyers.

CPAG'S HOUSING BENEFIT AND COMMUNITY CHARGE REBATE LEGISLATION, (3rd Revised Edition) contains the relevant legislation with a commentary.

ACTION ON RACIAL HARASSMENT, LEGAL REMEDIES AND LOCAL AUTHORITIES (1988), Legal Action Group and London Housing Unit, provides a comprehensive guide for local authorities to tackling racial harassment.

Conclusions

"We made the mistake of believing that scientific knowledge would enable us to solve all our human problems."

Sir Peter Medowar
after the Brixton disorders in 1981

Local authorities in Britain are elected bodies, responsible for implementing a wide range of national policies, for delivering many essential services to the communities or areas they represent and for developing local services in response to local needs. Because of the now very large area each local authority covers, they tend to be hierarchical, centrally organised office and paper-based organisations with many interlocking functions.

Decentralisation of local authority services in the 1980s represented a serious attempt by elected representatives to change the way local government was organised, the way people participated and the quality of service that was offered. But decentralisation of services is sometimes complex and cumbersome. Consequently, decentralisation does not always bring the benefits it promises. Other large organisations face similar problems when attempting to break up their operations into smaller units.

Meanwhile, estates often form discrete organisational and social entities quite separate from other parts of the local authority structure. Local housing management appears to work best if problems are looked at from the estate perspective – the bottom up – and if the local management organisation is developed "at the grass roots" or the "coal face". Many local authorities have found this as they have decentralised.

Central housing organisations can combine decentralisation from the top down with local initiative, flexible and varied solutions – the bottom-up – by adopting a simple decision-making structure for each local unit of organisation, by handing out as much autonomy as possible and by encouraging **local** involvement in uncovering **local** solutions which can be put into practice **locally** without having to take simple or day-to-day decisions back to the complex and remote centre.

This manual has emphatically adopted a bottom-up approach, which is developmental rather than schematic. In other words, the nature of the estate, the input of residents and staff, and surrounding factors such as the location, the nature of the central housing organisation and the size of the estate, all influence the shape of the project and its outcome. Drawing up a blueprint and imposing a package or formula on an estate are likely to be out of tune, particularly

on estates with a history of problems. There is no single successful approach to housing management.

Why then does the Priority Estates Project single-mindedly advocate local housing management with resident involvement? Is this not just another imposed solution? We have found that while situations and solutions vary greatly, two basic preconditions are widely supported by residents and housing staff alike. Without a local office and without the residents, we would not be able to start.

There is a long history of poor landlord–tenant relations in this country, particularly in low-income areas, which requires special effort to overcome. "Intensive housing management", a phrase which describes a localised and personal housing service, was coined in the wake of the reforming zeal of Octavia Hill and the Society of Women Housing Managers early this century (Darnley, 1990). The idea carried over into local authority slum clearance initiatives in the 1930s. But in the post-war public housing boom, it was largely regarded either as a luxurious extra or as outmoded paternalism, only needed in very special circumstances (see Macey & Baker, 1961, and Macey, 1982). However, intensive housing management made a fairly dramatic and welcome comeback in the late seventies and early eighties as problems mounted on council estates that were difficult to let and manage.

The landlord–tenant relationship places fundamental responsibilities on the landlord. For example, communal maintenance, repair and a tenant's right to peaceful enjoyment of the home. The tenant must also by law act in a responsible way towards the property, towards neighbours and towards the landlord. Someone has to broker that relationship and ensure that rented housing works within agreed boundaries. This is the local management and maintenance role which this manual tries to describe.

Although the idea is simple and popular, the practice is fraught with myriad difficulties. The poverty of many of the households, the layers of social, economic and management problems, the long neglect of repairs, the poor training of staff, the intense segregation and stigmatisation of some areas, are all indicators of a deep malaise that reaches far beyond the immediate boundaries of an estate or of housing management itself.

The problems in some areas seem overwhelming. Workable solutions can only be found if problems themselves are simplified. This brings us back to the bottom-up approach. A focus on action, on cutting out unnecessary layers of administration, on devising simple structures and systems, on adopting a creative, innovative and supportive management style, on immediate issues and reachable goals, shows quick benefits.

But basic resources, outside contacts, access to advice and skills are essential too. Therefore this manual has attempted to combine a highly localised method of housing management with a dynamic role for wider bodies, most essentially local authorities and housing associations, but also training and support organisations and the community at large. Residents themselves must be in partnership with the local management organisation.

Housing is an essential buttress of the economic and social organisation of any country. Managing such a valuable asset – 25 per cent of the nation's total wealth – must become an ever higher priority. For we will not rebuild on our scarce land either cheaply or quickly.

References

ARDEN, A. (1989): *Manual of housing law.* 4th Edition. Sweet and Maxwell, London.

BONNERJEA, LUCY (1987): The Future of Social Housing. Dept. of Social Science and Administration, London School of Economics Discussion Paper No. 1, April 1987. LSE, London.

BOOTSTRAP ENTERPRISES, HACKNEY and MACFARLANE, RICHARD (October 1989): Economic Development on Housing Estates. For Priority Estates Project, London.

BURBIDGE, MICHAEL *et al* (1981): *An investigation of difficult to let housing: Vol. 1: General findings; Vol. 2: Case studies of post-war housing; Vol. 3: Case studies of pre-war estates.* HMSO, London.

CHILD POVERTY ACTION GROUP (1990): *Guide to community charge.* CPAG, London.

CHILD POVERTY ACTION GROUP (1990): *National welfare rights handbook 1990/91.* CPAG, London.

COMMISSION FOR RACIAL EQUALITY: (1984): Race and Council Housing in Hackney – Report of a Formal Investigation. CRE, London.

COMMISSION FOR RACIAL EQUALITY (1988): Homelessness is Discrimination – Report of Investigation in Tower Hamlets. CRE, London.

DEPARTMENT OF THE ENVIRONMENT (1989; forthcoming): *Estate action handbook of estate improvement: Part 1: Appraising options; Part 2: External areas* (forthcoming); *Part 3: Dwellings (forthcoming).* HMSO, London.

DEPARTMENT OF THE ENVIRONMENT (1989): Nature and Effectiveness of Local Housing Management. Report to the DoE by the Centre for Housing Research, University of Glasgow. HMSO, London.

DEPARTMENT OF THE ENVIRONMENT (1989): *Tackling racial violence and harassment in local authority housing: a guide to good practice for local authorities.* DoE, London.

DEPARTMENT OF THE ENVIRONMENT (1989): *Tenants in the lead: the housing co-operatives review.* HMSO, London.

DOWNES, DAVID (ed.) (1989): *Crime and the city.* Macmillan, London.

DUNCAN, S. and KIRBY, K. (1984): *Preventing rent arrears.* HMSO, London.

ECONOMIST (17–23 March 1990): 'Economic Focus; European Unemployment – Swedish Lessons'. Aldbourne Associates, Marlborough.

ENSEMBLES, No. 6 (March 1990): 'Intégrer tous les enfants'. Délégation Interministérielle à la Ville, Paris.

FINKEL, A. (1989): Social Work within the Family Housing Association – justifiable expense or genuine benefit? Long Essay, London School of Economics, London.

FORREST, RAY and MURIE, ALAN (1984): Right to Buy? Issues of Need, Equity and Polarisation in the Sale of Council Houses. University of Bristol: School for Advanced Urban Studies, Bristol.

GREVE, JOHN and CURRIE, E. (1990): *Homelessness in Britain.* Joseph Rowntree Memorial Trust, York.

HENDERSON, J. and KARN, V. (1987): *Race, class and state housing: inequality and allocation of public housing in Britain.* Gower, Aldershot.

HILLS, JOHN (forthcoming): *Cat's Cradle.* Oxford University Press, Oxford.

HOPE, TIM and SHAW, M. (eds.) (1988): *Communities and crime reduction.* HMSO, London.

HOUGH, MIKE and MAYHEW, PATRICK (1983): The British Crime Survey, Home Office Research Study: 76. HMSO, London.

INSTITUTE OF HOUSING and TENANT PARTICIPATION ADVISORY SERVICE ENGLAND (1989): *Tenant participation in housing management.* IOH/TPAS, London/Salford.

JONES, T., MACLEAN, B. D., and YOUNG, K. (1986): Preliminary Report on Islington Crime Survey. Centre for Criminology and Police Studies, London.

KING, MARTIN LUTHER (1963): Why we can't wait? 'Letter from a Birmingham Jail'. Harper and Row, New York.

LSE HOUSING (1990): A Report to Bethnal Green Neighbourhood, L. B. Tower Hamlets, on Allocation Policies and Practices. LSE Housing, London.

McDONALD, ALAN (1986): *Weller Way – The Story of the Weller Street Housing Co-operative.* Faber & Faber, London.

MAX, GRAHAM DE (1988): Violence against Housing Staff with special reference to Sheffield MDC Housing Department. Long Essay, London School of Economics, LSE Housing, London.

PARKER, JOHN and BARRILEA (1989): Review of Housing Allocations for the London Borough of Ealing, May 1989. London Research Centre, London.

PARKER, JOHN and DUGMORE, KEITH (1976): Colour and the Allocation of GLC Housing. The Report of the GLC Lettings Survey 1974–75, Research Report 21. Greater London Council, London.

PETERS, T. J. (1987): *Thriving on chaos – a handbook for a management revolution.* Macmillan, London.

POWER, ANNE (19 April 1979): 'Council estates caught in a vicious racial spiral', *New Society,* London.

POWER, ANNE (1979): Facts and Figures about The Holloway Tenant Co-operative – A Survey of all rehoused members. Holloway Tenant Co-operative and the North Islington Housing Rights Project.

POWER, ANNE (April 1987): The PEP Guide to Local Housing Management, Vols. 1, 2 and 3. Priority Estates Project, London.

POWER, ANNE (1987): *Property before people – the management of twentieth-century council housing.* Unwin Hyman, Hemel Hempstead.

POWER, ANNE (9 December 1987): 'Reversing the spiral', *Architects Journal.* Architectural Press, London.

POWER, ANNE (November 1988): Under New Management – The experience of thirteen Islington Tenant Management Co-operatives. Priority Estates Project, London.

PRESCOTT-CLARKE, PATRICIA, ALLEN, PATRICK and MORRISSEY,

KATRIN (1988): *Queueing for housing: a study of council housing waiting lists.* HMSO, London.

PRIORITY ESTATES PROJECT (1986): Working Paper on PEP Household Survey Forms. Priority Estates Project, London.

PRIORITY ESTATES PROJECT (March 1988): Working Paper on Small-Scale Employment Creation on Unpopular Estates. Priority Estates Project, London.

PRIORITY ESTATES PROJECT (1990): Working Paper on Monitoring. Priority Estates Project, London.

READE, E. J. (1982): Residential decay, household movement and class structure, *Policy and Politics,* Vol. 10, No. 1, January. Sage Publications, London.

REYNOLDS, F. (1986): *The problem housing estate: an account of omega and its people.* Gower, London.

SCARMAN, LORD (1986): *The Scarman report – the Brixton disorders.* Pelican Books, Harmondsworth.

SHENTON, NEIL (1980): Deneside – a Council Estate. Papers in Community Studies No. 8, University of York, 1976, reprinted 1980.

WELSH OFFICE PRIORITY ESTATES PROJECT REPORT (1987). Welsh Office, Cardiff.

ZIPFEL, TRICIA (1989): Estate Management Boards – An Introduction. Priority Estates Project, London.

ZULAUF, MONIKA (1990): Women and Children on PEP Estates. Priority Estates Project, London.

Appendices

1. PEP estates providing examples and illustrations in the manual
2. Priority Estates Project publications list
3. Some useful organisations
4. Additional information relating to the sections of the manual:
   a) Code of practice for tenants' board and other organisations
   b) Tenant participation grants (section 16 grant regime)
   c) The role of the project co-ordinator
   d) Tenancy agreements
   e) Some useful sources on race and housing
   f) Additional tenant training information
   g) Co-ordination and development of other services – case study of Broadwater Farm
   h) Public sector contracts

APPENDIX 1: PEP ESTATES PROVIDING EXAMPLES AND ILLUSTRATIONS IN THE MANUAL

The Priority Estates Project is an independent non-profit-making organisation that works with local authorities and other housing organisations to set up locally-based, autonomous management on housing estates.

PEP was set up in 1979 by the Department of the Environment. Since then PEP has worked with 22 local authorities on 39 estates in England. Its aim has been to demonstrate that any area of rented housing can be made to work better with a full-time local management office, with committed staff in control of key functions and, more importantly, with the involvement and participation of the residents. The results are most dramatic on run-down, unpopular estates.

Abbey Park Estate
(Calderdale) West Bolton,
Illingworth, Halifax

320 dwellings
(non-traditional Wimpey 'no-fine' houses)

Back O' Th' Moss Estate
(Rochdale) Heywood
Rochdale

561 dwellings
(traditional brick-built houses)

Bacup Estate (Rossendale)
26–28 St James Street, Bacup,
Rossendale OL13 9NJ

1301 dwellings
(traditional cottage houses)

Barnfield Estate (Greenwich)
Barnfield Road,
London SE18

575 dwellings
(1930s/1940s traditional brick built flats)

Bloomsbury Estate
(Birmingham)
88 Bradburne Way, Nechells,
Birmingham B7 4PA

1153 dwellings
(1960s flatted estate)

Broadwater Farm Estate
(Haringey)
2–6 Tangmere, Willan Road
London N17

1063 dwellings
(1970s concrete, system-built estate of flats, tower blocks)

Chell Heath Estate
(Stoke-on-Trent)
90 Bishop Road,
Stoke-on-Trent

810 dwellings
(early post-war brick-built and a few BISF-system-built houses)

Cloverhall Estate (Rochdale)
14 Farm Walk,
Rochdale OL16 2TN

236 dwellings
(traditional brick-built houses and a few Wimpey 'no-fines')

Danes Estate
(Kingston Upon Hull)
Dibsdane, Orchard Park,
Hull

976 dwellings
(Wimpey 'no-fine' houses and tower blocks)

Digmoor Estate (Skelmersdale)
West Lancs D.C., 158 Birkrig
Digmoor Shopping Parade,
Skelmersdale, West Lancs.

973 dwellings
('Reema' panel pre-cast concrete and brick-built houses)

Freehold Estate (Rochdale)
271 Olney, Freehold Estate,
Rochdale

414 dwellings
(4-storey deck access blocks)

Huncoat Estate (Hyndburn)
6a Within Grove, Huncoat,
Accrington, Lancs.

500 dwellings
(traditional inter-war houses)

ISLE OF DOGS ESTATES:

early 20th century brick-built blocks, 1960s/1970s industrially-built flats early 1980s houses and tower blocks

Millwall Estate
38 Montcalm House,
London E14

455 dwellings

Barkantine
6 The Quarterdeck,
London E14

939 dwellings

Cubitt Town
Seyssel Street, London E14

634 dwellings

Poplar
Woodstock Terrace,
117 Poplar High Street,
London E14

695 dwellings

Robin Hood Gardens
4 Anderson House,
Woolmore Street,
London E14 OHG

761 dwellings

St. John's
Thorne House, Launch Street,
London E14

654 dwellings

St. Vincents/Birchfield
Limehouse Causeway,
London E14

553 dwellings

Samuda
Community Centre,
Stewart Street
London E14

496 dwellings

West Ferry
361/363 West Ferry Road,
London E14

484 dwellings

Kelvin Estate (Sheffield)
53 Kelvin Walk, Kelvin Flats,
Sheffield S6 3JR

945 dwellings
(system-built flats)

Kirkholt Estate (Rochdale)
Area Housing Office,
46 The Strand
Rochdale OL11 2JG

2228 dwellings
(late 1940s/early 1950s traditional houses, some bungalows)

Millers Lane Estate (Wigan)
Platt Bridge NH Centre,
80–90 Ribble Road,
Platt Bridge, Wigan, Lancs.

1144 dwellings
(1960's/1970's non-traditional houses)

Newton Court Estate (Kingston Upon Hull) 187 Newton Court, Hull	196 dwellings (late 1920s brick-built 3-storey blocks)
Norley Hall Estate (Wigan) 5–7 Lamberhead Road, Wigan, Lancs. WN5 9TL	1500 dwellings (cottages, traditional construction)
Ocean Estate (Tower Hamlets) 4–5 Aden House, Duckett Street London E1	1975 dwellings (mix of traditional and non-traditional brick-built flats and a few houses)
Penrhys Estate (Rhondda) Ferndale, Mid Glamorgan	948 dwellings (late 1960s Wimpey 'no-fine' houses, flats and maisonettes
Shadsworth Estate (Blackburn) 52/54 Arran Avenue, Shadsworth Blackburn BB1 2ET	420 dwellings (1950s traditional brick-built and system-built houses)
South Bank Estate (Langbaurgh) 11/13 Steele Crescent, South Bank, Middlesbrough	841 dwellings (1950s/1960s traditional cottage style houses and bungalows)

St. Paul's Gardens Estate (Bristol) 62a Halston Drive, St Pauls, Bristol BS2 9JN	200 dwellings (1970s purpose built estate)
Stoops & Hargher Clough Estate (Burnley) 2–4 Venice Avenue, Stoops Estate, Burnley, Lancs. BB11 5JX	900 dwellings (inter-war period traditional brick-built houses and a few Wimpey 'no fine' houses)
Thorpes Estate (Kingston Upon Hull) Homethorpe, Orchard Part Estate, Hull HU6 9HP	1061 dwellings (1960s Wimpey 'no-fine' houses and tower blocks)

Current Partnership Projects
Bloomsbury (Birmingham)
Shadsworth (Blackburn)
St Pauls (Bristol)
Stoops and Hargher Clough (Burnley)
Barnfield (Greenwich)
The Thorpes (Hull)
The Danes (Hull)
Bacup (Rossendale)
Chell Heath (Stoke on Trent)

APPENDIX 2: PRIORITY ESTATES PROJECT PUBLICATIONS LIST, MAY 1990

	Price
Estate Management Boards: an Introduction by Tricia Zipfel PEP: 1989	£2.95
Economic Development on Council Estates by Bootstrap (Hackney) and Richard MacFarlane PEP: 1989	£5.95
Under New Management: The Experience of Thirteen Islington Tenant Management Co-operatives by Anne Power PEP: 1989	£7.95
Tenant Involvement on Priority Estates by Chris Holmes PEP: 1988	£2.95
Small Scale Employment Creation on Unpopular Estates PEP: 1988	£2.50
Women & Children on Priority Estates PEP: 1990	£2.50

Furnished Accommodation for Single People £7.95
by Chris Holmes and Virginia Shaw
PEP: 1990

PEP Guide to Local Housing Management FREE
  Volume 1: The PEP Model
  Volume 2: The PEP Experience
  Volume 3: Guidelines for Setting up New Projects
DoE: 1987

Priority Estates Project – Annual Review FREE
1988–1989

Newsletter: PEPtalk
PEPtalk is a free quarterly newsletter to keep people up-to-date with the development and progress of PEP and other local management initiatives in England and Wales. To put your name on the mailing list, write to PEPtalk, 62 Eden Grove, London N7 8EN

Film/Video: Priority for People
Illustrates the success of the PEP approach on four estates. It is available on free loan or purchase in VHS or 16mm film format.

Loan Copies from PEP Publications, 62 Eden Grove, London N7 8EN

Video Sales from DoE Publications & Sales Division, Building No. 1 Victoria Road, Ruislip, Middx. HA ONZ (Tel: 081-845 1200 Ext. 200) Price: £5 incl. p & p

Film Sales enquiries to Andrew Godden, DoE, Room N13/05, 2 Marsham Street, London SW1P 3EB   (Tel: 071-276 3243)

APPENDIX 3: SOME USEFUL ORGANISATIONS

Child Poverty Action Group
1 Bath Street, London EC1V 9PY
Tel: 071/253 3406
Contact: Publication Department

CPAG campaigns for changes in policy. It brings together a wealth of information on poverty and uses this to press for an end to poor benefits for the poor, and to fight for a fairer future for all children. CPAG helps to set the agenda for the debate on longer-term reform towards a welfare state that puts the 'security' back into social security. It presses for changes in practice, publicising what is wrong with the benefit system, and trying to put it right. It advises social workers, CABs, advice agencies and others on the complexities of social security. CPAG's regular journal, Poverty, and a range of pamphlets explore the politics of poverty, providing in-depth analysis and challenging views.

CIPFA
Chartered Institute of Public Finance and Accountancy
2–3 Robert Street, London WC2 6BH
Tel: 071/895 8823
Contact: Anna Harrington (Assistant Secretary Local Authority Technical & Development)

CIPFA aims to advance the science of public finance and of accountancy and cognate subjects as applied to all or any of the duties imposed upon the functions undertaken by public service bodies. It aims to promote public education therein and to promote and to publish results of studies and research work therein and related subjects.

Companies House
Crown Way, Cardiff CS4 3UZ
Tel: 0222/ 380 801
Contact: Enquiry Unit

Companies House is the DTI agency responsible for incorporating limited companies in the UK. It also holds information on these companies and makes this available to the public.

Commission of the European Communities
Jean Monnet House, 8 Storey's Gate, London SW1P 3AT
Tel: 071/222 8122
Contact: Information Unit

The European Communities' general aims and objectives are to provide a harmonious development of economic activities, a continuous and balanced expansion, an increase in stability, an accelerated raising of the standard of living and closer relations between the States belonging to it. (EEC Treaty, Art. 2)

Department of the Environment
2 Marsham Street, Room N10/05, London SW1P 3EP
Contact: Section 16 Grant Regime

The Department of the Environment leaflet describes the grant regime available for the expansion of co-operatives and other tenant-led participation initiatives as follows:

The Department will give 100% funding to Advice Agencies to provide promotional advice, educational materials, visits and training for tenants and local authority officials and members who are interested in developing tenant participation options. This will include funding for an initial feasibility study of the options including Estate Management Boards, Tenant Management Co-operatives and other options. This will include discussing and agreeing the proposals with the local authority.

If the tenants select a particular option which has the backing of the Council, then the Department will provide 75% funding, with the Council providing the balance, directly to the tenants so that their choice of scheme can be developed. The tenants will have the resources to choose an Advice Agency to develop their chosen tenant management option.

An Advice Agency can help tenants and local authorities find out more about tenant participation. A list of Advice Agencies, currently funded by the Department, who will help tenants and local authorities with information and advice on tenant participation options is given in the leaflet.

Institute of Housing
Angel House, White Lion Street, London N1
Tel: 071/837 4280
Contact: Sian Jones (Press Officer)

The Institute of Housing is the only organisation in the United Kingdom dealing with every aspect of housing. It is a professional body representing staff involved with the development, management and maintenance of properties mainly owned by local authorities and housing associations. The Institute's main role is to argue the case for housing by presenting a clear and independent view to all agencies, groups and individuals involved in this vital service. The Institute has developed policy initiatives over a wide range of housing issues and is expanding its role as a major provider of housing education and training.

National Federation of Housing Co-ops
88 Old Street, London EC1
Tel: 071/608 2494
Contact: Michele Bristol

The NFHC was set up in 1984. Its aim is to represent co-ops to the government and to give advice for co-ops and lobby the government on behalf of co-ops. The NFHC gives management advice, supplies training and publications to existing co-ops and advises the public.

National Federation of Housing Associations
175 Gray's Inn Road, London WC1X 8UP
Tel: 071/278 6571
Contact: Housing Policy Section

The NFHA was formed in 1935 as the central agency for housing associations, trusts and societies. It is a wholly independent body that seeks to spread ideas and information among its members, it provides common services for them and represents housing associations to government, local authorities and other bodies.

Registry of Friendly Societies
15 Great Marlborough Street, London W1V 2AX
Tel: 071/437 9992
Contact: Registration Branch

For information concerning the RFS please refer to 'The Guide to the Law Relating to Industrial & Provident Societies', HMSO

Safe Neighbourhood Units
485 Bethnal Green Road
London E2 9HQ
Tel: 071/739 4388
Contact: Tim Kendrick (Director)

Birmingham Office:
2nd floor, Spencer House
Digbeth, Birmingham B5 6DD
Tel: 021/622 1097

Bristol Office:
7 Surrey Road
Bristol BS7 9DJ
Tel: 0272/246 279

The SNU is an independent non-profit making organisation which provides a range of specialist consultancy services in the field of public housing, local authority service delivery and community safety. These include survey research, project development and advisory services.

Tenants Participation Advisory Service England
48 The Crescent, Salford M5 4NY
Tel: 061/745 7903
Contact: Marianne Hood (Director)

TPAS is the Tenant Participation Advisory Service for England. It works with tenants, councils and housing associations to develop tenant involvement in housing management.

TPAS provides information, advice and consultancy. It has a range of publications and runs regular seminars on aspects of tenant participation.

TPAS is a company run by its members. Membership is open to all tenants' groups, local councils, housing associations and tenants' federations.

Helping Tenants to run their Homes

COUNCIL TENANTS

Do you want more say in how your homes are run?

Are you ready to take part in local decisions?

Do you want to play a bigger part in community affairs?

DEPARTMENT OF THE ENVIRONMENT

Having more say

Tenants can now have a bigger say in the way their homes are run. This can include taking over the management for themselves. Now there is **free** advice to help tenants decide. For those who want to take charge of the management of their homes, there are new grants to help them do this. Just think, you and your neighbours can decide how to look after and take control of:

- repairs and maintenance
- lettings (including equal opportunities)
- security and control of vandalism
- cleanliness and quality of the environment

Within the framework of a legal management agreement between your group and the Council, approved by the Secretary of State for the Environment, you would have a clear set of responsibilities including a budget and agreed policies on all these things, or as many of them as you wished. You can decide how far you want to take part in these decisions about your homes.

How does it work?

There are two main ways of taking charge of the management of your homes whilst the properties are still owned by the council

- a tenant management co-operative — tenants take responsibility for all or part of the management of their homes
- an estate management board — management responsibilities are given to a board made up of tenants (who will be in a majority), council officers, and others.

We call these **Tenant Management Options.**

Other possibilities are for tenants to use the *Tenants' Choice* provisions to get the council to transfer ownership either to another landlord — with the possibility of establishing a tenant management board — or to the tenants themselves to form tenant ownership co-operatives. A separate leaflet explaining *Tenants' Choice* in detail is available from Room N10/06 at the Department of the Environment. Further leaflets and advice are available from the Housing Corporation.

Councils and their tenants may sometimes develop new ways for tenants to take charge of management, or of ownership too.

How to get started

You will need to consider which tenant management option, if any, is right for you. You can get **free independent advice** to help you decide from an Advice Agency funded by the Department of the Environment. They will:

- tell you about the choices you can make
- talk to the Council to find out their views
- help you choose the right option
- carry out a **free** feasibility study to see if enough tenants support the idea, and make sure it is workable
- help you join with your neighbours to take on the management of your homes with the Council's agreement
- help you learn the skills you will need
- work with you and the Council to find out what its responsibilities and yours could be, within the legal management agreement which will guide you if you decide you do want to run your homes.

Some local authorities have tenant management co-operative Advice Agencies of their own. They may also help you decide what to do.

How to turn the idea into reality

After a lot of hard work by you (the tenants), the Council and the Advice Agency, an option will be chosen by the tenants with a democratic vote. Then the Agency can, if the Council agrees, help your tenants group to apply to the Department of the Environment for a *Tenant Participation (Section 16) Development Grant*. Your tenants group can then choose an Advice Agency — the same one or a different one — to help you develop the co-op or board and draw up the legal agreement with the Council.

Then it's up to *you!*

Who pays for it?

While you are deciding which tenant participation option you want, the Department of the Environment pays the Advice Agency for all the advice and training you need, and the feasibility study if this is needed.

After that, when you have chosen the management option you want, you apply to the Department of the Environment for a development grant. The Department of the Environment will pay for 75 per cent and the Council will pay for 25 per cent. The money goes direct to the tenant group. So you can *choose* which Advice Agency your group wants to help them get the right arrangements, the skills and legal agreement needed to run your homes.

What's next?

If you want to run your own homes and estate:

- get in touch with your Tenants' Association or find out how to form a Tenants' Association by asking an Advice Agency or your Council for information

- get in touch with your local Advice Agencies and ask for further information about 'tenant participation options'. The Advice Agency you choose will give **free advice** to help your group decide the right kind of tenant participation for you

- if you decide to take over all or part of the management of your homes yourselves, you can apply for a grant with the help of the Advice Agency.

The Review of Housing Co-operatives in England

LAST YEAR the Government published a report called *Tenants in the Lead* which confirmed that housing co-operatives and other sorts of tenant participation options were popular with tenants. These provide real opportunities for many local management initiatives. In its response to the report, the Government agreed to an expansion of co-operatives and other tenant-led participation initiatives. Additional resources are being made available to secure this.

Promotion: The Department will give 100 per cent funding to Advice Agencies to provide promotional advice, educational materials, visits and training for tenants and local authority officials and members who are interested in developing tenant participation options. This will include funding for an initial feasibility study of the options including Estate Management Boards, Tenant Management Co-operatives and other options. This will include discussing and agreeing the proposals with the local authority.

Development: If the tenants select a particular option which has the backing of the Council, then the Department will provide 75 per cent funding, with the Council providing the balance, directly *to the tenants* so that their choice of scheme can be developed. The tenants will have the resources to choose an Advice Agency to develop their chosen tenant management option.

Advice Agencies: An Advice Agency can help tenants and local authorities find out more about 'tenant participation'. A list of Advice Agencies, currently funded by the Department, who will help tenants and local authorities with information and advice on tenant participation options is given elsewhere in this leaflet.

If you would like a copy of Tenants in the Lead *or a Section 16 application form, please apply to: Department of the Environment, Room N10/05, 2 Marsham Street, London SW1P 3EB.*

Where to go next

The Department of the Environment currently fund the following Advice Agencies which may be able to help you. There are other agencies who can help and we will be providing a full list in May 1990.

LOCAL ADVICE AGENCIES

Banks of the Wear Co-operative Housing Services Ltd
3rd Floor, Mea House, Ellison Place, Newcastle NE1 8XS. Tel: 091 32 6446

Birmingham Co-operative Housing Services Ltd
510a Coventry Road, Small Heath, Birmingham B10 0UN. Tel: 021-773 3583

Church Housing Association
Welford House, 112a Shirland Road, London W9 2BT. Tel: 01-289 2241

Co-operative Development Services CHS (London) Ltd
140-142 Stockwell Road, London SW9 9TQ. Tel: 01-737 3512

Co-operative Development Services CHS (Liverpool) Ltd
39-41 Bold Street, Liverpool L1 4E. Tel: 051 708 0674

Co-operative Housing in South-East London (Chisel) Ltd
184A Brownhill Road, London SE6 2DJ. Tel: 01-698 9855

Co-operative and Housing Services (NW) Ltd
823A Stockport Road, Levenshulme, Manchester M19 3PN. Tel: 061 257 2636

East London Housing Association Ltd
187A Romford Road, Stratford, London E15 4JF. Tel: 01-519 2233

Great Western Region CHS Ltd
23 Bennet Street, Bath, Avon BA1 2QL. Tel: 0225 480099

Leicester Federation of Housing Societies Ltd
131 Loughborough Road, Leicester LE4 5LQ. Tel: 0533 666123

Merseyside Improved Houses SPHA Ltd
46 Watertree Road, Liverpool L7 1PH. Tel: 051 709 9375

SOLON East CHS Ltd
218 Whitechapel Road, London E1 1BJ. Tel: 01-247 9835

SOLON NW Co-operative Ltd
233A Kentish Town Road, London NW5 2JT. Tel: 01-267 2005

SOLON South-East Housing Association Ltd
235 Queens Road, Peckham, London SE15 2NG. Tel: 01-639 3634

SOLON Wandsworth Housing Association Ltd
49A Lavender Hill, Battersea, London SW11 5QN. Tel: 01-223 7376/7/8/9

South London Family Housing Association
Rochester House, 2-10 Belvedere Road, London SE19 2HL. Tel: 01-653 8433

Yorkshire CHS Ltd
2 Eastgate, Barnsley, S. Yorkshire S70 2EP. Tel: 0226 732 200

NATIONAL AGENCIES:

Priority Estates Project Ltd
62 Eden Grove, London N7 8EN. Tel: 01-607 8186
or Co-op Unit, 2 Mellor Road, Leicester LE3 6HN. Tel: 0533 858908

National Federation of Housing Co-operatives
88 Old Street, London EC1V 9AX. Tel: 01-608 2494

Tenant Participation Advisory Service
48 The Crescent, Salford, Manchester M5 4NY. Tel: 061 745 7903

PiC Services
Head Office: The Coach House, Kempshott Park, Dummer, Basingstoke, Hants RG23 7LP. Tel: 0256 75661

Published by the Department of the Environment. April 1990.

APPENDIX 4A: ESTATE MANAGEMENT BOARD – CODE OF PRACTICE FOR COMMITTEE MEMBERS

The Code of Practice for Estate Management Board members is intended to give guidance to Board members about the way in which they should carry out their duties once elected to the Board.

As a representative of other residents, dealing with difficult and confidential issues will require discretion and care to be exercised by members in the performance of their duties and responsibilities.

Training and advice will be provided for newly elected Board members who should be prepared to ask for support and assistance wherever necessary.

The EMB has many responsibilities which must be met effectively and fairly. In doing so the Board must protect the rights of individual tenants and the Council employees who have been seconded to the Board. At the same time the Board must operate within the rules laid down for the EMB as an organisation and within the terms of the Management Agreement with the Council.

The Code of Practice must be adhered to by all Board members and deliberate or frequent breaches of the Code must be treated by the Board as grounds for recommending removal from the Committee.

Induction Training

Each new member of the Board will be provided with induction training with regard to the Code of Practice relating to the role of Board members. All newly elected Board members will be required to attend these training sessions.

Confidentiality

Confidential information made available to the Board or individual Board members must not be divulged to any person or persons without the approval of the Board or the individual(s) concerned.

Personal Interest of Committee Members

Board members must not use their position as a Committee member to seek preferential treatment by the EMB nor should they be treated any less favourably.

They must use the agreed procedure for reporting repairs and in pursuing other enquiries relating to their own tenancy.

Rule 37b of the Society's Rules states that Committee members must declare any involvement they have in any organisation with which the EMB may be considering doing business. They must also notify the Committee if they have a personal interest in any other matters being considered by the Committee. In some cases it may be necessary for individual Committee members to abstain from discussion or leave the meeting during the discussion on a particular item.

Staff Relations

Committee members should at all times be courteous to staff and should seek to support and assist the staff in order to achieve the best possible service.

Individual Committee members must not issue instructions to staff directly and the management responsibilities of the Neighbourhood Officer for the staff is to be recognised at all times.

If a Committee member has a complaint about the performance of any member of staff this must be made in writing to the Neighbourhood Officer who will investigate and take any necessary action.

The Management Agreement (Schedule 4 Part 6) sets out procedures to be followed if a complaint is to be made against the Neighbourhood Officer.

If a Committee member requires an agenda item to be considered by the Board the decision whether or not to include the item on a future Board agenda will be made by the Board or in cases of urgency by the Neighbourhood Officer in consultation with the Chair of the Board.

Committee members should take care in their dealings with staff and should not expect favourable treatment for their enquiries taken up on behalf of other residents, eg completion of repair works or allocation of properties. All such enquiries will be dealt with in accordance with policies and procedures of the Council and the Board as set out in the Management Agreement.

If a Committee member is requested to raise a matter on behalf of a resident, this should be raised in the first instance with the Neighbourhood Officer. Such matters should be raised at Board meetings only if the Neighbourhood Officer has not resolved the matter to the satisfaction of the Committee member.

Committee members must take account in their dealings with staff of their responsibilities as elected representatives and act at all times in accordance with the guidelines included in the Code of Practice.

APPENDIX 4B: TENANT PARTICIPATION GRANTS (SECTION 16 GRANT REGIME)

The Department of the Environment (DoE) and the Housing Corporation (HC) provide grants to start up initiatives in which tenants participate in housing management. The DoE grants are for initiatives in council housing. The HC grants are for tenant participation initiatives in registered housing associations.

Promotion and feasibility

There are two main kinds of grant. First, the DoE and the HC give 100% grants to Advice Agencies to provide promotional advice, educational materials, visits and training for tenants and others interested in developing tenant participation options. This will include funding for initial feasibility studies of the options for particular estates including Estate Management Boards, Tenant Management Co-operatives, Tenant Ownership Co-operatives, and other ways forward. This stage includes discussing and agreeing the selected option with the local authority or housing association.

Development

Secondly, if the tenants on an estate select a particular option which has the backing of their landlord, they can receive a grant themselves to fund the development of the chosen option, up to the point where the Estate Management Board, Tenant Management Co-operative or other option begins operation. In the case of council housing, the DoE will provide a grant for 75% of the costs of developing the proposal, with the Council providing the balance. In the case of housing association tenants, the HC provides a 100% grant for this purpose. These development grants give the tenants the resources themselves to choose an Advice Agency to develop their chosen tenant participation or control option.

Advice Agencies

An Advice Agency can help tenants and landlords find out more about tenant participation options, as well as carry out feasibility studies and undertake development work. For information contact the Tenant Participation Unit, Room N10/05, Department of the Environment, 2 Marsham Street, London SW1P 3EB, or phone 071-276 3970. Housing association tenants should contact the Housing Corporation, 149 Tottenham Court Road, London W1P 0BN, telephone 071-387 9466. Information and application forms for grant can be obtained from the DoE.

APPENDIX 4C: THE ROLE OF THE PROJECT CO-ORDINATOR IN EMB & SIMILAR PROJECTS – LONG TERM ARRANGEMENTS

PEP has been considering the question of support for Estate Management Boards in the long term particularly having in mind that key parts of the support, up to now have been provided by 'temporary' staff either on short term Council contracts or via PEP.

The temporary input has most usually involved Project Associates and Project Assistants from PEP and a Project Co-ordinator employed short term (for 2 or 3 years) by the Council.

The pilot projects were set up on the basis that this input was mainly developmental and would cease to be needed once the EMBs were up and running. From experience, however, it seems that some longer term support must be built into the permanent staff structure. In most of the pilot projects the temporary input will not be totally withdrawn until 1991 but it is already apparent that the remaining permanent estate manager will find it difficult to sustain the routine housing management tasks and at the same time absorb into the team a range of new duties.

This transition has not been made easy by the fact that the Project Co-ordinators have generally been the project leaders whilst in post with responsibility for ensuring successful tenant involvement in the project. In some cases the estate managers have become distant from that part of the project and have focussed on housing management specifically. The outlook and skills involved in supporting tenant involvement have not, as a result, been developed in the estate manager and the transition to a broader role is more difficult.

There seem to be two main lessons emerging which are underlined by views put to us by project staff:

1) Some additional long-term, permanent resource is needed to support the EMB (over and above the resources that would be needed in a more traditional local office with line management at the centre).

2) It may be advisable to have a single permanent team leader from the outset. (i.e. a Project Manager rather than a temporary Project Co-ordinator plus an Estate Manager).

Additional long term resources

Looking at the work of the Project Co-ordinators and Project Assistants we have identified the following tasks that will need to be built into the permanent team:

'Project Assistant' Tasks:

Servicing of meetings/reminder to tenants.
Ensuring accountability of groups.
Producing publicity material.
Tenant support/community work.

'Project Co-ordinator' Tasks:

Overall co-ordination, making things happen.
Monitoring and reporting.
Advice to the EMB on strategy.
Training (tenants and staff).
Input into budget negotiations.
Protection of the Project's interests with the Council.
Attracting resources.
Managing the capital programme.

Ideally all of these tasks need to be built into the local team although some might be carried out by a permanent central post with a brief involving other estates.

It would seem that this additional work can be best built into the team partly by redesignating the Estate Manager to the broader 'Project Manager' role to include overall responsibility for servicing and supporting the EMB. In addition the project assistant/community work function might be built in in either of the following ways:

(a) One 'specialist' employed (either part-time or full-time), but accountable to the Housing Manager. Supervision might have to come from outside the staff team (either elsewhere in the Local Authority or brought in from outside) as the Manager may not have the necessary experience/skills for this. But the Manager should have line management responsibility for the work.

(b) The work to be shared out amongst staff – primarily amongst the Estate Officers and Clerical Staff, e.g. clerical staff may take on the role of servicing the Board (i.e. minutes, agendas, notices), but Estate Officers having responsibility for assisting with accountability of the group or helping produce publicity. This would imply an additional Estate Officer or Clerical Officer in the team.

The additional funding involved must be offset against identified savings at the centre where supervisory and clerical work will be reduced in the long term. If there is a net additional cost of tenant involvement then this must be weighed against other benefits which may flow from the EMB.

Summary

1. The work currently done by PEP or by project Co-ordinators, but needed long term for an EMB to thrive, should be done by the local estate office.

2. The community work could be done by a 'specialist'

community worker, or divided between Estate Officers/ Clerical Staff.

3. The 'Project Co-ordinator' job to be done by the Housing Manager in an enhanced role, with some tasks delegated to the rest of the team.

4. These tasks will be paid for out of the estate budget, but should be part of all housing management practice. 'Savings' will be made at the centre.

APPENDIX 4D: HOUSING CO-OPERATIVE TENANCY AGREEMENT

(The notes give a brief explanation of each section and sometimes give a little more information on the reasons for having a particular clause.)

This Tenancy Agreement is made on the.................... day of...19......... between
HOUSING CO-OPERATIVE LIMITED
(The Co-operative) and.......................................(The Member) of
....

1. Background to the agreement

The background to the agreement defines certain terms and describes the co-operative as a 'fully mutual co-operative housing association'. Fully mutual means that all tenants are members and all members are tenants or are going to be tenants. The consequence of being fully mutual is that the Co-operative does not grant secure tenancies, so that for example, members would not have the right to buy their homes and would not have security of tenure.

a. The co-operative is an Industrial and Provident Society registered under the Industrial and Provident Societies Act 1965, registered no.   and the members attention is drawn to the Rules of the Co-operative available from the Secretary. This registration means that the Co-operative is a co-operative housing association as defined in section 1(2) of the Housing Associations Act 1985 and within the meaning of section 5(2) of the Housing Act 1985.

b. The Co-operative is also a Housing Association registered with the Housing Corporation – registered no. C
– as a fully mutual Housing Co-operative, as provided in section 3 of the Housing Associations Act 1985 and is therefore a registered housing association as defined in section 5 (4) of the Housing Act 1985.

c. The Member is a member of
Housing Co-operative Limited.

d. Where a joint tenancy has been granted, the term 'member' in this agreement shall mean all joint tenants. Each joint tenant is individually liable under this Agreement, the joint tenants jointly have the full rights set out in this agreement.

e. Members tenancies are not secure tenancies as defined by section 80(2) of the Housing Act 1985, because the co-operative is a fully mutual co-operative housing association (see section 5 of the Housing Act 1985.) The right to buy does not arise within the meaning of Schedule 5 of the Housing Act 1985.

2. Agreement to let:

The Co-operative shall let, and the Member shall accept:

No..............................   (hereinafter called 'the Property') for a term of one week from

.... 19.......... and thereafter from week to week until brought to an end by either the Co-operative or the Member, each giving to the other no less than 4 weeks notice in writing.

3. Member's payments

a. The rent shall be £............................. per week,

including services of £............................. per week

to be paid in advance on Monday of each week until the rent is increased or decreased in accordance with the provisions of this agreement.

The first rent payment shall be on Monday.............................
19..........

b. **Services:**

This element represents services and outgoings payable by the Co-operative in respect of the Property and may be increased or decreased in accordance with 3d and 3e below. Any increase in the cost of providing services much be reasonably incurred by the Co-operative.

Services will be:

1. Provision and maintenance of security gates to property.

2. Maintaining entry phones

3. External lighting

4. Flower bed planting

5. Such administrative costs as may be incurred from time in the provision of these services

c. **Rates/Community Charge:**

It is the Member's responsibility to pay general, water and sewerage rates in respect of the Property, and any Community Charge payable by the member.

d. The Co-operative shall decide in general meeting held in accordance with the Co-operatives registered Rules what amount of increase or decrease is needed to account for the provision of the services and outgoings referred to in 3b above.

e. The rent is set by the Co-op in accordance with Co-op policy as decided by members at general meetings of the Co-op. Members shall be given four weeks written notice or any increase or decrease in the rent. The notice shall give a date when the increased or decreased rent shall be payable. The Co-operative may not increase the services element more than once in any period of six months, and no increase shall take effect without first giving the Member four weeks written notice.

f. In accordance with Rules of the Co-operative, a copy of the audited accounts is available to any member, and if the Member has any objection to the amount that is from time to time charged by the Co-operative, the Co-operative will abide by the decision of any independent accountant appointed jointly by the Members and the Co-operative or in default of agreement, such accountant being appointed by the National Federation of Housing Co-operatives.

4. The Co-operative's responsibilities

This section is intended to set out clearly the Co-operative's responsibilities as a landlord. Mostly, these are things that the Co-operative is required to do by law, particularly as regards maintenance and insurance, and they are written into the Tenancy Agreement for the tenant's information. The clauses relating to the maintenance are written in such a way as to give tenants the opportunity of getting work done themselves should the Co-operative not carry out work within a reasonable time. An appendix will be prepared at a later date setting out time limits in which the co-operative must carry out different types of repairs.

a. Not to interfere or disturb the Member in his or her peaceful occupation of the Property.

b. To provide the services listed in section 3b of this agreement.

c. To redecorate and maintain the exterior and interior common areas of the Property when required and to keep the common areas in good habitable repair and condition.

d. To keep in good repair and condition the roof and external parts and main structures of the Property including rainwater guttering, downpipes, and sewers.

Note:

With reference to 4c and 4d above, the Co-operative shall inspect the Property every year and carry out such work as is necessary: and the Member shall pay the reasonable cost of any maintenance or repair made necessary by the Member's misuse or negligence. In the event of a dispute between the member and the Co-operative, final arbitration shall be made in accordance with procedures laid down by a General Meeting held in accordance with the Co-operative's registered Rules.

e. To keep all boundary fences, the grounds, paths and walls in good condition and repair where deterioration has occured.

f. The Co-operative shall carry out repairs listed in Appendix A to this Agreement (which may be amended or altered by the Co-operative in accordance with the Co-operatives registered Rules) after having received notification in writing from the Member that such repairs are required. The Co-operative shall carry out the repairs within the time stated in Appendix A and if the Co-operative has not taken steps to carry out the repairs within the stated time the Member shall be empowered to arrange for the repairs to be carried out independently and the Co-operative shall bear the cost of the necessary repairs. The Member shall pay the reasonable cost of any maintenance or repair made necessary by the Member's misuse or negligence.

g. To make good any damage to the inside of the Property resulting from an inspection or from carrying out of any works by the Co-operative, its staff, workers, or agents.

h. To insure fully the building against fire and public liability. (This does not include the Member's personal possessions.)

i. So far as it is legally able to maintain the supply of water and electricity and proper functioning of other services provided to or for the Property, provided that the Co-operative shall not be liable to the Member if such supply or service fails, breaks down, leaks or is defected or malfunctions.

j. To issue a copy of the Co-operatives Rules on request.

5. **Member's Responsibilities:**

This section sets out the Member's responsibilities as a tenant. Some of the clauses are included to enable the Co-operative to fulfil its legal responsibilities, for example, the Co-operative could not allow any part of the Property to be used for a business because it would then be breaking its planning permission from   Borough.

Rent

a. To pay the rent on the days and in the manner shown in section 3. Where a joint tenancy has been granted, each Member is both jointly and severally responsible for the total rent shown in section 3, and for any increases made in accordance with the terms of section 3.

Repairs

b. To keep the Property including its doors, windows, walls, floors, fixtures, and fittings in good clean and tenantable condition.

c. To report to the Co-operative without delay any disrepair or defects within the Property which are the Co-operative's responsibility. Reporting shall be by the method as determined in the Co-operative's Repairs Policy.

d. To make good any damage done to the Property through the fault of the tenant, anybody living with the tenant, or an invited guest.

e. Not to make any structural changes to the Property without the prior agreement of the Co-operative. The member may carry out improvements to the premises but only if the Co-operative first consents in writing, and such consent not to be unreasonably withheld.

f. The Member shall at the end of the tenancy give the Premises back with vacant possession and leave the Premises in good lettable condition and repair. The Member must make good any damage caused by the removal of any installations and must return to the Co-operative's offices all keys to the premises replacing any that are lost. The Co-operative takes no responsibility for anything left at the premises by the Member at the end of the Tenancy.

Subletting and lodgers

g. The Member shall not sub-let or part with possession or occupation of the whole or any part of the premises. The Member may however transfer the Tenancy in accordance with a Court Order resulting from the divorce or separation of the Member. If the Member wishes to take in a lodger, he/she must first seek the written consent of the Co-operative. Consent will normally only be granted in exceptional circumstances including any application for a disabled person's carer.

Common areas

h. To keep common areas clean and free from obstruction, and to carry out a reasonable amount of work in order to ensure this.

Inflammable materials

i. Not to keep or use any paraffin heaters or bottled gas heaters/cookers on the Property. Not to store any inflammable materials on the property.

Access for inspection

j. On having received 48 hours notice from the Co-operative or its managing agents, to allow the Co-operative or its managing agents representatives to enter the Property for the purpose of inspection and to allow the Co-operative or its managing agent's workers or contractors to enter the Property at reasonable hours to carry out necessary repairs or alterations and to allow entry at any time in the case of an emergency.

Not to cause nuisance

k. To allow at all times all other members and other persons lawfully on the Property peaceably to occupy and enjoy the Property and every part of it and to permit such persons to exercise their rights under the Agreement without interference, nuisance or annoyance caused by the Member whether by noise, anti-social behaviour or otherwise.

l. Not to behave in a threatening or violent manner or cause wilful damage to any member or other person lawfully on the Property or against any property belonging to any such person or the Co-operative.

Responsibility for guests

m. To ensure that guests do not cause any disturbance or cause nuisance to other members living in the Co-operative nor wilfully damage any part of the Co-operative's property and to remedy any such damage.

n. Not at any time to invite or allow to remain on any part of the Co-operative's property any persons in respect of whom the Member has received a written notice from the Co-operative requesting that such person or persons should not enter or remain on the property.

Harassment

o. The Member will not permit or allow members of the Member's household or invited visitors to commit any form of harrassment on the grounds of race, colour, religion, sex, sexual orientation or disability which may interfere with the peace and comfort of or cause offence to any other resident in the property or visitor to a member of the Co-operative or any agent, contractor or staff of the Co-operative.

Principal place of residence

p. To use the Property as a principal place of residence, and not to use any part of the Co-operative's property for business or commercial purposes, or for any illegal activities.

q. To use the Property for the exclusive single occupation of the Member and his/her dependents where applicable.

Pets

r. Members may keep pets on the Accommodation provided that they have obtained the prior permission of the Co-operative in writing. Pets which cause a nuisance or hazard to other people lawfully on the Property may not be kept and the Member is responsible for ensuring that his/her pets never cause any nuisance or hazard. Dogs are not to be allowed onto communal ground without a lead.

Participation

s. To attend all General Meetings and sub-committees as decided by the Co-operative General Meeting, and to share in the work fairly unless specifically exempted by the Co-operative at a General Meeting.

Interior decorations

t. To redecorate the interior parts of the Property.

General

u. To abide by the terms of this Agreement.

v. The Member will be liable to pay the Co-operative for any money the Co-operative as to spend as a result of any breach by the Member of any part of this Agreement. Any money due under this Clause shall be a debt due to the Co-operative even if the Tenancy granted by this Agreement has ended.

6. Ending the Tenancy:

a. This Agreement may be ended at any time by either the Co-operative or the Member giving to the other party not less than four weeks written notice.

b. The Co-operative may give the Member four weeks written notice that the tenancy shall be terminated only for **the following reasons:**

   i. Any rent due from the Member has not been paid, and the Member, after having been given notice of the amount of arrears, has made no offer to pay those arrears within a reasonable period, or has unreasonably failed to fulfil an undertaking previously given to clear the arrears.

   ii. The Member is in breach of the conditions laid down in the Agreement concerning subtenants, lodgers and guests, sharing or parting with possession or occupation of the Property or any part of it and has taken no steps to remedy this situation after having received written notice of the breach of the Agreement from the Co-operative.

   iii. By his or her conduct, the Member or his or her guests, is the cause of persistent nuisance or annoyance to neighbours or wilful damage or neglect to the Property, including the Property, or adjoining property or common parts or the Co-operative's furniture or fittings and no steps have been taken by the Member to remedy this after receiving written notice

of the breach of the Agreement from the Co-operative.

   iv. The Member has been using the Property or allowing it to be used for illegal purposes.

   v. Possession is required for redevelopment or major rehabilitation and after consultation the Co-operative has offered the Member suitable alternative Property which has been refused.

   vi. The Co-operative was induced to grant the tenancy by a false statement made knowingly by the Member.

   vii. The dwelling is overcrowded within the meaning of the Housing Act 1957 in such circumstances as to render the occupier guilty of an offence.

   viii. The dwelling was made available for occupation by the Member while their own home was being improved on the understanding that they would return to their own home when those works were completed, and those works have been completed.

   ix. The Member has ceased to be a Member of the Co-operative.

   x. The Member is not using the Property as a principal place of residence.

   xi. The Member has benefitted financially or materially by virtue of his or her membership of the Co-operative.

   xii. A Member has allowed a pet to stay in the Property without the written permission of the Co-operative and no steps have been taken by the Member to remedy this after receiving written notice of the breach of the Agreement from the Co-operative.

   xiii. The Property was provided for persons with disabilities and it contains features or adaptations which make it especially suitable for such persons and (a) there is no longer such a person living there, and (b) the Co-operative requires the dwelling for occupation by such a person, and (c) suitable alternative Property is offered to the displaced tenant.

c. Notice to Quit may be withdrawn if the grounds on which eviction is granted are rectified within a period of time stated by the Co-operative.

IT IS HEREBY AGREED that all notices shall be deemed served on the date they are fixed to the door of the Property as shown in section 2 of this Agreement.

MEMBER'S SIGNATURE:

SIGNED..

DATE...

FOR **HOUSING CO-OPERATIVE:**

SIGNED..
(Authorised signatory)

DATE...

APPENDIX A: REPAIRS RESPONSIBILITIES OF CO-OP

This classification is referred to in clause 4(f) of the tenancy agreement, and becomes operable from the end of the builders defects liability period. It can be amended or altered by a general meeting of the Co-operative held in accordance with the Co-operative rules.

1. Emergency repairs

This section is intended to include items which are urgent. Repair work must commence as quickly as possible after being reported to the appropriate Co-op Officer, and within 48 hours at the latest. The full repair must be carried out as quickly as possible.

A. **Electrical & Mechanical**

No lights and/or power   permanent or emergency
Exposed wires
Overheating of switches and sockets outlets
Flickering lights
Damage through water penetration
Central heating and hot water supply
Fractured pipes
Flooding

B. **Carpentry**

All lockable doors that cannot be locked or made secure
due to faulty fitting.

C. **Plumbing**

Make safe missing or broken manhole or gulley covers
Repair leaks on water supplies
Replace broken toilet pan
Replace cone to flush pipe
Clear blockage of drain or waste pipe
Re-make joint of toilet pan to soil pipe
Repair to soil pipe
Repair or renew ball valve in storage tank
Failure of cold water supply
Storage tank and hot water cylinder

D. **Glazing**

Glazing where security or danger to life is involved
Completing repair work where emergency temporary
repairs have been carried out

E. **Emergency Repairs Also Include:**

Blocked toilets
Blocked or leaking drains
Serious storm, accident or flood damage to rooms
Dangerous structures

2. **Essential repairs**

This section is intended to cover items which cannot be
used but which are not considered to be emergencies.
Repair work must commence as quickly as possible after
being reported to the appropriate Co-operative officer
and within 5 working days at the latest. A full repair must
then be completed as quickly as possible.

A. **Mechanical & Electrical**

Extract ventilation systems
Mechanical ventilation unit

B. **Plumbing**

Sink unit and kitchen cupboards
Repair or replace waste water pipe
Defective ball valve in storage tank
Wash hand basin brackets
Waste trap and fitting
Faulty stop valve
Faulty drain down cock
Replace missing or broken manhole covers and gulley
covers
Clear blocked gutters and gulleys
Replace toilet seat
Replace missing or broken sections of guttering or rain
water pipe

C. **Building**

Plaster failure to walls and ceilings

D. **Roofs**

Replace cracked tiles or slates
Refix loose or slipped slates or tiles
Flat roof and railings

E. **Glazing**

Reglaze common parts
Reglaze windows and doors not covered until Emergency
Repairs

F. **Stair Safety**

3. **Routine inspection of the building at least every 2 years**

The property is to be inspected every other year. The
purpose of the inspection is to check that all mechanical
fittings are in good working order, that maintenance
contracts are operating efficiently, to identify faults or
repairs and to identify possible future maintenance costs.

A. **Services within flats**

Plumbing installation
Heating installation
Gas installation

B. **External**

Clean drains and gulleys
Check and clean roofs and guttering and down pipes
Check external envelope, pointing and sills
Check refuse bin store
(Equipment required for this work will be a ladder, drain
rods and stoppers plus cleaning fluids)

C. **Common Areas**

External paths, fencing, swings and sheds
Check planting
TV Aerial (including a check on the quality of reception)

Tenancy conditions for Islington Borough Council, London

1 Definitions, notices and permissions

1.1 DEFINITIONS

In these conditions:

You refers to you as the tenant of Council premises.

The tenant refers in the case of a joint tenancy, to the joint
tenants jointly and individually.

The Council means the Council of the London Borough of
Islington as your landlord.

The premises means the house, flat, room, maisonette, or
other dwelling in which you live but includes the structure only
if you have the tenancy of the whole of a house.

The block means the building in which the premises are
situated but excludes any part which the Council does not own
or have an obligation to repair under a lease. The term **block** is
used in relation to flats, maisonettes and rooms only.

The estate means the estate (if any) in which the premises
are situated (and which is named in the tenancy agreement).*

The common parts means any part of the block or of the
estate other than the premises to which the tenant, the
tenant's household or visitors are permitted to go from time to
time.

The household includes the tenant's family and other persons
living with the tenant in the premises.

1.2 NOTICES

1.2/1 Where you have to give the Council written notice under
any of these conditions, you must post or deliver it by hand,
either to the Housing Department at its main office or to the
local housing office shown on your rent card.

1.2/2 Where the Council has to give you written notice under
any of these conditions this may be done either by handing it to
you or by posting, or delivering it by hand to your premises, or
your last known address.

1.3 PERMISSIONS

1.3/1 Some of the clauses in these conditions refer to the need for you to obtain the Council's permission. Such a permission may be subject to conditions which you must keep.

2 Security of tenure and termination of tenancy

a So long as the tenancy is a secure tenancy, (most tenancies usually remain so during the lifetime of the tenant) the Council may seek possession of the premises through the courts only on one or more of the grounds set out in Schedule 2 to the Housing Act 1985 and summarised in the Schedule to this agreement. Before going to court the Council must give you at least four weeks written notice.

b The Council will not seize a tenant's belongings to pay off rent arrears without going through the courts.

c If you wish to end your tenancy and leave the premises, you must give the Council at least four weeks written notice before you do so.

3 Council's duty to repair and maintain the premises

3.1 COUNCIL'S OBLIGATIONS TO REPAIR STRUCTURE AND EXTERIOR

The Council must keep in good repair the structure and outside of the premises. This includes but is not limited to:

a Drains, gutters and outside pipes.

b The roof.

c External walls, outside doors (including frames, thresholds, hinges, handles, locks, jambs, lintels and letter boxes) and windows (including frames, sills, catches, hinges, stays, sash cords, glazing and putties) including decoration necessary to prevent deterioration of the fabric.

d Internal walls, floors, ceilings, plaster, tiling, skirting boards and internal doors (including frames, thresholds, hinges, handles, lock, jambs and lintels),

e Chimneys and chimney stacks.

3.2 COUNCIL'S OBLIGATIONS TO REPAIR AND MAINTAIN INSTALLATIONS

The Council must keep in good repair and proper working order, the installations in the premises for the supply of water, gas and electricity and for sanitation and the installation for space heating and heating water. Installations include but are not limited to:

a Water pipes, gas pipes and electrical wiring.

b Sockets and light fittings.

c Basins, sinks, baths, toilets, flushing systems and waste pipes.

d Water heaters, hot water tanks, radiators, heating controls, fire places, fitted fires, heaters and boilers.

3.3 NOTIFICATION OF DISREPAIR

The Council will only be breaking its obligations under 3.1 and 3.2 if it knows about the disrepair and the repair works have not been carried out within a reasonable time.

3.4 COUNCIL'S OBLIGATIONS TO MAINTAIN COMMON PARTS

The Council must take reasonable care to:

a keep the common parts in a reasonable state of repair and in safe condition fit for the use of the tenant, members of the tenant's household, any sub-tenant or visitor. This includes but is not limited to paths, steps, stairs, landings, corridors, halls, play areas and communal open spaces and fire escapes.

b keep the installations situated in the common parts in a reasonable state of repair and working order fit for the use of the tenant, members of the tenant's household, any sub-tenant or visitor. Installations include but are not limited to lifts, entryphones, rubbish chutes and bins, fire alarms and other fire prevention devices, fire extinguishers, lighting, communal laundries and communal drying facilities provided that in the case of each of the last two mentioned installations the Council's obligations shall not apply if the Council has withdrawn the service.

3.5 EXCEPTIONS TO REPAIR LIABILITIES

The Council shall not be liable under Clause 3:

a for any disrepair arising from the failure of you, your household, sub-tenant or visitor to use the premises in a reasonable manner or failure to observe these conditions of tenancy.

b to rebuild or reinstate the premises in the case of destruction or damage by fire, or by tempest, flood or other inevitable accident.

c to keep in repair any structural alteration made by you to the premises or installation fitted by you, if
   (i) the structural alteration has been made or the installation fitted without the written consent of the Council; or
   (ii) the Council has made it a condition of its consent that it will not be liable to repair the installation.

d to keep in repair or maintain anything which you are entitled to remove from the premises.

e to keep in repair or maintain any installation, equipment or similar object belonging to the London Electricity Board, North Thames Gas, Thames Water Authority, or other statutory undertaker.

3.6 MAKING GOOD

Where the Council carries out repairs or improvements which involve damaging the decorations in the premises, it must make good the damage so caused and must clear up and carry away all rubbish resulting from the works.

3.7 REGULAR INSPECTIONS

The Council must inspect the common parts, block and estate at regular intervals to ensure that the Council is complying with its obligations under the tenancy agreement. The Council will do its best to notify the chairperson or secretary of the appropriate tenants' association, if any, of an intended inspection so that arrangements can be made for a representative of the association to accompany the inspecting officer.

3.8 MAJOR WORKS – DEFINITION

Major works are works of repair (but not improvement) which by their extent or nature cannot in the opinion of the Council, reasonably be carried out with you and your household remaining in occupation of the premises.

3.9 MAJOR WORKS – OPTIONS

a Where the Council wishes to undertake major works it may, according to the circumstances and after consultation with you (see 3.10 below) require you to move from the premises while the work is carried out.

b Where you are required to move to enable major works to be carried out, you may choose:
   (i)   to be transferred to temporary accommodation and to return to the premises once the works are completed; or
   (ii) to make your own arrangements for temporary accommodation and to return to the premises when the Council notifies you that the works are completed; or
   (iii) to be transferred permanently to suitable alternative accommodation but only if,
        firstly such accommodation is available; and secondly the work is estimated by the Council to take more than four weeks to complete from the date of commencement.

3.10 MAJOR WORKS – NOTICE AND CONSULTATION

a The Council must give you written notice of its intention to carry out major works to the premises. The notice shall include details of and reasons for the proposed works, explain the provisions of clauses 3.8 and 3.9 in these conditions of tenancy and invite comments from you.

b The period of notice must be the maximum which the Council considers practicable. Except in the case of emergency major works, the notice must allow you time to comment on the proposed works.

c Where the Council intends to carry out a planned programme of major works to a number of premises, including yours, it must also give the same notice to the chairperson or secretary of the appropriate tenants' association, if any.

d The Council must have regard to any written comments made by you and/or the tenants' association in response to such notice.

3.11 CARETAKING

The Council must provide a caretaking service on flatted estates between such hours and at such frequency as the Council shall determine taking account of the general views expressed by tenants' representatives through the normal consultation procedures.

4 Tenant's duties

4.1 RENT

a Your rent and other charges are payable weekly in advance on Monday. You must pay them promptly when due.

b If at any time before you took up your present tenancy you occupied other Council premises then it should be open to the Council at any time:
(i) to debit your current rent account with any rent or charges you owe (on previous premises) and use any money paid by you to reduce your debt;
(ii) to credit your current rent account with any overpayment of rent or charges on the previous premises.

4.2 LOOKING AFTER COUNCIL PROPERTY/END OF TENANCY

a You must take care of Council property and make sure that your household and any sub-tenant and visitor does so.

b In particular, you must not allow them intentionally or recklessly to damage or deface the premises, any Council furnishings, fixtures and fittings or any part of the common parts, block or estate; nor must you do so yourself.

c You must on demand by the Council repay to it the cost (including where necessary replacement cost) of making good any such damage or defacement caused in any of these ways.

d You must notify the Council as soon as possible about any defects you find which you consider should be repaired by the Council under 3.1 and 3.2 of these conditions.

e At the end of your tenancy, you must:
(i) leave the premises and the Council's fixtures and fittings in as good a state of repair as they were at the beginning of the tenancy, except for deterioration caused by fair wear and tear or the Council's failure to carry out its obligations.
(ii) leave the premises in a clean condition and remove all rubbish.
(iii) take with you all your personal belongings. Anything left behind will be deemed abandoned. The Council may thereafter dispose of it without accounting to you.
(iv) secure the premises.
(v) immediately hand in the keys to the premises to the Council which will give you a receipt.

4.3 CONDUCT TOWARDS YOUR NEIGHBOURS AND RACIAL HARASSMENT

a You must not cause any nuisance, annoyance or disturbance to any of your neighbours, their children or visitors or to the Council. Nor must you allow any member of your household or any sub-tenant or visitor to do so.

b Your neighbours are the persons living or working in the vicinity of your premises.

c The phrase 'nuisance, annoyance or disturbance' includes (amongst other things):
(i) racial harassment;
(ii) violence or threats of violence towards the person or property;
(iii) threats, abuse or any harassment (sexual or otherwise) or any act or omission causing disturbance, discomfort or inconvenience;
(iv) obstructions of any of the common parts, doorways and other exits and entrances in the block and in the estate;
(v) making an unreasonably loud noise by shouting, screaming, playing any musical instruments or sound reproduction equipment (including television, radio and hi fi) or using other machinery;
(vi) any act or omission which creates a danger to the well-being of any neighbour or to his/her belongings.

4.4 CONDUCT TOWARDS THE HOUSEHOLD

4.4/1 You must not evict any person from your household otherwise than in accordance with the law.

4.4/2
a You must not commit or threaten to commit any violence to a member of your household which would justify that member leaving the premises.

b The Council will consider it to be evidence of a failure to keep to a above if (among other things):
(i) You have been convicted of an offence against the person of a member of your household; or
(ii) A court order has been made against you either to leave the premises, temporarily or permanently, or concerning your future conduct towards a member of your household.

4.5 CONTROL OF ANIMALS

a (i) The following animals may be kept in or brought to your premises without permission:
☐ A cat;
☐ Rabbits, guinea pigs, hamsters, and similar small animals normally kept in cages as pets;
☐ Budgerigars, canaries or similar small caged birds;
☐ Fish in aquaria.

(ii) You must ensure that no other animal is kept in or brought to your premises unless you obtain the written permission of the Council, which will be given only in certain specified circumstances.

b You must not let any animal kept in or brought to your premises:
☐ cause any nuisance or annoyance to the Council or to any other person;
☐ foul the premises, common parts, the block and estate;
☐ be out of proper control at any time in those places.

c You must on demand by the Council repay to it the cost of cleansing and of making good any damage or defacement to the premises, common parts, the block or estate caused by any such animal.

d In this clause the term 'animal' includes any mammal, bird, reptile, amphibian, fish and insect.

4.6 CONTROL OF USE OF CALOR GAS AND PARAFFIN

a You must not use or store liquid petroleum gas (calor gas) in your premises or your block or estate (if any) without the written permission of the Council. Such permission is not given in any circumstances for a flat or maisonnette in a block.

b You must not use or store paraffin in your premises, block or estate (if any).

4.7 GARAGES, PARKING SPACES AND VEHICLES ON ESTATES

a You must not, without the Council's written permission:
  (i) park a vehicle, trailer, caravan or similar object on any part of the estate;
  keep a vehicle, trailer, caravan or similar object in any garage belonging to the Council.
  Nor must you allow any of your household, sub-tenants or visitors to do so.

b If you are given permission to use a numbered parking space on any estate or a Council garage, you will be required to enter into a separate agreement with the Council. This agreement will contain detailed conditions regulating the use of the parking space or garage and also specify the relevant charge for such use.

c The Council may remove without notice any vehicle, trailer, caravan or similar object parked on the estate, which it considers:
  (i) is causing, or may cause, an obstruction to an emergency vehicle:
  (ii) by reason of its position or condition is a risk to the safety of any person living, working on or visiting the estate of his/her property;
  and the Council may charge for the cost of such removal and will not be liable for any loss or damage howsoever caused.

4.8 RESIDING IN YOUR PREMISES

a You must live in the premises and nowhere else.

b If you intend to stay away from the premises temporarily for any period of more than three months, you must notify the Council in writing not later than two weeks before you leave, stating:
  (i) your intended date of departure;
  (ii) your intended date of return;
  (iii) the arrangements you have made for the payment of your rent and the care of the premises;
  (iv) (where possible) the address and telephone number where you can be contacted by the Council.

c If you are staying away from the premises without being able to give prior notice due to circumstances beyond your control you must, as soon as you are able to do so, notify the Council in writing about your absence, giving the details listed in (ii), (iii), and (iv) above.

4.9 USE OF YOUR PREMISES

You must not use the premises or any part of it for business or other non-residential use. This means that your living accommodation should be used for living in; any garage for parking your own private vehicle; and any store only for your own personal belongings.

4.10 TENANT'S IMPROVEMENTS

a You must not, without the Council's written permission, which will not be unreasonably withheld:
  (i) make any alteration or addition to the premises or to the Council's fixtures and fittings therein or to the provision of services;
  (ii) erect any radio or television aerial;
  (iii) carry out any external decoration of the premises.

b If you do any of these things without the written permission of the Council, the Council may, in addition to any other action it may take against you for breaking this condition:
  (i) require you to take down and remove the alteration, addition or erection and reinstate the premises to their original state; or
  (ii) take it down and remove it itself, reinstate the premises and require you to pay the cost.

4.11 LODGERS

a Subject to subclause b below, you may take in lodgers without asking permission of the Council, but if you do so, you must notify the Council in writing of the fact within four weeks of the date on which any lodger is taken in.

b If your tenancy ceases to be secure (which will only happen in exceptional circumstances), you must obtain the written permission of the Council to take in or keep lodgers and you must comply with any conditions laid down in that permission.

4.12 SUBLETTING

a You must not sublet or part with possession of the whole of the premises.

b You must not without the written give consent of the Council, which will not be unreasonably withheld, sublet or part with possession of part of the premises.

c In considering a request for consent the Council must take into account the following matters, among others;
  (i) whether consent would lead to overcrowding of the premises:
  (ii) whether the Council proposes to carry out works on the premises or on the block (if any) which would affect the accommodation likely to be used by the sub tenant:
  (iii) the suitability of the proposed sub-tenant:
  (iv) the terms of the proposed sub-tenancy.

d Where the Council refuses consent it must give you written reasons.

e If the Council neither gives nor refuses to give consent within four weeks from the receipt of the application, it may be taken to have withheld its consent.

5 Assignment and succession

5.1 TRANSFER OF TENANCY DURING TENANT'S LIFETIME – ASSIGNMENT

a Subject to clauses b and c below, you must not assign (that is, transfer) the tenancy.

b You may, with the Council's written permission, which must not be unreasonably withheld, assign the tenancy:
  (i) to a person who would qualify to succeed to the tenancy if you were to die immediately before the assignment; or
  (ii) by way of exchange, to a secure tenant who has the written consent of his or her landlord (whether or not the Council) to assign his or her tenancy to you or to another secure tenant.

c The tenancy may be assigned if the assignment is made under or following a Court Order in matrimonial proceedings. You must give the Council written notice of such an assignment within fourteen days of its having taken effect.

5.2 TRANSFER OF TENANCY ON A TENANT'S DEATH – SUCCESSION

a In the case of a joint tenancy, if one tenant dies, the tenancy continues in the name of the surviving joint tenant or tenants.

b In any other case, on the death of the tenant:
  (i) the tenancy of the premises transfer to the tenant's surviving spouse (if any) provided he or she occupied the premises as his or her home at the date of death;
  (ii) If there is no such spouse, or if he or she does not wish to take over the tenancy, but there is another member of the tenant's family who lived in the premises continuously for a period of at least twelve months up to the date of death, the tenancy of the premises transfers to that person. Where more than one person is qualified to succeed in this way and they are unable to agree between them who shall have the tenancy, the Council must choose the successor from among them.
This subclause does not apply where the tenant is the last survivor under a former joint tenancy.

c Where the tenancy is transferred on the death of the tenant, the Council may seek possession of the premises if:
  (i) the premises are larger than the new tenant reasonably requires, he or she is not the spouse of the tenant and action to seek possession is taken between six and twelve months after the tenant's death; or
  (ii) the premises are specifically adapted for a physically disabled person, there is no longer such a person resident in the premises and the Council requires possession to relet to such a person; or

(iii) the premises are part of a group used for persons with special needs, a social service or service facility is provided nearby for such persons, there is no longer any such person resident in the premises and the Council require possession to relet to such a person.

If the Council seeks possession on any of the above grounds, it will make available suitable alternative accommodation to the new tenant.

d In this clause 'member of the tenant's family' means the tenant's parent, grandparent, child, grandchild, brother, sister, uncle, aunt, nephew, niece or common law spouse.

e Where, following the death of the tenant, there is no succession under b above and the tenancy comes to an end, if there is a co-habitee residing in the premises at the date of the death of the tenant, the Council shall offer the cohabitee a tenancy of the premises or of other premises which the Council consider suitable for the co-habitee. The co-habitee is a person who lives as the partner of the tenant in a permanent relationship whether or not of the opposite sex to the tenant.

f The provisions in this clause shall not apply if the tenancy has already been inherited or transferred voluntarily to the tenant (otherwise than by way of exchange).

6   Miscellaneous Provisions

6.1 TRANSFERS

If you apply for a transfer to other housing accommodation, the Council must thereafter make available to you on request at all reasonable times and without charge:

a the recorded particulars about yourself and your family which you have given to the Council;

b the priority which your transfer application has been given;

c the basis upon which that priority has been calculated.

6.2 ACCESS TO PREMISES BY THE COUNCIL

a In this clause the term 'agent' includes any contractor or consultant or other person authorised to act on behalf of the Council including any employee of such contractor, consultant or other person.

b You must give the employees and agents of the Council access to your premises for the purpose of:
   (i) carrying out the Council's powers and duties under these conditions of tenancy including the power to inspect the state of repair;
   (ii) carrying out the Council's statutory functions as a local authority including those relating to the provision, management and improvement of housing;
   (iii) finding out whether you or the occupiers of adjoining or adjacent premises are complying with these conditions of tenancy;
   (iv) enabling the execution of works to adjoining or adjacent land or premises including the block.

c If the Council employees or agents cannot get into the premises for repair or maintenance work on a first visit, then, unless it is an emergency (see e below), they will leave a notice giving another date. You will be given at least seven days notice of the further visit but if the date is not convenient, you must tell the Council as soon as possible and agree another date.

d The provisions of sub-clause c shall not apply in either of the following circumstances:
   (i) If you and the Council have already agreed the date of the first visit; or
   (ii) If on the first visit, you are present but are unable or unwilling to give access and on that occasion you agree with the Council's employee or agent a new date when you will be able and willing to do so.

e Council employees or agents may enter the premises without notice, using such means as are necessary, if there is an emergency involving injury to any person or property or if the Council believes that this is probable. If this happens, the Council will make good any damage caused.

f At all times before entering the premises employees and agents of the Council must product identification to you, or in your absence, to the person in charge of your premises.
   (i) The term 'identification' means in the case of an employee of the Council, the current identification card issued by the Council; in any other case, it means an official works order for the premises or a letter of engagement or authority issued by the Council.
   (ii) You will not be in breach of Clause 6.2 in refusing access to any employee or agent of the Council if he or she does not produce such identification.

6.3 VARIATION OF RENT, RATES AND OTHER CHARGES

a In this clause the term 'gross rent' includes all the elements of the amount you are required to pay for your premises including net rent, general rates, water rates and service charges including heating charges.

b The Council must give you at least four weeks prior written notice before varying the gross rent except that:
   (i) where the variation is due to a decision to alter any service charge, the Council must give at least two weeks notice; and
   (ii) where the variation is in relation to general rates and water rates, the Council are not required to give any notice but will do so, if practicable.

6.4 APPLICATION OF THESE CONDITIONS TO NON-SECURE TENANTS SUCCESSION

If your tenancy is not a secure tenancy under the Housing Act 1980 or if, having been a secure tenancy it ceases to be one (for example, by the subletting of the whole of it) then:

a You must not assign, sublet or part with possession of the premises or part of them;

b Clauses 2, 3.8, 3.9, 3.10, 4.10, 4.12, and 5 shall not apply; and

c Nothing in these Conditions are to be taken as meaning that the Council regards your tenancy as secure.

6.5 TENANT'S RIGHT TO QUIET ENJOYMENT

Except as set out in these conditions, you are entitled to have the use of your premises without any interruption or disturbance by the Council or anyone acting on its behalf.

Schedule to Clause 2a

GROUNDS UPON WHICH THE COUNCIL MAY SEEK POSSESSION

1 The tenant has failed to pay the rent.

2 The tenant has committed a breach of tenancy conditions.

3 The tenant or other person residing in the premises has caused nuisance or annoyance to neighbours.

4 The tenant or other person residing in the premises has been convicted of using such premises for immoral or illegal purposes.

5 The condition of the premises or the common parts has deteriorated owing to the act or default, of the tenant or any person residing in the premises.

6 The condition of any furniture provided by the Council has deteriorated owing to ill-treatment by the tenant or any person residing in the premises.

7 The tenant persuaded the Council to give him/her the tenancy by knowingly or recklessly making a false statement.

8 The tenancy of the premises was granted to the tenant on a temporary basis while work was carried out to his or her usual accommodation and that accommodation is now ready for re-occupation.

9 The premises are overcrowded within the meaning of Part IX of the Housing Action 1985.

10 The Council intends within a reasonable time to demolish, reconstruct or carry out work on the premises or the building in which the premises are situated and cannot reasonably do so without obtaining possession.

11 The premises are specifically adapted for a physically disabled person, there is no longer any such person residing in the premises and the Council require possession to relet to such a person.

12 The premises are part of a group used for persons with special needs (e.g. sheltered housing), a social service or special facility is provided nearby for such persons, there is no longer any such person resident in the premises and the Council require possession to relet to such a person.

13 The premises are larger than the tenant reasonably requires, the tenant only succeeded to the tenancy as a member of the family other than the spouse of the tenant who died and action to seek possession is taken between six and twelve months after the original tenant died.

14 The tenancy was assigned to the tenant by way of exchange and a premium was paid in connection with the assignment.

15 The premises form part of a building which is held by the Council mainly for purposes other than housing accommodation, they were let to the tenant in consequence of him/her being in the employment of the Council and the tenant or other person residing in the premises has been guilty of conduct incompatible with the purpose for which the building is used.

16 The premises form part of a building which is held by the Council mainly for purposes other than housing accommodation, they were let to the tenant in consequence of him/her being in the employment of the council, the tenant is no longer in that employment and the Council reasonably requires the premises as a residence for some person employed by the Council.

APPENDIX 4E: SOME USEFUL SOURCES ON RACE AND HOUSING

ASSOCIATION OF METROPOLITAN AUTHORITIES (London) (1987): Reports of the Local Authority Housing & Racial Equality Working Party on: Allocations; Homelessness; Local Housing Strategies; Racial Harassment

BELL W S (1988): Put in Your Place – Race & Council Housing in Enfield. LB of Enfield Community Relations Council

COMMISSION FOR RACIAL EQUALITY (1987): Living in Terror – A report on racial violence and harassment in housing. London

—— (1989): Race Relations Code of Practice. For the elimination of racial discrimination and the promotion of equal opportunity in the field of rented housing. HMSO

—— (1989): Race, Housing and Immigration. A Guide

—— (1988): Housing and Ethnic Minorities – Statistical Information

—— (1986): Ethnic Minorities in Britain: Statistical Information on the Pattern of Settlement

—— (1984): Hackney Housing Investigated. Summary of a Formal Investigation Report

—— (1988): Homelessness and Discrimination. Report of a Formal Investigation into the London Borough of Tower Hamlets

—— (1987): Racial and Ethnic Relations in Britain: Past, Present & Future

—— (1986): Review of the Race Relations Act 1976: Proposals for Change

DALTON M & DAGHLIAN S (1989): Race and Housing in Glasgow. The Role of Housing Associations. CRE, London

DEANE T (undated): An Anti-Racist Housing Policy. Labour Housing Group, London

DEPARTMENT OF THE ENVIRONMENT (1989): Tackling Racial Violence & Harassment in Local Authority Housing: A Guide to Good Practice for Local Authorities. HMSO

EADE J (1989): The Politics of Community – The Bangladeshi Community in East London. Gower, Aldershot

FEDERATION OF BLACK HOUSING ORGANISATIONS AND MERSEYSIDE AREA PROFILE GROUP (1986): Black People Do Not Cause Slums. They are forced to live in them. London

FORBES D (1988): Action on Racial Harassment – Legal Remedies & Local Authorities. Institute of Housing, London

GREATER LONDON COUNCIL (1976): Colour and the Allocation of GLC Housing. London

HENDERSON J & KAHN V (1987): Race, Class & State Housing. Gower, London

HOME AFFAIRS COMMITTEE (House of Commons) (1986–7): Bangladeshis in Britain. London

KING M L (1963): Why we can't wait. Harper & Row, New York

LOCAL AUTHORITY HOUSING AND RACIAL EQUALITY WORKING PARTY (1988): Local Housing Strategies. AMA, London

NATIONAL FEDERATION OF HOUSING ASSOCIATIONS (1982): Race & Housing: A Guide for Housing Associations. London

—— (1985): Ethnic record keeping and monitoring

PHILLIPS D (1986): What Price Equality? A report on the allocation of GLC housing in Tower Hamlets. GLC Housing Research & Policy Report No. 9, London

SMITH S & MERCER J (1987): Race & Housing – New Perspectives. University of Glasgow, Centre for Housing Research

THE ECONOMIST (28.10.89): Britain's Browns. East meets West

APPENDIX 4F: ADDITIONAL TENANT TRAINING INFORMATION

Thorpes Estate Steering Group – Training Course in Housing Management April/May 1989

Session 1 3rd April 1989	How the council works – and how the neighbourhood management committee fits in (Ginnie Shaw, PEP Associate)
Session 2	Housing finance, estate budgets and Housing Management (Sally Phillips, PEP Training Organiser)
Session 3 17th April 1989	What makes a good repair service? (Michael Hatchett, Bartlett School of Architecture). (Steering Group meets on 24 April; Bank Holiday – on 1st May)
Session 4 8th May 1989	Local lettings – how to get new tenants and keep down empty properties (George Varughese, PEP Associate)
Session 5 15th May 1989	Being a represenative – the responsibilities and the rewards (Chris Holmes, PEP Associate)
Session 6 22nd May 1989	Final session – what the course has taught; where to from here? (Roger Saunders, PEP Training Assistant, or Sally Phillips)

Note: 1. All sessions are on Monday evenings – Timing to be notified. (They will last for 1½–2 hours.) 2. So that the course works best for everyone, you are asked to attend **all** the sessions in the programme. 3. The programme has been designed especially for the members of the Thorpes Estate Steering Group.

Priority Estates Project

Residential Training Course for Members of the Neighbourhood Management Committees at the Danes and Thorpes Projects, Hull

12th to 14th January 1990

Venue: Esplanade Hotel, Belmont Road, Scarborough.

Programme

Friday 12th January

5.00 onwards	Arrivals and Dinner
7.30 – 9.00	**Introduction:** Background to the Neighbourhood Management Committees and the principles behind them. By **Ginnie Shaw.**
	Discussion: Members' hopes and aims for the NMCs. Potential difficulties and how they might be overcome.

Saturday 13th January

9.30 – 11.00	**The Partnership Agreements** What will the NMCs' duties and responsibilities be? What sort of decisions will the NMCs have to take? What information and other support/resources will the NMCs need to be able to fulfill their responsibilities? Session led by **Richard Veale,** Area Manager.
11.00	Coffee/Tea
11.30 – 1.00	**Running a budget** Where does the money come from and how is the budget worked out? What will the estate budgets cover? How much discretion will the NMCs have over how the budget is spent? What information on the budgets will the NMCs need? Session led by **Ginnie Shaw and Lester Quayle.**
1.00	Lunch
2.30 – 4.00	**Relationship with estate staff and management priorities** What will be the relationship between the NMCs and estate staff? How can NMC responsibilities towards staff be fulfilled? How should priorities for housing management be established, monitored, and reviewed? Session led by **Ginnie Shaw and Andy Toft.**
4.00	Tea
4.30 – 6.00	**Involving other tenants** How can NMC tenant reps be truly representative and accountable? How can the interest of other tenants be encouraged and sustained? What is the role of the Community Association? Session led by **Anne McLauchlan,** PEP Training.
	Dinner

Sunday 14th January

9.00 – 11.00	**Meetings Skills** What skills do NMC members need for meetings to be effective? Session led by **Roger Saunders,** PEP Training.
11.00	Coffee/Tea
11.30 – 1.00	**Communication and Presentation Skills** What skills do NMC members need to be able to communicate effectively with one another, with Council officers, and with tenants? Session led by **Roger Saunders.**
1.00	Lunch
2.00	**Planning Session** The NMCs' Aims and Objectives for their first year, together with an Action Plan.
3.30	Feedback and Summing up.
4.00	Tea and Finish.

TRAINING BODIES AND APPROVED HOUSING COURSES (Institute of Housing)

Institute of Housing
Angel House, White Lion Street, London N1

Tel: 071/837-4280

National Federation of Housing Associations
175 Gray's Inn Road, London WC1X 8UP

Tel: 071/278 6571

National Federation of Housing Co-operatives
88 Old Street, London EC1V 9AX

Tel: 071/608 2494

Local Government Training Board
Arndale House, Arndale Centre, Luton LU1 2TS

Tel: 0582/45 11 66

Priority Estates Project
62 Eden Grove, London N7 8EN

Tel: 071/607 8186

Royal Institute of British Architects
66 Portland Place, London W1

Tel: 071/580 5533

Royal Institution of Chartered Surveyors
12 Great George Street, London SW1

Tel: 071/222 7000

Housing Centre Trust
33 Alfred Place, London WC1

Tel: 071/637 4202

Tenants Participation Advisory Service England
48 The Crescent, Salford M5 4NY

Tel: 061/745 7903

EDUCATION INSTITUTIONS OFFERING FULLY RECOGNISED COURSES

These courses are awarded full exemption from the PQ written exams. Only students who enrolled on the Postgraduate diploma at Sheffield on or after September 1986 will be eligible for full exemption. Students who enrolled on the course prior to September 1987 are still required to sit two examinations (Social Structure & Social Change; Social Policy & Administration) unless otherwise exempt.

Please note that details of fees etc. for these courses should be obtained direct from the Institution concerned.

1.0 Postgraduate diplomas (full-time)

1.1 Birmingham Polytechnic/University of Birmingham
Course director: **Veronica Coatham,** Department of Planning and Landscape, Birmingham Polytechnic, Perry Barr, Birmingham B42 2SU   (021 331-5000)
Postgraduate Diploma in Housing

1.2 Bristol Polytechnic/University of Bristol
Course director: **Dr Peter Malpass,** Department of Surveying, Bristol Polytechnic, Unity Street, Bristol BS1 5HP   (0272 273016)
Postgraduate Diploma in Housing Studies

1.3 Edinburgh College of Art/Heriot Watt University
Course director: **Anne Yanetta,** Department of Town and Country Planning, Lauriston Place, Edinburgh EH3 9DF   (031 229-9311)
Postgraduate Diploma in Housing

1.4 London School of Economics
Course director: **Dr Anne Power** MBE, Department of Social Administration, Houghton Street, London WC2A 2AE   (071 405-7686)
Postgraduate Diploma in Housing

1.5 Newcastle Polytechnic/University of Newcastle
Course directors: **Stuart Cameron,** Department of Town and Country Planning, University of Newcastle 7 Park Terrace, Newcastle Upon Tyne NE1 7RU (091 222-6000), **Paul Crompton,** Department of Economics and Government, Newcastle Upon Tyne Polytechnic, Newcastle Upon Tyne NE1 8ST   (091 232-6002)
Postgraduate Diploma in Housing Policy and Management

1.6 Oxford Polytechnic
Course director: **Glenn McDougall,** School of Planning, Oxford Polytechnic, Gypsy Lane, Headington, Oxford OX3 0BP   (0865 741111)
Postgraduate Diploma in Housing Studies

1.7 Salford Centre for Housing Studies
Course director: **Dr Patricia Garside,** Environmental Studies Division, Department of Civil Engineering, University of Salford, Salford M5 4WT   (061 745-5000)
Postgraduate Diploma in Housing Studies

1.8 Sheffield Polytechnic
Course director: **Ian Cole,** Department of Urban and Regional Studies, Pond Street, Sheffield S1 1WB   (0742 720911)
Postgraduate Diploma in Housing

1.9 Stirling University
Course director: **David Alexander,** Department of Sociology, Stirling FK9 4LA   (0786 73171)
Postgraduate Diploma in Housing Administration

1.10 University of Wales, College of Cardiff
Course director: **Professor Peter Williams,** Department of Town Planning, UWCC, P.O. Box 906, Aberconway Building, Colum Drive, Cardiff CF1 3YN   (0222 874000)
Postgraduate Diploma in Housing

2.0 Postgraduate diploma (part-time)

2.1 Bristol Polytechnic
Course director: **Ms Barbara Reid,** Department of Surveying, Bristol Polytechnic, Unity Street, Bristol BS1 5HP   (0272 273016)
Postgraduate Diploma in Housing Studies

2.2 Humberside College
Course director: **Bill Spink,** School of Applied Social Studies, Humberside College, Inglemire Avenue, Hull HUG 7LU   (0482 440550)
Postgraduate Diploma in Housing Management and Administration

2.3 London School of Economics
Course director: **Dr Anne Power,** Department of Social Administration, Houghton Street, London WC2A 2AE (071 405-7686)
Postgraduate Diploma in Housing

2.4 Middlesex Polytechnic/Tottenham College of Technology
Course directors: **Dennis Hardy,** Middlesex Polytechnic, School of Geography and Planning, Queensway, Enfield, Middlesex EN3 4SF   (081 368 1299), **Marion Brion,** Tottenham College of Technology, High Road, Tottenham N15 4RU   (081 802-3111)
Postgraduate Diploma in Housing (part-time)

2.5 Newcastle Polytechnic/University of Newcastle
Course directors: **Stuart Cameron,** University of Newcastle Upon Tyne, 7 Park Terrace, Newcastle Upon Tyne NE1 7RU   (091 232-2391), **Paul Crompton,** Department of Economics and Government, Newcastle Upon Tyne Polytechnic, Newcastle Upon Tyne NE1 8ST   (091 232-6002)
Postgraduate Diploma in Housing Policy and Management

2.6 Oxford Polytechnic
Course director: **Glenn McDougall,** School of Planning, Oxford Polytechnic, Gypsy Lane, Headington, Oxford OX3 0BP   (0865 64777)
Postgraduate Diploma in Housing Studies

2.7 Polytechnic of the South Bank
Course director: **Charlie Cooper,** Department of Town Planning, Faculty of the Built Environment, Polytechnic of the South Bank, Wandsworth Road, London SW8   (071 928-8989)
Postgraduate Diploma in Housing Studies

2.8 Sheffield Polytechnic
Course director: **Ian Cole,** Department of Urban and Regional Studies, Pond Street, Sheffield S1 1WB   (0742 20911)
Postgraduate Diploma in Housing

2.9 University of Wales, College of Cardiff
Course director: **Professor Peter Williams,** Department of Town Planning, UWCC, P.O. Box 906, Aberconway Building, Column Drive, Cardiff CF1 3YN   (0222 874000)
Postgraduate Diploma in Housing

3.0 Undergraduate degrees (full-time)

3.1 Anglia Higher Education College
Course director: **Bernard Bourdillon,** School of the Built Environment, Anglia Higher Education College, Victoria Road South, Chelmsford, Essex CM1 1LL   (0245 493131)
BSc (hons) Housing Studies

3.2 Bristol Polytechnic
Course director: **Geoff Winn,** Department of Surveying, Bristol Polytechnic, Unity Street, Bristol BS1 5HP   (0272 273016)
BA (hons) Housing

3.3 Polytechnic of Central London
Course director: **Bill Smith-Bowers,** School of Construction, Housing and Surveying, Polytechnic of Central

London, 35 Marylebone Road, London NW1 5LS   (071 486-5811 Ext 433)
BA (hons) Housing Studies (Full-time)

3.4 **Sheffield Polytechnic**
Course director: **Colin Foster,** Department of Urban and Regional Studies, Pond Street, Sheffield S1 1WB   (0742 720911)
BA Hons Housing Studies

3.5 **Nottingham Polytechnic**
Course director: **Derek Fox,** Department of Surveying, Nottingham Polytechnic, Burton Street, Nottingham NG1 4BU   (0602 418418)
BSc Hons Urban Estate Surveying (Housing Option)

3.6 **University of Ulster**
Course director: **Chris Mackay,** Department of Social Administration, Coleraine, N. Ireland BT52 1SA   (0265 44141)
BSc Hons Social Administration and Social Studies

4.0 **Undergraduate degree (part-time)**

4.1 **Polytechnic of Central London**
Course director: **Bill Smith-Bowers,** School of Construction, Housing and Surveying, Polytechnic of Central London, 35 Marylebone Road, London NW1 5LS   (071 486 5811 Ext 433)
BA (hons) Housing Studies (part-time)

5.0 **Graduate/Non-Graduate Diploma Courses (part-time)**

5.1 **University of Glasgow**
Course director: **Robina Goodlad,** Centre for Housing Research, 25 Bute Gardens, Glasgow G12 8RT   (041 339-8855)
Diploma in Housing Studies (part-time)

6.0 **Hong Kong**

6.1 **University of Hong Kong**
Course director: **Dr Rebecca Chiu,** Department of Extra Mural Studies, Pokfulam Road, Hong Kong.
Certificate in Housing Management (part-time)

6.2 **Hong Kong City Polytechnic**
Course director: **Dr Roy Le Herissier,** Department of Public and Social Administration, Tat Chee Avenue, Hong Kong
BA (Hons) Public and Social Administration (Housing Stream) and Postgraduate Bridging Course

APPENDIX 4G: CO-ORDINATION AND DEVELOPMENT OF OTHER SERVICES

The following case study is an updated extract from the PEP Working Paper on small-scale employment creation on unpopular estates.

Employment initiatives – Broadwater Farm Estate

1. Unemployment on Broadwater Farm, especially among the youth, has always been a serious problem, estimated in 1986 as 45% of those eligible for work. This is very high for London and higher than in the Tottenham area as a whole. Large numbers of young people, mainly black and many of them without jobs, have tended to congregate on the estate.

2. In 1981, the Broadwater Farm Youth Association was formed. In 1983 Haringey Council established a comprehensive housing management office on the estate

which quickly tackled basic management problems: repairs, empty dwellings, cleaning, security. PEP worked with the estate team and the residents from October 1983–March 1990.

3. Job creation has been a priority since 1983, resulting in over 120 estate-based jobs for residents.

Job creation has developed in FOUR key ways:

A. **Council Recruitment:**
– When the estate-based housing office, the repairs team and the cleansing team were established in 1983, the Council recruited many Broadwater Farm residents into the team.
– By 1984, 19 out of 42 Broadwater Farm estate-based staff were residents.
– These permanent posts were funded from the Housing Revenue Account.
– Giving priority to local recruitment helped create a high level of service and commitment from the staff and won the co-operation and respect of residents. Housing management on Broadwater Farm is to a very high standard according to the PEP Guide (1987) and the Gifford Report (1986).

B. **Self Help Schemes:**
– From 1983 the Youth Association developed a range of community-based services, e.g. day care, playschemes, pensioners' club, meals-on-wheels, youth programme, sports, etc.
– These projects were grant-aided via the Urban Programme, Haringey Council and the GLC.
– The Youth Association has had a contract with Haringey Social Services to run the meals-on-wheels service on the estate.
– By 1987, these community services employed 14 residents. Since then, these projects have been affected by cuts across all services in Haringey.

C. **Small Enterprises:**
– Three small co-operative enterprises were established on the estate including a launderette, a fruit shop and a hairdressers.
– They were subsidised by the local authority's Economic Development Unit but the intention was that they become self-financing within three years. There is a limit to how much these small businesses can expand economically in a poor community. They are probably the least successful of all the job creation initiatives.

D. **Broadwater Farm Youth Assoc. Co-op Ltd:**
– In 1985, the Youth Association trustees set up a small company, the 'BWFYA Co-op', to develop workshop premises, provide training, and advise and assist in the development of new co-operatives and community enterprises. The management committee included Youth Association and Residents' Association representatives, Council officers and outside advisers.
– Two people were employed to do the development work.
– Prior to this, the Council had established a large programme of structural repairs, major maintenance and improvement works to Broadwater Farm, most of which was being done by **outside** contractors using **outside** labour, making profits which **left** the estate.

Residents decided to bid for this work, through the 'BWFYA Co-op'.

a) With Council support, they persuaded **private contractors** to recruit labour from within the estate and to provide training.

Between 1985 and 1988, seven contractors recruited approximately 20 young people. The arrangement worked well and some of these jobs became permanent.

b) The **Council DLO** also recruited c. 24 residents to work on a fire prevention contract. These jobs were also intended to be permanent but in 1989 they were lost when the DLO was forced to make major cutbacks.

Most of the contract work was financed through the local authority's HIP allocation for Broadwater Farm. An annual pest control contract was revenue-funded.

Based on American experience of 'affirmative action', all contracts were required by Haringey to tender on the basis of maximising local employment and providing training. This practice was made illegal by the Local Government Act 1988.

c) **The Co-operative itself** also negotiated with Haringey Council to become the contractor for some of the improvement works. By 1987/88 this included:

Under deck painting	:	15 jobs
Community gardens, landscaping and planting	:	24 jobs
Mosaic mural	:	3 jobs
Painted mural	:	2 jobs
		—
TOTAL		44 jobs

Most of this work was financed through Haringey's Estate Action targetted HIP.

These jobs, however, ceased at the end of each contract but the Co-operative went on to do further painting and landscaping work on the estate and is currently (1989/90) engaged in extensive renewal work in the Lordship Recreation Park adjacent to the estate.

d) **Enterprise Workshops**

Through the co-operative, plans emerged in 1988 to build workshops under the walkways, develop training and set up small businesses which could be competitive and tap markets outside the estate.

An Urban Aid grant has been agreed by the Department of the Environment and it is hoped that work will begin during 1990.

A new community-based company has now been established by tenants to oversee the development and management of the enterprise workshops.

Summary

Between 1983 and 1989, approximately **120 jobs** were created for residents on Broadwater Farm, some of them short-term, some of them permanent.

This success has raised expectations, but all these jobs depend either directly or indirectly on continuing investment of **public money,** either in the form of grants or capital expenditure. Residents realise that there is a limit to this type of investment.

The community's immediate aim now is to develop more individual skills, confidence, and work discipline through experience and training, then to establish self-sufficient small enterprises which can compete successfully in the wider economy beyond the estate.

A key factor in the development of jobs and training on Broadwater Farm has been the efficiency and effectiveness of the local management effort. If tenants have to spend all their energy chasing repairs and complaining about rubbish, they cannot hope to make progress on the complex task of building an economic base for the community. Also a good local office is essential if capital contracts are to be organised and co-ordinated in a way which involves the local community.

Since 1983, Broadwater Farm has been managed to a high standard. Community groups are well organised, imaginative and ambitious in their attempts to improve the estate. Between 1983 and 1985 the crime rate dropped by over 50%. In January/February 1987 the estate accounted for 1% of the crime in Tottenham, yet constituted 3% of the population.

Key Issues

A. Broadwater Farm has made a significant impact on local unemployment but, as a result, the **expectations** of young people have been raised. There is a question as to how momentum can be kept up when many schemes are short-term or vulnerable to withdrawal of funds.

B. Establishing the right kind of legal and financial framework to be able to handle major contracts is a complex and time-consuming task.

C. Professional advice and support is essential yet establishing a constructive relationship between community groups and professionals can sometimes be difficult.

D. A constant process of evaluation and adjustment is needed to establish successful and stable projects.

E. The support of the local authority and central government is essential if community projects of this kind are to flourish.

APPENDIX 4H

PUBLIC SECTOR CONTRACTS fall into three groups which are distinguished by methods of measurement and valuation rather than by the nature of the work.

1. **Lump sum contracts.** The client specifies the work to be done, either by drawings and bills of quantities or by drawings and specifications, and these are priced by the tendering contractors. The prices are called "lump sums" and may be fixed, or fluctuations may be allowed according to predetermined formulae. Lump sum contracts are liked because their value is fixed before work starts. They place constraints upon the client because lump sum contracts allow variations to their terms whilst work is in progress.

2. **Measured term contracts.** The chart specifies the contract period and the geographical area, or buildings to be covered by the contract, together with a schedule of the works to be undertaken, which sometimes includes approximate quantities. Tendering contractors compete either by inserting their rates or by adding or deducting percentages to rates provided by the client. Under measured term contracts, the contractor is required to complete any works listed on the schedule as and when directed by the client. The value of measured

term contracts can only be determined at the end of the term, because they give maximum flexibility to the client. They provide many opportunities for maladministration and fraud.

3. **Daywork contracts.** The client appoints a daywork contractor using non-commercial methods of selection. The contractor then undertakes any works for which instructions are received from the client. The contractor then charges for this work by using nationally agreed rates for labour, materials. Sometimes tendering daywork contrac-

tors insert their own rates against lists of items provided by the client. Because of the limited competition element, daywork contractors are considered unsuitable for compulsory competitive tendering. They provide maximum flexibility to the client, but the value of the work is determined by the ability of the contractor to record the work adequately and apply the agreed rates creatively.

Useful additional information may be found in "Buildings and Engineering Contracts" by A. Hudson, Sweet & Maxwell, London 1970, plus supplement 1979.

PROGRESS TOWARDS LOCAL EMPLOYMENT 1983/1987 - BROADWATER FARM ESTATE

TYPE	NUMBER	FINANCE
(1) **COUNCIL RECRUITMENT** (Local Office - Housing, Maintenance and cleaning staff)	19 (out of total of 42)	H.R.A. Management expenses
(2) **SELF HELP SCHEMES** (Day-care, Playschemes, Sports Programmes, Meals on Wheels, Youth Programme).	14	Grant aid via Urban Programme, Haringey Council or G.L.C.
(3) **SMALL CO-OP ENTERPRISES** (Laundrette, Fruit Shop, Hairdressers).	7	Local Authority subsidy via Economic Development Unit - aim to be self financing in 3 years
(4) **BROADWATER FARM YOUTH ASSOCIATION CO-OP LTD**	2	Grant aid from Local Authority.
(a) Private Contractors:		
Pest Control (i)	2	(i) Annual Contract - H.R.A. funded
Cladding (ii)	1	(ii) H.I.P. allocation 1987/88
Window Renewal (ii)	4	
Major Maintenance (ii)	6	
Tangmere Patios (ii)	2	
Flooring (ii)	3	(iii) Estate Action H.I.P. allocation 1987/88.
U-deck Painting (iii)	2	*NOTE: Contractors are invited to tender on the basis of providing training and maximising local employment. All the people who have been recruited are permanent employees and will move off the estate as contracts are completed.*
	20 TOTAL	
(b) D.L.O.:		
Store	1	
	23	
Firestopping (i)	24 TOTAL	
(c) Co-op Contracts:		
Mosaic Mural (i)	3	(iv) Estate Action H.I.P. allocation. Co-op jobs will end when contracts are completed.
Painted Mural (ii)	2	
U-deck Painting (iv)	15	
Community gardens (i)	24	(v) Permanent maintenance jobs are to be created and Garden Centre proposed in order to establish permanent employment.
Hard Landscaping (iv)	44 TOTAL	
PENDING		
(d) Enterprise Worksops (pending)	?	Urban Programme Funding.
(e) European Social Fund Grant (pending)	15 trainees + Manager	Funding for 1-2 years.

TOTAL NUMBER OF JOBS SINCE 1983 : 128

JOB CREATION ON BROADWATER FARM (prior to April 1988)

Proportion of jobs within existing contracts going to local recruits.

1.	Private Contracts:	Outside	Broadwater	% local labour
*	Pest control contract	1	2	66%
*	Window renewal (Kenley)	16	4	20%
*	Willan Road contracts (Groves)	4	6	58%
*	Tangmere window repairs	4	2	30%
*	Tangmere roofs/asphalting	3	3	50%
2.	**Incomplete information**			
	Cladding contracts	?	1	?
	U-deck painting (private)	?	2	?
	New flooring	?	3	?
	Rehabilitation Tangmere shops	?	?	50%
3.	**DLO**			
*	Maintenance store		1	
*	Firestopping contract	18	23	57%
4.	**Co-operative Contracts**			
*	Murals	–	5	100%
*	U-deck painting	–	10	100%
*	Landscaping	4	16	80%

* Where information is available, the proportion of jobs being filled by local recruits is on average 60% and 40% by workers from off the estate. Obviously, the Co-operative contracts have some impact on these figures.
  Excluding the Co-operative contracts, the breakdown is 47% local labour, 53% non-local labour.

STRUCTURE OF BROADWATER FARM YOUTH ASSOCIATION CO-OP LTD.

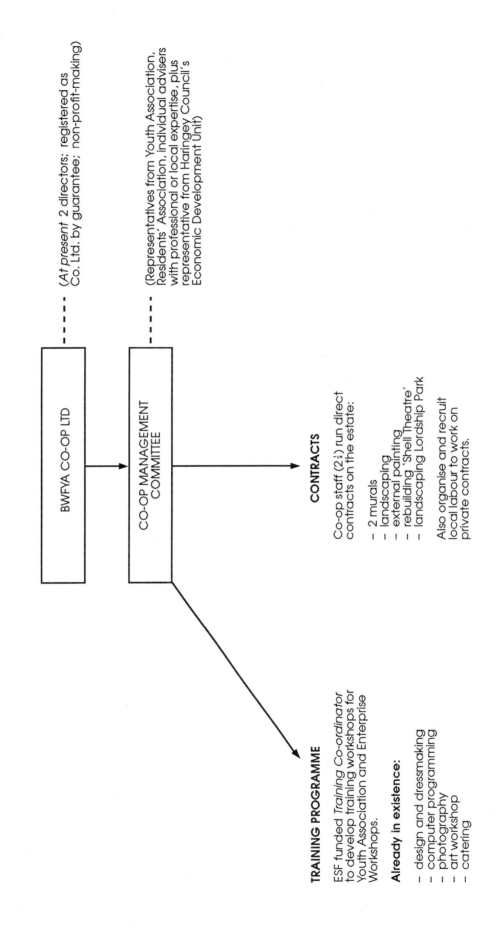

BWFYA CO-OP LTD ---- *(At present* 2 directors; registered as Co. Ltd. by guarantee; non-profit-making)

CO-OP MANAGEMENT COMMITTEE ---- (Representatives from Youth Association, Residents' Association, individual advisers with professional or local expertise, plus representative from Haringey Council's Economic Development Unit)

CONTRACTS

Co-op staff (2½) run direct contracts on the estate:

- 2 murals
- landscaping
- external painting
- rebuilding 'Shell Theatre'
- landscaping Lordship Park

Also organise and recruit local labour to work on private contracts.

TRAINING PROGRAMME

ESF funded *Training Co-ordinator* to develop training workshops for Youth Association and Enterprise Workshops.

Already in existence:

- design and dressmaking
- computer programming
- photography
- art workshop
- catering

LANDSCAPING OF THE REMEMBRANCE AND NATIONS' GARDENS ON BROADWATER FARM – FUNDING AND CONTRACTUAL ARRANGEMENTS

MAY-DECEMBER 1987

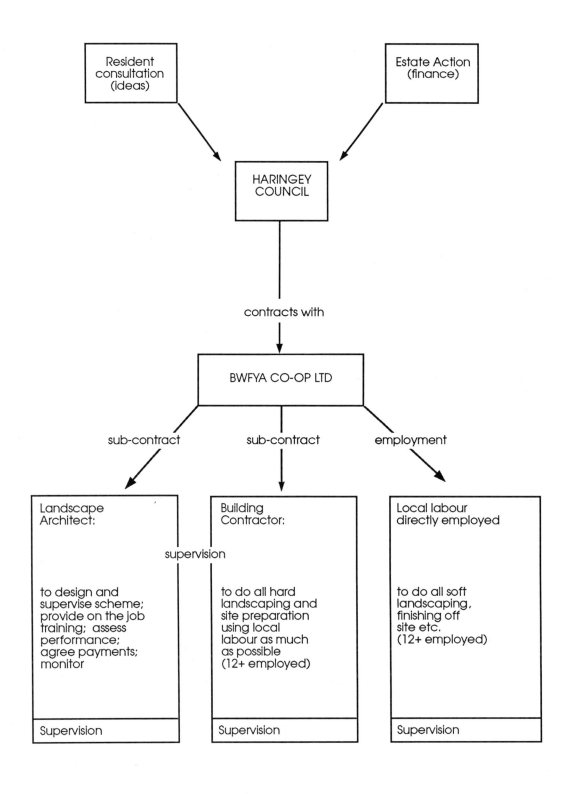

Index